Association of American State Geologists
Centennial History: 1908–2008

Edited by

James C. Cobb, AASG Historian

AASG
Association of American State Geologists

Published by the
Association of American State Geologists

2008

FRONT COVER PHOTO:

The three geologists circa 1909 standing in the doorway of the old geological survey and museum building in downtown Tallahassee, Fla., are *(left to right)*: the first Florida state geologist, Dr. Elias H. Sellards, who served from 1907 to 1919, and then as the Texas state geologist from 1932 to 1945; Dr. Roland Harper, Florida Geological Survey from 1908 to 1931, whose published works exceeded 500 titles; and Dr. Herman Gunter, state geologist of Florida from 1919 to 1958. The current Florida Geological Survey building is named the Gunter Building after Dr. Gunter. Photo courtesy Florida Geological Survey.

BACK COVER PHOTOS: *(FROM TOP TO BOTTOM)*

PHOTO ONE:

Iowa State Geologist Samuel Calvin in the field in an undated photograph Dr. Calvin is fourth person from left. Photo courtesy Iowa Geological Survey.

PHOTO TWO:

Florida Geological Survey field camp circa 1908 with (from left to right) Elias H. Sellards, Roland Harper, and Herman Gunter. Photo courtesy Florida Geological Survey.

PHOTO THREE:

Kentucky State Geological Survey party at Camp Cumberland River, circa 1908. George H. Ashley is seated third from left in front row. He would become state geologist of Pennsylvania in 1919. Photo courtesy Kentucky Geological Survey.

PHOTO FOUR:

U.S. and Kentucky State Geological Survey parties at Camp Martin circa 1908. Photo courtesy Kentucky Geological Survey.

Contents

Foreword...i

Letter from 2008 AASG President, Chacko John...ii

Letter from USGS Director, Mark Myers..iii

Acknowledgments...iv

Chapter 1: Introduction..1

Chapter 2: Creation of the Association of American State Geologists........9

Chapter 3: Minutes of the Founding Meeting...19

Chapter 4: The USGS–AASG Connection..27

Chapter 5: AASG Business and Accomplishments by Decade.....................39

Chapter 6: Ian Campbell, an Exemplary State Geologist,
            and the Ian Campbell Medal...183

Chapter 7: Genevieve Atwood, the First Woman State Geologist............189

Chapter 8: Raymond C. Moore Portrait Sketches.......................................193

Chapter 9: The Honorary Members Caucus..197

Chapter 10: The Pick and Gavel Award...201

Chapter 11: The John C. Frye Memorial Award..205

Chapter 12: The National Geologic Mapping Act..211

Chapter 13: The AASG–AGI Connection..233

Chapter 14: Workings of AASG in 2007..237

Chapter 15: History of the AASG Foundation...249

Appendix 1: Officers of the AASG..253

Appendix 2: Summaries of Annual Meetings, 1906–98...............................271

Appendix 3: Biographies of Founding Members of AASG...........................421

Appendix 4: Historical Directory of State Geological Surveys...................471

Appendix 5: Selected Group Photographs..519

Foreword

The *Association of American State Geologists Centennial History: 1908–2008* provides historical context for AASG and the state geologists past and present who did so much to advance geology and public policy in America. In the American system of government, states are important but can lose their voice in federal programs unless they work together for a common goal. AASG has been that voice for the states for federal programs dealing with topographic and geologic mapping; water, mineral, and energy resources; geologic hazards; and other geology-related issues important to society. In the 100 years of AASG there have been countless meetings with federal agencies, policy-makers, and Congress to initiate and influence programs for the benefit of the states and the nation. This history shows just how important AASG has been in these programs. Few people living today realize the significant role AASG played in getting topographic mapping for the nation. The same is true for geologic mapping, which is still under way, and other important geology- and resources-related issues. It is also true that people may not fully appreciate the role of the state geological surveys in this era of huge federal government programs. Day in and day out, state geological survey personnel respond to the needs of the citizens of their states for geologic, mapping, water, hazards, and mineral information. This is a celebration of their efforts too.

This history spans the time from horse and buggy geology to global positioning systems and laser mapping of outcrops using LIDAR (light detection and ranging); from the birth of aerophotography for mapping to satellite imagery; from benchtop flame mineralogy to electron microscopy, microprobes, and isotope geochemistry; from notebook and pencil to Internet-connected wireless laptops on the outcrop; and the entire development of plate tectonics. These are just a few examples of the great strides geology has made in the 100 years of AASG's existence.

It is the hope of the authors of this volume that historians of science and government will find subject matter in these pages intriguing enough for more scholarly work. We offer this history as just a beginning. We know there are many great stories to be told.

Dear State Geologists,
Friends, and Colleagues:

AASG began 100 years ago in a U.S. Geological Survey conference room in Washington, D.C., and here we are in 2008, celebrating this auspicious anniversary with the USGS, just outside Washington, D.C. Many historical events have occurred during these 100 years, such as world wars, natural disasters, depressions, environmental and political challenges, and enormous changes in the science. The common element throughout has been the very close relationship we have with the USGS. This federal-state, science-government relationship may be unique among all government agencies and scientific disciplines. Therefore on this centennial anniversary we also celebrate the century-long relationship we have shared together.

The very first AASG meeting was attended by 23 state geologists. Dr. Henry B. Kummel, state geologist of New Jersey, was elected the first president. Over these 100 years an enormous amount of planning was required to achieve what in some cases we now take for granted, such as topographic and geologic mapping, stratigraphic nomenclature, mineral-resource assessments, geologic-hazard assessments, and water-resource assessments. These achievements are the blueprints upon which our nation was built, but during nearly every decade, unforeseen events curtailed or even threatened to derail the best of plans. Topographic mapping was interrupted by World War I and the Great Depression. Other upheavals of the 20th century took a toll on other national and state geologic programs, but work was completed and great accomplishments were the result. The minutes of AASG meetings preserved in the archives attest to the cooperation and spirit of *being in this together,* the AASG and the USGS. This was enough to conquer adversity and get the job done.

It is my great honor to be president of the Association of American State Geologists during our centennial year. My hope for this Association is for another 100 years as successful as the first 100. I congratulate all the officers and members past and present who made this day possible by all of their hard work and dedication. There has been a tremendous amount of effort to build this organization into what it is today. AASG has stood for excellence in the geological sciences for the benefit of our states, citizens, and nation. The growth of AASG in the 20th century has paralleled the growth and success of our nation. Our states' resources and environment collectively have contributed enormously to making our nation the strongest in the world. I believe the state geological surveys and AASG have played a major role in our nation's success.

I see a very bright future for AASG for the next 100 years. The demands from society for mineral, water, and energy resources; the need to mitigate geologic hazards; and the need to protect our land, water, and air make geological surveys indispensable to our states' and nation's future. The AASG has come a long way from the 23 men who created this Association to the hundreds of people who participate today. I think all of us share a common belief that the next 100 years will be as productive as the past and AASG will be celebrating its 200th anniversary stronger than it is today. At that 200th anniversary I envision a celebration of the second century of partnership with the U.S. Geological Survey. I would like to thank the contributors to this AASG centennial history publication and especially the coordinator Jim Cobb, state Geologist of Kentucky, who along with staff at the Kentucky Geological Survey have put in many hours of hard work and research to make this possible. I hope all of you enjoy the activities planned for the centennial celebration and thank those from AASG and the U.S. Geological Survey who worked so hard to make this celebration a memorable one.

Sincerely,

Chacko J. John, *AASG President 2008*
Director and State Geologist,
Louisiana Geological Survey

To my friends and colleagues of
the Association of American State Geologists:

On the occasion of the 100th anniversary of the Association of American State Geologists, I would like to offer my warmest congratulations. The AASG and the U.S. Geological Survey share a strong history of service to the public at the state and national levels. We hold in common a mission to provide information about natural hazards, energy, mineral, and water resources to decision-makers in public service. In May of 1908, the fourth director of the USGS, George (Otis) Smith, invited all state geologists to attend a conference in Washington, D.C. The purpose of the conference was to discuss plans for work in geology, topography, hydrography, and mineral statistics. It was during this conference that the AASG was formed. The AASG now represents the state geologists in all 50 United States and Puerto Rico.

Celebrating this anniversary together in Shepherdstown, W.Va., offers us the wonderful opportunity to look at both our past and at our future. This volume records the long and proud history of AASG, and reminds us of the tremendous accomplishments of state geological surveys since the North Carolina Geological Survey started the grand adventure in 1823. As the former state geologist of Alaska, I feel part of this history, and as the director of the USGS I look forward to our future as we continue to work together to bring high-quality science to the table of public policy.

In recent years, our partnership with AASG has been especially important in our National Cooperative Geologic Mapping Program, our Geophysical and Data Preservation Program, our Energy Program, and our Water Programs. Together, the AASG and the USGS have many more opportunities to advance and provide the science to address the nation's pressing natural resource needs. Several stand out to me: understanding and responding to the impacts of climate change; understanding the water, energy, and mineral resources of the nation; and recognizing that our security is dependent on their sustainable and environmentally responsible use, and rebuilding one of our most fundamental products—the modern digital topographic map. All are critically important. Let us use this 100th anniversary of AASG to pledge that we will find ways to make real progress in these, and in many more areas.

The USGS staff and I congratulate you all.

Mark D. Myers, *Director*
U.S. Geological Survey

Acknowledgments

Many AASG members past and present participated in the making of this centennial history. Current and previous AASG secretaries, editors, officers, and historians all participated because of the work they did in compiling, recording, and archiving minutes, records, correspondence, and reports of this organization. For an organization with no permanent offices or staff, this job has been done for 100 years. The planning for this publication extended over many years, starting in 2001 with simple outlines of topics and subject matter, to this finished book. The Kentucky Geological Survey organized the archives, prepared documents for digital access, and undertook the coordination and communications with authors of chapters, editing of manuscripts, and preparation of the text for publication. The Texas Bureau of Economic Geology, handled the layout, image enhancement, graphic design, cover art, and printing. The work of all of the persons involved is greatly appreciated.

Kentucky Geological Survey personnel who worked on this project:

James C. Cobb, *Centennial History Project Coordinator, Compiler*

Margaret Luther Smath, *Editor*

Richard A. Smath, *Scanning supervisor, indexing, and programming*

Collie Rulo, *Scanning and graphic design*

Josh Reynolds, *Scanning*

Jill Bramwell, *Scanning*

Amanda Long, *Preparation of Historical Directory of State Geologists*

Texas Bureau of Economic Geology personnel who worked on this project:

Scott W. Tinker, *Director*

Joel L. Lardon, *Media Services Manager*

Jamie H. Coggin, *Senior Graphics Designer*

Introduction

James C. Cobb *(Kentucky; AASG Historian)*

This centennial volume was prepared in celebration of the 100th anniversary of the founding of the Association of American State Geologists. It gives the history of the AASG and the principal issues, activities, and accomplishments of the organization over these 100 years (1908–2008). This history was compiled from the AASG archives that include *The State Geologists Journal,* annual meeting minutes, committee reports, correspondence of the organization, and personal notes. In preparation for compiling this history, 45,000 pages of archives were scanned, indexed, and converted into searchable and computer-usable formats. Researchers delving into topics of historic significance in the future should find the digital archive an efficient, invaluable, and indispensable tool.

AASG was founded in 1908 when there were 46 states in the union, of which 42 had state geological surveys. The first state geological survey, North Carolina, was established 85 years earlier in 1823. The U.S. Geological Survey, established in 1879, had been in existence for 29 years. There was both support and disagreement between the USGS and state geological surveys. A number of state geologists were employed at least part-time by the USGS, so there was a complex and involved relationship among state surveys and the USGS. Since state geological surveys are a fundamental part of state governments, state surveys needed a unifying organization in which ideas could be exchanged, efforts to influence the federal government could be focused, and cooperation and coordination of efforts could be fostered. A new organization was needed.

As an organization, AASG is unique and special, not because it deals with geology, natural resources, public policy, and environmental issues (other organizations also deal with these subjects), but because it is governed by representatives of all 50 states and Puerto Rico, with each state having one vote. It is a remarkable reflection of the nation, embodying all the state and regional similarities and differences. AASG played a vital role in the history of the United States during the 20th century, a time of great changes and challenges; activities included topographic mapping, resource assessments, groundwater supply and protection, geologic hazards, geologic mapping, and support for and feedback to federal programs in all of these areas. The history of AASG is a study in public policy, government actions and inactions, state-federal cooperation and dissent, but ultimately the history of advocacy for geology-related programs needed by society.

AASG is an organization of people: the state geologists of each state plus Puerto Rico, associate state geologists, and honorary members who retired as state geologists or left their positions after serving as state geologists. This history is dominated by the accomplishments of people with vision and determination to make a positive difference in their states and the nation. What cannot be adequately captured is the personalities of the people who did so much to build not only this organization and the state geological surveys they directed, but also contributed to many national and societal endeavors. Unfortunately, the essence of the real people behind these accomplishments cannot be gleaned from the pages of journals, notes, and minutes. What can be learned is that a remarkable number of members have made tremendous contributions and were much admired by their peers.

On June 19, 1908, *Science* magazine announced the organization of AASG. The article reported the actions taken, provisions for annual meetings, appointment of committees, amendments offered, and officers elected. Henry B. Kummel (New Jersey) became the first president, H. Foster Bain (Illinois) the first secretary, and Joseph H. Pratt (North Carolina) the first executive committeeman. The first resolution, of May 12, 1908, was also reported (AASG, 1908):

> Whereas, our country and the sovereign states composing it now face serious problems relating to the preservation of our natural resources, and,
>
> Whereas, these problems,—of wisely administering our forests, our minerals, our soils, our water resources,—are tomorrow to be the subject of a conference between the Governors of the various states and the President of the United States, and,
>
> Whereas, we deem a contour-topographic map of our country so necessary to the intelligent solution of these and equally important problems,
>
> BE IT RESOLVED, that we most earnestly ask of state and Federal authorities in conference assembled, their support in securing such a map, and, since state and national interests are here so closely one, we most respectfully suggest: That state and Federal appropriation for topographic surveys be increased and that more immediately the Federal appropriation be increased for this work to meet the state appropriations now available.

> Be it resolved also, that a copy of these resolutions be presented to said confer-
> ence of the Governors with President Roosevelt with our greetings and respect.

The minutes of this first meeting also reported that "upon motion the resolution was unanimously adopted and the Secretary instructed to present it to the conference of Governors."

AASG was a proactive organization from its very beginning, pursuing federal programs of importance to the states. It is obvious from this first resolution that programs of national importance would be its highest priority.

In 1908, Theodore Roosevelt was president and the nation was undergoing rapid changes. Roosevelt, the youngest man to be president, served as vice president to William McKinley and became president when McKinley was assassinated in 1901. He brought a tremendous emphasis on the natural resources of the nation. The population of the United States was 88 million. The Dow Jones increased 48 percent from the previous year, and the economy improved dramatically. The Panama Canal was under construction and President Roosevelt sent the "Great White Fleet" on a goodwill mission around the world, underscoring his philosophy: "Walk softly but carry a big stick." President Roosevelt created the departments of Labor and Commerce and the National Conservation Commission to inventory and protect the nation's resources. Also in 1908, the Federal Bureau of Investigation was founded, the National Governors Association was founded, the first New Year's Eve ball-drop in Times Square took place, the Grand Canyon National Monument was created, the first Model-T Ford rolled off the assembly line, the Chicago Cubs won the World Series, coffee filters and tea bags were invented, the Hughes Tool Co. developed the rotary drill bit, the Geiger counter was invented, and Orville Wright made the first plane flight of 1 hour duration. In the rest of the world, the Nobel Prize in chemistry went to Ernst Rutherford for research on radioactivity, the Nobel Prize in physics went to Gabriel Lippman for color photography, the Tunguska impact occurred in Siberia, an earthquake destroyed Messina, Sicily, the Boy Scout movement was founded in Great Britain, and the first major oil strike in the Persian Gulf was made.

State surveys were established to collect information about the minerals, soils, hazards, and waters of each state. Many surveys were also given responsibility for mapping their state. The missions for state geological surveys were similar, requiring the surveys to investigate the geology and make information available to citizens through published reports and maps. Two state surveys were in existence in the 1820's (North and South Carolina), 15 in the 1830's (Massachusetts, Tennessee, Maryland, New Jersey, Virginia, Maine, New York, Georgia, Pennsylvania, Kentucky, Delaware, Indiana, Michigan, New Hampshire, Ohio, and Rhode Island), two in the 1840's (Vermont and Alabama), eight in the 1850's (Mississippi, Missouri, Illinois, Florida, Wisconsin, Montana, Iowa, Arkansas, and Texas), four in the 1860's (Kansas, Minnesota, Nebraska, and Louisiana), two in the 1870's (Nevada and Wyoming), two in 1880 (California and Arizona Territory), four in the 1890's (Washington, South Dakota, North Dakota, and West Virginia), and three in the 1900's (Connecticut, Colorado, and Oklahoma). The other state surveys, including Puerto Rico, were established after 1908.

In 1908, when AASG was founded, the budgets for state surveys were modest—only a few thousand dollars—and staff was few—only a handful of people. The magnitude of the state geological survey enterprise today is approximately $207 million (2006 data). This is the combined total for 47 states reporting their funding from all sources (state, federal, private). State funding accounted for $100 million (48 percent), nonfederal $71 million (34 percent), and federal $37 million (18 percent). The total expended by surveys for geologic research alone was $152 million in 2006. State surveys employed 1,953 full-time and 347 part-time employees in 2006. State geological surveys have not just maintained, but grown tremendously in importance, as measured by their funding levels since 1908.

The success of state geological surveys as a societal good can be demonstrated by comparing the growth in state appropriations for surveys from 1911 to 2006. USGS Bulletin 465 (Hayes, 1911) gives state appropriations for 28 surveys in 1911 whose state budgets are also given in the 2006 AASG statistician's report. The combined total for these 28 surveys increased from $244,000 in 1911 to $81 million in 2006. When corrected for inflation, the growth in state geological surveys as represented by these 28 is 16.2 times the 1911 level. Clearly, state surveys would not have reached this level of support from society if not for the value they provide their states.

There is no tally for the number of maps and publications produced by state geological surveys. In earlier times, *The State Geologists Journal* listed new publications from each state, but that practice was discontinued when the lists became too cumbersome. Survey publications have undergone more than 150 years of change from the formal hard-bound volumes of the 19th and early 20th centuries to the great diversity of today, including digital and Web-based. Estimates of state survey publications can be made by extrapolating data, giving numbers in the hundreds of thousands of titles. It follows that for the 50 states, millions of state survey publications and maps have been in circulation from the beginning to the present. Even greater is the explosion in public-service requests being served over the World Wide Web. Some states are reporting more than 1 million transactions per year in which data were downloaded to a client computer from a state survey Website. Data, maps, and publications are all being served over the Web in volumes per week that formerly were not achieved in a year's time. Clearly, state surveys are filling important and significant needs of government, industry, and citizens.

Throughout the 100 years of the AASG, many officers, secretaries, historians, journal editors, statisticians, and members have recorded and preserved important materials that made this history possible. AASG secretaries were the first to organize and preserve documents. John H. Melvin (Ohio) was the first AASG historian, beginning in 1952. Although he was not the first to compile AASG records, he was a key person in organizing the records we have today. Since Melvin, there have been 12 other historians, and we should thank them for their efforts (see officers in Appendix 1).

George Hanson (Wisconsin) served as historian for 11 years (1961–72), longer than anyone else. He compiled a booklet, *Historical Directory of State Geological Surveys,* edited by Edwin A. Noble (North Dakota). This booklet gives official names of state surveys and the names and years of service of state geologists up to 1972. The cover is a picture of Denison Olmsted (North Carolina), the first state geologist in the United States. The directory has been updated and is included as Appendix 4.

Charles Doll (Vermont), historian from 1972 to 1976, created a chronology of annual meetings, officers, and topics of discussion at annual meetings from 1906 to 1976. This document organized and indexed relevant facts for each year. He also found in the archives constitutional changes such as creation of new officers (editor, statistician, historian, and president-elect), the beginning of the *Journal,* levying of dues, and attendees at meetings. See annual meetings, officers, members present, and topics of discussion in Appendix 2. In 2004, James C. Cobb (Kentucky), current historian, and staff at the Kentucky Geological Survey continued this compilation, and it is included in Appendix 2 of this volume. These summaries give relevant information about the annual meetings such as location and host, officers, members present, topics discussed, and actions taken at the business sessions.

Very special tribute goes to Arthur Socolow (Pennsylvania) for being the editor and driving force for the 1988 volume, *The State Geological Surveys: A History,* published by the AASG. This book gives the history of individual state geological surveys, in detail for many surveys. The state geologists who served and the accomplishments of these surveys are also given. These books are still available, and the inventory of remaining books is with the Ohio Geological Survey.

George P. Merrill (1854–1929) was a historian of North American geology who graduated from the University of Maine with a Ph.D. in 1889.

In his work for the U.S. National Museum, he wrote a volume on state geological surveys that was published in 1920. This volume, *Contributions to a History of American State Geological Surveys and Natural History Surveys* (Merrill, 1920), gives details about the founding and early history of 36 state geological surveys. Included are pictures of 72 state geologists, covering the period up to about 1890. Appendix 1 of this volume gives budgets for state surveys up to 1900, and appendix 2 gives details about the Northern Transcontinental Survey from 1881–84, of Washington, Oregon, Montana, the Dakotas, and Minnesota. Other publications about state geological surveys include U.S. Geological Survey Bulletin 465, *The State Geological Surveys of the United States,* compiled under the direction of C.W. Hayes in 1911. This volume begins with the assertion that information such as mission, budget, staff, and current work about state geological surveys was difficult to obtain because it was spread among the 46 state surveys. The information was in demand by federal agencies interested in developing cooperative programs with state surveys. This bulletin covered 34 state surveys and is an interesting historic look at budgets and programs at state surveys in 1911.

In 1932, the National Research Council prepared a report on geological surveys (National Research Council, Committee on State Geological Surveys, 1932). The NRC had a standing committee on state geological surveys at that time, and a close relationship between NRC and AASG has continued to the present. The NRC report is very similar in content to USGS Bulletin 465. State geologists on this committee included Morris M. Leighton (Illinois), chair, Ernest F. Bean (Wisconsin), Henry A. Buehler (Missouri), and Henry B. Kummel (New Jersey), plus Arthur Keith (NRC). The outline for each survey included history, scope of activities, organization, appropriations, publications, principal accomplishments, and current projects. A total of 48 states and the USGS were covered in the report.

Staff at the Kentucky Geological Survey spent more than 4 years scanning and indexing AASG records and converting them into computer- and Web-usable formats. More than 45,000 pages of documents from microfilm and paper records were processed. These records have been placed on the AASG Website in the members-only section, organized by year and type of document for easy search and download. The records were indispensable for compiling this history. The University of Kansas library maintains the paper archives of the AASG, which are overseen by the Kansas Geological Survey. Currently, the Alaska Geological Survey manages the AASG online archives at www.stategeologists.org. As a note to future AASG officers and historians, I hope that the archives will be maintained and each year's minutes, journals, correspondence, and committee reports will be added. Please keep the archives growing!

References Cited

AASG, 1908, Minutes of the organization meeting of the Association of American State Geologists, Washington, D.C., May 12, 1908: AASG scanned archives, www.stategeologist.org.

Hayes, C.W., 1911, The state geological surveys of the United States: U.S. Geological Survey Bulletin 465, 177 p.

Merrill, G.P., 1920, Contributions to a history of American state geological surveys and natural history surveys: Bulletin of the U.S. National Museum, no. 109, 549 p.

National Research Council, Committee on State Geological Surveys, 1932, Summary information on the state geological surveys and the United States Geological Survey: Bulletin of the National Research Council, no. 88, 136 p.

Socolow, A.A., ed., 1988, The state geological surveys: A history: Association of American State Geologists, 499 p.

Creation of the
Association of American State Geologists

Jonathan H. Goodwin *(Illinois, Associate)*

H. Foster Bain, the director of the newly formed Illinois State Geological Survey, seems to have been the main catalyst in starting the organization that became the Association of American State Geologists, although state geologists from most of the eastern states also played significant roles. When Bain proposed that the state geologists of the Mississippi Valley gather in Chicago in early 1906, the idea met with an enthusiastic reception. He found that the concept of an organization of state geologists had been discussed in the past, but no action had been taken so far. Bain's leadership in organizing the Mississippi Valley Association of State Geologists, in cooperation with several colleagues and supporters from the academic community, started the ball rolling toward an almost inevitable result, the formation of the national Association of American State Geologists.

Around June 1905, Illinois Gov. Charles S. Deneen met in Springfield with Professors Edmund J. James, president of the University of Illinois, and Thomas C. Chamberlin, the noted Quaternary geologist at the University of Chicago, who was also the governor's friend and neighbor, for the purpose of selecting the person who would head the newly organized Illinois State Geological Survey. Acting as the three-person commission overseeing the new agency, they selected H. Foster Bain, a native of Seymour, Ind., who had received his Ph.D. in geology from the University of Chicago just 8 years before. Bain was then working for the U.S. Geological Survey in the western United States, and his appointment (by his choice) did not become effective until September 1, 1905 (Bain, 1907, 1931). It seems reasonable to guess, however, that as he was finishing his USGS duties and preparing to move his household, he must have conversed extensively by telephone, telegraph, and letter with the members of the commission, with several faculty of the University of Illinois, and with other state geologists, for he apparently had the new survey up and running at full tilt by early November of 1905 (Bain, 1907, 1931).

In February 1906, just 6 months after beginning work for the ISGS, Bain wrote to "the State Geologists of the Mississippi Valley," inviting them to "signalize the organization of the Illinois Geological Survey" by being his guest at a luncheon at the Quadrangle Club in Chicago on Saturday, March 24 or March 31. Bain noted in his letter that "the purpose is primarily social [but] Dr. Buckley [state geologist of Missouri] and I thought that an informal conference might lead to good and open up the way to cooperation in the matter of standardizing tests, etc." (Bain, 1906a). The correspondence found in the archives does not indicate how many of the then-active state geologists received Bain's invitation, but the limited evidence available suggests that his definition of the "Mississippi Valley" extended to all the states touched at all by that river's watershed.

On March 21, Bain sent a second letter to his invited guests, enclosing a suggested program for the meeting to be held on March 31. (This program has not been found in the AASG archives.) In his letter to Edward Orton (Ohio state geologist), Bain indicated that "Michigan, Indiana, Illinois, Wisconsin, Iowa, Missouri and Kansas will certainly be represented, with strong probability in favor of Kentucky and the possibility of Mississippi sending a delegate." He went on to say, "I have been on the whole surprised to find how much interest there is in the matter, and there seems to be a sentiment in favor of some sort of permanent organization for our mutual advice and assistance, as well as to stimulate a wider interest in geology throughout the Mississippi Valley" (Bain, 1906b).

According to the minutes of the March 31, 1906, meeting, delegates were present from Illinois (Bain), Indiana (Willis S. Blatchley), Kansas (Erasmus Haworth), Kentucky (Charles J. Norwood), Michigan (Alfred C. Lane), Missouri (Ernest R. Buckley), and Ohio (John A. Bownocker) (Bain, 1906c). The meeting itself was held at Walker Museum on the University of Chicago campus, a building that still exists. The group may well have dined at the Quadrangle Club, for the original location of that club was less than one block from Walker Museum.

The object of the meeting, as stated by the temporary chair, Mr. Buckley, was (according to the minutes)

> to consider the needs and possible benefits of some organization whereby the state geologists of the Mississippi Valley could, when desirable, act in concert and through which they might confer with and advise one another.

Following "a long, informal discussion in which all took part," according to Bain, who acted as secretary, the assembled decided that such an organization was desirable and that it should be "as informal as possible" (Bain, 1906c). Mr. Lane of Michigan moved that the organization be known as the Association of State Geologists of the Mississippi Valley and that voting membership be confined to one executive officer from each geological survey or equivalent organization (Bain, 1906c).

This motion apparently is the basis for two significant aspects of the bylaws of the current Association of American State Geologists: (1) that the first word in the organization's name would forever be "Association" rather than "American" (to the frequent confounding of the uninitiated) and (2) that only duly appointed state geologists (or the holder of an equivalent appointment in a state) could be full voting members.

The assembled members of the newborn association elected Willis S. Blatchley of Indiana as chairman and Bain as secretary, "to serve until his successor should be elected." The minutes do not state whether Mr. Blatchley assumed the chairmanship of the meeting immediately upon his election or later, perhaps upon the adjournment of this first meeting of the Association of State Geologists of the Mississippi Valley. Nevertheless, it is clear from the record of the actions taken during the March 31 organizing meeting that Mr. Blatchley should be regarded as chairman of the AMVSG, and Bain as secretary, beginning in the spring of 1906, presumably on April 1 of that year, at the latest (Table 1).

Table 1. Officers of the Association of Mississippi Valley State Geologists, 1906–08, compiled and inferred from minutes of meetings and correspondence.

March 31, 1906 (only)
Temporary Chairman: Ernest R. Buckley (Missouri)
Temporary Secretary: H. Foster Bain (Illinois)
April 1, 1906–May 12, 1908
Chairman: Willis S. Blatchley (Indiana)
Secretary: H Foster Bain (Illinois)
May 1907–May 12, 1908
Third member of Executive Committee: Alfred C. Lane (Michigan)

To conduct the association's business outside of meetings, the method moved by Mr. Buckley of Missouri was adopted (Bain, 1906c):

Any member desiring to raise a question shall make a brief of it and forward [it] for comment to another member of the association who shall attach his comment or recommendations and send it to another who shall in turn forward it until all members shall have had an opportunity to examine the case. The last man receiving the papers shall return them to the originator who shall then prepare copies of the entire discussion and send it to each one participating.

The appointment of temporary committees or the calling of field conferences was expected to be necessary in some cases. After an informal discussion of ways of achieving greater uniformity in methods of testing and sampling materials, and lunch, the conference reassembled and was joined by Professors Thomas C. Chamberlin, Rollin D. Salisbury, Samuel W. Williston, Stuart Weller, Wallace W. Atwood, and J. Paul Goode of the University of Chicago; Ulysses S. Grant and Alja R. Crook of Northwestern University; and August F. Foerste of the Kentucky Geological Survey. During the following discussion of the needs for some organization among the geologists of the Mississippi Valley, it was decided that the newly formed group should hold an annual spring conference. Professor Chamberlin also proposed, and the state geologists accepted, that "the members shall extend personal invitations to the other working geologists of the Mississippi Valley to meet with [the state geologists] during the spring conference in one or more sessions" (Bain, 1906c). It was the intention of the assembled that these open sessions should be "for the purpose of bringing about closer acquaintance and fuller informal discussion rather than reading of set papers" (Bain, 1906c).

Other subjects discussed informally as the meeting continued included "the relations of the state surveys to the Federal Survey, of the members of the state surveys to private professional work, the form and character of state publications and several other subjects" (Bain, 1906c).

Henry B. Kummel, the New Jersey state geologist, in an article published in the *Journal of the Association of American State Geologists* in 1941, recalled that around 1905 or 1906 a number of state surveys were "somewhat restive regarding their relations with the Federal Survey." Problems recalled by Kummel included concerns in West Virginia over the accuracy of early USGS 1:125,000-scale topographic maps and plans for remapping at larger scales. Also, New York's state geologist had taken strong exception to the conclusions contained in a recently published USGS geological folio of a part of his state, and the fact that he had not been informed by the USGS that the work was being done. According to Kummel, there had been "a lively exchange of comment between Albany and Washington" on this subject.

> Many of the state geologists felt very strongly…that their prestige in their own states might be seriously impaired and their appropriations threatened if the national organization invaded their territory without agreeing in advance upon some terms of cooperation,

Kummel observed.

We do not have evidence to indicate how widely the minutes of the March 31, 1906, conference were circulated, but it is clear that they were sent to state geologists who had not attended the meeting. In a letter dated

April 23, 1906, Bain, as secretary of the newly formed AMVSG, sent a copy of the minutes of the March meeting to Eugene A. Smith, the state geologist of Alabama, soliciting his comments and inviting him to join the association as his state's representative (Bain, 1906d). In his response dated May 2, 1906, Mr. Smith commented that he was "very glad to see this movement inaugurated." He continued as follows:

> A good many years ago at one of the New York meetings of the American Association, I tried to have an Association of State Geologists organized.... Such an organization should have been in existence all these years and I am very glad indeed to have the opportunity of helping it along right now, because there are certain matters in which the State Geologist ought to have a voice.... All of the State Geologists are bound, sooner or later, to run up against some opposing views as to nomenclature, as well as other matters probably more important held by members of the U.S. Geological Survey. At present the State Geologists are helpless, for what is one individual against a great organization. But if we all stand together and insist on obvious rights, I think we shall be in position to compel recognition [sic].

A letter dated April 17, 1908, authored by Bain (it is on ISGS stationery), signed by Willis S. Blatchley, Bain, and Alfred C. Lane of Michigan (Blatchley and others, 1908), and addressed to "Members of the Mississippi Valley Association of State Geologists," sheds some light on several aspects of the AMVSG. The letter begins as follows:

> It will be recalled that at the meeting in Washington in May 1907 a resolution was passed inviting the cooperation of the U.S. Geological Survey and the Geological Society of America in the formation of a general committee which should consider the fundamental basis upon which geologic nomenclature should be formulated. Pursuant to this proposition the U.S. Geological Survey has appointed Mr. Arthur Keith to serve upon such committee, and the Geological Society of America has agreed to appoint a representative. The Geological Society suggested, however, the enlargement of the committee to include representatives of the Canadian and Mexican geological surveys, and also suggested that a representative be chosen by the state geologists as a whole rather than by our own association. This is probably the best plan if the committee is to be small. If the committee should be somewhat larger it might be well to have a specific representative of our own Association. As you are aware, the state geologists in general have no organization to act for them, and it seems proper that our Association should take the initiative in proposing the representative.

First, from this text it is evident that the AMVSG held a meeting in Washington in May 1907. The occurrence of the meeting is included in a table of annual meetings and officers compiled in 1979 by Helen Nace and Daniel Miller Jr., then secretary of the Association, but we currently lack any other record of the actions taken at this meeting. This 1907 meeting had been overlooked in several pre-1979 summaries of the early history of the organization. It may be that action was taken at this May 1907 meeting to create a three-member Executive Committee and to name Alfred C. Lane of Michigan as the third member of that committee. He is listed as an officer in the 1979 table under the "Vice President" column, although no such office then existed. There is no reference to an Executive Committee in the minutes of the March 31, 1906, organizing meeting, but Bain's experience with his own agency's three-person oversight commission suggests a model for the association's Executive Committee. There is also, of course, the obvious need for a tie-breaking third voter among the officers.

Second, the April 1908 letter shows that the AMVSG had quickly become an active organization that sought to assume a leadership role in dealing with scientific and other issues that were of concern to its members. Reading between the lines, however, it is also clear that some geologic organizations did not regard the geographically limited AMVSG as empowered to speak on behalf of all the state geologists.

According to Henry Kummel's 1941 account of the early history of the AMVSG and AASG, during a meeting of the Geological Society of America held in New York in late 1906, Charles Walcott, the director of the U.S. Geological Survey, "seized the opportunity given by the presence of many State Geologists at the meeting to discuss privately in a friendly way with many of us the differences which had arisen" (Kummel, 1941, p. 12). In the following year, Walcott was succeeded by George Otis Smith and in May 1908, Smith invited all the state geologists to come to a conference of officers of state geological surveys and of the U.S. Geological Survey, to be held in Washington, May 11–12, 1908. The object of the conference was the discussion of plans for work in geology, topography, hydrography, and mineral statistics (Smith, 1908). The U.S. government, he said, would reimburse the state geologists for "railroad transportation from your State to Washington and return." It was during this conference, probably held in the downtown Washington offices of the U.S. Geological Survey, that the Association of American State Geologists came into existence. Henry Kummel recalled that, in the forenoon of the second day it was resolved to form an "Association of American State Geologists," and a committee of three was appointed to draw up a simple constitution and bylaws. The conference thereupon adjourned for luncheon, leaving the committee to wrestle with the problem (Kummel, 1941, p. 12).

Kummel (1941) reported that this three-person committee consisted of himself, Bain, and Israel C. White of West Virginia, but the minutes of the organizational meeting indicate that only Bain and Kummel were appointed to this committee (AASG, 1908a). The minutes of the meeting also indicate that, although the suggestion to create a new organization had been made during the conference with the U.S. Geological Survey, actions by the committee to devise the bylaws of the organization did not begin until the state geologists gathered alone in the USGS conference room beginning at 2:30 p.m. By contrast, Kummel recalled that the bylaws writing committee

> was confronted with a very acute problem. Work fast or go without lunch. We chose the former alternative. Perhaps the brevity and simple form of the constitution was primarily due not to any special wisdom on the part of the committee, either individually or collectively, but to the fact that we were hungry (Kummel, 1941, p. 12).

The available evidence offers no way to resolve the discrepancies between the formal records and Mr. Kummel's recollections, written 33 years later. The minutes of the meeting state the following (AASG, 1908a):

> There was an informal discussion of the desirability of a closer organization of state geologists and of the object which might be accomplished by it. Upon motion, the meeting resolved itself into the Association of American State Geologists. Upon motion, the temporary chairman (Mr. Kummel) and Secretary (Mr. Bain) were appointed a committee on organization and Mr. Pratt (North Carolina State Geologist) being called to the chair, they retired to prepare a set of by-laws in accordance with the suggestions made during the discussion.

The following is pure speculation on my part. Perhaps during the conference in the morning there had been agreement on the need for a formal organization of state geologists and Messrs. Kummel and Bain (and perhaps Mr. White of West Virginia) volunteered to draft proposed bylaws for the Association for formal consideration during the afternoon meeting. And, perhaps, during the afternoon's informal discussion it was decided that some changes in the draft were necessary. And finally, perhaps Bain, first as temporary secretary of the organizational meeting and then as the duly elected secretary of the new Association, decided to combine these steps into one for the sake of simplifying the story without significantly altering its import.

The Association of Mississippi Valley State Geologists provided a fully functioning model for the new organization and, given Bain's presence on the bylaws drafting committee, it should come as no surprise that the bylaws of the Association of American State Geologists adopted that afternoon almost exactly duplicated the series of motions adopted at the Walker Museum in Chicago a little more than 2 years earlier. Although the minutes of the March 31, 1906, meeting do not record such an organizing motion, the AMVSG, like the AASG, ultimately operated with a three-person Executive Committee (see Blatchley and others, 1908). Outside of meetings called by the Executive Committee, the method of transacting business adopted in the AASG's new bylaws almost exactly duplicated that proposed by Mr. Buckley of Missouri and enacted by the AMVSG. The only difference was that the task of circulating to the membership a brief written by a member for discussion and comment, and of informing the members of any consensus of opinion that might develop regarding the brief, was left to the secretary rather than the originator of the brief (Bain, 1906c; Smith, 1908).

According to the minutes, there was no formal election of the president and secretary of the new AASG. Instead, by motion, the informally organized association turned itself into the formally organized AASG and the temporary chairman (Kummel) and temporary secretary (Bain) became the president and secretary, respectively. Mr. Pratt of North Carolina, who had served as acting chairman of the meeting while Kummel and Bain drafted the bylaws, was elected the third member of the Executive Committee.

The organizational meeting was attended by at least 22 of the then-active state geologists, but whether Israel C. White of West Virginia was among them is something of a mystery. His name is not in the list of attendees at the beginning of the minutes, but he is referenced on page 4 of the minutes as an appointed member of a committee. It seems unlikely (but certainly not impossible) that he would have been appointed to an ad hoc committee if he were not present (Smith, 1908), but the official record is rather murky. The reference to the committee in the May 12, 1908, minutes is parenthetical and states that the committee, comprising Messrs. William B. Clark (Maryland), Israel C. White (West Virginia), and Joseph H. Pratt (North Carolina), was appointed by the president *after adjournment*. Kummel's recollection 33 years later, and this oblique reference in the minutes, are the only indications of Mr. White's possible presence at this meeting. Despite this uncertainty over his presence at the organizational meeting, Mr. White clearly was an active member of the Association; he was elected president of the Association at a meeting held in December 1912 in New Haven, Conn. (De Wolf, 1912).

At the second meeting of the AASG, held in Baltimore, Md., on December 30, 1908, in conjunction with the Geological Society of America, Bain reported to the 14 members present that representatives of all the active geological surveys in the United States had been invited to join the new organization and had indicated their desire to do so. The list of state geologists compiled by Bain included 35 people, one of whom was the "Territorial Geologist" of the Arizona Territory (AASG, 1908b).

The ultimate fate of the Association of Mississippi Valley State Geologists was not recorded. The AMVSG seems never to have been organized with formal bylaws, however. With the development of a national association organized for essentially the same purpose, it seems likely that the members simply allowed their regional organization to die out by inaction.

Given H. Foster Bain's close connections with the origins of both the Illinois State Geological Survey and the Association of American State Geologists, it is a remarkable coincidence, I think, that both were formally organized on the same date, May 12—the ISGS by Gov. Deneen's signature on the organizing act in 1905, and the AASG 3 years later by the formal vote in Washington, D.C., of state geologists representing about half of all the United States then in existence.

References Cited

AASG, 1908a, Minutes of the organizational meeting of the Association of American State Geologists, Washington, D.C., May 12, 1908: AASG scanned archives, www.stategeologists.org.

AASG, 1908b, Minutes of the December 30, 1908, meeting and list of 1908 state geologists (as of January 1909): AASG scanned archives, www.stategeologists.org.

Bain, H.F., 1906a, Letter to Professor Edward Orton Jr., state geologist, Columbus, Ohio, Feb. 16, 1906: AASG archival holdings, Kansas Geological Survey, Lawrence, Kan.

Bain, H.F., 1906b, Letter to Professor Edward Orton Jr., state geologist, Columbus, Ohio, March 21, 1906: AASG archival holdings, Kansas Geological Survey, Lawrence, Kans.

Bain, H.F., 1906c, Minutes of the conference of state geologists held at Walker Museum, University of Chicago, March 31, 1906: AASG archival holdings, Kansas Geological Survey, Lawrence, Kans.

Bain, H.F., 1906d, Letter to E.A. Smith, state geologist, Tuscaloosa, Ala., April 23, 1906: Archives of the Geological Survey of Alabama, Tuscaloosa, Ala.

Bain, H.F., 1907, Year-book for 1906: Illinois State Geological Survey Bulletin 4, 260 p.

Bain, H.F., 1931, The initiation of the state geological survey, *in* Papers presented at the quarter centennial celebration of the Illinois State Geological Survey: Illinois State Geological Survey Bulletin 60, p. 29–33.

Blatchley, W.S., Bain, H.F., and Lane, A.C., 1908, Letter to members of the Association of Mississippi Valley State Geologists, April 17, 1908, on forming a committee to deal with geological nomenclature issues: AASG archival holdings, Kansas Geological Survey, Lawrence, Kans.

De Wolf, F.W., 1912, Minutes of the December 27, 1912, meeting of AASG: AASG scanned archives, www.stategeologists.org.

Kummel, H.B., 1941, Early history of the Association: Journal of the Association of American State Geologists, v. 12, no. 3, p. 11–14.

Smith, E.A., 1906, Letter to H.F. Bain, May 2, 1906: Archives of the Geological Survey of Alabama, Tuscaloosa, Ala.

Smith, G.O., 1908, Letter to John A. Bownocker, Ohio state geologist, Columbus, Ohio, May 5, 1908.

Minutes of the Founding Meeting

James C. Cobb *(Kentucky; AASG Historian)*

The minutes from the founding meeting have been preserved (Fig. 1). The copy reproduced in Figure 1 came from the Wisconsin Geological Survey; George Hanson (Wisconsin) was AASG historian from 1961 to 1972. The founding meeting was held May 12, 1908, in Washington, D.C. The USGS was the host and arranged the meeting space and train transportation expenses to and from the meeting for the state geologists who attended. The first elected officers were: Chairman: Henry B. Kummel (New Jersey), Secretary: H. Foster Bain (Illinois), and Executive Committeeman: Joseph H. Pratt (North Carolina).

Reading the biographies of the state geologists who attended the first meeting and established AASG, one sees 23 highly accomplished persons gifted in science, leadership, and vision (see Appendix 3). They dealt with governors, legislators, federal agencies, colleagues, staff members, and the difficulties of conducting geological surveys in the early 20th century. Many became legendary, having their names associated with such monumental discoveries as the anticlinal theory of oil accumulation and the same for salt domes, fossil discoveries, and great accomplishments in science, government, and industry. Some of these men founded other associations such as the American Association of Petroleum Geologists and the Ceramics Society. This group of men made discoveries in mineralogy, paleontology, structural geology, stratigraphy, and mapping. Many were academics associated with universities; others were involved with state governments. Some served in the military. A number of these men were so highly regarded by their respective states and universities that buildings were erected and named in their honor.

As previously mentioned, it is unclear whether Israel C. White (West Virginia) was actually in attendance. But Mr. White clearly was an active member of the AASG; therefore his biography is included along with those of the other 22 founding members in Appendix 3.

The following list gives the names of the members present at the inaugural meeting, May 12, 1908, in Washington, D.C.

Eugene A. Smith, Alabama

Albert H. Purdue, Arkansas

Elias H. Sellards, Florida

Samuel W. McCallie, Georgia

H. Foster Bain, Illinois

Samuel Calvin, Iowa

Erasmus Haworth, Kansas

Gilbert D. Harris, Louisiana

William B. Clark, Maryland

Alfred C. Lane, Michigan

Albert F. Crider, Mississippi

Henry A. Buehler, Missouri

Erwin H. Barbour, Nebraska

Henry B. Kummel, New Jersey

John H. Clarke, New York

Joseph H. Pratt, North Carolina

Arthur G. Leonard, North Dakota

John A. Bownocker, Ohio

Richard H. Hice, Pennsylvania

Earle Sloan, South Carolina

George H. Perkins, Vermont

Israel C. White*, West Virginia

William O. Hotchkiss, Wisconsin

*unclear whether White was actually in attendance.

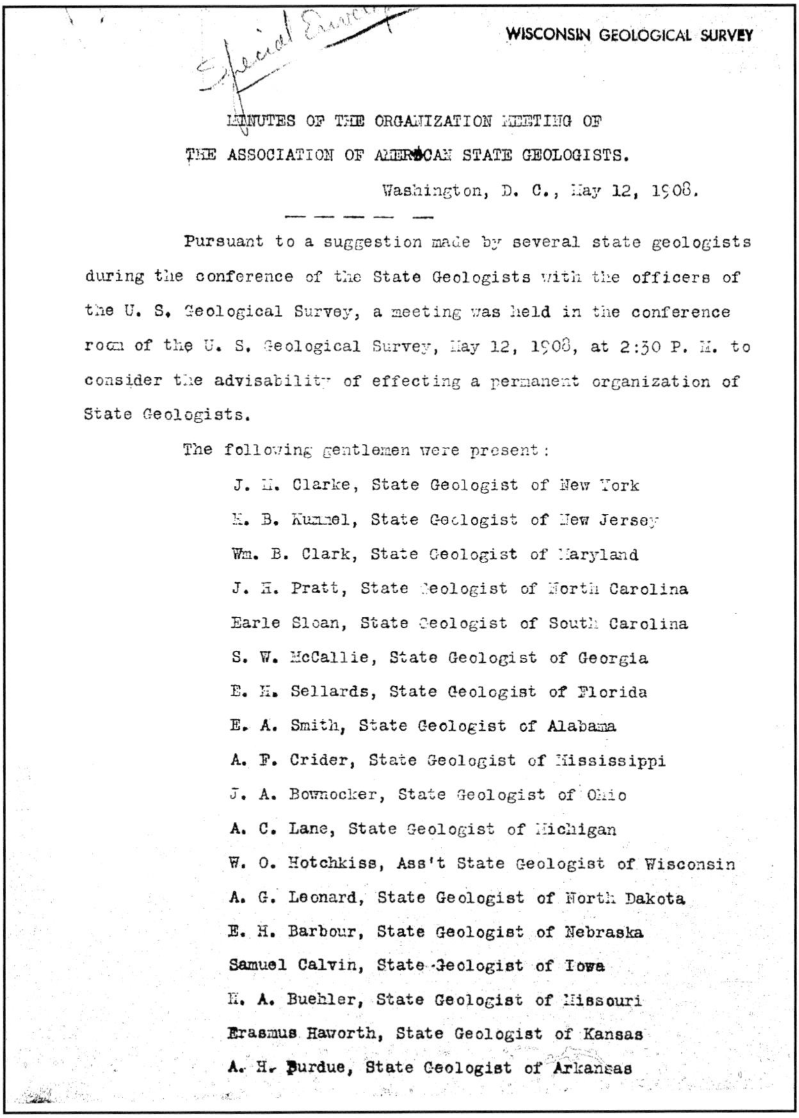

WISCONSIN GEOLOGICAL SURVEY

MINUTES OF THE ORGANIZATION MEETING OF
THE ASSOCIATION OF AMERICAN STATE GEOLOGISTS.

Washington, D. C., May 12, 1908.

— — — — —

Pursuant to a suggestion made by several state geologists
during the conference of the State Geologists with the officers of
the U. S. Geological Survey, a meeting was held in the conference
room of the U. S. Geological Survey, May 12, 1908, at 2:30 P. M. to
consider the advisability of effecting a permanent organization of
State Geologists.

The following gentlemen were present:

J. M. Clarke, State Geologist of New York

K. B. Kummel, State Geologist of New Jersey

Wm. B. Clark, State Geologist of Maryland

J. H. Pratt, State Geologist of North Carolina

Earle Sloan, State Geologist of South Carolina

S. W. McCallie, State Geologist of Georgia

E. H. Sellards, State Geologist of Florida

E. A. Smith, State Geologist of Alabama

A. F. Crider, State Geologist of Mississippi

J. A. Bownocker, State Geologist of Ohio

A. C. Lane, State Geologist of Michigan

W. O. Hotchkiss, Ass't State Geologist of Wisconsin

A. G. Leonard, State Geologist of North Dakota

E. H. Barbour, State Geologist of Nebraska

Samuel Calvin, State Geologist of Iowa

H. A. Buehler, State Geologist of Missouri

Erasmus Haworth, State Geologist of Kansas

A. H. Purdue, State Geologist of Arkansas

Figure 1. Minutes of the founding meeting of the AASG, May 12, 1908, Washington, D.C.

-- 2 --

G. D. Harris, State Geologist of Louisiana

H. F. Bain, State Geologist of Illinois

G. H. Perkins, State Geologist of Vermont

R. M. Hice, of the Geological Commission of Penn'a.

Upon motion Mr. H. B. Kummel was made temporary chairman of the meeting.   Upon motion Mr. H. F. Bain was made temporary secretary.

There was an informal discussion if the desirability of a closer organization of state geologists and of the object which might be accomplished by it.

Upon motion the meeting resolved itself into the Association of American State Geologists.

Upon motion the temporary Chairman and Secretary were appointed a committee on organization and Mr. Pratt being called to the chair, they retired to prepare a set of by-laws in accordance with the suggestions made during the discussion.

The Committee reported the following plan of organization.

(1)

NAME

This Association shall be called the Association of American State Geologists.

(2)

OFFICERS

The officers shall consist of a President and Secretary with the usual powers and duties of such offices who with a third member shall constitute the Executive Committee which committee shall have power to call, annual and special meetings of the Association and to arrange programs for the same.

(3)

ELECTIONS

All officers shall be elected annually and shall serve one year and until their successors are elected.

Figure 1. Minutes of the founding meeting of the AASG, May 12, 1908, Washington, D.C. (continued).

-- 3 --

(4)

COMMITTEES

The Association may from time to time authorize and appoint such additional committees with such instructions and power as may be desired.

(5)

TRANSACTION OF BUSINESS

Any member of the Association desiring concurrent consideration and action in any proposition may prepare a brief covering the case and forward it to the Secretary who shall circulate it among the members for discussion and comment and shall inform the members of the Association of any consensus of opinion which may in this way develop.

(6)

AMENDMENTS

These by-laws may be amended or changed by a majority vote at any meeting of the Association.

Upon motion the report of the Committee was adopted and the proposed by-laws became by-laws of the Association.

Upon motion the temporary organization was made the permanent organization of the Association.

Upon motion Mr. J. H. Pratt was elected to the Executive Committee.

After an informal discussion of the desirability, if possible, of obtaining the franking privilege of the use of the State Surveys, the President was authorized to appoint three members to form a Committee on Distribution of Documents with instructions to examine into the means, if any, by which the privilege might be obtained and to take the lead in an effort to obtain it in case such a move seemed likely to succeed.

Figure 1. Minutes of the founding meeting of the AASG, May 12, 1908, Washington, D.C. (continued).

-- 4 --

(After adjournment the President appointed W. B. Clark, Chairman, I. C. White and J. H. Pratt.)

A resolution regarding appropriations for topographic work was offered and read. After being informally discussed it was referred to the President and Secretary for amendment. They reported it in the following form.

Washington, D. C., May 12, 1908.

Whereas, our country and the sovereign states composing it now face serious problems relating to the preservation of our natural resources, and,

Whereas, these problems,- of wisely administering our forests, our minerals, our soils, our water resources,- are tomorrow to be the subject of a conference between the Governors of the various states and the President of the United States, and,

Whereas, we deem a contour-topographic map of our country so necessary to the intelligent solution of these and equally important problems,

BE IT RESOLVED, that we most earnestly ask of state and Federal authorities in conference assembled, their support in securing such a map, and, since state and national interests are here so closely one, we most respectfully suggest: That state and Federal appropriation for topographic surveys be increased and that more immediately the Federal appropriation be increased for this work to meet the state appropriations now available.

Be it resolved also, that a copy of these resolutions be presented to said conference of the Governors with President Roosevelt with our greetings and respect.

Upon motion the resolution was unanimously adopted and the Secretary instructed to present it to the conference of Governors.

Figure 1. Minutes of the founding meeting of the AASG, May 12, 1908, Washington, D.C. (continued).

-- 5 --

    Upon motion the matter of extending to representatives of state geological surveys and similar organizations not represented at the organization meeting, to join the Association, was placed in the hands of the Executive Committee with power to act.

    Adjourned to meet on call of the Executive Committee.

                                      Secretary.

Figure 1. Minutes of the founding meeting of the AASG, May 12, 1908, Washington, D.C. (continued).

The USGS–AASG Connection

Clifford M. Nelson *(U.S. Geological Survey)*

Cooperation by the U.S. Geological Survey with the state geological surveys, a mutually beneficial collaboration, began nearly a quarter century before the USGS facilitated the birth of the Association of American State Geologists in 1908. The movement to establish a national survey in America originated in 1878, 11 years after the federal government began continuous science and mapping surveys west of the 100th meridian. That June, as part of ongoing efforts toward financial retrenchment, the 45th U.S. Congress and President Rutherford Hayes sent to the National Academy of Sciences a formal request to devise a plan for improving economy and efficiency in the federal mapping and science surveys of government-held lands (the public domain) in states and territories—those mostly west of the Mississippi River.

Leadership of the NAS, Congress's statutory adviser "upon any subject of science or art" (U.S. Stat. L., v. 12 [March 3, 1863], p. 806) since 1863, passed to Yale's O.C. (Othniel Charles) Marsh, NAS vice president and acting president since the death in May 1878 of the Smithsonian Institution's Secretary Joseph Henry. Marsh, as required by NAS bylaws, formed and led a special committee to plan for improving these federal surveys. Marsh's committee, scientists and engineers not directly connected with the surveys, included Alexander Agassiz (Harvard), James Dana (Yale), John Newberry (Columbia), Simon Newcomb (Nautical Almanac Office), William Rogers (Massachusetts Institute of Technology), and William Trowbridge (Columbia). Federal geologist Clarence King, his own western survey for the U.S. Army Corps of Engineers nearly completed,[1] advised the committee, at Marsh's

---

[1] King (1842–1901) planned and led the U.S. Geological Exploration of the Fortieth Parallel (1867–79). Only its last two final reports remained in press: King's *Systematic Geology* (1878) and *Odontornithes* (1880) by Marsh (1831–99). For an overview, see Wilkins and Hinkley (1988).

request. In November, the NAS approved its committee's plan and sent it to Congress.

Early in 1879, Carl Schurz, President Hayes's reform-minded Secretary of the Interior, asked John Powell, who led one of the Department of the Interior's surveys[2], to rewrite the NAS plan for inclusion in Interior's portion of the sundry civil-expenses bill for fiscal year 1879–80. When Powell added his land-reform measures rejected by Congress in 1878, Schurz turned to King and industrialist Rep. Abram Hewitt (D-New York). Hewitt and King, in redrafting the measure, substituted "national" for "public" domain, to try to make the proposed new geological survey within Interior a nationwide agency, similar to Interior's Census Bureau (1790), the Agriculture Department (1862), and the Treasury's Coast and Geodetic Survey (renamed and expanded in 1878).

Congress, in a hotly contested but bipartisan decision, approved the USGS section and the remainder of the civil-expenses appropriations bill on March 3, 1879, and sent the legislation to President Hayes. Republican Hayes, a former governor of Ohio who reestablished his state's geological survey under Newberry (1869–74) (Hoogenboom, 1995, p. 218), signed the measure on the same day. Specifically, the founders established the USGS for "the [scientific] classification of the public lands and the examination of the Geological Structure; mineral resources and products of the national domain" (U.S. Stat. L., v. 20 [March 3, 1879], p. 394).[3] The politician and scientist reformers created the USGS as a bureau of practical geology: in Hewitt's view, one similar to the Geological Survey of New Jersey, whose operations he earlier helped to oversee. They intended the agency to aid the mineral-mining industry's efforts to provide materials in response to a construction and currency crisis in an increasingly industrialized America still recovering from the economic depression that followed the financial panic of 1873.

The law's USGS section also founded a Public Lands Commission (for codifying and improving the land laws), on which King and Powell served, and discontinued the three competing western surveys led by Ferdinand Hayden (Interior), Powell (Interior), and Lt. George Wheeler (Army Engineers)—although many of their functions passed to the USGS.[4] The reformers did not succeed in founding a "Coast and Interior Survey" (including the Coast and Geodetic Survey) to provide all federal geodetic, land-parceling (cadastral), and topographic surveys, or in restricting the General Land Office to public-land sales and records.

[2] The Smithsonian (until 1874) and the Department of the Interior (thereafter) supervised Maj. Powell (1834–1902) and his U.S. Geographical and Geological Survey of the Rocky Mountain Region (1871–79). See Worster (2001).

[3] For additional perspective on the founding of the USGS, see Rabbitt (1979, v. 1, p. 262–288).

[4] Hayden (1828–87) led the U.S. Geological and Geographical Survey of the Territories (1867–79); Wheeler (1842–1905) planned to have his U.S. Geographical Surveys West of the One-Hundredth Meridian (1871–79) map the entire nation. See Foster (1994) and Guth (1999).

Hayes's Attorney General's office upset Hewitt's and King's attempt to extend USGS operations countrywide by ruling that "national domain" in the agency's establishing statute meant the public lands. Hayes, influenced principally by Schurz and Newberry, but also by Newcomb, Marsh, James Hall, Powell,[5] and many other scientists within and outside the National Academy of Sciences, nominated King as USGS director in March 1879. The Senate confirmed King in April, he took his oath of office in May, and the USGS began official operations on July 1. King appointed five principal geologists: Hayden, Franklin Emmons and Arnold Hague (veterans of King's predecessor survey), G.K. (Grove Karl) Gilbert (who served with Wheeler and then Powell), and Raphael Pumpelly (Missouri's state geologist during 1871–73).

King had already sought statutory authority to overturn the decision by the Attorney General's office. On June 28, 1879, John Atkins (D-Tennessee), chairman of the House Committee on Appropriations in the Democratic-controlled 46th Congress, introduced, at King's request, a joint resolution (HR 116) to amend and explain without further ambiguity the USGS establishing statute by inserting "and the States" (U.S. Congressional Record, 46th congress, 1st Session, p. 2420) after "national domain." Subsequent debate modified the addition to "and he [the Director] may extend his examination into the States, not to interfere, however, with any geological survey now being made by the States" (U.S. Congressional Record, 46th Congress, 1st Session, p. 2423). The representatives passed HR 116 and sent it to the Senate that same day, but that chamber's Committee on Appropriations, chaired by Henry Davis (D-West Virginia), did not concur before the Senate adjourned on July 1.

Enacting HR 116 would have to wait until the 46th Congress convened its second session in December. To extend the geographic coverage of the federal work in economic geology in the meantime, King transferred 20 percent of the USGS direct appropriation of $100,000 for 1879–80 ($75,000 less than the total received by the three ongoing predecessor agencies in 1878–79) to Interior's 10th Census, led by Francis Walker, for the cooperative gathering and analysis of mineral and mining statistics nationwide. King and Pumpelly, now chief of the USGS Mining Geology Division, appointed geologist Bailey Willis and many other specialists to Pumpelly's Census unit (1879–81).

Four days after Congress's second session began on December 1, 1880, King tried again to extend officially USGS operations nationwide. King sent Schurz a copy of a letter, written under Davis's direction, "requesting an official construction of the law relating to the field of the U.S. Geological

---

[5] Powell, deciding that he could not defeat Hayden for USGS director, supported King's candidacy.

Survey" (King, 1879a) and what "national domain" meant thereby. Davis sent a copy of HR 116 to King on December 8, asking how passage would influence USGS work. King responded on December 15 that "the American people...cannot afford to grope in ignorance about its own vast [mineral] resources," soon, King estimated, to yield $1 billion annually. "Such accurate information," King continued, required a national effort. It "cannot be obtained by private individuals" or "by individual states" for reasons of great expense required, limited organizational size and geographic-geologic experience, and lack of comparative data about mineral occurrences nationwide (King, 1879b).

Marsh, again National Academy of Sciences vice president after Rogers's election as president in April 1879, continued to support King's goal. In February 1880, King sent Rogers a copy of a second and similar letter written to Davis in January and asked Rogers (Virginia's state geologist during 1835–43) for his opinion of the proposed extension nationwide. Agassiz, Edward Cope (formerly with Hayden and Wheeler, but still Marsh's bitter rival in paleontology), Dana, Archibald Geikie (British Geological Survey), Hayden, and Josiah Whitney (Harvard) campaigned actively in letters and in print against what they termed a usurpation. Rogers, in replying on March 20, enthusiastically supported the extension, emphasizing that members of Marsh's NAS committee should not object when Congress decided not to accept all their advice and reminding them that Congress did not ask the NAS to comment on HR 116 (Rogers, 1880).[6]

King then sent telegrams to 10 of the 15 active and two former state geologists, and agricultural chemist Eugene Hilgard[7] (Berkeley), to announce a second attempt at extension in Congress during the spring. To allay actively promoted fears of abridging state rights, King emphasized that the USGS would not make surveys of states. The USGS, he continued, only sought "to follow such general questions as happen at any time to be under investigation wherever the facts may lead regardless of political lines." King urged "the inauguration and continuance of State surveys" and wished "to cooperate with them to the mutual advantage of both parties." He asked his colleagues if they thought "the general extension...desirable to meet the practical and scientific needs of the people and the Government" and, if so, did they "wish to cooperate with him"[8] (King, 1880).

Thomas Chamberlin (Wisconsin), John Collett (Indiana), George Cook (New Jersey), James Hall (New York), Hilgard, Charles Hitchcock (New Hampshire, 1868–78), Peter Lesley (Pennsylvania), George Little (Georgia),

---

[6] Rogers's draft of this letter is in the William Barton Rogers Papers, Massachusetts Institute of Technology Archives, Cambridge, Mass.

[7] Hilgard (1833–1916) led the university's Agricultural Experiment Station. California had discontinued Whitney's state geological survey (1860–74) and did not appoint a state mineralogist until 1880 and that title changed to state geologist in 1961.

[8] The replies, by telegram and letter, are dated February 26 through March 1, 1880.

Newberry, James Safford (Tennessee), Nathaniel Shaler (Kentucky), and Eugene Smith (Alabama) all thought the cooperative work with the USGS important, necessary, and useful—economically, politically, and scientifically. Newberry demolished the state-rights argument by urging acceptance in science of the Civil War's outcome. All but Cook promised King their hearty cooperation. Cook thought the USGS should first prove itself by successful operation on the public lands before the agency went nationwide.[9]

King's second and third efforts to extend USGS operations into the eastern states also proved unsuccessful. Early in March 1880, Sen. Davis reported out of his committee an amended version of HR 116. After debate in May, the Senate and the House, despite pleas from Atkins, Davis, Hewitt, and others, voted to delete from USGS appropriations for fiscal year 1880–81 the phrase "when requested by the authorities thereof" (U.S. Congressional Record, 46th Congress, 2nd Session, p. 3159 [Senate, May 10], 3927 [House, May 28]), added after "States." Congress also reduced to $150,000 the $350,000 that King and Schurz requested as an initial increase toward the $500,000 needed for the expanded work and parity with the sum long given to the Coast and Geodetic Survey. King repeated his arguments for the extension in the USGS initial annual report finished in November, the month the Republicans kept the presidency and regained the House and the Senate. Davis renewed his efforts in the third session that began in December, and again in January 1881, but the often-revised HR 116 died when Congress adjourned on March 3.

King resigned on March 11, having planned to serve as director only long enough to staff the USGS and organize its work. Congressional opposition to increased funding and the extension reinforced this decision. New President James Garfield, who did not retain Schurz at Interior, consulted only King and Smithsonian Secretary Spencer Baird about a successor; both recommended Powell, and the Senate confirmed him a week later. Atkins, Davis, and other supporters of King and Powell in the new and Republican-dominated 47th Congress again strove to extend USGS operations nationwide. Atkins's initial attempt in 1882 to authorize USGS investigations in the Appalachian region died in committee.

On July 11, 1882, Atkins introduced to the full House an amendment to the USGS clause in the civil-expenses bill for 1882–83 to authorize the agency "to continue the preparation of a geological map of the United States" (U.S. Congressional Record, 47th Congress, 1st Session, p. 5923). Hewitt and many representatives who either supported or opposed founding the USGS and extending its work into the eastern states remained in the

---

[9] King did not similarly query State Geologists Samuel Aughey (Nebraska, "honorary"), Hiram Cutting (Vermont), Washington Kerr (North Carolina), Carl Rominger (Michigan), and Amos Worthen (Illinois).

House. Frank Hiscock (R-New York), who approved the Coast and Geodetic Survey's cross-country extension, but not the USGS's eastward expansion, objected (on a point of order) to Atkins's amendment as a new work. During the subsequent debate, Joseph Blackburn (D-Kentucky) and others again raised the state-right argument, but John White (R-Kentucky), Atkins, and others opposed it. Atkins, a Confederate colonel during the war, told his colleagues that "four years of experience taught me to modify my State-right views considerably" and "that the extreme views once entertained by that political school have passed away" (U.S. Congressional Record, 47th Congress, 1st Session, p. 5926). Abram Fulkerson (D-Virginia), in supporting the extension, also urged his colleagues to fund it by approving the proposed increase of the USGS direct appropriation to $222,000, noting that Britain provided "annually for geological purposes alone...near five times as much as the Appropriations Committee recommends for our vast and unexplored domain" (U.S. Congressional Record, 47th Congress, 1st Session, p. 5927). The representatives approved both the bill's extension of USGS authority and its larger appropriation, the senators agreed on August 2, and President Chester Arthur signed the legislation 5 days later. Of the USGS's new total, $10,000 would go to continue gathering statistics about "mines and mining other than gold and silver and in making chemical analyses of iron, coal, and oil" (U.S. Stat. L., v. 22 [Aug. 7, 1882], p. 329).

By 1882, the reformers had failed to revive Wheeler's survey, or establish an American equivalent of the British Ordnance Survey, to prepare all of the needed surveys of measurement and position. Under the new authorization for a national geologic map, Powell expanded USGS programs in topographic mapping (led by Henry Gannett, formerly with Hayden and then the 10th Census) and in general geology. Powell did so, to King's dismay, at the expense of those in economic geology, for which the USGS had been founded. King devoted most topographic mapping by the USGS to support its mining-district investigations. He also funded a lesser effort to continue Powell's earlier reconnaissance-scale mapping in the Southwest, as part of the General Geology Division's work toward acquiring a better understanding of America's geology to support the mandated economic work to help develop and discover deposits. Each part of King's USGS program in applied economic geology contained some basic research, so that, in King's words, as paraphrased by USGS Chief Geologist Walter Mendenhall, there always would be new "science to apply" (Mendenhall, 1929, p. 12). King's goals in increasing and diffusing geologic knowledge included preparing a more accurate geologic map of the United States than those published by the Ninth Census in the 1870's.

Powell, to support his goal of producing a national topographic map as a precursor to completing improved geologic coverage countrywide, began cooperative mapping programs with some of the eastern states. The participating states wished to have 15-minute (1:62,500-scale) coverage to use as base maps for compiling their geologic and other data, and for preparing improved topographic and other statewide maps. Powell, who succeeded in increasing USGS direct appropriations by the end of his initial decade to $200,000 more than King's yearly goal of $500,000, arranged cofunded and multiyear topographic programs with Massachusetts and New Jersey (1884), Connecticut and Rhode Island (1887), and New York (1892).

By then, the USGS had undergone major financial and organizational changes. The report in 1886 of the 2-year review of federal bureaus by the bipartisan Allison Commission (during the 48th and 49th Congresses) recorded criticisms of Powell's policies and programs that led to new statutes that required the USGS first to specify its estimates for publications (U.S. Stat. L., v. 24 [Aug. 4, 1886], p. 255) and then to line-itemize its entire budget (U.S. Stat. L., v. 24 [March 3, 1887], p. 527).[10] In 1888, the 50th Congress and President Grover Cleveland responded to appeals from Northern Plains farmers and ranchers for help following their devastating losses during recent summer droughts and harsh winters by establishing an Irrigation Survey within the USGS. Cleveland's Attorney General's office ruled the public lands closed to entry until Powell's new organization fixed the sites of the needed dams, reservoirs, and canals. The decision also denied federal dowry lands to six new states—Idaho, Montana, North Dakota, South Dakota, Washington, and Wyoming—that entered the union in 1889–90. When Powell's Irrigation Survey failed to provide the required information promptly and in full, the 51st Congress and President Benjamin Harrison in 1890 discontinued the Irrigation Survey and required half of USGS topographic funds to be expended west of the 100th meridian (U.S. Stat. L., v. 26 [Aug. 30, 1890], p. 391), reopened the public domain, and granted the new states their dowry lands.

When the USGS could not respond adequately to a renewed currency crisis in the early 1890's, the 52nd Congress and Harrison slashed USGS direct appropriations in August 1892 from $705,000 in 1891–92 to $470,000 for 1892–93 and reduced the agency's statutory scientific staff from 24 to 11 persons, but they kept the economic activities they thought practical and valuable (U.S. Stat. L., v. 27 [Aug. 5, 1892], p. 370–371). Powell responded by reducing the whole USGS force by 15 percent, a decrease that fell most heavily on the geologic unit. Economic geologists George Becker, Emmons, and Pumpelly, and paleontologist Marsh (who succeeded Rogers as National Academy of Sciences president in 1883), were among the casualties. Powell still refused to change his ways. He also ignored

---

[10] USGS block-funded appropriations were not restored until 1950.

King's warnings and a new congressional investigation, while lobbying (unsuccessfully) to have the USGS transferred from Interior to Agriculture.

Personal and professional reasons kept King from returning as director, as many in Congress, industry, and the USGS wished.[11] Instead, King facilitated the USGS's recovery. To restore the geologic unit in 1893, King recommended USGS Chief Paleontologist Charles Walcott[12] to Interior Secretary Hoke Smith to be the geologist-in-charge of geology.[13] The 53rd Congress and President Cleveland finally forced Powell to resign, effective June 30, 1894, by the time-honored method of reducing his salary.[14] Cleveland, at King's recommendation, nominated Walcott on May 11 to succeed Powell, and the Senate confirmed Walcott on May 28. By that time, the USGS had issued two editions (1884, 1893) of its own geologic map of the United States (at a scale of 1:7,100,000), compiled on bases produced by the Census and then by the USGS.[15]

Walcott, quickly demonstrating that the USGS would respond to America's principal economic and educational needs, restored congressional confidence in and funding for the agency, which rose to $1 million in the next decade. He also significantly expanded USGS–state cooperation. Walcott continued the topographic arrangement with New York and began similar programs with Maryland and North Carolina in 1896 (the year the USGS gained authority for benchmarks and map sales), and West Virginia in 1898. Walcott initiated similar cofunded efforts in geology, beginning with Pennsylvania in 1899. He also sought and gained continuous and growing federal funding "for gauging the streams and determining the water supply of the United States, including the investigation of underground currents and artesian wells [decried by Powell] in arid and semiarid sections" (U.S. Stat. L., v. 28 [Aug. 18, 1894], p. 398).[16] Walcott began cooperative work in hydrography with Nevada, New York, and Pennsylvania in 1900. For fiscal year 1907–08, 15 states contributed a total of almost $104,000 to the topographic portion of USGS "cooperative mapping and research." An additional $5,000 came from Pennsylvania for work in geology, and New York provided $2,450 for continuing joint investigations of water resources.

---

[11] King's double life after his clandestine marriage in 1888, the losses he sustained in the financial panic of 1893, and the lingering effects of injuries incurred during field work led to a nervous breakdown that October. King recovered mentally, but not financially, by May 1894. See Wilkins and Hinkley (1988, v. 1, p. 386–396), Nelson (2008a, p. 122), and Sandweiss (in press).

[12] King, at James Hall's suggestion, hired Walcott (1850–1927) in 1879 as the USGS's most junior geologist. For an overview, see Yochelson (1998, 2001).

[13] Walcott rehired Becker (1847–1919) and Emmons (1841–1911) in 1893 and gave Marsh an honorary appointment. Pumpelly (1837–1923) resumed his career as a consultant. See Champlin (1994).

[14] Powell's salary was reduced from $6,000 to $5,000, but he resigned before the reduction took place on July 1. For additional perspective on Powell's decline and fall, see Rabbitt (1980, p. 189–239) and Nelson (2008b, p. 150–151).

[15] For the evolution of these maps, see Nelson (1999a).

[16] The initial appropriation of $12,500 rose to $200,000 in 1902–03.

State geologists, as investigators as well as managers, also contributed to these cooperative efforts. By July 1907, when Walcott resigned as director to become secretary of the Smithsonian, a number of former or current state geologists had or still served as full-time, part-time, or honorary members of the USGS. Powell began the practice of appointing state and academic geologists to part-time (or "when-actually-employed") positions on the USGS staff to add their expertise to advance the agency's programs, but also to deflect any potential or real criticism. Walcott continued some of these appointments, now made less necessary by the USGS staff's growth in size and experience. By 1907, although Cook, Hall, and Newberry were dead, Foster Bain (Illinois), Ernest Buckley (Missouri), Thomas Chamberlin (at the University of Chicago since 1892), William Clark (Maryland), Erasmus Haworth (Kansas), Henry Kummel (New Jersey), and Israel White (West Virginia) still served as part-time USGS employees. John Branner (Arkansas, 1887–93) was no longer among them.

Branner, at Stanford since 1891, resigned his part-time appointment with the USGS in 1906 in a dispute with Walcott about Branner's delay in publishing the results of his USGS-funded work on Arkansas coals in 1886–87. The absence of these results became more significant in 1906 when President Theodore Roosevelt asked Interior Secretary James Garfield (the slain president's son) to determine which federal coal lands were so valuable economically that they should be withdrawn from entry to prevent further fraudulent acquisitions. That request changed the scientific classification of the public lands by the USGS to one made and reported to the General Land Office before their disposition. Walcott asked Branner to send in his unpublished results on the Arkansas fields and promised him full credit. When Branner asked for more time to publish, Walcott refused, choosing to have the required investigation completed more rapidly by a full-time USGS employee. Branner resigned, but Walcott held the resignation for several months until Branner went public in a letter to *Science*. Walcott replied in the same journal that responsibility for serving the public promptly and well overrode any continued professional courtesy (Rabbitt, 1986, v. 3, p. 45–46, 50–52).

To respond to other occasional complaints from some state geologists about USGS intrusions, lack of coordination in publications, and other issues, Walcott met informally twice in December 1906 with two groups. He arranged a meeting in Washington with several Atlantic Coast state geologists to plan cooperative studies, especially in groundwater. Walcott also discussed mutual concerns with Bain and some of his fellow state geologists at the annual meeting of the Geological Society of America in New York City. In May 1907, Walcott hosted a similar meeting—of the Association of the State Geologists of the Mississippi Valley, founded a year earlier at the University of Chicago by Bain and six other state geologists. The attending state geologists requested greater cooperation from the USGS and the GSA, especially in forming a general committee to stabilize American geologic nomenclature. GSA's national meeting in Albuquerque that December did not yield a similar turnout.

In 1908, the USGS again invited the state geologists to meet in Washington. George Smith (Fig. 2),[17] whom Garfield and Theodore Roosevelt chose during the preceding year to succeed Walcott as director, asked the 30 state geologists and one state mineralogist to convene in Washington May 11–12, just before the conference of governors[18] held at the White House (May 13–15) to promote better management of the nation's natural resources, and to plan for adding to and improving USGS–state cooperative work in geology, hydrography, mineral statistics, and topography (Rabbitt, 1986, p. 74–75). On May 12,[19] the 22 attendees agreed to form an Association of American State Geologists[20] to promote their mutual interests and their science. They chose Kummel (president), Bain (secretary), and Joseph Pratt (North Carolina) as their Executive Committee, and John Clarke (New York) to join Arthur Keith (USGS) on a North American Committee on Geological Nomenclature.

The AASG's members pledged to lobby for more federal and state funds for topographic mapping and to promote other joint interests, and sent copies of their resolutions to Roosevelt. From efforts based on these and other resolves came the U.S. Bureau of Mines, founded in 1910[21] (U.S. Stat. L., v. 36 [May 16, 1910], p. 369) by transferring to it the USGS Technologic Branch, established in 1907 by Walcott, who appointed USGS geologist Joseph Holmes (North Carolina, 1891–1905) to direct the branch's fuels- and structural-materials testing. Interior Secretary Richard Ballinger and President William Taft selected Holmes to lead the USBM. The joint drive to increase funding for topographic mapping yielded greater sums and statutory requirements in 1926 (U.S. Stat. L., v. 44 [May 10, 1926], p. 486) and 1928 (U.S. Stat. L., v. 45 [March 7, 1928], p. 232) that ensured an equal sharing of the costs by the federal and state governments for continuing cooperative work in topography and water resources. Subsequent

---

[17] Smith (1871–1944) joined the USGS in 1896 and served with Secretary Garfield on the Keep Commission. When Garfield chose Smith, rather than USGS Chief Geologist Willard Hayes, to replace Walcott in 1907, Smith had only been chief of the Section of Petrology for a year. For a brief overview, see Nelson (1999b).

[18] Thomas Chamberlin was among the conference's speakers.

[19] The minutes name Israel White as the 23rd participant, but he is not listed among the attendees; see AASG (1908).

[20] The state geologists' Board of Geologists, organized in the 1830's, passed into the American Association of Geologists (1840) and Naturalists (1842), and then to the American Association for the Advancement of Science (1848), with its Special Committee to Memorialize the State Governments on Geological Surveys (1849). The 15-member special committee initially included Louis Agassiz, Joseph Henry, and William Rogers.

[21] Structural-materials testing passed to the Bureau of Standards.

Figure 2. Dr. George (Otis) Smith, fourth director of the U.S. Geological Survey, who served from 1907 to 1930. He was instrumental in planning the founding meeting of AASG in 1908.

mutual efforts produced the USGS–Kentucky Geological Survey mapping project (topography, 1949–59; geology, 1960–78) that provided 1:24,000-scale geologic coverage of Kentucky's 707 quadrangles and state geologic maps at scales of 1:250,000 (McDowell and others, 1981) and 1:500,000 (Noger, 1988). The cooperative COGEOMAP project followed in the 1980's and included 31 states by 1987. The 5-year renewals of the National Geologic Mapping Act (U.S. Stat. L., v. 106 [May 18, 1992], p. 166) have, so far, ensured the continuity of its three programs—FEDMAP (federal mapping and support activities), STATEMAP (state-mapping operations), and EDMAP (educational-support activities)—to extend USGS–state cooperation beyond its 125th anniversary.

References Cited

AASG, 1908, Minutes of the organizational meeting of the Association of American State Geologists, Washington, D.C., May 12, 1908: AASG scanned archives, www.stategeologists.org.

Champlin, P., 1994, Raphael Pumpelly: Gentleman geologist of the Gilded Age: Tuscaloosa, Ala., University of Alabama Press, 273 p.

Foster, M., 1994, Strange genius: The life of Ferdinand Vandeveer Hayden: Niwot, Colo., Roberts Rinehart, 443 p.

Guth, P.L., 1999, Wheeler, George Montague, *in* Garraty, J.A., and Carnes, M.C., eds., American national biography: New York, Oxford University Press, v. 23, p. 136–138.

Hoogenboom, A., 1995, Rutherford B. Hayes: Warrior and president: Lawrence, Kans., University Press of Kansas, 626 p.

King, C., 1878, Systematic geology: Washington, D.C., U.S. Government Printing Office.

King, C., 1879a, Letter to C. Schurz, Dec. 5, 1879: National Archives and Records Administration, microfilm 152, record group 57, USGS letters sent, 1879–1895, roll 1.

King, C., 1879b, Letter to H. Davis, Dec. 15, 1879: National Archives and Records Administration, microfilm 152, record group 57, USGS letters sent, 1879–1895, roll 1.

King, C., 1880, Telegram to state geologists, Feb. 26, 1880: National Archives and Records Administration, microfilm 152, record group 57, USGS letters sent, 1879–1895, roll 1.

Marsh, O.C., 1880, Odontornithes: A monograph on the extinct toothed birds of North America: New Haven, Conn., Printed for the Museum, 201 p.

McDowell, R.C., Grabowski, G.J., and Moore, S.L., 1981, Geologic map of Kentucky: U.S. Geological Survey, scale 1:250,000, 3 sheets.

Mendenhall, W.C., 1929, Geologic Branch, *in* U.S. Geological Survey 50th annual report: U.S. Geological Survey, p. 9–29.

Nelson, C.M., 1999a, Toward a reliable geologic map of the United States, 1803–1893, *in* Carter, E.C., II, ed., Surveying the record: North American scientific exploration to 1930: Memoirs of the American Philosophical Society, v. 231, p. 51–74.

Nelson, C.M., 1999b, Smith, George Otis, *in*, Garraty, J.A., and Carnes, M.C., eds., American national biography: New York, Oxford University Press, v. 20, p. 182–184.

Nelson, C.M., 2008a, King, Clarence Rivers, *in* Koertge, N., ed., New dictionary of scientific biography: Detroit, Charles Scribner's Sons, v. 4, p. 120–123.

Nelson, C.M., 2008b, Powell, John Wesley, *in* Koertge, N., ed., New dictionary of scientific biography: Detroit, Charles Scribner's Sons, v. 6, p. 149–152.

Noger, M.C., comp., 1988, Geologic map of Kentucky: U.S. Geological Survey, scale 1:500,000.

Rabbitt, M.C., 1979, Minerals, lands, and geology for the common defence and general welfare: Volume 1, before 1879: U.S. Government Printing Office, 331 p.

Rabbitt, M.C., 1980, Minerals, lands, and geology for the common defence and general welfare: Volume 2, 1879–1904: U.S. Government Printing Office, 407 p.

Rabbitt, M.C., 1986, Minerals, lands, and geology for the common defence and general welfare: Volume 3, 1904–1939: U.S. Government Printing Office, 479 p.

Rogers, W., 1880, Letter to C. King, March 20, 1880: National Archives and Records Administration, microfilm 590, record group 57, USGS letters received, 1879–1901, roll 4.

Sandweiss, M.A., in press, Passing strange: The secret life of Clarence King: New York, Penguin Press.

Wilkins, T., and Hinkley, C.L., 1988, Clarence King: A biography [rev. and enlarged ed.]: Albuquerque, N.M., University of New Mexico Press, 524 p.

Worster, D., 2001, A river running west: The life of John Wesley Powell: New York, Oxford University Press, 673 p.

Yochelson, E.L., 1998, Charles Doolittle Walcott, paleontologist: Kent, Ohio, Kent State University Press, 510 p.

Yochelson, E.L., 2001, Smithsonian Institution secretary, Charles Doolittle Walcott: Kent, Ohio, Kent State University Press, 589 p.

AASG Business and Accomplishments by Decade

This chapter is a decade-by-decade summary of Association of American State Geologists' events, issues, and accomplishments. Several different authors contributed to this chapter, so the approach to summarizing each decade varies from author to author. The activities of AASG have been recorded in minutes, correspondence, reports, and other documents preserved in the archives, some for more than 100 years. The hard-copy archives of AASG are maintained by the Kansas Geological Survey at the University of Kansas Library. More than 45,000 pages of these archives have been scanned and converted into a format that is accessible from the Internet. Currently, the Alaska Geological Survey maintains the AASG Website. The Kentucky Geological Survey created and maintains the online archives. The work of scanning and conversion of the archives for an online retrieval system was the work of Richard Smath and James Cobb at the Kentucky Geological Survey. The scanning and indexing process started in 2002 and was completed in 2006. The authors of each decade summary worked from the scanned records that could be displayed on their computer screens while composing their summaries. This technique, plus the use of optical character recognition software, proved to be an effective method for gathering information for this chapter. Appendix 2: Summaries of Annual Meetings also gives names, dates, places, attendees, and topics of discussion for each annual meeting. That appendix serves as a table of contents to the business, activities, and people of AASG over 100 years.

Accounts of the activities of state geologists in the first decade of the 1900's to create AASG and collaborate with and influence the federal government are given in several previous chapters of this volume (chapters 1, 2, 3, and 4).

Before 1909:
The Founding and Organizing of AASG
James C. Cobb *(Kentucky; AASG Historian)*

There is a description in the archives of a meeting on August 8, 1891, in New York City, hosted by Columbia University, to form the U.S. Association of Government Geologists. The meeting was chaired by Maj. John W. Powell, with Arthur Winslow (Missouri) serving as secretary. The agenda included remarks by Powell for calling the meeting, a plan of organization, purpose, and results to be derived. The official name and subsequent meeting in December 1891 were proposed. The meeting was attended by the following state geologists: James Hall (New York), James M. Safford (Tennessee), J.W. Spenser (Georgia), Eugene A. Smith (Alabama), J.A. Holmes (North Carolina), Arthur Winslow (Missouri), Edwin T. Dumble (Texas), and Joshua Lindahl (Illinois). Details of the discussions and subsequent meeting are unfortunately not available, but the idea for government geologists to organize for the common good started before 1900.

The tasks needing to be done in the first decade of 1900 were to formalize the organization, create bylaws and a system of governance, select leaders, obtain support from all existing state geological surveys, and embark on the mission of influencing the federal government and state geological surveys on issues related to geology, mineral resources, water, hazards, and topographic mapping for the good of the states and the nation. Chapters 2 and 4 of this volume cover in detail the founding of AASG. Details from the 1908 annual meeting minutes give a flavor of the first meeting, however. On May 12, 1908, at 2:30 p.m., 22 state geologists met in a USGS conference room in Washington, D.C., with officers of the USGS to consider forming a permanent organization of state geologists. Henry B. Kummel, state geologist of New Jersey, was made temporary chairman of the meeting and H. Foster Bain, state geologist of Illinois, was made temporary secretary. They discussed forming the organization and what objectives might be accomplished by it. A motion was made to form the Association of American State Geologists. Kummel and Bain were appointed to form a committee to prepare bylaws in accordance with the suggestions made during the discussions. Out of the bylaws came the Association name, offices to be filled, and power to call meetings and arrange programs. Officers would be elected annually. Committees would be formed to conduct business as desired. The business of the Association would initially be conducted through briefs circulated among the members. A motion was made to accept the committee's bylaws as the bylaws of the Association, and thus the AASG was created. The temporary officers, Kummel and Bain, were installed as the first president and secretary, and Joseph H. Pratt, state geologist of North Carolina, was elected as the executive committeeman. A committee of William B. Clark (Maryland), Israel C. White (West Virginia), and Pratt was appointed by the president to look into the possibilities of gaining franking privileges for state surveys. The first external business considered was a resolution regarding an increase in federal appropriations for topographic work, because state and national interests so closely coincided in this area. The resolution recommended that the federal appropriation match the available state appropriations. It passed by unanimous vote. The text of this resolution is given in its entirety in chapter 1 of this volume. It is interesting to read in the minutes given in chapter 3 that a copy of the resolution was to be presented to the first Governors Conference and President Roosevelt at the White House with greetings and respect of the AASG. Several founders had personal invitations to the Governors Conservation Conference, as can be seen in the biographies in Appendix 3 of this volume.

The first Governors Conference was called by President Theodore Roosevelt and held at the White House May 13–15, 1908. It was to address the importance of conservation of natural resources and was attended by all but 12 governors as well as cabinet secretaries, federal officials, members of Congress, Supreme Court justices, leaders of industry, experts in the field of conservation, representatives of trade and professional organizations, and other dignitaries. Minutes of this meeting, as well as President Roosevelt's address, are on the National Governors Association Website.

Was it a coincidence that the Governors Conference began on the day following AASG's founding meeting or was there prior planning to achieve some direct effect on those proceedings? The AASG minutes shed no light on this question, but the coincidence is too obvious to ignore, and the fact that the resolution on topographic mapping was to be delivered to the Governors Conference makes the coincidence even more likely to have been planned. The National Governors Association marks its founding from the meeting in 1908, the same as AASG.

The Executive Committee called the second meeting for December 30, 1908. Fourteen members met for lunch at the Hopkins Club in Baltimore, hosted by William B. Clark, state geologist of Maryland. Secretary Foster Bain (Illinois) informed the group that all active state geological surveys had expressed a desire to join AASG. A corrected list of active state geologists was provided. A motion was made to empower the president to appoint a committee on conservation to cooperate with the National Conservation Commission. Also, the secretary was instructed to bring the desirability of appointing state geologists to the state conservation commissions to the attention of the governors.

Legislation creating the U.S. Bureau of Mines had passed in the House and was in the Senate. AASG members discussed the desirability of the new bureau being nonpolitical and technical in character and therefore that members should make their opinions known in Congress on this matter. The AASG strongly supported creation of the Bureau of Mines and took an active role in lobbying for it in Congress.

A letter about topographic mapping, federal appropriations, and cost sharing had been circulated to all state geologists in October 1908. That letter is reproduced below, because although written 100 years ago, its issues, arguments, and questions are as relevant today as they were then. Anyone in AASG who worked on the National Geologic Mapping Act and subsequent reauthorizations will certainly appreciate the points made in this letter about shifting of costs to the states and rescinding the 50-50 cost sharing for an increased burden to the states.

Trenton, N.J., October 31, 1908

To the Members of the Association of State Geologists:

Gentlemen:

Your executive committee takes the liberty of presenting for your consideration the following regarding topographic surveys.

As you are aware, for many years the U.S. Geological Survey has been engaged in making a topographic map of the United States. This was originally taken up to afford a proper base for geologic maps but the work has expanded until at present general purpose maps are being made and the sheets are probably in as much demand and of as much use to non-geologists as to ourselves. The law has in the meantime remained unchanged and there is now no specific provision for any such maps except for the original purpose-base maps for geology. The topographic mapping has gone forward faster than the geologic mapping so that two years ago the House Committee on Appropriations felt warranted in reducing the current appropriation from $350,000 to $300,000; at which sum the appropriation has since remained.

From time to time various states, desiring to obtain maps showing greater detail than the Federal standard or to provide for more rapid extension of the work in their territory, have entered into agreement with the Director of the U.S.G.S. for a division of expense on a basis of half and half. There is no specific authority authorizing this nor none forbidding it and the basis of division has always been considered an equal one in view of the dual use of the maps for State and Federal purposes.

With the cut in the appropriation it became necessary to drop some of the work and the Secretary of the Interior has ruled that not more than one third of the appropriation, or in this case $100,000, may be used in these cooperative surveys. To meet all the cooperation offered by the States this year would have required $150,000. In many states the appropriation is contingent on this cooperation so that money has been turned back into the state treasuries at the time that there was a large and unsatisfied demand for the maps.

It is evident that there is a disposition on the part of Congress to throw the burden of this work more and more on the states and it becomes our duty to consider whether this is equitable or in accord with sound policy. In most, but not all, the states the cooperation has been through the state geologist so that in the main the burden of action rest on us.

It needs no argument we believe to show that the maps are properly the work of both State and Federal organizations and that the division of expense which has heretofore obtained is essentially just. In the western public land states where the Federal Government has large holdings it may be expected to assume a larger share of the cost and at any point where either State or Federal government has land or other special interests it is manifestly proper for either to make at its own expense any special maps needed. Over the country as a whole however it does not seem proper that the states should be put to the whole expense of a general purpose map since the Federal uses for such a map are so many and widespread.

As a matter of policy and also of economy it is believed that the work is better done under the general direction of a single corps than for each state to build up its own topographic survey. This is the opinion of your Chairman whose state is the only one which has made its own survey (the Federal Government contributing to the expense) and who feels that the eminent success in New Jersey was due to exceptional conditions not likely to obtain elsewhere. In our judgment therefore there can be no escape from the conclusion that the historical basis of division of expense is the correct one. If this basis is to be maintained it will be necessary in order to meet the entirely reasonable demands for progress made by the cooperating states, to either secure from the Secretary of the Interior a change in his ruling or from Congress an increase in the appropriation. The basis upon which the Secretary decided that one third only of the appropriation might be spent in cooperation is not known. It is possible that he could be induced to change. The better way however is evidently to have Congress fix the amount, if that can be done. Any attempt to do this will doubtless bring up the whole matter of the authority for a general purpose map and may require an amendment to the existing law. The initiative in this, as it seems to us, should come from the U.S. Geological Survey rather than from us.

We have ventured to lay this whole matter before you and to invite your instructions by letter. It is evidently a matter vital to many if not all of us and one eminently fitted for joint action. In order to bring it to a focus we would be glad to have you express yourselves as to:

(1) Do you think it advisable and would you join in an
effort to induce Congress to increase the existing
appropriation without any change in the law?

(2) Do you favor the Executive Committee asking the Secretary of the
Interior for his reasons in fixing the limit of one third and requesting him if
possible to remove it and make larger allotments for cooperative work?

(3) Do you consider the old basis of division equitable or
do you favor the State doing its own topographic work?

(4) Do you consider a change in the existing Federal law
necessary to provide for general purpose maps, and
if so will you support an effort to have this change made?

> Attention is called to the fact that prompt action is desirable since the month of November, between election and the assembling of Congress, is the time when Congressmen make their plans for the winter work. A letter or personal visit then is more effective then at any other time.
>
> Respectfully,
> Henry B. Kummel, Joseph Hyde Pratt, and H. Foster Bain
>
> P.S. Please address all replies to Mr. H. Foster Bain, Urbana, Ill.

It is obvious from this letter that the state geologist of that time faced obstacles in getting adequate and equitable funding for topographic mapping, as were encountered in enacting the National Geologic Mapping Act of 1992. The tactics of the federal government to shift financial burdens to the states have not changed in 100 years (see the chapter on the National Geologic Mapping Act and also the decade of the 1990's in this chapter).

The motivation of the USGS in hosting and providing logistical support for the fledgling AASG was possibly the support in Congress that state geologists could bring. Since many states at that time were conducting geologic investigations and mapping, there was also a strong motivation to bring better coordination, standards, and efficiencies to the geologic enterprise: motivations that remain strong to the present time. From its beginning, AASG pushed for federal funding for topographic mapping, creation of the Bureau of Mines, and proper credit for the states in the mineral resources work they did for the USGS.

The first decade of AASG was highly successful, with creation of a viable and effective organization, all states having geological surveys becoming members, lobbying for increased appropriations for topographic mapping, lobbying for the U.S. Bureau of Mines, and cooperation with the USGS. Some of the traditions set in the first decade have carried on to the present time. The foundation for a successful AASG in 2008 was solidly laid down in its first decade.

1910–19

James C. Cobb *(Kentucky; AASG Historian)*

The 1910 meeting was held in Washington, D.C., in May. President Henry B. Kummel presided, with Frank W. De Wolf, state geologist of Illinois, as secretary, and Israel C. White as executive committeeman. Eighteen state geologists attended the meeting. A plan was approved for a cooperative bulletin with the USGS on operations of geological surveys. This bulletin was published in 1911 as USGS Bulletin 465 (Hayes, 1911). This bulletin is discussed in chapter 1 and gives data on budgets and programs of the state geological surveys in 1910. The AASG statistician's report probably dates back to this bulletin. Some states were successful at getting state funding for important projects but needed more federal participation. The idea of collecting information on programs and levels of funding from the states was to show the amount of state money available and therefore the amount of federal matching money to be lobbied for in Congress.

Another topic that appears a number of times in this decade was publication rights and proper credit for cooperation with the USGS mineral resources program—state surveys receiving credit for the work they did in compiling mineral resources information for the USGS. Evidently the policy of the USGS had been to not give credit to state surveys or their staff for the data they provided. Also, the USGS did not allow the states to publish the data independently. This topic generated considerable discussion during the decade and was on the annual meeting agenda a number of times.

In 1912, Joseph H. Pratt moved to change the bylaws of the Association to elect officers at the winter meeting rather than the spring meeting, as had been the practice. Nominations for new officers were called and Richard Hice (Pennsylvania), Eugene Smith (Alabama), and Israel White (West Virginia) were nominated. Dr. Smith withdrew and White was elected. It was moved and carried that Frank De Wolf (Illinois) be elected secretary by acclamation. Henry Kummel (New Jersey) was elected executive committeeman. The first subject on the program was the proper construction of oil and gas wells to safeguard coal and water supplies. It was presented by Hice and discussed by White and De Wolf. On motions of Albert Purdue (Arkansas), a committee consisting of Hice, White, and De Wolf was selected to study the problem and to confer with the director of the Bureau of Mines, with a view to forming a uniform law for adoption by the states. It was understood that a later meeting would be called for those state geologists interested in the subject, for discussion of measures recommended by the committee.

In 1913, AASG was formally invited by Georgia Gov. Joseph W. Brown to meet in Atlanta in that year, but the AASG was already committed to meet with the Geological Society of America and could not accept the invitation. The 1913 annual meeting was held in December at Princeton, N.J., in conjunction with the Geological Society of America, with Princeton University acting as host. A listing for 1913 gives the names of state geologists for 48 states and territories, and the cooperative agreements each state had with the USGS in geology, topography, water resources, and mineral resources. For example, the Illinois State Geological Survey had cooperative programs in geology, topography, and mineral resources, but the Illinois Rivers and Lakes Commission had a cooperative program in water resources. The Iowa survey had cooperatives in all four areas, but the Kentucky Geological Survey had cooperatives only in geology, topography, and water resources. This list gives similar information for every state. One can speculate about the development of programs at each state geological survey and the influence, which was probably considerable, these cooperatives had on them.

Only scant information can be found about the 1914 annual meeting. It was held in December in Philadelphia, again in conjunction with the Geological Society of America. The business session approved support for the Kern-Foster Bill (selection of locations of mining experiment and safety stations under the U.S. Bureau of Mines). The efforts of previous lobbying must have been effective, because in 1914 there was a congressional hearing on the funding of topographic mapping. The title page of the report on that hearing, showing the names of the members of the committee, is reproduced here:

TOPOGRAPHIC AND HYDROGRAPHIC SURVEYS

No. 1
HEARINGS
BEFORE THE
COMMITTEE ON EXPENDITURES IN THE
INTERIOR DEPARTMENT
OF THE
HOUSE OF REPRESENTATIVES
ON
H.R. 13457
A BILL TO PROVIDE FOR A MORE EQUITABLE MEANS OF DISTRIBUTION OF
TOPOGRAPHIC AND HYDROGRAPHIC SURVEYS AND OTHER WORK OF THE
UNITED STATES GEOLOGICAL SURVEY AMONG THE SEVERAL STATES, AND
TO MAKE SUCH WORK MORE EFFECTIVE AND SERVICEABLE IN THE SEVERAL
STATES IN THE WORK OF IMPROVEMENT AND DEVELOPMENT

FEBRUARY 20, 1914
WASHINGTON, D.C.
GOVERNMENT PRINTING OFFICE

Rep. James M. Graham of Illinois was chair. Other members were Rep. Oscar Callaway (Texas), Rep. Tom Stout (Montana), Rep. Joseph A. Goulden (New York), Rep. Frank W. Mondell (Wyoming), Rep. Dudley M. Hughes (Georgia), and Rep. Charles H. Burke (South Dakota). John F. McCarron (Illinois) was clerk.

The 29 pages of testimony and responses to questions by USGS Director George O. Smith in this hearing show that the purpose of topographic mapping for the federal government was to create a base for geologic mapping in order to encourage mineral development in the United States. The states were seeing the great needs for detailed topographic mapping for many vital issues such as flood control, irrigation, roads, political boundaries, and many other applications essential to state interests. The wide philosophical gap between the federal and state concepts for topographic mapping led to inevitable differences over federal appropriations.

The first AASG field meeting was held in 1914 in Houghton, Mich., from August 27–September 1. Visits were planned to the Keweenaw Copper and Marquette Iron Districts. Field stops were planned at outcrops, mines, smelters, and the Michigan College of Mines, plus side trips to Mackinac Island and St. Ignace. Fourteen state geologists had reservations for the trip 17 days prior to its start. Accommodations on the ship *St. Ignace* from Detroit to Ishpeming and return had been reserved for the state geologists. The topics announced in advance for the business session were: (1) relations with the USGS, (2) topographic mapping and the distribution of federal efforts, and (3) Mississippian stratigraphic problems. The 1914 field meeting was a very ambitious undertaking and probably set a standard that has been followed to the present time.

The annual meeting for 1915 was held December 27 in Washington, D.C., and hosted by the USGS. The business session was very full, with AASG internal business, business of state surveys, and relations with federal agencies on the agenda. That scope of business was similar to what has been addressed at all AASG annual meetings for the past 90 years. The AASG internal business included the election of current officers for a second year by acclamation. An invitation from Oklahoma to hold a field meeting in the fall of 1916 was considered. The business of state geological surveys included exhibits of new maps and reports; encouragement for state surveys to assist in the war effort by locating deposits of pyrite, platinum, fluorite, iron, tin, tungsten, etc.; review of California laws governing drilling of oil and gas wells; role of state surveys in appraising mining property and mineral land for taxation; discussion of motorcycles and automobiles in survey field work and related expenses; policies for survey employees to engage in private work in their own states or in other states; policies regarding the distribution of oil reports to operators, landowners, and the press; the proper care of samples from well drillings; and finally, discussion of the maintenance of museums. What makes the 1915 meeting different was the long list of state geological survey issues that were discussed. AASG had become a mentoring organization for its members for the development of state survey programs. This focus on state geological survey methods and programs as a means of sharing information among the members has been carried on to the present time.

Under the topic of federal affairs, the U.S. Bureau of Mines was urged not to locate experiment stations without recommendations from state geologists; there were reports and discussions on allocations of federal funds for topographic surveys; a resolution passed requesting the director of the U.S. Geological Survey to notify state geologists regarding hearings on formation names and also to provide advance notice about each season's field programs. Was this move for better coordination a predecessor to what became in the 1980's the "AASG–USGS Cooperative Planning Agreement"? There were also expressions of a lean budget year for congressional appropriations for the USGS and the Bureau of Mines and suggestions were made for lobbying help from the state geologists through their delegations in Congress. This was 1915, and World War I was raging in Europe. The United States officially entered the war in 1917.

The following letter to AASG members reproduced below is included to show the style of communications in 1915 and the topics offered for the members to consider. Note that the address given for the meeting in 1915 was Ebbitt House in Washington, D.C.; much as the Cosmos Club has been in recent decades, the Ebbitt House may have been an early meeting place for state geologists. From information gained from the Ebbitt House Website, it was founded in 1856. President McKinley is said to have lived there during his tenure in Congress. Presidents Grant, Andrew Johnson, Cleveland, Theodore Roosevelt, and Harding supposedly refreshed themselves at the bar. Perhaps the state geologists used this for business and gatherings in the early 1900's.

ANNUAL BUSINESS MEETING
ASSOCIATION OF AMERICAN STATE GEOLOGISTS
2:30, December 27, 1915, Ebbitt House, Washington, D.C.

To Members of the Association:

Gentlemen:

The Executive Committee has called a meeting for the time and place mentioned above, and believes that enough members will be present to properly hold an election of officers and discuss the topics on the program to advantage. The meeting is set one day before that of the Geological Society in response to a resolution passed at the last meeting.

A field meeting in the spring or fall should probably be arranged for the coming year, and that will be a more appropriate occasion for a comprehensive program than the present time with its conflicting and overlapping meetings at Columbus and Washington.

PROGRAM

1: Exhibit of new maps and reports....

2: Laws governing the drilling of oil and gas wells....

3: Function of State Surveys in appraising mining properties and mineral land for taxation purposes....

4: Experience and expense of using motorcycles and automobiles in survey work. Bring your records.

5: New experiences with exhibits, high school collections, and publicity movements.

6: Private work. Should assistants be permitted to engage in private work within their state or in adjoining states or for local companies outside the state?

7: Should oil reports be distributed first to operators, the press, or to land owners? How to avoid "scoops."

8: Office key maps as guides to field notebooks and detailed office files. New Jersey and Illinois experiences. Have you any?

9: Care for sample drillings from wells—glass tubes, boxes, or other means? Experiences in Missouri and West Virginia. What is your method?

10: Results of interstate cooperation on the Mississippian will be presented by Professor Weller and others either to a later meeting of this Association or to a section of the Geological Society meeting.

11: A resolution of December 1911 requested the Director of the USGS to notify State Geologists regarding hearings of committee on formation names in cases affecting the several states; also a resolution requesting advice about each season's geological program in the several states. Have you received such advice from the Director?

This may be a lean year for congressional appropriations and both the Geological Survey and the Bureau of Mines in which all State Geologists have to intersect may need the help which we can easily give through home contact with our delegations in Congress. The Directors of both bureaus have been invited to bring to our meeting any topics desired.

It is hoped that two new State Geologists, W.H. Twenhofel of Kansas and Freeman Ward of South Dakota will be with us.

Very respectfully,
F.W. De Wolf, Secretary.

Annual meetings for 1916–18 were in New Albany, N.Y., St. Louis, Mo., and Baltimore, Md., respectively, showing that AASG was moving away from meetings only in East Coast cities and had ventured as far west as St. Louis, all in conjunction with the Geological Society of America. There was also a call for the president of AASG to be on the National Research Council during this period. This was the beginning of a valuable relationship between AASG and the National Research Council that has lasted for 90 years.

With few exceptions, the 1918 annual meeting business agenda could be used in 2008. Following is a list of issues from the 1918 annual meeting:

- Announced that the Mineral Administration Bill was approved.
- Called for closer cooperation with the U.S. Bureau of Mines.
- Discussed cooperative topographic mapping, costs and state allotments.
- Passed a motion for each state to prepare a statement of the amount of cooperative topographic funds asked from their legislature.
- Discussed cooperation between state geological surveys and university research.
- Passed a motion to appoint a committee to act with state highway and other organizations to secure sufficient appropriations for topographic maps.
- Passed a motion to encourage states without surveys to establish one.
- Passed a motion to appoint a committee to consider correlation problems between states.
- Discussed cooperative studies of formations extending into other states.
- Passed a motion that the question of the summer meeting in 1919 be left to the Executive Committee, with power to set.
- Passed a motion that the president of the Association should be on the National Research Council.
- Discussed budget systems, state surveys connected with other state departments, salaries paid by state surveys.

In 1919, the annual meeting was held September 1–6, in Birmingham, Ala.; host was Thomas L. Watson, Geological Survey of Alabama. Unfortunately the minutes of that meeting are not in the archives, but there is considerable material about the meeting. The following excerpt of the program gives a flavor of annual meeting communications of that time:

> Members and guests should arrange to reach Birmingham on or before Sunday, August 31. Headquarters will be at the Tutwiler Hotel, 5th Ave. and 20th St. (Rates $2.00 to $5.00 per day, European plan.)… There are two railroad stations in Birmingham, the Louisville & Nashville, in the center of the city, and the Terminal, about one-half mile to the northward. (Those coming by way of Cincinnati and Chattanooga should inquire about a possible delay at the bridge a few miles north of Chattanooga).

> Members can use their judgment about what to bring in the way of outing clothes, collecting outfits, photographic apparatus, maps and literature. Films can be bought in almost any city visited.

The published annual meeting program continued for 14 pages and included a three-page field guidebook for Bessemer, Ala., and graphite deposits, with description of arrangements and field geology.

The struggle for increased appropriation for topographic mapping was continuing in 1919. The elevated concern for this issue can be seen in the correspondence of the AASG for 1919. A letter to the Secretary of the Interior from the Engineering Council of Washington, D.C., signed by Morris M. Leighton, state geologist of Illinois, is reproduced in part below:

The Honorable,

The Secretary of the Interior,

Washington, D.C.

My dear Mr. Secretary:

It has become apparent to engineers, geologists, and others engaged, offi-cially or otherwise, in development work that the Geological Survey should be granted a more liberal appropriation for topographic mapping. The demand for a complete topographic map of the United States is the result of dearly bought experience, and a realization that such a map is an essential part of that program of development to which our country must resort if it is to respond to its own internal needs and to new world demands....

Very respectfully,
Morris M. Leighton
Chairman,
NATIONAL SERVICES COMMITTEE

There is no explanation in the archive about Leighton's role as chair-man of the National Service Committee of the Engineering Council nor the relationship between AASG and this group, but by these statements it was apparently a close and mutually supportive one. The all-important resolu-tion is reproduced below. This was 1919, and Leighton would not become state geologist of Illinois until 1923.

RESOLUTION CONCERNING TOPOGRAPHIC MAPPING PASSED BY ENGINEERS' ARCHITECTS' AND CONSTRUCTORS' CONFERENCE

CONVENED AT CHICAGO, ILLS.—APRIL 23–25, 1919.

The Engineers, Architects and Constructors Conference on National Public Works, composed of the representatives appointed by 80 National, State and Local Organizations, with an aggregate membership of over 100,000 men, realizes the great importance of adequate maps for the economical planning and construction of a large proportion of engineering works.

With much wisdom the Federal and State Governments are now entering upon a program of highway construction which constitutes the greatest engineering project ever undertaken by our Government, and which will result in the expenditure of many billions of dollars of public funds in the next decade. This highway construction, as well as many other important public and private engineering undertakings, such as drainage and reclamation projects and others—in the aggregate of tremendous magnitude—demand for economical accomplishment the best type of information such as is afforded by the Topographic Maps issued by the Federal Government in co-operation with many of the States. These maps are completed for only about 40% of the area of the country. The past rate of progress, if continued, will require between 80 and 103 years to complete the maps for the whole United States....

In view of the foregoing statements, which express the sense of this Conference,

BE IT RESOLVED: That the facts be presented to the President and to the Congress, and that they be urged to make adequate provision for the entire work of completing the Topographic Map of the United States in the shortest possible time, compatible with requisite accuracy; and

BE IT FURTHER RESOLVED: That inasmuch as the Engineering Council has already taken up this matter with Federal Government Departments, their efforts to hasten the completion of the Topographic Map be endorsed by this Conference and that this Resolution be entrusted to them to present to the President, The Secretary of the Interior, the members of the Congress, and to make such other disposition of it as will, in their judgment, further the end desired.

ADOPTED 4/25/19

Upon passage of the resolution by the National Service Committee of the Engineering Council, a copy was circulated to all state geologists for action. A copy of this transmittal is reproduced below:

From: National Service Committee

To: All State Geologists

Subject: Resolution Concerning Topographic Mapping.

In response to the suggestion of [AASG President] W.O. Hotchkiss I am sending you, herewith, twelve (12) copies of the resolution concerning topographic mapping, passed by the Chicago Conference of Technical Societies, April 25th. This resolution is intended to be used in connection with your campaign to secure from the present Congress an appropriation of $500,000, for the mapping work of the United States Geological Survey.

I assume that Mr. Hotchkiss or Dr. Watson, the Secretary of your association, has given you full information concerning this matter.

Very truly yours,
M.M. Leighton
Chairman
NATIONAL SERVICE COMMITTEE, ENGINEERING COUNCIL

The letter below from Interior Secretary Franklin K. Lane was sent to Morris M. Leighton, chairman, National Service Committee of the Engineering Council:

Dear Mr. Leighton:

I have before me your statement of the essential relation of the topographic mapping of the country to good engineering and the economic development of our resources, and your presentation of the matter strikes me as warranted by the facts of which I am cognizant. An adequate map of the United States at the earliest possible date is of course the program to be endorsed. Your information is correct that the Geological Survey now has available trained personnel sufficient to permit a large expansion of the Government's activities, in topographic surveys. This increase in number of topographic engineers is a happy by-product of the assistance rendered the Army by the Department of the Interior…. For this reason, an annual expenditure of $1,000,000 on the topographic map of the United States is now justified both by the public needs and the ability of this Department to perform this work economically and effectively. In such a program it is hoped that the States might increase their cooperative contributions to $500,000, especially as the cooperation for the two years past was necessarily interrupted by the military mapping being largely confined to a few border States.

The amount of state cooperative funding for topographic mapping was recommended by Lane to be raised from $350,000 to $500,000.

It is interesting to see nearly 90 years later what the issues and arguments were concerning support for topographic mapping for the nation. It was clearly a federal-state cooperative, with the states through AASG and its allies pushing hard to get the much-needed appropriations from Congress. In hindsight, one must wonder why it was such a struggle and why it took so long. One also wonders how AASG coordinated with 80 organizations, because those details are not found in the archives. It is intriguing that Morris M. Leighton played such an instrumental role, yet would not become state geologist of Illinois for another 4 years.

By the end of the decade 1910–19, AASG had developed into the organization that continues to the present time, with three major areas of focus: internal business of running the organization; lobbying, cooperation, and influence on federal programs; and operation and function of state geological surveys. World War I had taken a toll on topographic mapping as trained mappers had been recruited into the war service and had stopped their work in the various states. Also, budget issues related to the war arose, causing the funding for topographic mapping to greatly decrease. By the end of this decade, AASG annual meetings had moved out of the East Coast as far west as St. Louis. Summertime field meetings with business sessions and rather elaborate geologic field trips had come into being. Attendance at the annual meetings had increased to about 20 members in 1919. At this time, AASG was certainly making its influence felt at the federal level and was also mentoring its own members by encouraging innovations at the state geological surveys.

1920–29

James C. Cobb *(Kentucky; AASG Historian)*

The Roaring Twenties were a golden age for AASG, with tremendous growth in the depth and breadth of activities and influence. Many of the traditions still practiced today came into being during this decade. Influence and involvement in federal affairs, including Congress and the USGS, were at a high level because of the all-consuming efforts to fund topographic mapping for the nation. Topographic mapping was the top priority at nearly every meeting. The Temple Bill authorizing topographic mapping for the entire nation was passed after a tremendous campaign on the part of AASG.

AASG's focus also turned inward to the administration and functions of state geological surveys. This focus culminated in a National Research Council bulletin on state geological surveys. Traditions begun in the 1920's include:

- Modern look and organization of meetings and minutes.
- Began AASG dues.
- Created office of editor.
- Initiated the *Journal of the Association of American State Geologists* (first published in 1930).
- Elaborate summer field excursions.
- Created office of past-president.
- Created Nominations Committee, composed of the three immediate past-presidents.
- Developed structure of annual meetings with outside guests invited.
- Began committee visits to federal agencies and Congress (similar to modern AASG Liaison Committee, but not referred to as such).
- First successful lobbying effort to get legislation passed by Congress (Temple Bill for topographic mapping in 1925).
- Wrote and amended constitution.
- First visit to AASG meeting by representatives of foreign geological surveys: Canada, Australia, and Russia.
- First mention of the use of the Cosmos Club.
- First necrology for members.

- Strong interest in cooperative planning with the USGS and concerns about the relationship between state geological surveys and the USGS.
- First mention of the need for document and sample preservation.
- First cooperative work with the National Research Council.

The AASG leadership was outstanding during this decade. Both travel and communications were slow by today's standards, yet the level of activity and communications was very high. The AASG archives for this decade have minutes of meetings plus pages of correspondence. In terms of numbers, however, the leadership for this decade was by relatively few people. Only six men served as president during these 10 years: William O. Hotchkiss (Wisconsin), George H. Ashley (Pennsylvania), Edward B. Mathews (Maryland), Wilbur A. Nelson (Tennessee, Virginia), Henry A. Buehler (Missouri), and Ernest F. Bean (Wisconsin). Only three men served as secretary: Thomas L. Watson (Virginia), Nelson, and Morris M. Leighton (Illinois). The standard for minutes was largely set by Leighton, whose minutes were very complete and detailed. Only four men served as executive committeeman, although another officer, the past-president, was added to the Executive Committee (executive committeemen were Mathews, Buehler, and Nelson). These eight men rotated through the AASG offices, leading the group and carrying the burden. They succeeded in developing AASG into the organization we have today.

Close cooperation with the USGS in meetings and programs was very prominent because most states had cooperatives with the USGS in geology, topography, water resources, or mineral resources (or combinations of all of these). In fact, the topic of federal-state relationships became a subject for discussion at many of the meetings in the 1920's, initiated by both AASG and the USGS. The AASG met annually in the conference room of the director of the USGS, Dr. George O. Smith, and in some meetings AASG personnel were outnumbered by their USGS counterparts, indicating a strong interest on the part of the USGS in state geological surveys. Such notable USGS geologists as George O. Smith, C. David White, Walter C. Mendenhall, Edward O. Ulrich, Oscar E. Meinzer, Col. Claude H. Birdseye, and many others attended these meetings. Drs. Smith, White, Mendenhall, and Col. Birdseye attended a majority of the meetings.

In the 1920's, the USGS matched but not necessarily dollar for dollar the efforts of the state geological surveys in the four areas of cooperation mentioned above. The USGS also offered assistance to states in disciplines such as paleontology and mineralogy, because some states did not have these specialties. There was a spirit of cooperation, but inevitable conflicts arose. State geological surveys raised concerns with the USGS about stratigraphic correlations and names, funding for the cooperative programs, changes in requirements for cost sharing, and federal survey parties doing work in states without the knowledge of the state geologists. The AASG minutes record open and honest dialogue on these issues and actions taken to mitigate the conflicts. The value of the collaboration, cooperation, expertise, and assistance of the USGS cannot be overemphasized, and were in large part responsible for the success of AASG and state geological surveys that continues to this day.

AASG annual meetings throughout the 1920's were held in conjunction with the annual meetings of the Geological Society of America. The AASG minutes did not always record this, but a comparison of AASG annual meeting locations with GSA meeting locations does show this connection. These meetings were always held just after Christmas in late December, and some minutes are titled "Christmas meeting." Considering the number of northern cities involved, modes of transportation required, and the time of year, the state geologists of the 20's were fearless travelers. As previously stated, the Association also met annually with the USGS in Washington, D.C., in the spring. It is difficult to distinguish which meeting was the principal meeting of the year. In several years, field conferences were added to the schedule of AASG activities, and some state geologists attended as many as three meetings in a single year.

1920. The annual meeting for 1920 was held in Chicago on December 28, in conjunction with the Geological Society of America annual meeting. The Executive Committee proposed levying dues for the first time. A top priority in 1920 was the effort to increase federal appropriations for topographic mapping. The following letter reproduced in part below to AASG members from President William O. Hotchkiss (Wisconsin) and Secretary Thomas L. Watson (Virginia) shows how intensive the approach being pursued by AASG was for topographic mapping.

> As you are doubtless informed a complete plan for completing the topographic map of the United States by 1932 has been proposed by the United States Geological Survey. This contemplates state cooperation on the usual dollar for dollar basis. If you have not received this plan and the estimate of the cost for completing your state you can get it by writing Director George Otis Smith of the United States Geological Survey. Congress has been asked by Secretary Lane to appropriate for topography on this basis.
>
> This letter is written to urge you to get this matter under way in your state. These maps are urgently needed for the great program of highway construction; the great saving to the public in the highway work is the most pressing immediate need for these maps and gives you an opportunity to get your state highway department and other engineers interested to present this matter forcibly to your state legislature and secure the state appropriation necessary to complete

the plan by 1932. The National Association of State Highway Officials at its annual meeting in Louisville, Kentucky, passed a strong resolution urging the completion of this 1932 plan and directed its Executive Committee to appoint a special committee on topographic maps to urge the matter on Congress.

We feel that topographic mapping has been poorly supported in the past because we geologists have been urging it without the help of others just as vitally interested. We believe that success will come only as the engineers and others needing these maps are gotten into harness to pull for this plan. There are few services of greater benefit you can render your state than to get these maps completed, but to do it you most bring every influence to bear, both to get adequate state appropriations and to urge your congressmen to see that federal appropriations are forthcoming. This means work on your part. You must get the engineers and influential citizens enlisted. You will doubtless get much support from various departments of your state government handling maps—if you go after it—the Board of Health, the Railroad Commission, the Drainage Commission, Conservation Commission, the State Military Department, the Highway Department, and many others. You can also do what some states have done—get your legislative committee to ask the United States Geological Survey to send a representative to appear before them.

It is up to you. Will you get busy and do your share? Urge all influential engineers and others you know in each congressional district to write their Congressman to support the increased appropriations Secretary Lane has asked of Congress for topography, and bring every influence to bear you can.

(Signed) W.O. Hotchkiss,
President.
Thomas L. Watson,
Secretary

The Secretary of the Interior, Franklin K. Lane, was in support of the goal to map the nation by 1932 and requested that Congress fund it. A plan to do this work had been submitted by the USGS. The state geologists were charged with pushing for support from their senators and congressmen, their own state legislatures, various offices of state government, and engineers, especially highway engineers.

A list of budgets and salaries for state geological surveys and state geologists in the archives for 1920 shows the average state survey budget was about $30,000, ranging from zero for a few states to Illinois with a budget of $137,000. Salaries for state geologists also ranged up to $5,000 per year, and the average was about $3,500 per year. Several methods calculate the value of money through time; one method, based upon the cost of labor, suggests a salary in 1920 of $3,500 would be about $119,000 in 2007.

1921. The 1921 annual meeting was held in Amherst, Mass., hosted by Amherst College and also in conjunction with the annual meeting of the Geological Society of America. As had been started several years earlier, a list of state geological surveys and the cooperative programs they had with the USGS in geology, topography, water resources, or mineral resources was compiled for the year. USGS Director Smith informed the group that the topographic mapping budget would be $430,000 for the year. The state geological surveys would match this with state funds. A fall field meeting was held in Nashville, Tenn., at the Hermitage Hotel, with room rates from $2.50 to $5.00. The group visited the largest smokeless gunpowder plant in the world, built for World War I, and the Hermitage, President Andrew Jackson's home, as well as Pleistocene and Silurian fossil localities. On October 7, the members of AASG were treated to lunch at the Nashville Kiwanis Club, where the song reproduced in part below evidently had its debut.

(sung to the tune of "Reuben Reuben")

Gentleman of the Kiwanis
We would introduce to you
Ge-ol-o-gists so archaic
We hope their talk won't make you blue.

I.C. White of West Virginia
F. De Wolf of Illinois
Bachelor Beuhler of Missouri
He's the one for us Oh boys!

David White his name and station
He doesn't care to have us say
But when we meet his wife and children
We'll tell them all about today.

E.O. Ulrich calm and steady
Never is doubted by his wife
But when he is away on a survey
Shocking how he leads his life.

Hotchkiss, big gun from Wisconsin
Ulrich of th' Government Survey
David White, his old side partner
Having the times of their lives today.

Gentleman, gentleman we've been thinking
Wouldn't it be a great big joke?
If all geologist were translated
Into iron, steel, and coke.

Buehler is from
old Missouri
A great state
from which to be
When he goes to
choose a wife
Bet he'll come
to Tennessee.

(AASG anonymous)

This song shows the humorous side of AASG in 1921. It is equally interesting to see that the good-natured humor extended to guests E.O. Ulrich and David White, a good indication of the collegial relations. On October 8, the group left at 8:00 a.m. on the Nashville-Florence railroad by special coach to visit a phosphate deposit and enjoy a barbecue. Then on October 9, they departed Nashville by special Pullman train for Chattanooga for more field excursions. A menu by the

Figure 3. Lunch menu from the 1921 AASG field excursion.

American Zinc Company of Tennessee for the Association of American State Geologists is reproduced in Figure 3, and shows the clever use of the stratigraphic column for the food offerings for the luncheon.

AASG members were informed that the Temple Bill had passed in the U.S. House of Representatives. Dr. Temple was a congressman from Pennsylvania who sponsored this bill authorizing increases in funding and establishing a timetable for topographic mapping but not appropriating those increases. Much work was still needed to get the bill through the Senate and appropriations. The letter to state geologists on this issue from Wilbur A. Nelson, state geologist of Tennessee, requesting action by the state geologists is reproduced below:

> The different State Surveys of the country should be intensely interested in the passage of the Temple Bill—H.R. 5230, which was introduced in the House of Representatives April 26th. 1921. This bill provides for the completion of the topographic mapping of the United States. This bill was referred to the committee on interstate and foreign commerce.

I am enclosing copy of this bill with the request that you read same carefully and if it meets with your approval that you strongly urge the different engineering societies and organizations in your state to get behind the measure and request your congressmen and Senators to support this bill so that it may pass at an early date.

As you will note from reading the bill, it is only an authorization bill and does not carry any increase for topographic mapping for the coming year, and there should be no opposition by the present congress on the score that it asks for an increased appropriation for this fiscal year; the first increase being for the fiscal year ending June 1923.

I wish you would write me immediately concerning this bill, giving if possible a strong endorsement of same, so that our Association can take immediate favorable action on this measure.

1922–1924. Documents were not found for these years in the archives.

1925. AASG held three meetings in 1925, minutes of which are preserved in the archives. The Harrisburg meeting was most likely a field meeting, held on October 12, 1925. AASG was welcomed by Maj. Stewart, director of the Pennsylvania Department of Forestry and Waters. George Ashley (Pennsylvania) spoke about the importance of working with the USGS cooperatives in paleontology and water. Henry Kummel (New Jersey) reiterated Ashley's statements about cooperation with the USGS. President Nelson (Virginia) read a preliminary statement about the needs for comprehensive scientific work by federal and state agencies for the benefit of the nation, which was to be sent to President Calvin Coolidge. Ashley moved adoption and Raymond C. Moore (Kansas) and Morris M. Leighton (Illinois) seconded the motion to finalize by the end of that week the statement for presentation to the president of the United States. The group was informed by President Nelson that the Department of Interior was asked to cut $10 million from its budget. A total of $350,000 would possibly be taken from the USGS topographic mapping program. Once again, members were asked to muster congressional support to keep on the timetable set forth by the Temple Bill.

AASG approved tentative support for a water-resources assessment being pushed by the American Engineering Council. AASG members at this meeting were concerned that a national water program might hurt progress in topographic mapping. Therefore, action on this water proposal would wait until the Temple Bill was implemented. Word reached the group that John M. Clarke (New York), a founding member, had died. A resolution was passed to send condolences to his wife and the New York Geological Survey.

The traditional December meeting with the Geological Society of America in New Haven, Conn., conflicted with a meeting in Kansas City, Mo., with the American Association for the Advancement of Science. Therefore, AASG members split between these meetings. At the Kansas City meeting on December 29, attended by 10 members, the group discussed the budget worries for topographic mapping that would wipe out the provisions of the Temple Bill. Again action was needed in Congress and the Department of Interior. A motion passed to send President Nelson with a committee to see Gen. Lord, director of the Bureau of the Budget, and Congressman Louis C. Cramton (R-Michigan), chairman of the Department of Interior Appropriations Committee, to secure agreement that the federal government would conform to the funding and timetable in the Temple Bill. The group also decided officially not to support the new water proposal until the matters confronting topographic mapping were solved. Dr. Mendenhall (USGS) spoke about the cooperative relationships with the state geological surveys and Dr. David White (USGS, National Research Council) spoke about the need to have a summary of the research activities of the state geological surveys. He also relayed the interest by the NRC in the activities of the state geological surveys.

Ten members attended the New Haven meeting December 28–30. They were joined by Mr. Kindle, who represented the Canadian Geological Survey. This meeting had an outcome similar to the other meeting in supporting topographic mapping but advising against active support for the water proposal until the Temple Bill was fully implemented. The American Engineering Council had requested that AASG join the council as an affiliate member, but this was rejected because the members felt that AASG could be more effective as an independent group working with the council on issues of common interest.

1926. In 1926 the annual meeting was held in Madison, Wis., in conjunction with the Geological Society of America meeting. Dr. C. David White of the USGS reiterated the need for well records, samples, and cores for research and education. There was a discussion about the desirability of forming state well drillers' associations to facilitate the collection of records and samples. William H. Emmons (Minnesota) moved and George F. Kay (Iowa) seconded a motion that the Association cooperate with the National Research Council in its endeavors to salvage well records. The motion passed unanimously. This was perhaps the first attempt to preserve samples and records, a movement that is undergoing a resurgence in the 2000's.

The Newton Water Bill to increase federal appropriations for water-resources investigations was discussed. Chief Buehler (Missouri) stated that his state was spending $20,000 a year for water-resources work, but the U.S. Geological Survey could only match that amount with $650. Kay moved and H.E. Culver (Washington) seconded that the Newton Bill be endorsed by

AASG. This motion carried unanimously. The secretary was instructed to send a letter to the congressional committee that had this bill under consideration.

1927. AASG held three meetings in 1927: April 25–26 in Washington, D.C.; October 19–21, in Urbana, Ill.; and December 30 in Cleveland.

The April meeting was held in the conference room of the director of the USGS and called to order by President Buehler (Missouri). Fifteen members attended. The morning session was devoted to Association business and the afternoon session to federal survey and other business. The American Society for Testing and Materials had requested help in creating a system of coal classification. Ashley (Pennsylvania), Leighton (Illinois), and Harold Culver (Washington) were appointed to the resulting committee. The sentiments prevailing at the meeting were for the classification system to give full consideration to all coal-producing states. Gould (Oklahoma) spoke highly of the services of the USGS on the Committee on Geologic Names, and especially the services of Miss M. Grace Wilmarth, secretary of the committee. The morning session adjourned for lunch at the Cosmos Club, where the officials of the USGS were guests of the Association.

The afternoon session involved outside agencies, especially the USGS and the U.S. Coast and Geodetic Survey. USGS Director George Smith updated the group on the Temple Bill. Although it was not yet fully implemented, the legislation did help increase appropriations for topographic mapping. Some additional states had state funds to match the federal program, others had lost their appropriations, and some had not yet reported their funds. Dr. Temple was still a strong supporter 7 years after the bill's introduction. Mr. N.C. Grover, chief of the Water Resources Division of USGS, spoke about the Newton Bill. He stated that this bill would not affect the Temple Bill, but could help, because surface-water studies needed topographic maps. The Topographic Division of the USGS was represented by Col. C.H. Birdseye, chief topographic engineer, Col. Smith, and Maj. Herron. They expressed the opinion that 1:24,000-scale maps with 1:48,000-scale details would increase costs because of the extra line work needed. They encouraged actual testing to be done, however.

Dr. E.C. Andrews, state geologist of New South Wales, Australia, addressed the group. The states of Australia were united in the conviction that a federal survey was needed for Australia. His trip to the United States was to see firsthand how the relationships worked between the USGS and the state geological surveys. Dr. William Bowie, chief of the Geodesy Division, U.S. Coast and Geodetic Survey, addressed the group about the national horizontal and vertical control system, leveling surveys, traverses, and triangulations. In terms of the topographic mapping program, this work was extremely important. The necrology was read for Dr. Eugene A. Smith (Alabama),

Dr. Israel C. White (West Virginia), Dr. George H. Perkins (Vermont), and Dr. Samuel W. McCallie (Georgia), all founding members of AASG.

Dr. Morris M. Leighton (Illinois) addressed the group about his meeting with the Bureau of the Budget. The federal budget officials were optimistic about the availability of federal support for topographic mapping and the horizontal and vertical control work. It seems awkward today that the job of topographic control was vested with one agency, the U.S. Coast and Geodetic Survey, but topographic mapping with another, the USGS and its mapping partners, the state geological surveys. But, according to these officials, the U.S. Coast and Geodetic Survey together with the Bureau of the Budget were willing and ready to provide the necessary funds to cooperate with the states for lines of levels, traverse, or arcs of triangulation. From these statements it seems odd that at every meeting the subject of availability of funds was a major topic and concern.

Dr. Walter C. Mendenhall reiterated the USGS's willingness to assist state geological surveys with scientific services, particularly with expertise not readily available at the state level. The subject of federal survey parties working in states without making contact with the state geologist also came up for discussion. It was pointed out that in such cases there was likely a loss of information for both parties, because information was not exchanged. USGS Director Smith said he would arrange for state geologists to receive in advanced the personnel notices for federal survey parties, which would contain the locations of proposed federal field work.

A motion by Wilbur Nelson (Virginia), seconded by Ernest Bean (Wisconsin), was passed to send letters to heads of geology departments at colleges and universities where graduate research was being done, inviting their interest in the research problems of the states and extending the facilities of the geological surveys to the graduate students to the extent possible. There was a discussion of the U.S. Board of Geographic Names and how to get more influence by state geologists on the names chosen for topographic maps.

A motion was made by Kummel (New Jersey) and seconded by Nelson (Virginia) to extend hearty thanks to Director George Smith and other cooperating officials of the USGS for the fine hospitality that had been extended to the members of the Association at the conference. The motion passed unanimously.

The meeting in Urbana was a field meeting hosted by Morris M. Leighton (Illinois; AASG secretary) and the Illinois State Geological Survey. It was in conjunction with the Geology Section of the National Academy of Sciences. A memorial service was held for the late Stuart Weller, professor of geology at the University of Chicago and expert on Mississippian geology. He had passed away unexpectedly while in the field. He participated in many activities of the state geological surveys, as seen by the tributes to him. Tributes were read by T.C. Chamberlin (University of Chicago), W.C. Mendenhall (USGS), Henry Kummel (New Jersey), Willard R. Jillson (Kentucky), E.S. Bastin (University of Chicago), and Morris M. Leighton (Illinois), who also presided. A special lecture was given by D.J. Mushketov, director of the Russian Geological Survey. He was on a 2-month visit to investigate the function and organization of geological surveys for the development of mineral resources in Russia. The group departed Urbana for Bloomington, Ill., for the business session.

Secretary Leighton reported on the activities of the Executive Committee regarding the Flood Control Conference recently held in Chicago. On April 15, 1927, the Mississippi River flooded along a large part of its course from Illinois to Louisiana. The resulting flood in the lower Mississippi Valley took more than 200 lives, 600,000 people were displaced, and millions of dollars in property damage occurred. This was a traumatic event for the nation, so it is no wonder that flood control was a major topic. The Executive Committee was attempting to have a geologist appointed to the flood commission being recommended to President Calvin Coolidge. Charles N. Gould (Oklahoma) moved and Walter F. Pond (Tennessee) seconded that Henry Buehler (Missouri) be appointed to that commission. The AASG Resolutions Committee offered a resolution on flood control that passed unanimously. Unfortunately, the text of this resolution was not found.

The Cleveland meeting was held December 30 in conjunction with the Geological Society of America. President Buehler presided and Gould (Oklahoma) was appointed secretary pro tem in the absence of Secretary Leighton (Illinois). A committee to prepare a resolution on the life of Israel White (West Virginia) was appointed. A resolution by Leighton on appropriations for the USGS and Bureau of Mines was read and referred to the Executive Committee, and giving the Executive Committee the power to act. Dr. Wilbur Nelson (Virginia) sent a telegram stating that noncoastal work by the U.S. Coast and Geodetic Survey in the Department of Commerce was being transferred to the USGS. After considerable discussion, the following resolution was adopted:

> Resolved that, it is the sense of the Association of American State Geologists that Congress should delay action on house bill 7048 until the National Academy of Science can determine whether the changes proposed therein would increase the efficiency of the scientific work to be accomplished.

In the election of officers for 1928, President Buehler suggested that the Nominations Committee be composed of the past-presidents of the Association. The past-presidents present at the meeting were Kummel (New Jersey), Mathews (Maryland), and Ashley (Pennsylvania). It was moved and seconded that the past-president be added as a third member of the

Executive Committee. It was also suggested that when needed, an additional member residing in the vicinity of Washington, D.C., be added to the Executive Committee. The officers elected were Ernest F. Bean (Wisconsin), president; Morris M. Leighton (Illinois), secretary; Henry A. Buehler (Missouri) and Wilbur A. Nelson (Virginia), executive committeemen.

1928. The first meeting of 1928 was on April 24 in Washington, D.C. President Ernest Bean (Wisconsin) called the meeting to order in the conference room of the director of the U.S. Geological Survey, with 14 state geologists and 26 invited guests in attendance. The first business was legislation on flood control, inspired by the Mississippi River flood of April 1927, and its relationship to topographic mapping. Col. C.H. Birdseye, chief topographic engineer of the U.S. Geological Survey, stated that the Mississippi River Commission did not contemplate topographic mapping or scientific research of any sort. It was contemplating strengthening and raising the levies. The U.S. Army Corps of Engineers proposed $1 million for topographic mapping, but no stream gaging. Congressman Temple thought there would be a prolonged fight in Congress over the actions to take concerning flood control and mapping. The only point of agreement between the plans being offered was that topographic mapping and stream gaging must be done.

Secretary Wallace of the American Engineering Council said the new Temple Bill should not be considered part of the flood-control measures but should be considered a fundamental undertaking for its own sake. Sentiment was that this attitude should appeal to Congress so they could say that they acted on flood relief. Mr. Wallace also spoke on the Newton Bill, HR 8111, and said that the bill had positive responses for early hearings.

Further discussion of the new Temple Bill brought out a budget item for $500,000 for stream gaging in the Mississippi River and its tributaries. The gaging was intended to study the quantity and source of water carried in the lower Mississippi River.

Airplane mapping was discussed at length because private firms had complained that the Army Air Corps was undercutting them on price and that they were unable to compete because of unfair practices. They were also asking that government aerial photographs be kept confidential so that private companies would not lose business. An Air Coordination Committee comprising three secretaries (Secretary of the Army for Aeronautics, Secretary of the Navy, and Secretary of Commerce) was convened to hear these complaints. The private firms presented evidence that it cost $75 to $100 per flying hour to keep the plane and camera in the air. The two military services were in favor of having the Army Air Corps do the mapping work, but the Secretary of Commerce pushed to prevent the army from providing photographs for mapping. The committee worked out a deal that required the geological surveys to advertise for bids from aerial photography firms and then if those bids were not satisfactory, then the army would do the work.

The USGS had purchased a new *aerocartograph*. This new equipment could draw contour lines from overlapping aerial photographs, and all details could be accurately delineated.

The firm of Brock and Weymuth had recently sued all government and private firms doing aerial photography work for patent infringement. Their claim was that their process of overlapping aerial photographs for mapping purposes was covered under their patent. If they won their case, then all parties doing this work would be required to stop, but that prospect did not appear likely.

A discussion ensued about map scale, and using 1:48,000-scale accuracy on 1:24,000-scale scale maps for efficiency was rehashed year after year. It was decide to run a field trial to collect more information about this oft-debated issue.

The work of the U.S. Coast and Geodetic Survey was questioned because although much topographic mapping had been done in the nation, the work of the USCGS did not fit in with any of the past or current mapping. Col. Birdseye, chief topographic engineer for the USGS, had written a letter to *Science* magazine defending the USGS program but alluding to the deficiencies of the USCGS. A bill was introduced to Congress transferring the work of the USCGS to the USGS, but it was deemed unlikely to pass.

The relationships of geologic work by state and federal surveys were discussed by Director George O. Smith and Chief Geologist Walter C. Mendenhall of the USGS. They pointed out that the federal survey was not required to observe 50-50 cost-sharing when operating with the states, but the USGS share could not exceed 50 percent. It was common at that time for the USGS to match every state dollar with 20 cents of federal money. The federal survey had done work in Alabama and was now requested in Virginia, Arkansas, Texas, Kansas, and other states. Dr. Mendenhall welcomed the opportunity to work with the states because "there was infinitely more geology work needed than could be done with all our efforts in this and the next century" (Leighton, 1928). Director George Otis Smith said the USGS was duty bound to match every dollar put up by the states, and that if necessary he would ask for a supplemental appropriation. Following the Mississippi River flood, the need for stream gaging on the river had been raised by engineers, and the Appropriation Committee was glad to increase appropriations for that. Now that the topographic mapping program had established a 50-50 cost-sharing precedent, and that was being approached in water resources, Dr. Leighton (Illinois) asked if this would be carried over into geologic cooperation. Director Smith replied that the effort would be to build on this precedent.

Drilling and completion of water wells was a topic for discussion by O.E. Meinzer, USGS, who spoke on the merits of state water well drillers' associations. He felt these groups should be encouraged and supported by state geological surveys as they provided opportunities for outreach and education. There were also plans for a National Well Drillers Association. The sentiment was that all drillers should be knowledgeable about geology. Dr. Leighton (Illinois) spoke about activities at the University of Illinois, where five separate organizations came together to promote water-well drilling and an association was started. The Illinois State Geological Survey was hopeful that by working with the drillers, better subsurface information could be collected.

Mr. Bowie of the U.S. Coast and Geodetic Survey spoke about a new initiative to complete the survey control, leveling, and triangulation program for the nation. The American Society of Civil Engineers was pursuing a $5 million appropriation to finish this work without matching funds from the states. Bowie stated that after first- and second-order control, leveling, and triangulation was completed, the geographic position of any place in the United States would be no more than 25 miles from a known location. A problem arose because Minnesota had been turned down for control work. The Bureau of the Budget had refused their state's match because the state legislation had not passed in time. Some criticism had been directed toward the USGS and the USCGS for possible duplication of efforts. The western United States had been completed for triangulation work. The U.S. Supreme Court had ordered the Oklahoma–Texas boundary placed on the 100th meridian and marked on the ground with monuments spaced 10 miles apart. Mr. Garnett was appointed commissioner for this survey, and with the approval of Chief Justice William Howard Taft, the USCGS ran an arc of triangulation from the Rio Grande River. Henry Buehler (Missouri) wanted to know if the arc of triangulation would hold from the Rio Grande to Canada. Bowie replied that the arc would be "fixed" and then the eastern half of the country would be adjusted. Buehler asked whether earth movements would affect the triangulation and leveling. Edward Mathews (Maryland) asked about readjustments at Sandy Hook and Point Lookout, to which Bowie replied he doubted there would be any.

1929. AASG held two meetings in 1929, both occurring before the stock market crash on Black Tuesday, October 29, 1929. The first meeting, chaired by President Ernest Bean (Wisconsin), was February 15–16 in Washington, D.C., attended by 10 state geologists and one assistant. In answer to a request from Sen. Tasker L. Oddie (R-Nevada), a committee of Buehler (Missouri),

Reger (West Virginia), and Bean (Wisconsin) was formed to appear in the afternoon before his subcommittee. The topic of correlating physiographic features and its utility was discussed. Wilbur Stout (Ohio) described the situation in Ohio. The discussion included examples from Wisconsin and West Virginia. A resolution developed from the discussion: that state geologists request the U.S. Geological Survey to appoint conferees on the broad correlation of physiographic features covering the several states and that the state geologists appoint as conferees Stout (Ohio), Gould (Oklahoma), and Ashley (Pennsylvania). The purpose of a conference would be to correlate physiographic features in several states. Henry Kummel (New Jersey) gave an in-depth report on developing deep water wells to assist municipalities, using New Jersey's example. A discussion about ways to get people thinking intelligently about their investments in order to combat unscrupulous oil and gas promoters recommended newspaper articles, radio, and presentations to civic groups. The coal classification system of the American Society for Testing and Materials was discussed by Dr. Ashley (Pennsylvania), who reported that the system would have three separate methods: one for science, one for coal use, and one for marketing. Ashley gave his opinion that the coal market would decline over the next decade, then level off and increase as the oil and gas pools declined. Was he being prophetic?

The following day, Morris Leighton (Illinois) chaired a session on topographic mapping. This was the major topic at every AASG meeting in the 1920's, and most often led by Col. C.H. Birdseye, chief topographic engineer for the USGS. Col. Birdseye reported that the topographic budget for the next fiscal year was $635,000, to be matched by $497,000 in state funds. He called attention to the resolution by the American Society of Engineers calling upon the federal government to take control and finish topographic mapping where it is a national priority. The resolution demonstrated the renewed interest by engineers, and was sent to secretaries in departments involved, the president, and Congress. He also stated that the largest amount of appropriations was going to northern states that had short field seasons because of bad winter weather. He was hoping for cooperation in the southern states, so that topographic personnel could be active mapping there during the winter. He also said that the Mississippi River Commission might undertake some topographic mapping. The Mississippi River alluvial plain was being mapped for the War Department. With regard to aerial mapping, Col. Birdseye stated that the *aerocartograph* machine for making contours on maps from aerial photographs was very satisfactory for land with high relief, but not for land with low relief. Regarding the cooperation with the army and navy, the Interior Department appropriations bill for 1930 authorized the Secretary of War and the Secretary of the Navy to take aerial photographs needed by the geological survey in their mapping program. The act also allowed contracting with commercial firms if the army and navy could not do it in the time needed. In the continuing debate over map scale, Maj. Herron (USGS) reported that a test was done in Illinois during the past mapping season. The result of that test was that 1:24,000-scale mapping was $3 per square mile versus $2 for 1:48,000-scale mapping. To complicate this issue, the mappers doing the 1:24,000-scale maps did so using 1:48,000-scale accuracy. It was felt that mapping could be done to 1:48,000-scale accuracy on 1:24,000-scale maps if a rule allowing such a change was made. Col. Birdseye expressed the opinion that if the states adopted the 1:24,000 scale, then the state share in the cooperative would have to be larger than the federal contribution.

Dr. E.O. Ulrich discussed interstate correlation at length, with comments by Gould, Buehler, Leighton, Stout, Reger, White, Moore, and Smith. This was obviously an important topic. The prevailing sentiment was that the regional viewpoint rather than the state's viewpoint should prevail in the study of stratigraphy and stratigraphic correlations, and that each state should seek to have the detailed information that it gathered considered by a regional specialist at the USGS or a university. Much has changed since 1929, and many states have developed stratigraphic nomenclature and correlations. The USGS has played an important role in this, and the North American Code of Stratigraphic Nomenclature did not begin until 1946.

A resolution was moved by Buehler and seconded by Gould that the state geologists draft a strong resolution outlining the need for more work on theoretical and fundamental problems, upon which the future development of this country would be based, and that this resolution be transmitted to the president and interested members of Congress.

Dr. Mendenhall (USGS) expressed interest in state geologic maps because they were the most useful and popular publications. New maps had been engraved for Wyoming, New Mexico, Oklahoma, Arkansas, Alabama, Virginia, and Colorado. Kentucky, Minnesota, and Texas were proposing new geologic maps. New York, Tennessee, Missouri, Illinois, Michigan, and Wisconsin had recently published new geologic maps. A universal scale of 1:500,000 was recommended, and the adoption of this scale would facilitate an eventual new geologic map of the United States at a scale of 40 miles to the inch.

The topic of state geological survey organization was raised. It was announced that Maine and Montana were organizing geological surveys and California was reorganizing its survey. The fundamental principles for organizing state geological surveys were discussed. The first principle mentioned was that state geologists should be full-time and have no teaching duties. Ohio and Virginia had recently divorced their surveys from any teaching connections. The second principle was for funding to be sufficient to permit the formation of an effective organization. It was pointed out that even in small states, miscellaneous appropriations were made for hundreds of thousands of dollars for useless purposes, but state geological surveys were investments in the future. The third principle was that the work of the state geological survey should fit the conditions of that state. The fourth principle was that surveys should be controlled by nonpolitical bodies. It was announced that general organizational material about state geological surveys was being compiled by the National Research Council.

A letter from Secretary W.O. Tuffs of the Advisory Council of the Federal Board of Surveys and Maps, requesting contributions to his office expenses, was discussed. Mr. Wheat of the Federal Board of Surveys and Maps explained that representatives from engineering and technical societies were named to the advisory council. The societies involved included the American Society of Civil Engineers, American Institute of Mining Engineers, American Society of Mechanical Engineers, American Institute of Electrical Engineers, Association of American State Geologists, American Association of State Highway Engineers, National Research Council, and American Engineering Council. A motion was made to accept the letter. A motion passed to appoint Mathews (Maryland) to the council because Nelson (Tennessee) had resigned.

Publicity for state geological surveys was discussed. Charles Gould (Oklahoma) pointed out the desirability of translating technical literature into language useful to all citizens. The Oklahoma survey was making an effort for this through radio, newspapers, and presentations to civic organizations. Leighton (Illinois) stated that county teacher institutes might appreciate lectures on their local geology. The Illinois survey had started a new educational publication series. George Kay (Iowa) had done lectures in Kansas for county teachers. Samuel W. McCallie (Georgia) said that Georgia was supplying all school libraries with a complete set of reports for students to use in assigned reports.

The minutes by Leighton for this meeting were "largely transcribed from short-hand notes," perhaps the reason they were so detailed.

The following letter preserved in the archives gives details about organizing for a publication of state geological surveys being undertaken by the National Research Council. This letter lays out the justification, purpose, and members of the committee. It was on National Research Council–Division of Geology and Geography letterhead and signed by Leighton (Illinois), chair of the committee and secretary of AASG.

March 30, 1929

Directors of State Geological Surveys, State Mining Bureaus and related organizations:

On April 28, 1929, the Division of Geology and Geography of the National Research Council authorized the publication of a bulletin to be published by the National Research Council on the recent work of the official surveys as regards appropriations for geological surveys and their activities in geological and geographical research. A committee was appointed by Dr. Waldemar Lindgren, then Chairman of the Division of Geology and Geography of the Council, to consist of E.F. Bean, H.A. Buehler, Arthur Keith, Henry B. Kummel, Waldemar Lindgren, and M.M. Leighton, Chairman.

According to a statement made by Dr. Lindgren, the object of this bulletin would be to give briefly the organization at the present time of the various state geological surveys, bureaus of mines and related organizations, and the allotments available for the last period. There would also be included a statement regarding how much of this money is available for geological and geographical research and how much expended for other purposes such as mining investigations, forestry service. etc. This would give a comprehensive view of the amount spent for geological purposes in the United States by the various states. This should be followed by a statement of the work performed by the surveys along geological and geographical lines during the last 20 years, enough to give a general outline of the number and character of the publications. Where special scientific researches have been carried out in addition to the areal and economic work, an account should be given of such researches.

It is desired that the whole compilation be compressed in a bulletin of about 100 pages. It is Dr. Lindgren's feeling that this would make an extremely valuable document, not only for general information for geologists, but also in order to make the various state geologists conversant with the surveys of the other states.

At a recent meeting of the committee on state geological surveys above named, it was decided to prepare an outline of the data desired for this bulletin which might be helpful to the respective state geologists in preparing their copy. Inasmuch as the surveys vary widely in their names, methods of control, legal requirements, sources of financial support, range of activities, etc., the form of the outline must be adjusted by each executive officer to the requirements of his survey. If your geological survey is a part of a state department or of a museum, the information which you give should be restricted to activities included ordinarily in a geological survey.

In order that the final bulletin can be limited to approximately 100 pages, and inasmuch as there are some 41 surveys or bureaus, this will set a space limit of about 1000 words for each organization. Please keep within that limit if it is possible.

It seems likely that the amount of work involved for each state geologist in preparing his outline will be relatively small. I should appreciate it greatly if you can favor me with your manuscript by April 12. This will enable the chairman of the committee to make a preliminary compilation of the material for the bulletin before the annual meeting of the Division of Geology and Geography of the National Research Council.

Thanking you, I am
Very truly yours,
Morris M. Leighton

A report by the National Research Council gives the criteria and list of information to be collected for the NRC bulletin on state geological surveys. This committee had met in Urbana, Ill., in April to begin their work. The report lays out 10 topics of information needed for the bulletin. They are given below.

NATIONAL RESEARCH COUNCIL

Division of Geology and Geography

Report of the Committee on State Geological Surveys

The Chairman and Members of the Division:

The Committee on State Geological Surveys was created at last year's annual meeting of your Division of Geology and Geography, for the purpose of preparing a bulletin on the organization, character of work, and accomplishments of the various state surveys and bureaus, which is to be published by the said Division. The committee, as appointed by the Division, consists of E.F. Bean, Wisconsin, H.A. Buehler, Missouri, H.B. Kummel, New Jersey, Waldemar Lindgren and Arthur Keith, ex officio, and M.M. Leighton, Chairman.

By correspondence and by oral discussion at the meeting of the committee at Hotel Astor, New York, December 27th, a decision was reached regarding the items of information which this bulletin should include, and an outline prepared of the data to be secured from the officials of the various state organizations. This outline includes the following principal items:

1. The name, location and date of organization.

2. The scope of the functions of each survey as determined by the laws or the governing boards.

3. The size, character, method of appointment, terms of office and compensation of the governing boards. If there is no governing board, a statement is to be made of the organization's connection with the State.

4. The title, name, method of appointment, date of appointment of present incumbent, and term of office of the executive officer. If the executive officer holds an ex-officio appointment or other state or educational position, this will be given and also the proportion of time spent on Survey work.

5. The number, method of appointment, term of service, and range of salaries of the geologic, topographic or engineering, and clerical members of the survey staffs; also the extent to which advanced college students and college professors are employed.

6. The relations of the respective surveys to a University, College, State Museum, Highway Board, etc.

7. The sources of support and amounts, contingent factors upon which appropriations are made, and source and amount of support from royalties; also the continuing nature of the appropriations, whether annual, biennial or for an indefinite period.

8. Average expenditures for administrative and routine clerical, geologic work, topographic work, geographic work, and miscellaneous purposes such as mine inspection, oil and gas well inspection, review of mineral land values, water investigations, soil surveys, archeology, forestry, testing road materials, museum work, etc.

9. The kinds of series of reports and number of volumes published on geology and geography, and on other subjects; also the extent to which publishing is limited by lack of funds.

10. A statement of the work accomplished since 1911, including cooperative work which would be specified; also the lines of work now being undertaken.

11. A brief statement of previous survey organizations.

It is the recommendation of Dr. Lindgren, who proposed this undertaking to the Division of Geology and Geography while he was Chairman, that the final bulletin be compressed to about 100 pages.

The above outline has been mailed to all of the state geologists or executive officers, and the majority have sent in their first drafts. The work of compiling and editing will be prosecuted as rapidly as possible.

Inasmuch as the old bulletin (No. 465) on State Geological Surveys, published by the U.S. Geological Survey, did not include the Federal and Geological Survey or the U.S. Coast and Geodetic Survey, and inasmuch as the complete annual reports of these surveys are published regularly by their directors and are readily accessible, it does not seem imperative that statements of their work be included, but regarding this the committee awaits the action of the Division.

The Committee:

E.F. Bean
H.A. Buehler
H.B. Kummel
Waldemar Lindgren
Arthur Keith (ex-officio)
M.M. Leighton, Chairman.

Urbana, Illinois.

April 18, 1929.

The AASG archives contain drafts and correspondence about the process from state surveys as the requested information was collected. NRC bulletin 88 was published in 1932 and titled "Summary Information on the State Geological Surveys and the United States Geological Survey." A total of 48 states were included. Alaska and Hawaii were not yet states, so all the states at that time participated. This does not mean, however, that all states had geological surveys. Some of the entries state that there was no formal survey but geologic work was carried out by other organizations.

The second meeting for 1929 was on October 5 at the Ardmore Hotel in Ardmore, Okla. It was just 24 days before the infamous stock market crash. The minutes were titled "Annual Field Conference." President Bean (Wisconsin) called the meeting to order with 11 state geologists in attendance. A motion passed to urge the Bureau of the Budget to grant $180,000 to the U.S. Coast and Geodetic Survey. A committee to carry out this action was requested. President Bean postponed the announcement of this committee. A motion passed to take up the matter of administrative costs and encourage faster response in invoicing of charges to the states by the USGS. President Bean appointed Pond (Tennessee) and Condra (Nebraska) to carry this out. George Branner (Arkansas) opened the discussion of starting a medium of publication for the AASG. This issue was then discussed by Sellards (Texas), Moore (Kansas), Bevan (Virginia), Condra (Nebraska), and Pond (Tennessee). The result was the creation of an office of editor and naming Branner as the first editor for AASG. His responsibility would be to prepare and mimeograph reports on activities of state geological surveys. These reports would be distributed at intervals of 3 months. Gratitude was expressed to the organizers of the field conference: the Oklahoma and Texas geological surveys; Dr. Gould, state geologist of Oklahoma; the Geological Society of Ardmore; Dr. C.W. Tomlinson; the Lions Club of Ardmore; Dr. Sellards, the acting director of the Texas Bureau of Economic Geology; and Dr. Bullard and staff of the University of Texas. The motion passed unanimously. Leighton announced the quarter centennial of the Illinois State Geological Survey, which would be celebrated by a symposium on the Pennsylvanian System. Walter Pond (Tennessee) announced the 100th anniversary of the Tennessee survey.

An informal discussion of office filing systems was held. The group debated the time of the next meeting with the USGS, because there would be conflicts between the Geological Society of America meeting in Washington, D.C., and the American Institute of Mining Engineers meeting in New York. Secretary Leighton was requested to ascertain the preference of the director of the USGS and to canvass the members. A dinner was held at the University Club, and Mr. Leverson of the Tulsa Geological Society gave a talk. The following evening, Condra gave a talk, followed by talks by Gould and Bevan. There was an expression of gratitude for the arrangements for the trip and it was placed in the minutes, which stated that it was one of the best conferences held by AASG thus far.

The decade of the 20's was a golden age, with frequent meetings covering a wide variety of topics, despite the fact that topographic mapping was the overwhelming priority. Changes were made to AASG, such as the addition of the offices of past-president and editor. The planning for the *State Geologists Journal* was initiated. Liaison groups were very active on Capitol Hill, giving testimony and meeting with federal officials. Relationships with the USGS were very close, and coordinating meetings were held annually to plan programs and strategy for funding from Congress. There was a big emphasis on the functions and organization of state geological surveys as AASG reached out to assist states attempting to start a survey. Even the minutes took on a modern appearance, and technology of the day, shorthand, was employed. A special mention should be made of the enormous amount of work by Morris M. Leighton, state geologist of Illinois. He served as secretary for 6 years, attended most of the AASG meetings during this decade, and organized an annual field meeting in Illinois. His name is attached to communication to AASG from allied organizations, so he was also active in organizations helpful to AASG such as the American Engineering Council and the National Research Council. The amount of material in the archives increased a great deal during his time as secretary. A relatively few very dedicated members rotated through the AASG offices, but participation grew, and meetings and field conferences moved away from the East Coast. Members of the AASG in the 2000's would readily understand the issues and debates of the 20's and vice versa. The actions and activities of the 20's set the stage for the AASG of 2008.

1930–39

Donald M. Hoskins *(Pennsylvania, Honorary)*

The year 1930 marked the beginning of a major change in communications between and among state geologists about issues they and their surveys faced. Meeting in Urbana, Ill., AASG members discussed having a medium of publication (Leighton, 1927). George Branner, Arkansas state geologist, was appointed to the newly created position of editor to prepare quarterly mimeographed reports to include "discussions of administrative practices and activities of the various surveys." Additional recommended topics included interstate cooperation and relationships with federal agencies.

As reported in the first issue of the *Journal of the Association of American State Geologists* (1930), Branner's December 1929 letter to all state surveys announcing the new quarterly report and requesting articles produced an excellent response. The letter cited the types of articles suitable for the new

Journal: office administration and procedures, methods and equipment of field work, types of survey work in progress, cooperation with private, state, and federal entities, specifications for and lists of reports and maps, state legislative and congressional relations, varieties of publicity, and news and announcements were all acceptable *Journal* topics. Members adopted a motion (AASG, 1930) that the *Journal* be regarded as confidential and not for public release. Twenty-one of the 41 listed member states subscribed during 1930.

Implementing the adopted content guidelines, AASG's subsequent 1930 issues of the *Journal* principally contained informative articles on survey administration, organization, and procedures (Kansas, California, Alabama, Arkansas, Colorado, Illinois), field work in progress (Wisconsin[22]), map publication specifications (Oklahoma), publicity (Oklahoma, Illinois), and new publications (Florida, Pennsylvania, Iowa, Kansas, Arkansas, Oklahoma). Following 1930, the AASG *Journal* regularly included similar informative articles about state survey activities and reports and maps issued.

AASG's *Journal* became the principal communication method for informing the many members who could not attend annual, special, and field meetings of the Association about accomplished business. Further, the *Journal* provided a means of sharing with all AASG members information on programs of the U.S. Geological Survey and other federal agencies. Issues discussed and questions raised during AASG's annual meeting, which were usually attended by fewer than 20 of its members, were included in the *Journal,* as were letters and reports provided by federal agencies.

Issues facing AASG members in the 1930's continued from earlier decades and included cooperation with the USGS in topographic map preparation, stream gaging, interstate stratigraphic correlations, use of geologic names, the need for a standard basis for coal classification, and a proposal by the USGS that all geologic reports contain an abstract.

At its 1930 annual meeting (AASG, 1930), the 15 attending AASG members were informed that the USGS appropriation bill for 1931, while containing most desired items, also would newly require that states share 50 percent of the cost of engraving and printing topographic maps. Because of the difficulties this would create for many states with appropriation periods differing from the federal appropriation, members immediately appealed to Congress for a delay in implementing the requirement. During the 1930 meeting, AASG President Bean received a letter from Rep. Louis C. Cramton (R-Michigan) offering an amendment that would defer the implementation of the 50-50 requirement until 1932. Issues and concerns of Association

---

[22] The article, "The Cost of the Magnetic Survey in Wisconsin" by H.R. Aldrich (1930), provides a very full description of what field geology work was like in the 1930's. "Magnetic" is explained as actually being mineral lands classification.

members relating to topographic mapping were often included in the *Journal* during the 1930's.

Recognizing the need for more structure in Association activities, at its 1930 annual meeting the Association also adopted a new statement of organization recommended by an ad hoc committee. Eight members would constitute a quorum for transacting business. Included in the proposed bylaws was provision for assistant state geologists to have membership at meetings of the Association. Nominations for officers would be made by three past-presidents.

Seeking to publicize the work of AASG members, AASG Secretary George C. Branner prepared a lengthy article summarizing the geologic and other activities of all 41 state surveys for 1929. Submitted for publication to the *American Year Book,* the report was also printed in AASG's *Journal* (Branner, 1931a). Described were general, basic, and economic geologic activities, including subsections on fuel, metallic and nonmetallic minerals, and groundwater. Similar annual reports for 1930, 1931, 1933, 1934, 1935, and 1936 were printed in the AASG *Journal.*

Sharing 50 percent of the cost of publication of geologic reports and topographic maps, concern over the delay in printing of completed topographic maps, and other federal-state cooperative activities were issues that continued into 1931. Both topics were discussed at AASG's annual meeting in February, which was held, following past practice, in conjunction with a meeting with the USGS. At this meeting, USGS Acting Director Mendenhall related that the

> U.S. Geological Survey must be in a position to state definitely to Congress
> that they had not contributed more than 50% of the total amount expended
> on cooperative projects...(AASG, 1931a, p. 11).

Organizations other than AASG did not support the 50 percent cost sharing. As an example, the Colorado Mining Association, through two resolutions printed in AASG's 1931 *Journal* (AASG, 1931a, p. 11–12), strongly opposed the federal requirement that states share in this cost.

Included in AASG's 1931 annual meeting was a presentation of federal appropriations for the USGS, noting that the cost of stream gaging formerly borne by the Army was now transferred to them. Following this presentation, acting USGS Director W.C. Mendenhall, in response to a request from AASG, provided a lengthy and detailed letter relating the expenses incurred in the cooperative topographic mapping and stream gaging programs. Mendenhall's (1931a) letter revealed (perhaps for the first time) that USGS assessed an overhead charge of 12.5 percent to cover costs of cooperative work conducted by USGS's Topographic Branch office in Washington. Coupled with the requirement that all costs of engraving and printing of topographic maps had to be shared by state cooperators, this information was likely surprising.

Not all was well within the states in 1931 as the Great Depression began to affect state government operations. Staff of the Oklahoma survey was reported by AASG (Journal of the Association of American State Geologists, 1931) not to have been paid since March because of lack of a deficiency appropriation. In addition, Oklahoma Gov. Murray vetoed its state survey appropriations for the biennium starting July 1, 1931. Dr. Gould, Oklahoma state geologist, announced, "he is going fishing." This was the first reported instance in AASG communications of state geological surveys being affected by the 1930's depression. Others would follow.

The first history of the Association's activities, including tables of business and field meetings with principal topics discussed, was compiled by Secretary Branner and printed in the July 1931 issue of AASG's *Journal* (Branner, 1931b).

Reprinted in AASG's *Journal,* regarding the issue of preparation and completion of topographic maps, was the statement originally published in June 1931 in the *American Engineering Council's Bulletin* endorsing the letter written by Dr. H.W. Temple, Congressman from Pennsylvania, and principal author of the "Temple Bill" (publication 498, 68th Congress, Feb. 25, 1925) "authorizing completion of the topographic mapping of the United States within a period of 20 years" (American Engineering Council, 1931). Included in the Engineering Council's statement was a strong resolution addressing the director of the Bureau of the Budget to provide "sufficient appropriations to carry out the intent of the Temple Act," and "the removal of restrictive clauses in the appropriation bills which hinder or defeat the intent of the original Temple Act" (American Engineering Council, 1931).

A very lengthy letter written to Congressman Temple from acting USGS Director Mendenhall (1931b) explained that it was the policy of the Appropriations Committee that "has molded the appropriations and plans for topographic mapping...." Mendenhall further wrote, "Apparently the Committee has assumed that the spirit of the Temple Act is met if sufficient Federal appropriations are made annually to meet the cooperation offered by states."

The Great Depression had an impact on AASG member surveys. In early 1932, legislation slated the Kentucky Geological Survey for abolishment. Later legislation transferred the Kentucky survey to the University of Kentucky. The Pennsylvania Topographic and Geologic Survey received a one-third funding cut, stopping most field work and reducing most salaries. The year 1932 also brought the reinstatement of the Ohio survey, following gubernatorial veto of its 1932 appropriation. Ohio's State Board of Control provided funds from an emergency fund. AASG also postponed its planned 1932 summer field meeting (AASG, 1932, p. 2).

That state geological surveys were important to state economic interests was apparent with the 1932 initiative by the Massachusetts Forestry Association to institute "a land economic survey of which the Geological Survey will probably be the most important phase." Organized by AASG, 21 state geologists wrote to the Massachusetts Forestry Association in late 1931 in support of this initiative, describing the benefits that their state surveys provided to their states' industry (Reynolds, 1932).

Topographic maps continued to be a public concern, as well as a concern to AASG members, as evidenced in the *New York Times* editorial of May 24, 1932. Decrying that only 44 percent of the nation had been mapped, the editorial stated, "A topographic map is as important and as much of a tangible asset as any highway, dam, or harbor improvement...."

At its 1932 annual meeting (AASG, 1932, p. 4), AASG considered the request from the North Carolina Highway Commission to jointly meet with the American Association of Highway Officials regarding "geodetic control for highways ... [and] general state topographic mapping as an aid to highway location...." The requested joint meeting was held in December 1932. AASG's Committee on Topographic Mapping attended, led by President Leighton. At this meeting, AASG presented a succinct statement under headings of "The Unsatisfactory Progress in the Program of Geodetic and Topographic Surveys" and "Proposed Plan for Adequate Geodetic and Topographic Surveys to Meet the Special and Immediate Needs of Highway Building."

AASG's plan

> ...suggested that in such States, the State Highway Commissions or State Highway Engineers consider the advisability of matching Federal funds or supplementing the inadequate funds of the State mapping agencies already existing to bring forth standard surveys in those areas where road building is under consideration. It is estimated that...the allotment by State Highway Commissions on the average of the equivalent in cost of one mile of concrete paving per year would be sufficient.

An AASG-drafted resolution presented to the American Association of Highway Officials was then adopted (Bevan and others, 1933).

Also considered at the 1932 annual meeting was the proposed reduction in the Department of the Interior appropriation. The proposal resulted in an AASG letter being sent to the chairman and all members of the Senate Interior Appropriation Subcommittee, supporting the president's recommended budget for geological surveys, topographic maps, and stream gaging.

The year 1933 was very active for AASG and its members as they, their states, other national associations, the federal government, and the country reacted to the impacts of the Great Depression. The effect of the Great Depression was reported to AASG members (Branner, 1933c) in January 1933, and noted that the overall decrease in 1932 appropriations to state surveys was 23.8 percent (from $1,381,357 to $1,051,292). At its 1933 annual meeting (Branner, 1933a), many AASG members reported the effect of reduced state appropriations, including that the Washington state survey was "almost non-existent." July's issue of AASG's *Journal* (v. 4, no. 3) announced that the Alabama, Connecticut, and Maine surveys were without funds to operate and that many more states were operating with reduced appropriations. Late in 1933, the Alabama survey was reinstated, but Indiana and Ohio reported reductions.

USGS Director Mendenhall reported at AASG's 1933 annual meeting (Branner, 1933a) that the USGS's proposed appropriations for 1934 were cut, with fundamental research eliminated and cooperative funds reduced, under the assumption that state cooperative funds were overestimated.

The federal appropriation for topographic maps for 1933 was also a matter of concern to AASG members, following receipt of a letter from J. Clawson Roop, director of the Bureau of Budget (Staack, 1933) in which he stated that the "suggestion of Congressman Temple of Pennsylvania, for a change in the language of the appropriation for topographic surveys ... would involve such a departure from the existing governmental policy ... as would require ... the obtaining of authorizing legislation," meaning that the disliked policy of 50-50 cost sharing for engraving and printing to topographic maps would be continued.

On July 25, 1933, seven AASG members attending the International Geological Congress in Washington, D.C., met and adopted a motion instructing that a letter be sent to the chairman of the Special Board for Public Works urging that $10 million be provided to the USGS and the U.S. Coast and Geodetic Survey "for topographic mapping, for water resource investigations, for conservation work, and for continuation of geodetic work" (Journal of the Association of American State Geologists, 1933). AASG's Executive Committee sent this letter August 5 on behalf of the Association.

Late in August, by telegram, AASG members were asked to attend a special meeting on August 29 in Chicago. The meeting was called to address "(1) employment of unemployed engineers, and (2) the need for topographic mapping in various parts of the country." President Leighton informed the meeting that the $2.4 million allotted to the USGS from the

National Recovery Act for topographic mapping "was not to be used cooperatively" (Landes, 1933).

At this meeting attended by 16 members, numerous motions were adopted. Included were that "state geologists offer every cooperation to the U.S. Geological Survey." The motion was followed by a suggestion that AASG's offer "include a diplomatic request that the state geological surveys be consulted in the expenditure of funds." A following adopted motion stated that "the Association of American State Geologists recommend that funds be allotted to the U.S. Geological Survey to study the mineral resources of the country to relieve unemployment among geologists, petroleum geologists, and mining engineers" (Landes, 1933). Following the meeting, an August 29 telegram and letter were sent to Harold Ickes, chairman of the Federal Emergency Administration of Public Works, listing the adopted motions and other recommendations from this meeting. A later letter emphasized the needed work on the mineral resources to aid in industrial recovery of the nation.

Addressed at AASG's August meeting also was a request forwarded from the National Research Council for AASG comments regarding the organizational position and structure of the USGS and U.S. Bureau of Mines, including possible transfer of work or relocation of the USGS into a Bureau of Surveys and Maps that would include the Coast and Geodetic Survey.

Responding to an October 14 letter from AASG Secretary Branner, USGS Director Mendenhall provided a state-by-state list of amounts allotted to the USGS from the Federal Emergency Administration of Public Works for topographic surveys, stream gaging, and underground water surveys (Mendenhall, 1933). Inasmuch as these funds were not allowed to be matched by state funds, the largest allotments were allocated by the USGS to many of the states with extensive public-domain land.

The year 1933 ended with a special meeting of AASG (Branner, 1933b), attended by 16 members and USGS Director Mendenhall, to address a request from the National Research Council "to prepare a report for the Division of Geology and Geography of the National Research Council on 'A Model State Geological Survey.'" Sixteen subcommittees were listed, with nine state geologists or state survey staff as subcommittee chairmen. The meeting minutes reported that

> the ultimate goal sought is to produce a report to be published by the National Research Council, which will clearly reveal the importance that this high body attaches to state geological surveys and related bureaus, and which can be used by the state surveys in their formulations of programs of work and in seeking and obtaining better legislative support (Branner, 1933b).

During the special meeting, USGS Director Mendenhall

stated that the present financial situation affecting the state and federal surveys was indicative of the fact that it was incumbent upon scientific men generally to unite for the purpose giving legitimate publicity of the value of their efforts and place in the state and national life (Branner, 1933b).

The year 1934 began with a list of ongoing and planned activities of AASG member surveys using funds obtained from the Civil Works Administration, one example of which was that the Arkansas survey would be hiring 29 employees in various capacities (Branner, 1934a).

The AASG *Journal* changed editors in 1934. Virginia State Geologist Arthur Bevan became secretary of AASG following elections at the 1934 annual meeting and assumed the role of editor. With volume 5, number 2, Bevan noticeably modified its format and changed the content to include lengthier, member-written articles on more general topics. The first such article, written by AASG President M.M. Leighton (1934), was entitled "The Functions of State Geological Surveys." Also reported, in abstract format, in this issue of the *Journal* were eight papers presented at a symposium, Relations between Government Surveys and the Mining Industry, sponsored by the American Institute of Mining Engineers. State Geologist George Ashley of Pennsylvania presented "The Function of State Surveys" at the symposium.

As related during AASG's 1934 annual meeting (Bevan, 1934), one included symposium paper, "Relations between Government Surveys and the Mining Industry," presented by Reno Sales, chief geologist, Anaconda Copper Mining Co., provided suggestions to surveys

that they should (1) stick to their objectives, (2) speed up field and office work, (3) issue adequate editions of reports, (4) have maps for distribution independently of reports, (5) keep adequate underground records of mines, (6) aid prospectors, (7) see that there is no overlapping of bureau functions with those of private surveys, (8) revise data periodically, and (9) properly advertise publications, state where and how such could be obtained (Sales, 1934).

Discussion by AASG members followed.

Cooperative topographic map production continued to be a matter of concern to AASG members in 1934. Public Works funds used for topographic mapping could not be matched by states. The regular appropriation provided to the USGS did not include sufficient amounts to match expected state cooperator funds. President Leighton suggested that there was a "breakdown of the agreement of the Government to see through this cooperative work of topographic mapping on a 50-50 basis with the states." A motion was then adopted to prepare a resolution addressing "the failure of Congress to appropriate adequate funds to meet available state cooperation" for topographic mapping and stream gaging (Bevan, 1934, p. 7–8).

The concluding issue of AASG's 1934 *Journal* began with a letter to the Association from its Executive Committee appealing to Association members and their staff to

> prepare well-illustrated articles on topics of national interest, bearing on mineral resources, water resources, mapping…or any phase of the work of state geological surveys or of geologists (Branner and others, 1934).

These articles would be edited "by someone familiar with the technique of popular writing" and distributed to national circulation periodicals such as *Harper's, New Republic, Popular Science, Scientific American,* and the *New York Times Magazine Sunday Supplement.*

> It is the considered opinion, therefore, of the Executive Committee that one of the most important activities which our Association can undertake is to bring about a more widespread understanding of the work and economic values of geological surveys and of geologists generally (Branner and others, 1934).

At a meeting of the AASG in December 1934 (Bevan, 1935), a motion was adopted amending section VI of AASG's bylaws relating to the *Journal.* The amendment included, "the *Journal* is not regarded as a confidential publication and the secretary may receive subscriptions from any responsible persons" (Bevan, 1935).

On January 14, 1935, the report of the federal Board of Surveys and Maps to the Natural Resources Board was released. Printed in AASG's January 1935 *Journal* (Wilby, 1935), the report was of considerable interest to Association members who were cooperators with the USGS in topographic mapping. The report described a new "National Mapping Plan," and stated (Wilby, 1935)

> the Board has made an exhaustive investigation and finds much evidence that the actual loss of money due to the lack of adequate maps is greater than the estimated cost of completion of the standard maps of the United States…. The Board has prepared a program which, if adopted and carried out, will provide for the completion in ten years of the standard surveying and mapping of the United States…. The Board recommends that the program be 100 percent Federal, and that it be financed from Federal funds….

At AASG's February 1935 annual meeting in Washington, D.C., Claude H. Birdseye, chairman of the federal Board of Surveys and Maps, presented a discussion of the National Mapping Plan, which was later printed in AASG's *Journal* (Birdseye, 1935a).

At its 1935 annual meeting, Association members described "the relations of State Geological Surveys to public works projects as they pertain to the natural resources of states falling within the provinces of the Surveys" (Bevan, 1935a).

On July 15, 1935, Arthur Bevan, AASG secretary, sent a telegram to President Franklin D. Roosevelt. Printed in AASG's *Journal,* excerpts include (Bevan, 1935b):

> Associated Press dispatches indicate that National Planning Committee program has been abandoned. Because of the great and immediate need of extensive topographic mapping and ground-water surveys and inventories of mineral resources by the Federal government in coordination with the several states ... the Association of American State Geologists deplores this apparent change in the establishment of a permanent policy of orderly development....

In October 1935, AASG President George Branner prepared and sent a lengthy and impassioned letter to President Roosevelt on this matter (Branner, 1935a). Included in the letter was:

> I have learned with both astonishment and regret that the National mapping program ... approved by the National Resources Board, and which, according to press reports, was approved by you, has not been put into effect.... It is well known that you are convinced of the need for making inventories of all our natural resources and planning for their utilization and conservation for the benefit of present and future generations. As it is impossible to begin to plan effectively without the accurate picture of the terrain which is furnished only by modern topographic maps, it must be clear that the need for accurate maps is imperative for this purpose.

President Roosevelt (1935) responded from Warm Springs, Ga., with a letter in which he wrote,

> Since the [Natural Resource] Board's April report, various work relief projects have been submitted by the U.S. Geological Survey, the U.S. Coast and Geodetic Survey and the Corps of Engineers for proposed work in agreement with the national mapping program. These have been reviewed and coordinated by the National Resources Committee, successor to the Board. None of them have been approved or placed in operation under the current work program, *because of the high cost per man-year of employment* [emphasis added].

At a meeting held in conjunction with the meeting of the Geological Society of America, AASG members adopted a resolution in regard to mapping services of the federal government. The motion passed unanimously, and the secretary was directed to mail copies to President Roosevelt, Secretary Ickes, and a lengthy list of federal officials and members of Congress. The resolution stated (Bevan, 1936b):

> 1. That the nation-wide mapping program as outlined in 1934 by the Board of Surveys and Maps and endorsed by the National Planning Board is of such moment that it is imperative that every effort be made to put the program into effect at the coming session of the Congress.

2. While agreeing with the broad principle of the consolidation of the basic mapping agencies of the Federal Government, as advocated in the report of the Science Advisory Board, we believe that certain of the recommendations are of a highly controversial character and any action on them should be held in abeyance pending further study. It is believed that such controversial recommendations should not be allowed to obscure the major objective of initiating at once the nation-wide mapping program.

In addition to hearing lengthy reports of federal agencies (U.S. Geological Survey, U.S. Bureau of Mines, U.S. Coast and Geodetic Survey, National Resources Committee, National Park Service) during AASG's February 1936 annual meeting, six of which were published in volume 7, number 2 of AASG's *Journal,* President Branner proposed forming a National Defense Committee of AASG. A motion was adopted forming the Association as a whole in a "Committee on Strategic Mineral Resources" (Bevan, 1936a). Responding to President Branner's reference to the report of the Planning Committee for Mineral Policy (part IV of the National Resources Board Report, 1935), a motion was adopted for the secretary to "prepare a resolution requesting the establishment of a permanent National Planning Agency, so that the work of the National Resources Committee might be continued on a more definitely permanent basis" (Bevan, 1936b). An additional AASG resolution was adopted expressing "the hope that the computations and adjustments of the existing field data for control surveys may be undertaken and carried to a rapid completion as a step towards preventing waste of public funds" (Bevan, 1936b).

In late 1936, AASG Past-president Morris M. Leighton presented to AASG members a proposal for the creation of a national Mineral States Committee by the American Mining Congress. Prepared by request of the Program Committee of the Congress, and provided to its members in 1936 for implementation, the proposal would involve the president of AASG in a national committee and state geologists of each mineral-producing state in state committees. AASG members would join in committees composed of mining executives and mineral producers in "the important task of assembling and preparing information for the education of the people" on mineral matters (Leighton, 1936).

At AASG's 1937 annual meeting, the structure of its Executive Committee was modified by changing the title of "third member of the Executive Committee" to "vice president," effective March 1, 1937 (Bevan, 1937). At this meeting, potential changes to the date of the annual meeting were considered, in part because of the conflict of the usual February date, when many state legislatures were in session. Adopted also at this meeting was a resolution to be sent to the director of the U.S. Coast and Geodetic Survey stating that AASG "favors strongly the establishment of a nation-wide system of gravity and magnetic bench marks and that the location of all such bench marks be established in conjunction of the State Geologists of the respective states" (Bevan, 1937). As in the prior year, the many presentations made by federal officials were printed as articles in volume 8, number 2 of AASG's *Journal*. Added as presentations in 1937 were reports and articles of the U.S. Soil Conservation Service and the U.S. Forest Service.

Newly elected as AASG secretary at AASG's 1937 annual meeting, Raymond C. Moore edited the third (July) issue of AASG's 1937 *Journal*. Moore was aided in editing by Kenneth Landes, Kansas assistant state geologist. With one minor exception, this was the first issue of the *Journal* to use graphics to illustrate an article, and the first to use graphics for the cover design.

Discussed at length by Moore was the topic of AASG's annual meeting, specifically its date, location, and limited attendance, and including the question "Is it desirable to hold at least some of the annual meetings of the association at a place more centrally located than Washington?" (Moore, 1937a).

In response to a questionnaire sent by AASG Secretary Moore, the final issue of the 1937 *Journal* included responses to questions, plotted graphically on U.S. maps with state boundaries. Most responding AASG members preferred abandoning the pending February 1938 meeting and to meet instead in conjunction with the annual meeting of the Geological Society of America. Included comments, however, indicated a wide variety of opinions as to the most beneficial meeting date and location and the extreme difficulty for some to attend because of distance or expense (Moore, 1937b).

The National Mapping Program was again directed to the attention of members of AASG, with an appeal from Secretary Moore to contact "our representatives in the House and Senate" (Moore, 1937c). Provided in the final 1937 issue of AASG's *Journal* as background material were a series of letters, including letters by AASG members to Sen. Carl Hayden (D-Arizona), a supporter of appropriations for topographic mapping, and to President Roosevelt (Moore, 1937b).

At AASG's late December 1937 special meeting held in Washington, D.C., the Association's attention was directed (Moore, 1938a) to the

> subject of formulating specific programs for future meetings of the Association to embody matters of greatest practical value of attending State Geologists. The view was expressed that increase in value of the meetings might be obtained by laying more stress on exchange of observations and judgments concerning various matters that are of importance to State Geologists, and giving less time to requested addresses from Federal officials.... It is the evident purpose of meetings in Washington (1) to consider in joint sessions of Federal officials and

State Geologists subjects that affect cooperation and interrelation of the work of these two groups, not merely for State Geologists to hear in person reports... that otherwise might be read at convenience, and (2) to permit special individual conferences between State Geologists and Federal officials.

During the part of the meeting involving federal officials, Secretary Moore outlined AASG's viewpoint regarding future meetings and indicated the desire for somewhat informal presentations. "There was evident relief on the part of Federal officials in being asked to help develop the conference along these lines" (Moore, 1938a, p. 35). Also discussed at this 1937 special meeting was the likelihood that there was little prospect of appropriations to implement the Temple Act. Reasons offered for lack of mapping prospects included numerous overlapping mapping agencies and wastefulness of present policies.

Communications to AASG members from professionals concerned over lack of action on the National Mapping Plan were discussed at the 1938 AASG annual meeting, and resulted in appointment of an AASG committee to draft a resolution "reaffirming support of the Hayden-Ickes Bill" (Landes, 1938, p. 22). Correspondence from President Roosevelt (1938) provided to AASG from the American Engineering Council included ".... It seems to me that the adoption of any general mapping program should be deferred pending the enactment of Congress of general legislation for the reorganization of governmental activities." The resolution referred to Senate Document 14, 75th Congress, which outlines a 20-year program of control and mapping in the United States, "known as the Hayden-Ickes Plan."

The resolution (AASG, 1938) stated:

> The Association of American State Geologists declare that it is the consensus of opinion of its members that an expenditure of $5,000,000 a year for basic topographic mapping, as recommended in the Hayden-Ickes Plan, would be so fruitful of public benefits that the plea of the necessity for economy is to be regarded as a lack of understanding of the significance of the undertaking; and that the reorganization of governmental agencies has no connection with the adoption of the Hayden-Ickes Plan....

Candid comments provided by U.S. Geological Survey Director Mendenhall during AASG's 1938 annual meeting and printed in AASG *Journal* (Landes, 1938, p. 46–47) provide a federal perspective on the mapping and reorganization issues of concern to AASG members:

> The older scientific organizations, by and large, may be said to have reverted financially, about to the positions they occupied before the big depression of 1929.... You know Secretary Ickes' proposal, backed by Senator Hayden. You know that the Budget is not accepting that proposal. Therefore, the proposed appropriations are essentially on the old basis. You are acquainted with the

reason given by the Budget as spokesman for the President, for failure to make funds available in accordance with the Ickes-Hayden Plan.... I gather that the real reason undoubtedly is the anxiety of the Administration over the prospect of greatly decreased income and increased outgo, for as you know, the National budget is unbalanced and there is no prospect of balance.... So far as reorganization is concerned, that will doubtless reach down into the details of government. Every indication that comes to us is that the President is thoroughly map-conscious, is very greatly interested in and desirous of stimulating mapping in the United States, but I have not the remotest idea whether he has in mind the creation of a new mapping unit. I gravely doubt whether has had time to think very much about it.

The year 1938 brought a new topic. New was the availability of strategic and critical minerals, a concern because of "rumors of wars." Correspondence from the Office of the Assistant Secretary of War suggested "it might be more advantageous if coordinated data were forwarded through the Association of American State Geologists" (Moore, 1938b). Utilizing lists of strategic and critical minerals and their products, it was suggested that state geologists send publications on the listed minerals and products to the Commodities Division of the Assistant Secretary of War.

Explaining to AASG members the lack of the fourth issue of 1938's AASG *Journal*, Secretary Moore said in the first issue of 1939 that "nothing appeared worthy of...publication in the *Journal*..." (Moore, 1939).

Important motions were adopted at AASG's 1939 meeting (Bevan, 1939b). The first adopted motion was "that the Secretary of the Association be directed to provide for honorary membership without dues." The motion made it possible for Association members who had reached retirement age to be elected honorary members of the Association. Dr. Henry B. Kummel, retired New Jersey state geologist, was elected the initial honorary member of AASG. Also discussed was the feasibility of AASG having a meeting annually in conjunction with the Geological Society of America, as a joint session similar to that of affiliated or other societies. Following discussion, a second adopted motion was:

> Be it resolved that the Association of American State Geologists favors an afternoon session in conjunction with the annual meeting of the Geological Society of America for the purpose of presenting a program of the research work of the State Geological Surveys, and it is hereby recommended that a committee with power to act be appointed by the President to carry out these purposes.

As part of its meeting with federal officials, USGS Director Mendenhall shared a letter written by the Secretary of War addressed to the Secretary of the Interior (Bevan, 1939a). Mendenhall stated, "It expresses the official War Department attitude toward topographic mapping." Included in the letter was: "The work being undertaken by the U.S. Geological Survey and the U.S. Coast and Geodetic Survey ... constitutes a material contribution to the national defense."

Col. Rogers, chief of the Commodities Office of the Assistant Secretary of War, also addressed AASG members at length regarding "proper utilization of our mineral resources and their relation to industrial mobilization." Resulting from his presentation, AASG adopted a motion that the AASG president be empowered to appoint a committee of three to confer with Col. Rogers for the purpose of working out a specific relationship and coordination of this work with the army and navy (AASG, 1939b).

Extensive correspondence between AASG members during midyear 1939 focused on whether or not AASG should appoint a committee to study federal reorganization. Lacking AASG action for such a committee, newly elected AASG Secretary and Editor Price circulated a poll; 25 responses were received by the due date of July 5, 1939, of which 20 favored the proposal and four did not (AASG, 1939a).

1940–49

Donald M. Hoskins *(Pennsylvania, Honorary)*

The 1940's began with the attention of state geologists directed to natural resource issues related to conflicts ongoing in Europe.

A full report of AASG's Military Liaison Committee (Branner and others, 1940), appointed following AASG's 1939 annual meeting, was prepared late in 1939 for consideration at the February 1940 annual meeting. Included was a joint letter of the directors of the U.S. Geological Survey and the U.S. Bureau of Mines: "To this end, the two Federal Bureaus concerned bespeak the cooperation of the members of the Association." The U.S. Geological Survey and the U.S. Bureau of Mines had been directed by Public Law 117, Section 7, enacted in mid 1939 by the 76th Congress, to investigate ores and mineral substances essential to the national defense. AASG's committee "recommended that all state geologists...cooperate fully with the two Federal agencies" and prepare "lists of the kind and amount of information they possess regarding each deposit of these minerals...."

AASG's 1940 annual meeting, attended by 19 members, produced a policy statement regarding interrelations between public geological surveys and commercial consultants and laboratories following a discussion: "Competition of State Geologists versus Private Consultants." Public relations, critical minerals, work being accomplished through the Works Progress Administration, mineral taxation, industrial mineral laboratory investigations, state survey relations to highway construction, and soil surveys all were discussed.

Past-president Bevan's presentation at the meeting, "Public Education in Geology," was printed in the *Journal* in two parts (Bevan, 1940, 1941), and was highly recommended to all state geologists by Association officers.

The statement of organization of AASG, with amendments (AASG, 1940) addressed concerns over the procedure for AASG officer nomination and election. The feasibility of AASG conducting a meeting at the annual Geological Society of America meeting was considered, as well as what should be the relation of state surveys to regional geological society meetings. Distribution of the *Journal,* minus confidential information, to anyone was adopted. AASG also adopted a motion that "it is not wise policy for the Association to prepare a report on reorganizing the U.S. Geological Survey and the U.S. Bureau of Mines without being requested to do so by the organizations concerned or by the Executive Department" (Price, 1940).

Presentations made at the 1940 meeting by U.S. Geological Survey staff were later published (Meinzer, 1940; Staack, 1940). J.G. Staack, chief topographic engineer, reported on formulation of new standard policies for topographic maps affecting cooperation with state agencies. Included were contour intervals, map scales, and uniform indexing based on latitude and longitude. New map publication processes augmenting copper plate engraving, and stereophotogrammetric preparation of topographic maps were described. O.E. Meinzer, chief of the Division of Ground Water, discussed the increasing national demand for groundwater. Meinzer urged that federal and state surveys develop a well-coordinated program of work recognizing the limits that congressionally earmarked appropriations impose, which had resulted in federal-state tensions.

"National Defense and how the different States through the State Geological Surveys can aid in our Nation's defense program" was the main theme of AASG's 1941 annual meeting, with 22 states attending. Incoming President Raymond C. Moore (1941c) expressed his opinion of the reasons for AASG existing:

> The objectives of the Association of American State Geologists have not been formulated in a published statement of purpose. Naturally we have no political aim, although we may properly consider joint action to influence public policy in certain directions, such as adequate support for a national topographic mapping program, for researches needed by mineral industries of several states, and similar matters.

During the 1941 annual meeting, topics discussed included printing of bulletins, cost and financial return, Federal Stockpiling Act, mineral development legislation, the Interstate Oil Compact program, and improving the

Journal through active participation. Dinner included a USGS presentation titled "Domestic Strategic Mineral Investigations" and included two congressmen as guests. Their participation resulted in a recommendation to invite such guests on future occasions. The bulk of the open session of the 1941 annual meeting addressed strategic minerals, groundwater-use legislation, and federal (multiagency) mapping programs.

Regarding strategic minerals, the presenter, Charles K. Leith (1941) of the USGS, suggested

> that the Geological Surveys could be of assistance in attempting to curb the tendency of certain individuals or groups with the respective States who are requesting Government aid in developing what frequently prove to be worthless mineral deposits on their land. The State Geologists should be able to aid in sorting out the better prospects.

The Association amended its bylaws during the 1941 meeting to state that the AASG Nominating Committee would consist of the three most recent active past-presidents, with the senior member as chairman. Also adopted was a resolution on the qualifications and tenure of office of state geologists. Resolved was that "the duties of a State Geologist are such as can be discharged properly only by a person who is thoroughly trained in geology, mineralogy and allied fields of science and who has had several years of practical experience in geological work" and is a "graduate of an accredited college or university" and has "pursued an extended course of study along geological lines..." (Dott, 1941).

At AASG's 1941 meeting, the report on reorganization of the U.S. Geological Survey and the U.S. Bureau of Mines was disapproved. Retiring AASG President R.A. Smith (Michigan) was directed to send the report to the director of the U.S. Bureau of the Budget, noting that it was merely a report of an AASG committee and disapproved by vote of the Association members.

The year 1941 was also the year in which, starting with the third issue of the *Journal,* its cover featured a sketch by then–AASG President Raymond C. Moore (Kansas) of a past-president of AASG. The initial person sketched was Missouri's "Chief" Buehler, AASG president in 1926. Many more portrait sketches by Moore were to follow (see chapter 8).

A second "Early History of the Association" (Kummel, 1941) was published in the *Journal* in 1941. Written by Henry B. Kummel, AASG president from 1908 to 1911, it provided recollections for the period when limited records were kept of Association activities and actions. The first historical compilation was prepared by AASG Past-president George C. Branner and published in the *Journal's* July 1931 issue. Additional historical information on Association members was presented by Branner in "Growing Import of

State Geological Surveys," published in September 1941 in *Mining and Metallurgy,* and reprinted in the *Journal.*

AASG President Moore (1941a, b), through correspondence in 1941, recommended renewal of the combined geological society/agency committee that developed a "stratigraphic code." Forming of the committee was initiated by AASG in 1930. Following publication of the "code" in 1933 by the Geological Society of America and American Association of Petroleum Geologists, the committee disbanded. AASG proposed to AAPG, GSA, the Geological Survey of Canada, and the USGS that three representatives of each organization meet in conjunction with GSA's 1941 meeting to consider revisions or additions to the "code." At this meeting, Moore was appointed chairman. Two questions were addressed:

> (1) Is establishment of a Commission on Classifications and Nomenclature of Rock Units likely to promote advancement of geology in North America, and (2) If such a Commission is agreed to be desirable, what should be its scope and methods of work? Attending members unanimously agreed that the proposed commission should be organized then, "recognizing that the exigencies of war may severely restrict its activities..." (Hake and Moore, 1941).

AASG's 1942 annual meeting began with presentations of war activities of several state surveys, mostly related to strategic minerals. Following a lengthy, detailed USGS status report of strategic materials, Association members were advised that they could principally help in "shaking down" propositions that were submitted to the War Production Board and other Washington agencies, as well as cooperating in regional and district studies of critical commodities such as manganese. Included in a resolution adopted unanimously on February 14 was that AASG

> hereby tenders the services of its organization and of each of the State Geological Surveys and Mining Bureaus to all Federal agencies concerned in augmenting and stimulating the production of war minerals (Dott and Moore, 1942).

Earlier, in 1941, AASG President Moore charged a committee with preparing a report addressing the accumulation of experience on the technique of building state geological organizations. Fulfilling this charge in 1942, in addition to detailed recommendations on organization and procedures, using the Illinois and West Virginia surveys as examples, the committee's report included specific recommendations to new survey chiefs to develop a program with fundamental and applied aspects, providing full credit to all participants, and to address legislative committees with "... frankness, expert knowledge and definite convictions ..." (Committee on Aid to State Geological Surveys, 1942).

The role that state surveys could and should play with regard to war minerals was addressed in a proposal by AASG's vice president, Earl Nixon

(Oregon), for an Advisory Committee on War Matters that would address issues in addition to the then-critical need for a more effective domestic mineral production (Nixon, 1942).

AASG polled active surveys early in 1943 to develop information on mineral production used in the war effort and address apparent short-comings, of which some members were aware. AASG Past-president Moore (Kansas) was called to military service.

Early in 1943, Virginia State Geologist Bevan described new trends in survey work, including "greater emphasis upon the practical usefulness of all kinds of field and laboratory data" and from general to precise data using geophysical and precise laboratory techniques (Bevan, 1943). He said that much of the work of his survey was focused upon projects that aided in the war, principally related to minerals, including the urgent demand for large amounts of high-grade limestones. Groundwater was also very important to the armed forces, with rapid expansion of armed forces facilities.

While AASG's 1943 annual meeting mainly focused on World War II effects on state survey programs, the Association initiated new committees that were to continue thenceforth: Ballot, Auditing, and Resolutions. An ad hoc committee of past presidents was charged with preparing a communication to the Secretary of the Interior relative to the qualifications of the successor to U.S. Geological Survey Director Mendenhall. On recommendation of this committee, the Association unanimously adopted and ordered transmitted a letter that included (Dott, 1943a)

> ... The Director should be a geologist recognized for his integrity, high, un-questioned professional standing in Geology, proved administrative ability....
> In addition, the State Geologists place high value on the ability of the Director to cooperate with the States, and on such relationships today in war, and tomorrow in peace....

A lengthy report of AASG's ad hoc Advisory Committee on War Matters was presented (Dott, 1943c). Principal issues addressed in the report included (1) concern over the new decentralized program of the U.S. Bureau of Mines, with complaints of Association members of deliberate disregard of state surveys, lack of qualification of USBM local engineers, and waste in its program of exploration, and (2) locating military establishments without understanding of local groundwater and terrain.

Because of the extensive negative information received regarding U.S. Bureau of Mines activities, AASG's Executive Committee met with USBM Director Sayers to convey AASG members' concerns. In this regard, AASG's *Journal* quoted a *New York Times* editorial: "Misrepresentation, dishonesty, and deception must in the end reflect unfavorably on the Bureau's integrity and damage its reputation ..." (Dott, 1943b). Later reports by state geologists indicated that AASG's concerns were not addressed (Lloyd, 1943).

In mid 1943, AASG President Price (West Virginia) became a major with the provost marshal as a natural resource specialist. Assuming the post of AASG president, Vice President Earl Nixon (Oregon) addressed the Association with "National Trends Inimical to State Geological Organizations," recommending that the

> ... Association should study and analyze the present situation, with all its implications that may be detrimental to state and national welfare, scientific progress in our own states, and the self-interest of our state organizations (Nixon, 1943).

The *Journal* noted (Dott, 1944b) that in preparing for AASG's 1944 annual meeting,

> the officers feel that the meeting this year will be one of the most important ever held. Serious problems affecting State Geological Surveys and equivalent bureaus exist now, and different, but probably equally serious ones will stare us in the face as soon as the war is won. It is not too early to consider a broad, national, peace-time policy of geological, mineral and ground water investigations, a policy that will define the whole job, and will also define the respective responsibilities of state and federal agencies.

At the 1944 meeting, the Resolutions Committee prepared a resolution to Department of the Interior Secretary Ickes regarding the respective functions of the U.S. Geological Survey and the U.S. Bureau of Mines, with specific reference to the investigation of deposits of minerals. Responding for Secretary Ickes, acting Secretary Abe Fortas (1944) responded,

> We appreciate the interest shown by your organization.... We hope in the near future to arrive at a mutually satisfactory formula, which will provide a blueprint for efficient conduct of the Department's exploration work for mineral resources....

In addition, at the 1944 meeting, the Association appointed a continuing committee "... to study the matter of ground-water work in the States, with special reference to cooperation with the U.S. Geological Survey" (Johnson, 1944a, p. 6). To this end, the committee prepared a resolution that was adopted by AASG members to be sent to the director of the USGS (Johnson, 1944a, p. 8–9). An extended series of communications addressing many unresolved issues to and from AASG and the Water Resource Division of the U.S. Geological Survey and between AASG members began with this resolution.

Discussions during the 1944 meeting of exploration and investigation of mineral deposits brought out that duplication, with consequent waste of public funds, had occurred, and that there was considerable local resentment toward the expanding federal usurpation. Responding to a letter sent to him, USBM Director Royd R. Sayers (1944, p. 10) responded,

> The matters enumerated by the Association…are contrary to the policy of the U.S. Bureau of Mines, and I shall be glad to take the steps that are necessary to remedy any of them when specific instances of such departure from the policy of the Bureau is reported.

Circulation of the *Journal* was discussed again, and a motion passed to restrict it to AASG members and directors of the USGS, USBM, and Canadian geological survey. Adopted by motion and implemented with issuance of the third issue of 1944 was the addition of the pages of the *American Year Book* pertaining to state survey activities. Retiring editor of the *Journal,* Meredith Johnson (New Jersey), wrote to the members that the present policy was not wholly satisfactory, had weaknesses, and recommended that the *Journal* be devoted to noncontroversial, nonconfidential material and that confidential matter be provided by circular letters (Johnson, 1944b, p. 14).

Acting AASG President Robert Dott (Oklahoma) inquired whether AASG should and could be represented in a proposed council of geological organizations that was considered at a 1943 meeting (Dott, 1944a). First reported to AASG members in 1943 in the AASG *Journal,* the new organization was initially identified as "American Geological Association" (Dott, 1943b, p. 37). The 1943 meeting attendees, including AASG Past-president Paul Price (West Virginia), resolved that the AASG would not, for the present, be invited to be a part of the new organization, being similar in category to the USGS.

Plans for the 1945 annual meeting included a special pre-meeting session of the Groundwater Committee with USGS Director Wrather, addressing continuing unresolved problems in connection with the cooperative investigation of groundwater (Johnson, 1945a).

At the 1945 AASG annual meeting, three standing committees (Ground Water, 40th Anniversary, and Regional Correlations) were continued, although little had been accomplished by the latter two because attention had been directed to war activities.

The Ground Water Committee submitted a progress report (Clark, 1945), noting that although discussions were held with USGS Director Wrather,

> It is clear that there is still considerable dissatisfaction with federal-state cooperative ground water programs, budgets and agreements in the states where the geological surveys are the state cooperating agents. Some states now cooperating may withdraw…. The most difficult items are federal funds charged to the cooperation….

A resolution supporting a recommendation of mining delegates from western states regarding public access to confidential geologic and engineering reports made by federal agencies was adopted, noting that (Johnson, 1945b, p. 14–15)

> the Association is in thorough sympathy with this recommendation, not only because the information has been obtained by use of public funds, but also because inquiries on such mineral resources go to the State officials, rather than federal agencies in ratio of about 40 to 50 to one, and the information should be readily available to the public.

The resolution resulted in the introduction of congressional legislation (HR 3148 and SB 1034). Soon after the introduction of the legislation, letters from U.S. Bureau of Mines Director Sayers (1945) and Assistant Secretary of the Interior Strauss (1945) to the congressional committees noted changes in Bureau policy to release data previously held confidential.

Topographic mapping was also considered during AASG's 1945 meeting, with a motion adopted

> ...that the topographic mapping of the United States should be completed as rapidly as possible, the work to be done under the supervision of the U.S. Geological Survey, and with the use of the best available photographic mapping methods (Johnson, 1945b, p. 9).

U.S. Geological Survey Director Wrather later discussed their extensive topographic mapping program producing military maps and for the War Production Board, describing the use of multiplex methods for producing the maps and inviting the members to a demonstration. Announced were USGS plans for a series of state geologic maps at a uniform scale of 1:500,000.

Following the 1945 meeting, a mail vote was taken of the 44 then-current members. Of these, 26 voted that the 1946 meeting be held in Urbana, Ill., rather than in Washington, D.C. (Johnson, 1946b, p. 6). The tentative program included invited presentations by the U.S. Geological Survey and the U.S. Bureau of Mines. The Water Resources Committee presented eight "guiding principles," including "...The charge against cooperative funds for administrative costs in the Washington Office, and for field inspections by Washington officials, is unfair to State Geological Surveys, and should be eliminated" (Johnson, 1946a, p. 2). The Association adopted the eight principles.

The Correlations Committee reported that it had not reached consensus on its objectives, with some members, including Chairman Horace Thomas (Wyoming), recommending that it serve chiefly in an advisory capacity. The 40th Anniversary Committee outlined plans for celebrating "the maturity" of AASG at a field conference in the Colorado-Wyoming area in late

August or early September. The general plan for a field conference with evening sessions addressing the general theme of "The Next 40 Years" was approved.

Elmer Pehrson, representing the U.S. Bureau of Mines, described work of the Bureau that included a description of statistical data collected. Following his presentation, the Association resolved that

> the U.S. Bureau of Mines, in cooperation with the appropriate state agencies, should assemble and publish as state reports in a separate volume the mass of statistical data on the mineral industry of the nation...(Johnson, 1946a, p. 14).

U.S. Geological Survey Director Wrather's presentation included an exhibit of a new topographic map for Orbisonia, Pa., with shaded overprint to bring out topography as in a relief map. The Association extended especial thanks to Director Wrather for his "sincere cooperation with this association and its members and for his presence at this session" and, in a resolution (Johnson, 1946a, p. 14–15), urged

> Congress to appropriate to the official map-making agency of the nation, the U.S. Geological Survey, sufficient funds to permit completing the Topographic Map of the whole of Continental United States as fast as accuracy permits, but that this shall not preclude matching appropriated funds from those states desiring to speed up the program within their area....

The Association then voted to hold its 1947 meeting in Washington, D.C., and in 1948 in Alabama in celebration of the centennial year of the Alabama Geological Survey.

Subsequent to the 1946 annual meeting, President Johnson (New Jersey) proposed that an index of articles appearing in AASG's *Journal* be prepared and that Raymond C. Moore be appointed chairman of an AASG delegation to the Commission on Classification and Nomenclature of Rock Units (Johnson, 1947, p. 1–2). Moore was elected chairman of the commission at its 1947 meeting.

President Johnson (1946d) paraphrased Arthur Bevan (Virginia) in commenting on the 40th anniversary field conference thus:

> It is indeed timely that the Association recognize and review the accomplishments of four most significant decades in the progress of state geological surveys and the roles of the surveys in building a sound and stable national economy. It is appropriate that this be done by a field conference, where the stress of war years can be laid away and field science and good fellowship may be the order of the day....

Seventeen AASG members, along with additional staff and guests, attended the field conference. Many, discounting the encountered "rotten" weather, recommended that such field conferences be held annually or semiannually (Troxell, 1946).

In October 1946, AASG's Executive Committee (AASG, 1947b, p. 22) wrote to U.S. Geological Survey Director Wrather, saying,

> It has been called to our attention that those members of our Association having cooperative agreements with the U.S. Geological Survey for the study of ground waters, have a very real interest in the appointment of a successor to O.E. Meinzer.... [W]e feel that the interests of our members should permit us to voice the hope that the ground water work of the U.S. Geological Survey will continue under the direction of a trained geologist with experience in that field....

Signed by AASG's Executive Committee, the letter was airmailed to Washington. Following a prompt response by U.S. Geological Survey Director Wrather, noting that Dr. Nelson Sayre, geologist, had been appointed to replace O.E. Meinzer, President Johnson (1947) wrote:

> Speaking as a representative of the Association of American State Geologists, I am sure that even those members who have not yet had the pleasure of meeting Dr. Sayre will be pleased by the consideration given their viewpoint in connection with the selection of an appointee....

In preparation for AASG's 1947 annual meeting, a committee of past-presidents made recommendations for amendments to "Outline of Organization of the Association of American State Geologists." As stated therein (Price and others, 1947),

> As the years have elapsed, the value of interchanges among state geological surveys made possible through the Association and importance of the Association as a medium of concerted action has become increasingly evident.... To this end, we suggest enlargement of the executive committee so that, in addition to the present three members (president, vice-president, and secretary), the retiring past-president and a president-elect shall serve as active administrative officers of the Association.

These recommendations were unanimously adopted by the Association, "for the purpose of having more members actively engaged in the affairs of the Association and in order to spread interest and influence in the respective states..." (AASG, 1947a).

Following presentations during the 1947 meeting on "The Role of State Surveys in Problems of Water Supply," which concluded that "perhaps no phase of the work of a state geologist in many states is more important than the administrations of studies in water resources," the importance of having standing committees was discussed "to aid in the administration of the Association." Standing committees then voted were: (1) Water Resources Committee, "whose purpose shall be to keep members informed in all matters pertaining thereto," (2) *Journal* Committee, with the editor as chairman and two others as correspondents, and (3) Committee on Public Education, whose duties were "to promulgate geological information and to advise the members of the Association on methods of educating the public to our mutual advantage" (White, 1947).

Additional actions voted in 1947 were: (1) to convene the 1948 annual meeting in Tuscaloosa, Ala., to include a symposium on the role of geology in the national economy, with invitations to the U.S. Geological Survey for their participation, (2) to keep the *Journal* as is, with improvements expected, and adding distribution to former state geologists, and (3) to increase the Association dues-subscription from $7 to $15 to cover printing costs.

Following election to the previously created officer positions, and using a complex procedure that only the Association could arrange, the newly created position of president-elect was filled. The procedure used has to be read to be believed (Jones, 1947):

> *The Election of Officers:* After a sharp discussion, the impugning of motives, a threat to the sufferage (sic), challenges, and counter charges—not to mention a tardy explanation of and by the Committee (Bean, see front cover, and White, see back cover) the count of the votes was given; the report accepted and the following declared elected:
>
> President: Edward L. Troxell, Connecticut
> Vice President: A.C. Trowbridge, Iowa
> Secretary: Walter B. Jones, Alabama
>
> *Appointment of Peyton, President-Elect:*
> Because the law as presently constituted (page 20) comprehends an Executive Committee made up of the president, vice president, secretary, president-elect and past president,
>
> Because it provides for the filling of vacancies other than at times of election by the committee itself, and
>
> Because there was no election of a president-elect in 1947:
>
> The Executive Committee formally met on March 26th last, chose and appointed* Peyton, Georgia, as president-elect for and during 1947.
>
> Actually, to make this a legal procedure**, the following steps were taken: Trowbridge, as vice president, succeeded to the vacant office of president-elect, then willingly resigned from the Association. The Committee appointed Peyton to the vacant office of vice president; on the withdrawal of Trowbridge, Peyton advanced to the position of president-elect; Trowbridge was once more named to the office of vice president. Explanation: Peyton was selected because he had been named by a nominating committee of past presidents on a tentative slate of officers in January; further explication: Trowbridge, through modesty or for some other reason, positively refused to accept the position of president-elect.
>
> The Executive Committee as currently set up is as follows:
>
> President: Edward L. Troxell, Conn.
> Vice President: A.C. Trowbridge, Iowa
> Secretary-Treasurer: Walter Jones, Alabama
> President-Elect: Garland Peyton, Georgia
> Past President: Meredith E. Johnson, N.J.
> _____
> *The Executive Committee has no authority to appoint a president-elect.
> **See if you can figure it out.

Discussions during AASG's 1948 annual meeting held in Alabama dealt with issues relating to federal groundwater and topographic mapping programs. Included were reports on cooperation between states in resolving boundary-line issues related to Pennsylvanian rock nomenclature. A resolution was adopted recommending to state geological surveys that they adopt "...the practice of publishing authors abstracts with geological reports published by the surveys" (Jones, 1948, p. 68).

In the absence of U.S. Geological Survey Director Wrather, the Ground Water Division representative reported that the Minneapolis, Minn., Engineers Club had recommended to Congress to remove all funding for cooperative groundwater investigations, as well as funding for the entire USGS, objecting to the U.S. Geological Survey's "...supplying of any information regarding ground water resources of municipalities or municipal areas." Responding to member concerns, and prepared by motion, AASG adopted a resolution (AASG, 1948):

> Whereas the occurrence, development, and utilization of ground water resources are primarily geological in nature...essential to the healthy growth of a community...fundamental to the welfare of the nation; and
>
> Whereas, the United States Geological Survey is now in a position where it cannot meet the needs of the various state agencies cooperating in ground water studies,
>
> Be it resolved, the Association of American State Geologists goes on record approving the continuance and expansion of cooperative ground water studies between the various states and the United States Geological Survey....

The propriety of AASG making a recommendation for the appointment of the director of the U.S. Bureau of Mines was considered at the 1948 meeting. Congress had withheld approval of appointment of the acting director of the U.S. Bureau of Mines, a geologist (preferred by many AASG discussants), because he was not a mine operator. Concerns were voiced that AASG should not make recommendations for federal appointees. A resolution was adopted recommending that the Secretary of the Interior consult with the National Academy of Science in selecting and nominating the Bureau of Mines director. This resolution was provided to AASG's Executive Committee for its transmittal to the Interior Secretary at their discretion, pending resolution of congressional action.

Closing out the 1940's decade, AASG, at its 1949 annual meeting in San Francisco, created a formal Association office of editor of the *Journal,* and decided to cease publishing the *Journal* as a newsletter and publish it as a formal publication. The first two issues of the new *The State Geologists Journal* published during the second half of 1949 included sections on budgets, programs, and publications; mineral development and economics; educational extension and public service; and, in addition to exchange of news and other communications, provided a directory of state surveys. The new *Journal* was

> devoted to the dissemination of information concerning the organization, facilities, activities, accomplishments, and publications of the various geological surveys and mining bureaus of the states...(Leighton, 1949).

Following AASG's Rock Color Chart Committee report that the first 500 copies of the chart were sold in 5 months after its publication, a resolution was adopted recommending that AASG member surveys use as a standard the color chart prepared by the color chart commission and distributed by the National Research Council.

An extended discussion of the change in policy by the U.S. Geological Survey in the dual naming of 7½- and 15-minute topographic maps resulted in adoption of the following resolution (AASG, 1949):

> Whereas, the Association of American State Geologists recognizes the confusion which is certain to result from present practice of the Topographic Branch of the United States Geological Survey, of retaining the name of a previous topographic map when that quadrangle is subdivided and remapped at a larger scale, and

> Whereas, the Geologic Branch does not follow that practice in its use of geologic names

> Now therefore

> Be it resolved that the Association go on record as opposing existing practice of the Topographic Branch and further that the Director of the United States Geological Survey be requested to reopen the matter and that the cooperating state officials be consulted.

In order to renew relations with federal agencies, the Association members voted to hold the 1950 annual meeting in Washington, D.C., and to have a special meeting in conjunction with the meetings of the Geological Society of America in November 1949.

1950–59

William M. Kelly *(New York)*

The decade of the 1950's was a period of introspection during which the AASG sought to define its purpose and goals. Several actions were taken in support of these endeavors. First, the organization's constitution was revised and adopted in modern form in 1954. Second, a statement of aims and objectives was adopted. Henceforth it would be the mission of the AASG:

> 1. To advance the science and practical application of geology in the United States

2. To improve the work of the state geological surveys through interchange of ideas in regard to programs, techniques, and application to the needs of our modern economy

3. To improve methods of assembling data and disseminating the results of state geological survey work to the public, industries, schools, and civic organizations

4. To accomplish coordination and correlation of work with federal and associated state agencies working in similar or related fields.

Third, a statement of purpose was formally adopted for the *Journal* (Deiss, 1951, p. 4):

> "The State Geologist" Journal is devoted to the dissemination of information concerning the organization, facilities, activities, accomplishments, and publications of the various geological surveys and mining bureaus of the states, and of other information of interest to these agencies who are pursuing research in the natural resources.

Fourth, the AASG polled its membership to discover what specialized personnel and equipment was held by each state survey, and published the information in 1952. The most common piece of specialized equipment was the spectrograph, followed by differential thermal analysis instruments and electron microscopes. Not surprisingly, the most common specialized personnel were spectrographers and chemists.

Attendance at the annual meetings of the Association was steady during the 1950's, averaging 26 states in the first half of the decade and 31 states in the second. Total appropriations for the surveys increased from approximately $4 million to $7.5 million over the course of the decade. AASG funds increased from year-end balances of $1,700 to $3,000 in the same period. (Corrected for inflation to the centennial year, this is $14,000 and $26,000, respectively.) Annual dues were $15 per year. By the end of the decade, all states except Massachusetts had a state geologist. Massachusetts was considered "a hopeless case." Puerto Rico was elected to membership and Alaska had been invited to join.

The modern schedule of AASG meetings was adopted during this decade in that the practice of having two meetings per year was established. At the time these were a business meeting and a field trip meeting. Every other year, the annual meeting was to be held in Washington, D.C. In alternate years, the meetings would be held by a state survey as a field meeting. Early in the decade, honorary membership without dues upon retirement of state geologists, pending vote of the membership, became AASG policy. Furthermore, it was agreed that the Executive Committee meeting would be held the evening prior to the annual business meeting. The spread of succession for AASG officers was expanded to run from the secretary-treasurer to the vice president to the president-elect to the president rather than the then-established policy of merely the president-elect to the president.

The annual meetings allowed discussion of a wide range of issues. These included questions of ethics, consulting practices, registration of geologists, and publication practices. During a discussion regarding the scope and limits of services furnished by state surveys, it was noted that this "is a good question with apparently 48 answers." AASG was concerned about the problem of induction of state survey personnel into the armed forces for the Korean conflict. Also, as a holdover from World War II and the ongoing Koran Police Action, much information on mineral resources, production, and consumption was held confidential by the federal government. State geologists urged that the data be released.

Perennial guests at annual meetings were U.S. Geological Survey personnel, with all divisions represented, and personnel of the U.S. Bureau of Mines. Many state surveys had projects that involved one or both of these agencies. The National Water Well Association and the National Science Foundation sent representatives to request cooperative relations with the AASG. The USGS, in 1950, was "instructing" its project geologists to contact the state geologists when working in a state, hoping to devise a system to keep the state geologists informed of the work of federal geologists. USGS reported that, in the early part of the decade, they were still oriented toward the war emergency and that defense and topographic mapping had highest priority. The U.S. Geological Survey noted that states had a great deal of information on resources. USGS was trying to organize cooperation between the states and the Defense Minerals Authority in order to get that information to the national government. AASG offered to provide seasoned representatives on specific minerals instead of the U.S. Geological Survey sending "a young USGS man" into the field.

Two topics dealing with the mineral industry received AASG attention in the 1950's. There was concern and opposition among the membership to the proposal by the Bureau of Land Management to discredit U.S. mining law. The bureau and the U.S. Forest Service had combined, it was felt, with loggers, stockmen, and recreationalists to change mining law. The purported intent was to sever surface from subsurface mining rights, thus giving the bureau complete control of the surface. At issue was the possibility that the Interior and Agriculture departments might hinder mine development on federal lands. Also, the AASG repeatedly stressed the importance of preservation of drill cores and associated data. While supporting the need for a comprehensive library of core samples, well log data, and other geologic materials gathered from exploration and production, the consensus of the

AASG was that the archiving of drill core and data was a function primarily of the states and not of a national organization.

An annual topic of discussion was the distribution of individual geological survey publications. Questions of how many, to whom, content, and whether to send to overseas recipients were frequent topics. The same issues were debated regarding *The State Geologists Journal.* Cost was always a concern, but distribution was increased during the decade. Furthermore, it was resolved that all state surveys would send two copies of everything published to all other state surveys and Canadian provinces. Distribution of geologic specimens also entered the discussions, revealing wide variation in practice from state to state. It was noted that the California survey used prisoners to break rocks for kits and Ohio used football players "since we have them."

The American Geological Institute, established in 1948, approached the AASG in 1950. The president and executive director of AGI requested an official connection between AASG and AGI. Membership in AGI was a contentious subject among the state geologists. A motion was made and seconded to apply for affiliated membership. Reasons cited were: (1) AASG would be represented on the committees of other scientific organizations in an advisory capacity to the federal government on questions of use of scientific and technical personnel by the armed forces and could attend hearings on the question of the draft and (2) AASG needed professional representation in the field of education. This was immediately met with a motion *not* to join. Some state geologists thought that the AGI had no clearly established policy and would attempt to infiltrate AASG. A 3:1 majority defeated this latter motion. The motion to join carried, and the AASG became the 12th affiliate to join AGI. Delegates to AGI were elected for staggered 2-year terms.

Suggestions were entertained to provide AGI with additional funds for publication purposes. In 1954, after much discussion, AASG forwarded $50 to AGI. In 1956, this amount was increased to $100 and again to $200 at decade's end. In 1952, the AASG began to provide support for the concept and production of the AGI *Glossary of Geology.* Supporters stated that the desire of the AASG was an orderly science and that the glossary would be an aid to that end. Skeptics among the state geologists opposed the whole idea of the glossary, saying, "nobody will follow" the standardized definitions and usage. Those opposed to the idea expressed the opinion that the AASG was supposed to produce technical reports for mining engineers and industrialists, and supporting the glossary would detract from those aims. A resolution was forwarded in support of the *Glossary of Geology,* voted upon, and carried. An AASG representative was appointed to serve on the AGI Glossary Committee. The first edition of the AGI *Glossary of Geology* was published in 1956. In 1954, the American Association of Petroleum Geologists rescinded funding for AGI, referring to any contribution to AGI as "pouring…money down a bottomless rat hole." AASG steadfastly continued its support.

The vantage point of the AASG centennial year provides an opportunity to reflect on the attitudes that prevailed in the United States in the 1950's, which now seem unsettling, if not ethically and morally dubious. The chief of the Geological Division of the USGS is quoted in the AASG annual meeting minutes as follows on the issues of gender and race in the workforce: "Giving women geologists field experience so that they think in terms of geology is a problem. Most women geologists are just looking for a mate and only plan to work for about two years." And, decrying the data collected on federal employment: "Government forms are devoid of racial information so the USGS cannot tell until a candidate shows up what his race is." In the 100th year of the American Association of State Geologists, such opinions are, fortunately, well in the past.

1960–69

William M. Kelly *(New York)*

The 1960's were a time of apparent growth for the Association as it assumed new responsibilities and expanded interests. This is reflected in part by the size and duration of the annual meetings of the organization. At the beginning of the decade, the annual meetings attracted the state geologists from fewer than 30 states on average, and were conducted over a period of 2 days. By the end of the period, geologists from more than 40 states attended the meetings, which were held over 5 days. In 1962, the practice of holding the annual meeting between March 1 and June 30 was ratified by constitutional amendment. Prior meetings had been held in the fall. Financially, the Association maintained modest resources, with end-of-year balances of less than $1,000 to less than $2,000 for the period. In 1966, annual member dues were increased to $25 per year. During the period from the latest 1950's to 1968, total state survey expenditures increased from roughly $8 million to $20 million, and personnel approximately doubled to about 1,000.

The number of federal agencies represented at the meetings doubled during the decade. Perennial interests of the AASG during the 1960's were the programs of USGS, the Bureau of Reclamation, the Soil Conservation Service, and the Bureau of Mines. The USGS Geologic Division chief of operations summarized the repetitive theme of the day, saying "same old appropriations, increasing costs, too many projects." The Association routinely expressed, directly to USGS staff and via the Liaison Committee, a request that the USGS inform the state surveys of federal activities within their state borders and file material of local interest with the state. There was ongoing concern regarding federal programmatic encroachment (USGS, Soil Conservation Service, Corps of Engineers, etc.) on the work of state agencies.

Consistent with the purpose of the organization, AASG exhibited continual interest in matters dealing with geologic education. Throughout the decade, the Association was concerned about the organizational structure and viability of the American Geological Institute, as reflected by the appearance of this topic at every meeting, and financial support of AGI by AASG in the amount of $100, later $200, annually. The Association expressed strong support for earth science education at the elementary and secondary school level. Frequent topics of discussion were handouts, brochures, and free mineral samples for students. The Association noted the lack of university programs to train hydrologists. In 1963, AASG passed a resolution of support for Senate Bill 2 funding college-level scientific and technical training. AASG continued to be active on the American Committee on Stratigraphic Nomenclature throughout the decade.

In the early 1960's, many state geologists were appointed and did not hold civil service positions. Therefore, some complained of being "fair game" for political pressure in hiring and for campaign contributions. Discussions of licensure and certification, both pro and con, occurred for several years. In 1966, a motion was adopted to support the American Institute of Professional Geologists in the field of certification.

Technological changes were rapid in the 1960's, and the Association's activities reflected that fact. Early in the decade, discussions ensued on the use of computers to streamline publication procedures. By 1967, 15 states were involved in computerization of scientific data. AASG had discussions in 1962 on the role of state geological surveys in control of atomic waste disposal. By 1966, 23 states were involved in recommending locations for atomic accelerators.

The Liaison Committee was established on an ad hoc basis in 1962 and was formalized as a standing committee the following year. In the early to mid 1960's, the committee members were able to meet with cabinet-level officials in Washington, such as the Secretary of the Interior or the presidential science advisor. The activities of this committee became some of the most important of the organization. In 1965, the Association was classified as a 501(c)(3) organization, and as such was exempt from federal income tax. Contributions made to the AASG would henceforth be tax-deductible. Further, AASG would not be liable for Social Security or unemployment taxes.

By 1966, the Vietnam War began to encroach on funding for USGS programs and cooperative activities between the USGS and the states. In 1968, the loss of graduate student and occupational deferments from the military draft raised concerns about the availability of properly trained geologic personnel in the near future. Similarly, the Association expressed concern about the demise of certain academic programs nationwide, such as mining engineering, which declined from 36 programs to 17 by the end of the 1960's.

AASG was authorized to nominate a representative to the National Research Council in 1967. The AASG Personnel Committee and an ad hoc Environmental Committee were designated in 1968. As early as 1963, John Frye (Illinois state geologist) expressed his opinion that "environmental geology is coming." Indeed, in 1969, the Liaison Committee held meetings with the Department of Housing and Urban Development to discuss the role of environmental geology and its application to urban planning.

Late in the decade, a national system of wilderness areas was being discussed at the annual meetings, with briefings by appropriate federal managers. Many members of the Association took a dim view of the proposed federal legislation. AASG adopted a resolution strongly suggesting significant revision of the bill.

The State Geologists Journal was widely disseminated to libraries, surveys, and schools, with much information included from related agencies, such as mineral resources data from the Bureau of Mines. This increased the size, hence the cost, of production of the *Journal,* and led to annual discussions of how to cut costs or reduce the size. Early in the decade, the *Journal* subscription (two issues) was $5. It is recorded in the minutes of the 1969 annual meeting (Mankin, 1969) that a motion was entertained to "remove certain inappropriate phraseology" from the cover of *The State Geologists Journal.* Specifically, the motion was to remove the phrase "organ of the" from the front cover. The motion "was passed unanimously by the 'organic' membership of the Association." Also commonly queried was the confidentiality, or lack thereof, of the data published in the statistician's report.

The decade of the 1960's was, for the Association as well as the nation, a period of change. Reflecting this were the perhaps prescient comments of AASG President William Daoust in 1962. He noted "so many new ways of doing things, so many old procedures being shelved for the new." The pace and scope of activities of the AASG through the decade proved him to have been correct.

1970–79

L. Harvey Thorleifson *(Minnesota)*

AASG began the 1970's with only two members having more than two decades of experience: Leo Hough of Louisiana and Charles Doll of Vermont, both having served since 1947. In contrast, 14 members had been newly appointed in 1969. The membership entered the decade with the guidance of a committee consisting of John Frye (Illinois), Wallace Hagan (Kentucky), Robert Jordan (Delaware), John Patton (Indiana), and Ian Campbell (California), who had been directed by President Flawn of Texas to review the state of the Association.

The committee noted that the two activities of earliest origin were the annual meetings and the *Journal*. Recommendations on the annual meeting were designed to alleviate perennial difficulty in accommodating the large number of discussion topics requested by members, while also limiting the duration, including field trips, to 4 days. A third-day closed session was proposed, for review of the materials that had been presented, including private review of the presentations made by federal agencies and other invited guests, as well as to allow participants to break into discussion groups. To limit the meeting to 4 days, it was suggested that only 1 day be scheduled for a field trip.

It was recommended that the *Journal* be unchanged, although it was suggested that annual meeting minutes or a description of the meeting no longer be included, except for a brief review, thus allowing distribution of minutes to be restricted to members of the Association.

The committee recommended continued participation in the American Commission on Stratigraphic Nomenclature that had begun in 1946, as well as continuing the constituent society membership in the American Geological Institute that had begun in 1951, while it was recommended that a directory of specialized equipment and personnel compiled in 1952 and updated in 1954 not be revived.

On the longstanding publication exchange, the committee endorsed the policy of the time, that each state survey send one, two, or no copies of all formal publications to each state survey, depending on the advance stipulation of the receiving survey. It was further recommended that a survey-by-survey list of all series published be compiled, and that each survey update its list of the publications that it wished to receive from other surveys.

As a successor to a 1949–50 initiative for the secretary to distribute news, which was followed up on intermittently in later years, it was proposed that AASG establish a monthly news sheet to be sent to the membership, to include news submitted by members that had not been covered in the

AGI Report or *Geotimes,* in part to allow the Liaison Committee to alert members to developments within their purview.

Although special meetings of the Association were held in 1953, 1955, and 1957, the constitution of the time authorized only one annual meeting, to be held within the period March 1 to June 30. The committee recommended that special meetings, in addition to the annual meeting, be permitted on call of the Executive Committee when needed or desired and that special meetings, if held in conjunction with conferences of other organizations, be listed in the programs for those meetings.

The committee had no recommendations for changes in either the constitutional provision or the existing guidelines for honorary membership, which had been established in 1953 and later incorporated into the constitution, according to the report.

The committee recommended continuation of the annual statistical report that was in existence by 1943, and proposed that the statistical table carry a qualifying statement to the effect that the functions of the individual state organizations and the funding of geologic activities in the various states were not uniform, and that the raw figures in the statistical chart may therefore not necessarily provide basis for comparison.

It was recommended that the Liaison Committee, initiated on an ad hoc basis in 1962 and formalized as a standing committee in 1963, be continued and that the Association establish guidelines to determine the circumstances under which it could properly speak for the Association on issues that extended outside the mandate of state geological surveys.

The committee endorsed continued nomination of a representative to the National Research Council, a practice which had begun in 1967; that the Personnel Committee, established in 1968, be continued; and that the ad hoc Environmental Geology Committee designated in 1968 continue as a subcommittee of the Liaison Committee. The committee felt it desirable for AASG to make recommendations to the federal government, more as an initiator, rather than merely reacting, regarding topics for which there was near unanimity.

No changes to the constitution, bylaws, or committee structure were recommended, while it was recommended that the Liaison Committee have responsibility for all contacts with federal agencies. It also was suggested that AASG establish guidelines regarding official positions taken by the Association. In addition, it was recommended that AASG members send copies of their annual reports to the director of the U.S. Geological Survey and the director of the U.S. Bureau of Mines; that pertinent sections of the Liaison Committee reports be sent to the head of each federal agency that the Liaison Committee visited; that the Association conduct a comprehensive review of existing cooperative arrangements between state geological surveys and federal agencies; and that the resulting information be transmitted to the state geological surveys.

The 1970 AASG annual meeting was held in Rolla, Mo., with President Peter T. Flawn of Texas presiding and Missouri State Geologist William C. Hayes acting as host. Flawn had that year, for example, appeared before a House of Representatives subcommittee to speak on a national mining and minerals policy. In his *Journal* message, President Flawn begged members to support him in conducting Association business more efficiently, by having representatives to organizations and committee chairs submit a written report with recommendations for action by April 1, so the business meeting could consider recommended actions rather than the corpus of the report. He called for fellow state geologists to do their homework, and read the reports that they would receive in the mail. Prominent topics at the annual meeting were mineral policy, topographic mapping, and environmental geology (Flawn, 1970).

William C. Hayes of Missouri was president at the 1971 meeting in Kennebunkport, Maine, where Robert G. Doyle acted as host. In writing his first President's Page in the *Journal,* in addition to noting the decade that had passed since the first President's Page by President John Frye (Illinois), President Hayes discussed the overriding tone and genuine feeling expressed in previous columns that in spite of our diverse organizational structures, legislative charges, and emphasis on different disciplines, all surveys were deeply dedicated to providing the very best in geologic data to their respective states. He also noted that the Association had always been well received at various government levels in Washington, and that all should put their shoulders to the wheel and give wholehearted support to the basic programs of the USGS. The year 1971 also saw publication of "The Origin and Development of the State Geological Surveys," compiled and edited by Gordon B. Oakeshott, deputy chief, California Division of Mines and Geology, and published in *Journal of the West.* At the annual meeting, in addition to presenting the Prettiest State Geologist award to William H. Moore of Mississippi, the participants discussed the impending energy shortage and possible establishment of a federal natural resources department, and discussed national priorities, including topographic mapping, adequate funding to match the state role in cooperative water programs, and acceleration of environmental geology. It was stated that it was evident that AASG had been effective in encouraging Congress to support topographic mapping.

In his 1972 President's Page, President Philip E. LaMoreaux (Alabama) called for an action-oriented AASG, and commented that in an age of environmental awareness, the significance of good topographic, geologic, minerals, water, and energy resources maps and reports is largely lost on the general public, the same public that must provide the necessary support and funds to make much of this mapping possible. He pointed out that state geologists fully appreciate the need for good maps and reports, with which myriad environmental and other problems can be answered, and state geologists know that the adequacy of this important information determines to a great extent whether state surveys can successfully supply the information needed to develop the minerals, water, and energy resources of our respective states and nation and at the same time provide the necessary facts to protect our environment. He linked this awareness to the trend for AASG to become more of an action group, resulting in a new unified effort, for example, to bring about adequate appropriations for topographic and geologic work.

At the 1972 annual meeting hosted by William P. Hewitt in Moab, Utah, after establishing that there was some uncertainty over whether a certain caucus should be referred to as the honorary or the ornery members, the participants addressed several themes, with the environment and topographic mapping being prominent. Professional registration also was an active topic, focusing on a model bill for the registration of geologists and geophysicists prepared in Oklahoma. It was noted that several other states were considering registration, while legislation was already in force for registration in California, Arizona, and Idaho. A key issue was reciprocity, and discussion focused on the number of years necessary for qualification to take the examination, whether or not graduate education or teaching constituted professional experience, methods of distinction between geologists and geophysicists, and qualification for membership on the registration board.

The Liaison Committee reported concern that extensive USGS activity in foreign programs and in mapping the lunar and Martian surfaces could delay completion of the national topographic map. Discussion with the USGS emphasized the proposed National Assessment of Total Urban and Rural Environment (NATURE) program. State geologists expressed the concern that establishment of this data system would significantly reduce the role of the state geological survey in responding to local questions, formerly handled by their agencies. If the development of a national data center would permit nongeologists to have ready access to interpreted geologic information, the need for and the role of state geological surveys would be drastically changed. It was also pointed out that the bulk of the necessary information to establish a national data center would have to be obtained from the files of the state geological surveys. Considerable reluctance was expressed on the part of most state geologists to provide this information to a national data center without specific assurances that this information would have restricted application except through the offices of the respective state surveys. Concern was also expressed regarding the need for cooperative funding on many projects. The proposed NATURE program thus left many questions unanswered, and it was the opinion of many state geologists that answers to these questions needed to be forthcoming before they were willing to extend their support to the program.

Earnest discussions also were held on coordination of USGS offshore operations with coastal states, and concern was expressed regarding investigations centering on geologic hazards in the context of urban geology. Specifically, concerns were noted regarding the USGS role in attempting to at least influence the establishment of regulations concerning urban construction without consultation or cooperation with the appropriate state geological survey, as well as regarding USGS programs in geologic hazards that were being introduced in several states without consultation with state geological surveys. Such actions suggested a general insensitivity on the part of the USGS to the responsibilities and concerns of state surveys.

Finally, considerable displeasure was expressed by many state geologists for the lack of attention being shown by the USGS toward the completion of the national topographic map. Upon completion of the much-discussed report by the USGS, the Association received the shocking news that Gov. Wallace had been the victim of an attempted assassination while on a speaking engagement in Baltimore.

The discussion on USGS activity was followed up by a resolution expressing concern regarding the potential impact of the NATURE program on efforts to complete the national topographic coverage.

Also in 1972, *The State Geologists Journal* was reduced from two issues per year to one annual issue.

At the 1973 meeting hosted by Sam M. Pickering Jr. in Stone Mountain, Ga., Norman F. Williams of Arkansas was the presiding president. In his President's Page in the *Journal,* Williams had addressed the role of geology in dealing with the energy crisis of the day, and the impending shortages of minerals, and the role of nongeologists in allowing the crisis to develop as managers sought quick profits, or as governments sought council from nongeologists. Whereas 2 years earlier, geologists had held the positions of Undersecretary and Assistant Secretary of the Interior and directors of the Offices of Oil and Gas and of Water Resources Research, Williams noted that these able spokesmen were now gone, with the death of Bill Pecora and the retirement of Hollis Dole, Wilson Laird, and Garland Hershey.

At the Georgia meeting, USGS Director Vince McKelvey discussed rumors of a reorganization of the USGS by saying that perhaps the most significant observation he could make was that he was still a director, and what he was directing was still the USGS. He then described impending confirmed changes, such as the 70-person transfer of the seismological activities of the National Oceanic and Atmospheric Administration to the USGS.

Richard Sheldon spoke for the Geologic Division of the U.S. Geological Survey, focusing on follow-up to the 1970 Mining and Minerals Policy Act, designed to strengthen the role of the mining industry, and requiring that the Secretary of the Interior present an annual report to Congress on the health of the mining industry, and the production potential of minerals in the United States. Sheldon indicated that this needed to be a cooperative program, so exchange of data between the states and the USGS was called for.

Later in the meeting, Howard L. Edwards, vice president of Anaconda Co., presented an analysis of the minerals industry from the industrial viewpoint, pointing out that all indications suggested an impending energy crisis, and a minerals crisis soon to follow, because of environmental concerns, removal of land from exploration, poor profit picture, and increasing government restriction on all phases of the mineral industry's operations.

Charles Mankin of Oklahoma, speaking for the Committee on Registration, reported that four states had registration laws, 10 states either had an act under consideration or had considered such action in the recent past, 20 states had no reported plans under consideration for registration, and 16 states did not respond to the survey. The conclusion of the committee was that there was no major movement concerning registration and little widespread interest in such a movement at the present time. It was noted that the most important consideration in present registration laws as well as for future consideration was the matter of reciprocity among the states.

The Honorary Members Committee indicated that although they had met and examined a number of candidates, a few of whom were suggested by state geologists, they did not have any nominations. Instead, they recommended that a standing committee be appointed by the president to receive nominations from members, that nominations be accompanied by a supporting letter, that would include the number of years served in the capacity as state geologist, as well as attendance record and contributions to the welfare of the Association. A commitment to an AASG affirmative action plan was passed, noting that increased utilization of women and minorities in professional practice was recognized as a national objective, and that the AASG recognized its responsibility in achieving this objective.

At the 1974 conference, held in Bend, Ore., Raymond E. (Andy) Corcoran was the host, and the presiding president was Kenneth N. Weaver of Maryland. In his President's Page, Weaver had lamented the polarization of views on public policy, such as the discussion of the time regarding the energy crisis, in which environmentalists blamed industry, industry blamed the environmentalists, and both blamed the government for the predicament of the day, resulting in confidence in government at all levels being at an all-time low. Weaver saw the same tendency in the extreme positions being adopted by geologists on energy and environmental issues. Weaver pointed out that geologists have a unique role to play in addressing the complex interrelationships of society, because the geologist is trained to think in dynamic three dimension over geologic time, although he felt that this perspective could cause some to incorrectly discount human impact on the environment. Nevertheless, he saw a crucial role for state geologists and state surveys in occupying the middle ground, properly informing debate, and in supporting the rapid growth of environmental geology, thus softening the rhetoric and decreasing polarization.

At the meeting, the Liaison Committee report made reference to the cluster meeting program, begun by Dick Sheldon of the USGS Geology Division at the suggestion of the AASG Liaison Committee in October 1973, to facilitate consultation with states regarding new and upcoming USGS programs. A recorded and divided vote was taken on a resolution regarding balancing environmental objectives with the energy and material needs of the nation, making specific reference to what was seen as unnecessary and irrational constraints on surface mining of coal being considered in federal legislation.

In 1975, the annual meeting was held in Asheville, N.C., during the term of President James L. Calver of Virginia, and with North Carolina State Geologist Stephen G. Conrad acting as host. Calver's presidential column had dealt with the Mining and Minerals Policy Act, approved in late 1970 after nearly 2 years of consideration by Congress. The act declared a continuing policy for the federal government to foster and encourage private enterprise in the development of economically sound and stable domestic mining, minerals, metal, and mineral reclamation industries. But in noting many other legislative initiatives, Calver saw over-regulation, an overall negative attitude toward private enterprise, and a lack of understanding of the relationship of the mineral industry to the basic economy, so he called for efforts to promote awareness of the essential role of the resource industry.

A topic addressed at the meeting was needed liaison between state surveys and the Nuclear Regulatory Commission regarding geology and seismicity of sites proposed for nuclear plants. Resolutions also addressed topics such as the imminent minerals shortage. The Liaison Committee report included a summary of the move of USGS staff to Reston, Va., as well as contemplation of a federal Department of Energy and Natural Resources. In addition, incoming President Charles Mankin (Oklahoma) was granted the Royal Order of the Peacock, in recognition of his sartorial splendor.

Colorado State Geologist John W. Rold hosted the 1976 annual meeting in Vail, Colo., with President Charles J. Mankin presiding. Mankin's presidential column followed up on his predecessor's observations regarding legislative initiatives that would have a negative impact upon the minerals and energy industry, resulting in a need for state geologists to speak up for industry. In calling for wise natural resource development in a time of exploding population and loss of energy self-sufficiency, Mankin cited the U.S. bicentennial preparations, and quoted from the Constitution of the United States. At the Vail meeting, three resolutions were passed expressing concern over the United States becoming more dependent upon uncontrollable supplies of vital raw materials from foreign sources, presenting a serious threat to the nation's economy and security. The resolutions therefore endorsed the work of the USGS and the Bureau of Mines, and called for these agencies' budgets to be enhanced commensurate with their responsibilities in helping assure this nation's domestic mineral supply. In addition, it was stated that the withdrawal of public land from eligibility for development would adversely affect development of the nation's mineral resources, and must be avoided except in the most necessary and critical cases. A policy in which public lands would be administered under a policy of multiple use so as to permit essential development of the nation's natural resources for the benefit of all the public was called for.

At the 1977 annual meeting, which began at the University of Delaware north campus in Newark, N.J., and which was concluded at Rehoboth Beach, Del., Duncan J. McGregor of South Dakota was president, while host Robert R. Jordan missed the meetings because of illness, although he managed to recover and arrive in time for the banquet. McGregor's presidential column addressed the role of the AASG in proving to politicians and bureaucrats that we can be of help in solving problems related to fuels, minerals, water, and the environment. He acknowledged that many state geologists had to resist a sense of futility, as geologic facts were ignored by government entities. McGregor counseled acceptance that a politician will only be receptive to information that helps obtain votes, create jobs, or yield dollars. It was noted that although scientist, politician, and bureaucrat each use dramatically different criteria in decision-making, we simply must recast our geologic facts in a form that will convey to the politician and bureaucrat that following our advice will obtain for them those precious votes, jobs, and dollars. The meeting included further discussion on how the AASG could become more effective in influencing policy, in the context of crises regarding resources and environmental preservation. Arthur Socolow of Pennsylvania led discussion on whether the needed AASG role would be more effective by issue papers conveyed quickly to decision-makers in Congress, the media, and to congressional staff, rather than through resolutions, which were the practice in the past. Discussion called for an impartial stance on development, and sensitivity to local perspectives. Socolow advocated that simple, factual, nonadversarial information, possibly suggesting alternatives when appropriate, would inform a public that has differing perspectives, allowing them to make their own well-informed decisions.

The Liaison Committee report included discussion of topics such as the anticipated lack of impact that the new Department of Energy would have on the USGS, as well as discussion with Presidential Science Advisor Frank Press on the National Uranium Resource Evaluation.

The 1978 AASG annual meeting was held in Jackson, Wyo., and the presiding president was Arthur A. Socolow of Pennsylvania. Wyoming State Geologist Daniel M. Miller Jr. acted as host. Socolow's presidential column addressed the topic of communication. He noted that while geology had attained great preeminence in the context of strategic mineral resources, the great uranium rush, moon rocks, and the energy crisis, geologists were not high in public esteem, geologic research was struggling for support, and the role of geologists in providing the world with materials was viewed with suspicion rather than praise. He attributed this contradiction to our failure to communicate effectively, both in terms of conveying and listening. He saw state geologists, at the interface between science and the public and responding daily to issues, as well positioned to convey needed information, for the good of the nation, the public, and the geologic profession.

At the meeting, after welcoming new State Geologists Charles (Chip) Groat of Louisiana and James Davis of California (formerly of New York), President Socolow reported on his busy year, responding to topics such as nuclear waste management, surface-mining regulations, and energy legislation. The death of Ian Campbell in 1978 was acknowledged, and the establishment of the Ian Campbell Memorial Fund was announced.

A resolution was passed to endorse the Core Repository System project of the Bureau of Mines, to develop an efficient and economical national system of repositories for drill cores and other samples of geologic materials. The AASG recommended that a number of strategically located repositories be established throughout the United States and that possibilities be explored for providing federal aid to existing state core storage facilities, where they are available, to function as regional facilities.

At the 1979 annual meeting, held in Little Rock, Ark., Robert B. Erwin of West Virginia was president and Norman F. Williams was host. President Erwin dedicated his column to the AASG-cosponsored 9th International Congress of Carboniferous Stratigraphy and Geology that had been held in Illinois, and cited Carboniferous rock sequences as the source of many of the answers to the world's short-term energy problems. Erwin indicated that the end is in sight for many traditional energy supplies, that problems of massive utilization of fossil fuels, particularly coal, are surfacing throughout the world, so international understanding and cooperation are essential if we are to solve the complex, worldwide environmental, social, and political problems fostered by increasingly acute energy problems.

A report was presented on a contract between AASG, the Department of Energy, and the National Governors Association for the purpose of providing geologic expertise and communication with the states concerning Department of Energy activities relating to the National Waste Terminal Storage Program, implemented at a level of $10,074 as an amendment to an existing contract between the Department of Energy and the National Governors Association.

In another of many agenda items, Matt Walton of Minnesota reported for the AASG Core Storage Committee on discussions regarding a national core and sample storage and retrieval system for geologic materials. Through a questionnaire, it was found that few, if any, states expressed enthusiasm or even interest in a national center for core storage to which the individual states would contribute their cores, although about two-thirds of the states expressed interest in a national core storage system provided each state had a facility for the materials generated within that state. Only smaller states indicated a willingness to participate in a regional facility.

The Liaison Committee reported on the death of proposals for a federal Department of Natural Resources.

Arthur Socolow presented a report on the experience of the Pennsylvania survey resulting from the accident at the Three Mile Island nuclear power plant, located 10 miles from their offices in Harrisburg. He described how over 10 percent of the million residents within a 30-mile radius of the plant evacuated, including some staff members. Survey staff had helped respond to a run on topographic maps, had supported USGS in around-the-clock water sampling, had assisted with water-supply information for proposed evacuation centers, had provided groundwater information about the plant site, and had readied bedrock geologic information in case of a meltdown. It was noted that the types of data required in the emergency cannot be generated quickly, but must be acquired and prepared over years by basic geologic studies. Socolow praised the USGS for its response to

Pennsylvania's needs, observed that the Office of Emergency Preparedness had suffered from a lack of direction, and noted that Nuclear Regulatory Commission geologists did not appear to play an effective role.

In addition, among many other meeting topics, a resolution advocating a marine geology map series for the Continental Shelf was passed.

The 70's thus were a time of escalating conflict between resource and environmental objectives, and of concern over energy and material shortages and loss of self-sufficiency. State geologists took a leadership role in the rapid expansion of environmental geology, while in many cases seeing themselves as advocates of the energy and mining industries. Earnest discussions thus were held on the responsibilities of state geologists, as well as on the balance between advocacy and the provision of impartial information that would inform all sides of a debate. There was a dedication among the AASG membership to ensure that geology would play the prominent role that the public needed in these resource and environmental issues, so much discussion was directed to how state geologists can communicate effectively, thus assisting society and bolstering our role.

1980–89
John D. Kiefer *(Kentucky, Associate)*

To begin the discussion of the 1980's, we first need to take a look backward at the 70's. We might say that the issues of the 80's began with the first Earth Day, April 22, 1970, but the seeds had already been sown. The 70's also marked the beginning of a series of laws and regulations such as the Clean Water Act, the Clean Air Act, permitting waste discharge under the National Pollution Discharge Elimination System, the Resource Conservation and Recovery Act, the Surface Mining Control and Reclamation Act of 1977, and so on. Add to that the oil embargo of the mid 70's and we have set the stage for perhaps the biggest change in the way surveys do business. Many of the notes taken from the President's Page of *The State Geologists Journal* are a look back to the future.

In 1980, President Daniel M. Miller, state geologist of Wyoming, praised the AASG as one of the most progressive geologic organizations in the nation. Miller said that the AASG had moved forward and broadened its area of influence. Communication had been extended in the fields of underground waste disposal, oil and gas reserve assessment, and surface mining. He noted that while many in AASG "do not agree in principle or in fact" with many of the actions initiated by the federal government agencies, AASG had nevertheless maintained a clear channel of communication through the liaison meetings (Miller, 1980). Miller also singled out one of the past productive endeavors as being the "interfacing of AASG with the aims and objectives of the American Geological Institute." He noted that his tenure had been very rewarding and that this completed, for him, a record 7 years as an officer and member of the Executive Committee of AASG.

In a major issue of note, President Miller assigned a special committee of Robert Jordan (Delaware), Donald Haney (Kentucky), and Wallace Howe (Missouri) to investigate the successes and failures of a program presented by William Menard, director of the USGS, and William A. Radlinski, USGS, in 1978, at the Jackson, Wyo., AASG annual meeting, which would allow state geological surveys an opportunity to solicit financial support for state projects considered mutually beneficial to USGS and the states. The program had had mixed results, and the committee was charged with the task of developing a questionnaire to be circulated among the state surveys to gather reliable information concerning the success or lack of success of the USGS contracts/grants initiative. It appeared that the program, entered with high hopes, was not widely advertised nor accepted throughout the ranks of the federal survey. Results of the questionnaire were mixed, with some grants issued, but numerous roadblocks and delays reported. The program was poorly funded and few state geologists found the process to be working smoothly. It seemed that the difference between USGS and state priorities was a major stumbling block, with the result that the experience ranged from poor to very bad.

The AASG developed a position paper on joint planning with the USGS. The original version was presented by Robert Jordan, state geologist of Delaware, at the "Maxicluster" meeting in Reston, Va., in June 1980, and it was decided that Jordan and William Fisher, state geologist of Texas, would work with Rob Wesson and Dave Seyler of the USGS to generate parallel position papers to be exchanged in 1981. Because the foundation for this joint agreement was begun at the 1978 meeting in Jackson, Wyo., the agreement and subsequent revisions were informally named the "Jackson Accords."

Stephen Conrad, North Carolina state geologist, served as the AASG president in 1981. He reported on the general health of state surveys, but also noted the many changes in state survey leadership that had taken place during his 16 years as an AASG member. Some state geological surveys had had as many as five state geologists over that period, and only seven had the same state geologist throughout that 16-year time span. While some may view this as a sign of instability and uncertainty, Robert Jordan (Delaware) had noted in his position paper on joint planning with the USGS that "state geological surveys collectively and individually were vital, active, dynamic, and healthy organizations" (Conrad, 1981). Collectively, the surveys in 1981 employed some 1,500 professionals with a like number of staff and a combined budget of about $65 million. Conrad pointed out that while each state geologist may have his own special style, they all shared the same basic traits of "dedication to their organizations and a deep sense of commitment to public service." He noted the major problems that faced surveys at that time, such as disposal of hazardous waste and contaminated groundwater. At the same time, cutbacks in federal spending in programs that traditionally had supported state surveys would adversely affect state geologists' ability to deal with these issues. He expressed confidence that state surveys would find ways to continue to function at a high level of effectiveness and meet the challenges before them.

At the annual meeting, major concern was expressed over the rapidly rising cost of *The State Geologists Journal,* from $1.69 per copy in 1979 to $2.40 in 1981. Editor Vincent Dreeszen, state geologist of Nebraska, projected the cost at $3 per copy in 1982.

The USGS–AASG Joint Agreement ("Jackson Accords") noted that

> it is in the best interest of both the State and Federal Governments to seek the most efficient and cost effective means to achieve National and State objectives.... Both the state geological surveys and the USGS need to be mutually supportive in their response to changing needs and conditions, and new mechanisms are suggested for policy-making, communication and coordination between states and the USGS.

Cluster meetings were determined to be the logical vehicle for transfer of information on program and project potentials identified in project discussions, which should be initiated at the semiannual liaison meetings and the AASG annual meeting. Obtaining Outer Continental Shelf data continued to be a problem for the state surveys.

The first meeting of the National Research Council's Geological Sciences Board was held in April. The board seemed to be searching for a mission; however, its overall mission was to look after the health of the geological sciences in the United States. Charles Mankin, state geologist of Oklahoma, was on the board and Kenneth Weaver, state geologist of Maryland, was the AASG liaison.

In 1982, President William Fisher, state geologist of Texas, reviewed the President's Page statements for the past decade. In 1972, Philip LaMoreaux, state geologist of Alabama, had written about the environmental movement and how AASG had "come of age" in providing the data necessary as we moved into the age of environmental legislation and regulation. We then moved into a period of declining domestic production of energy, and significant parts of our resource supply being in the hands of foreign cartels. Areas covered by the geological surveys, such as energy, minerals, and environmental resources, were coming into public conflict. By 1978, Arthur Socolow, state geologist of Pennsylvania, was left to wonder why, with all the emphasis on resources, geology was riding so low, and he concluded that it must be because geologists were such poor communicators (Fisher, 1982).

Fisher (1982) noted that as state geologists

> we do reflect the major issues of our times, not…because we are more perceptive…but…because we exist at the boundary of science and public policy. We straddle these areas not because it is a…comfortable place to be, but because that is the way we are chartered. But therein lies the uniqueness and special contribution of state geological surveys. Nothing really changes. Society's need for the geologic facts of life has not, nor will not, lessen. But, emphasis and public perception do change, sometimes quickly and profoundly.

> We will again be tested and we need to be ready to meet that change.

According to 1983 AASG President Meredith E. (Buzz) Ostrom, Wisconsin state geologist, the past is the key to the present.

> The difference between the past and the present is that the problems have tended to increase in intensity, variety, and complexity in response principally to population increases, increased demand for resources, greater public aware-ness, technological advances, and other factors (Ostrom, 1983).

He might also have added environmental regulation. State geological surveys are unique in that they tend to be on the cutting edge of these issues. Initially, surveys were charged with delineation of mineral and water resources to feed the needs of a developing nation, but the emphasis has shifted through time to resource and environmental management, which in turn has shifted the role of geological surveys to becoming the major resource of geologic information for problem-solving, decision-making, and policy-setting in the natural resources and environmental protection arena. Ostrom noted how these changes have greatly added to the responsibilities and workload of state geological surveys, including their involvement in management and policy decisions. This carries over to the AASG, which

> grew out of a meeting in 1908 with the U.S. Geological Survey…to discuss "current plans for work in geology, topography, hydrography, and mineral statistics." Today, the involvement of our association extends beyond the USGS to many other key federal agencies and the Congress (Ostrom, 1983).

Ostrom said that AASG participated in liaison meetings with representatives of federal agencies to discuss national programs and priorities, and was called upon to provide them with critical reviews of these issues. This re-flected a growing realization of the importance of geologic information and that geological surveys were the principal source of that information. These issues could range from identifying strategic mineral reserves to the siting of landfills and nuclear waste repositories, providing information for surface mining and reclamation, and the prevention of groundwater pollution.

Ostrom (1983) then moved to the future: "I believe that if we intend to continue to effectively serve the public, we will be required to seek more cost-effective methods...." Survey budgets were declining in 1983 as a result of a depressed economy, "from which, some say, we may never recover." The ultimate impact would be staff reductions. This should lead to closer coordination with the geologic community, including the USGS, universities, and industry. Duplication of effort and data were unaffordable. Continuing on the path of uncoordinated efforts was not only uneconomic, but it was not in the best interest of the public we are supposed to serve.

Robert Jordan, state geologist of Delaware, in his 1984 presidential message looked at the camaraderie and mentoring aspect AASG shared among all the state geologists. He noted that while state geologists are generally well educated and trained, the

> unique attributes are in a large part passed on by our predecessors within the context of AASG.... In sum, my message is to enjoy the fellowship of AASG, be sustained by it, and extend it to our new friends and our associates elsewhere (Jordan, 1984).

In other words, it would be better to acknowledge our friends while they are still with us.

In other news of 1984, the USGS and the Bureau of Reclamation were moved into a new section of the Department of the Interior under Assistant Secretary for Water and Science Robert Broadbent. The Bureau of Reclamation was charged with focusing on desalinization, the USGS on water policy. Who would concentrate on groundwater was still in question. The USGS was hoping for better relations with the Minerals Management Service, inasmuch as contracts with coastal states had been going to the MMS, but the USGS believed they should be with the USGS. The AASG and MMS had a different interpretation. The Bureau of Land Management relationship on mineral evaluations was still evolving, since the Conservation Division was moved to MMS and BLM. It was hoped that that would provide a good opportunity for state surveys and BLM to communicate. The COGEOMAP program was introduced by USGS to counter the steadily declining geologic mapping role in the United States. It was a 50-50 cost-sharing effort with the states.

On July 31, the National Critical Minerals Act of 1984 was signed into law, with a budget of $500,000 and a chairman designated by the president. Its purpose was to advise the president in establishing a coherent national mineral policy and needs.

The petroleum industry was in the forefront of the news that year. Sharply dropping prices for oil decreased activity throughout the industry, resulting in budget reductions and the layoff of many geologists. A committee, to which AASG contributed significantly, developed information for the guidance of geologists considering career changes. This was presented in a symposium, a booklet, and on video and audio tapes.

Budget cuts had a cascading effect in 1985, and many state surveys were affected. AASG President James Davis, state geologist of California, pointed out that despite the pinches and swells of our funding support, which resembled a "boudinage" pattern, most of our surveys date back over a century, and many have been in continuous operation for more than a century. He said it was the responsibility of the state geologist to provide leadership to his staff, which should include a sharing of a vision and a collaboration and coordination with staff as to what the functions and the goals of the organization must be. Those in government for a long time were fully aware of the pinches and swells of budget and staff. Davis said state geologists had the responsibility of sharing this retrospective knowledge with their staffs, who are charged with providing to the public information related to the geology, geologic hazards, and mineral resources of their states. Some state surveys are also charged with monitoring surface- and groundwater resources. The need for this information will always exist, along with a continuous need for more current information and modern geologic interpretations for decision-makers. This assures us of the need for geological surveys well into the future. In addition, many states are confronted with land-use policy decisions, including those on federal lands, which may affect the future availability of mineral resources (Davis, 1985).

Frank Kottlowski, state geologist of New Mexico and 1986 AASG president, summarized 1986 by noting that, constitutionally, AASG objectives are to address the practical application and the science of geology and the related earth sciences in our states; to improve the work of state geological surveys through interchange of ideas pertaining to their organization, programs, techniques, application to the needs of the ever-changing economy, and other geological survey matters; to improve data collection and dissemination to the user community; and to accomplish better coordination of work with associated federal and state agencies. All of these objectives were important decades ago and were still the main focus of AASG and its members in 1986. Kottlowski reviewed statements by previous AASG presidents, and closed by quoting William Fisher, Texas state geologist: "We exist at the…boundary of science and public policy, wherein lies the uniqueness and special contributions of state geological surveys" (Kottlowski, 1986). Kottlowski pointed out that with many environmental issues, energy issues, public paranoia toward nuclear power, federal and state budget tightening, air pollution, a depressed mineral industry, and increased geologic hazards from population expansion, we would have much to challenge us in the future.

In 1987, President Charles W. (Bud) Hendry (Florida) wrote that the Association was "alive and well." He added that "it seems to be a sign of the times to have geological surveys reorganized and placed under new leadership in response to reduction in funding and reprogramming of functions by legislatures and host organizations," and 1987 was no exception. But AASG continued "to be the conduit from/to the general public for geological information needed in mineral development, waste disposal, growth management, and water availability." He concluded that the Association's liaison with federal agencies, professional associations, and congressional committees serves to improve coordination of geologic activities involving both federal and state participation.

At the 1987 annual meeting in Traverse City, Mich., Robert Horton announced that he was resigning as director of the U.S. Bureau of Mines, effective in July. He noted insolvable budget issues preventing the bureau from being effective. Carolita Kallaur and Michael Hunt of the U.S. Bureau of Mines noted that a depressed oil industry and political opposition to leasing areas outside of the Gulf of Mexico were curtailing the United States' ability to find new oil and gas reserves. The result was that the Middle East would exert even greater control over our economy and national security. C.Y. Chen, chief of mining engineering, U.S. Office of Surface Mining, made a presentation on the Surface Mining and Reclamation Act, Public Law 95-87, and the role of geology in the law. Twenty-five states then had primacy of the program, and OSM had oversight in eight states.

Doyle Frederic of the U.S. Geological Survey stated that they were making a significant investment in advanced cartographic systems and geographic information systems. He noted concern by the states about the need to participate more fully in geographic information system pilot projects. The USGS was close to completing once-over coverage at a scale of 1:24,000 for the country. These resources were being directed toward digital cartographic data development and 1:24,000-scale revision, and the National Mapping Division was beginning a national aerial photography program. Robert Milici, Virginia state geologist, presented the results of a survey made of the states regarding the proposed USGS National Mapping Program and COGEOMAP element. After a long discussion, it was noted that AASG had already adopted resolutions on those issues and gotten no response from USGS or the Department of the Interior. President Hendry then appointed a committee to prepare a resolution to include language in support of geologic mapping, a national geologic mapping plan, increased support for COGEOMAP, and a request for a response to the resolution from the USGS and the Department of the Interior.

In 1988, AASG President Charles (Chip) Groat, state geologist of Louisiana, reported on the AASG effort to raise the level of federal support for geologic mapping. He noted that geologic mapping is a fundamental responsibility of both federal and state geological surveys. In fact, it is the foundation of most of our geologic research, and many surveys have been working on mapping at various levels since their founding more than a century ago. The job is far from finished, however, and even those states like Kentucky, which completed mapping on a 7.5-minute-quadrangle base some 10 years earlier, still lack the detail and mapping products at a level consistent with the needs of geologic mapping to the nation. The AASG decided to make a concerted effort to raise the level of federal funding for geologic mapping. Groat stated that this would require not only a major effort at the federal level, but also commitments at the state and local levels to generate the funds necessary to support the program. It would require selling the importance and usefulness of geologic maps in dealing with a wide variety of land-use, resource, and environmental issues, not just on their scientific value. Only if their importance could be documented and the utility of these maps be effectively communicated to the user community would the program succeed. He also noted that state surveys must continually justify the financial support they receive. With the rapid increase in the need for resource and environmental information brought about by the explosion of new regulations in the past decade, this communication found a new audience not only with regulatory agencies, but with the general public (Groat, 1988).

The birth of the National Geologic Mapping Act marked the beginning of a new era for AASG. Few could envision the level of effort necessary to get the act passed by Congress, pursuing and defending levels of appropriations, and shepherding the act through numerous reauthorizations by Congress. Geology plays a central role in our lives, and it is up to geologists, particularly those at state geological surveys, to communicate and explain that role to the public and decision-makers. Groat pointed out that several state surveys have developed innovative programs aimed at earth science education and informing the public about resources, the environment, and geologic hazards.

In another example of looking back to the future, Groat stated,

> Geologic mapping and effective communication of geologic information [are] growth areas for the future. It is likely that state geologists were saying this when their state geological surveys were founded. It is clearly time for another push (Groat, 1988).

Larry Fellows, 1989 AASG president and state geologist of Arizona, used a unique approach in his 1989 President's Page by focusing on words beginning with the letter "p." He said that increasing *population* required more land, water, minerals, and energy. In addition, more *people* meant more *pollution*, which required more *physicians* and more services. Tax revenues were insufficient to fund the needed services, and tax increases were generally not being considered. Government agencies were being asked to operate more efficiently, improve *performance,* and be more *productive.* This required that state geologists clearly define what services, *products,* and activities are essential, and they must develop strategic *plans,* goals, and *priorities* to *provide* them to the user community and the public (Fellows, 1989). He added that

> most state geological surveys communicate regularly with their constituents. These constituents, in turn, need to know what reports, maps, and data are available. They want readily accessible computerized databases. Users need accurate and detailed bedrock and surficial geologic maps. Finally, they request a variety of objective, scientific, topical, and interpretive reports and maps, many of which are derived from the basic geologic maps.

This brought Fellows back to a need that AASG had been preaching for more than a century, and in 1989 AASG members were united in their support of a national geologic mapping program. Substantial progress had already been made on topographic and soils mapping, which required long-term commitments to goals, *plans, priorities, personnel,* and funding. Fellows concluded, "I encourage AASG members to continue to work together in stressing the importance of this [national geologic mapping] program to the Nation" (Fellows, 1989).

In addition to regular activities, AASG members completed three special projects in 1989: (1) *The State Geological Surveys: A History,* (2) a review at the request of the Department of the Interior of data used by the USGS and the Minerals Management Service to assess undiscovered recoverable oil and gas resources of the nation, and (3) a white paper and draft legislation for the National Geologic Mapping Act.

1990–99

Morris W. (Brud) Leighton *(Illinois, Honorary)*

Introduction. Clearly, the decade of the 90's was a period of major change in the growth, maturation, and influence of the AASG. The Association changed from one with relatively narrow interests to one with far-ranging influences in this decade. It was perhaps the most important period in the shaping of the AASG since it formed in the first decade of the 1900's. The decade witnessed sweeping changes in AASG's interactions with federal

Table 2. Annual and midyear meetings, decade of the 90's.

Annual Meetings

Place	Date	Meeting	President
Madison, Wis.	June 9–13, 1990	82nd	Donald Haney (Kentucky)
Saratoga Springs, N.Y.	May 4–7, 1991	83rd	Ernest Mancini (Alabama)
Tuscaloosa, Ala.	June 13–17, 1992	84th	Robert Fakundiny (New York)
Coeur d'Alene, Idaho	June 5–8, 1993	85th	Morris W. Leighton (Illinois)
Maumee Bay, Ohio	June 4–7, 1994	86th	Donald Hull (Oregon)
Reno, Nev.	June 12–14, 1995	87th	Donald Hoskins (Pennsylvania)
Charlottesville, Va.	June 2–4, 1996	88th	Walter Schmidt (Florida)
Breckenridge, Colo.	June 21–24, 1997	89th	Earl Bennett (Idaho)
Portland, Maine	June 12–16, 1998	90th	Charles Gardner (North Carolina)
Fairbanks, Alaska	June 5–9, 1999	91st	Larry Woodfork (West Virginia)

Midyear Meetings

Place	Date	President
Dallas, Tex.	October 29, 1990	Ernest Mancini (Alabama)
San Diego, Calif.	October 21, 1991	Robert Fakundiny (New York)
Cincinnati, Ohio	October 27, 1992	Morris W. Leighton (Illinois)
Boston, Mass.	October 26, 1993	Donald Hull (Oregon)
Seattle, Wash.	October 25, 1994	Donald Hoskins (Pennsylvania)
New Orleans, La.	November 7, 1995	Walter Schmidt (Florida)
Denver, Colo.	October 29, 1996	Earl Bennett (Idaho)
Salt Lake City, Utah	October 21, 1997	Charles Gardner (North Carolina)
Toronto, Canada	October 27, 1998	Larry Woodfork (West Virginia)
Denver, Colo.	October 26, 1999	Jamie Robertson (Wisconsin)

Table 3. AASG Liaison Committee meetings, decade of the 90's.

Year	Spring Meetings	Fall Meetings
1990	March 11–14	October 14–17
1991	March 25–27	September 30–October 2
1992	May 4–6	September 13–16
1993	April 18–22	September 12–15
1994	April 24–27	September 11–14
1995	April 23–26	September 18–20
1996	March 18–20	September 22–25
1997	March 9–12	September 14–17
1998	March 15–19	September 20–24
1999	March 14–17	September 12–15

agencies, Congress, and private organizations, as well as in the manner in which the Association was organized and conducted its business.

This section on the decade of the 90's is divided into topics, highlighting as the first and most important event of the 90's the enactment and implementation of the National Geologic Mapping Act and the role played by the AASG. Tables 2 and 3 provide background on the important meetings during the period to assist the reader in relating events and in providing timelines. The tables list the AASG annual and midyear meetings with their presiding officers and the Liaison Committee meetings, respectively (in the decade of the 90's, the AASG Liaison Committee met twice annually in Washington, D.C., to exchange information with federal agencies, national organizations, congressional committees, and members of Congress and their staffs on ongoing and new programs and legislation and to provide input on the efforts of the state geological surveys in related areas, their expertise, and available databases). A list of all the AASG officers during this period is provided in Appendix 1.

National Cooperative Geologic Mapping Program in the 90's. Following the bill's introduction in the Senate in 1991, the AASG witnessed the signing into law of the National Geologic Mapping Act of 1992 by President George H.W. Bush. This act provided for a program that was considered to be of paramount importance to the completion of detailed geologic mapping for all of the United States at a scale useful in decision-making by government, business, and private sectors—decisions affecting the prosperity, health, and welfare of the nation. The idea was to undertake the work cooperatively between the states and the federal government, within the authority and oversight of the U.S. Congress, through the USGS in partnership with the AASG. Details of this program, developed in cooperation with the USGS, may be found in chapter 12.

The passage of such a bill in Congress within 1 year of its introduction was a record made possible by the legwork, planning, coordination, and implementation activities carried out by the AASG in conjunction with the various state geological surveys, their constituents, national professional societies and organizations, state and federal agencies (including especially the USGS), congressional staffers, Congress, and the public. This work commenced in the 80's and carried through into the 90's. The various AASG committees and individuals involved in the early work in framing the program and developing the legislation are reviewed in chapter 12 and in the review of the decade 1980–89, also in this chapter.

At its midyear meeting held on October 29, 1990, the Association gave its approval to move ahead with a draft implementation plan and draft authorization bill for the National Cooperative Geologic Mapping Program submitted by Charles Mankin (Oklahoma). In June 1991, through the diligent efforts of Mankin and other AASG members, Senate Bill 1179 was introduced into Congress, thus initiating the formal congressional legislative process. A companion bill, HR 2763, was introduced in the House of Representatives. Initial hearings were held July 20, 1991, on the Senate bill and July 25 for the House bill. AASG's Earl Bennett (Idaho), Mankin, and Robert Fakundiny (New York) provided oral testimony for the Senate bill. Donald C. Haney (Kentucky), Morris W. Leighton (Illinois), and Jonathan G. Price (Nevada) provided written or oral testimony for both.

After the National Geologic Mapping Act became Public Law 102-2895 in May of 1992, AASG President Robert Fakundiny wrote that it was one of the more unusual laws to be passed in that it (1) was sponsored and supported by both political parties, (2) became law in the same congressional session in which it was introduced, (3) was sponsored or cosponsored by 23 senators and 49 representatives, and (4) would improve the nation's wealth, health, and wellbeing, at a positive benefit/cost ratio. Fakundiny personally thanked Charles J. Mankin, who moved the bill through all the stages in Congress; all of the Association's fellow state geologists and colleagues, who presented testimony before both houses of Congress; all who urged their own state delegations to support the program; and lastly, USGS Director Dallas L. Peck and his staff, for working closely with the Association to achieve this goal.

After passage of the authorizing legislation, the AASG shifted its focus to the implementation of the act and its four program elements: (1) geologic mapping by the U.S. Geological Survey under FEDMAP, (2) its program under SUPPORTMAP, (3) mapping under STATEMAP by the state surveys with state funds matching federal funds, and (4) training of students under EDMAP.

An AASG Implementation Committee was appointed by Fakundiny at the AASG annual meeting in Alabama in 1992. The committee worked with the USGS to develop procedures acceptable to both the AASG and the USGS and to ensure the procedures met federal requirements and the needs of the states. The committee comprised three AASG representatives chosen by regional clusters, two representatives chosen by the AASG Executive Committee, and the AASG president as an ex officio member. The three cluster representatives were Thomas Berg (Eastern Region), Charles Mankin (Central Region), and Jonathan Price (Western Region). At-large members appointed by the Executive Committee were Earl Bennett and Donald C. Haney. Morris W. Leighton served as the first ex officio member of the committee. In addition, Berg, Price, and Haney were asked to serve as AASG representatives on a 16-member federal Geologic Mapping

Advisory Committee (which first met in 1996 when federal appointments to the committee were confirmed).

In the meantime, the USGS, as program administrator, issued its first Program Opportunity Notice in fiscal year 1992, requesting mapping proposals. An early part of the implementation plan, worked out between the USGS and the AASG, called for a peer panel to review the various proposals and to make recommendations to the USGS for funding. The STATEMAP Peer Panel was established, to become effective on October 1, 1992, to make it coincide with the federal fiscal year. By ballot, the AASG selected Norman Hester (eastern region), Perry Wigley (central region), and Earl Bennett (western region), and at-large-members Robert Fakundiny (as past-president) and Charles Mankin. Peer panel members had staggered terms of 1 to 3 years to provide for continuity. Total dollars to be used for the program were made available to the USGS through congressional appropriations.

In accordance with the AASG–USGS Implementation Plan, Dr. Lehi Hintze, Utah Geological Survey geologist, was selected as the initial representative of the state geological surveys to serve on the EDMAP Peer Panel. His alternate was Dr. Thomas Smith, Alaska state geologist. The AASG representative was to join three university scientists, one each for the eastern, central, and western regions of the country. EDMAP, like the federal Advisory Mapping Committee, did not become fully functional until 1996, however. At that time, EDMAP, a matching-funds cooperative with universities, was funded for the first time.

Overall implementation of the program slowly took place from 1992 to 1996. During this time, it was realized that congressional appropriations to support the act were not keeping pace with the spending levels authorized in the bill. This was despite a heavy AASG effort on Capitol Hill urging more equitable funding between the four elements of the National Cooperative Geologic Mapping Program. Support for the mapping effort was found in a number of federal agencies, the National Governors Association, the states through their geologic mapping advisory groups, and a number of individual state surveys' own clientele and user groups. Numerous representations and testimonies followed on the Hill to argue for increased funds. They met with limited but growing success. Key to some of the success was an agreement reached in 1994 between AASG President Donald Hoskins and USGS Director Gordon Eaton. It was agreed that in the future, STATEMAP would be funded at 20 percent of the available National Cooperative Geologic Mapping Program funding. This produced a significant increase in fiscal year 1996 STATEMAP funds. This is reflected in Table 4, "Authorization and Funding under the National Geologic Mapping Act for the Decade of the

Table 4. Authorization and funding under the National Geologic Mapping Act for the decade of the 90's.[1]

Fiscal Year	Authorization ($M)		Funding ($M)[2]			
	Total	STATEMAP	STATEMAP	EDMAP	FEDMAP	Total
FY 93	37.5	15.0	1.34	0.0	20.64	21.98
FY 94	42.75	18.0	1.84	0.0	21.17	23.01
FY 95	48.5	21.0	1.34	0.0	20.54	21.80
FY 96	55.5	25.0	4.38	0.44	17.06	21.88
FY 97	(continuation)		4.38	0.44	17.06	21.88
FY 98	26.0	min. 20%	4.44[3]	0.44	17.28	22.16
FY 99	28.0	min. 20%	4.54[4]	0.45	17.56	22.55
FY 00	30.0	min. 20%	4.76[4]	0.46	14.56	19.78

[1] From ncgmp.usgs.gov/ncgmpabout/ngmact/ngmact1992 [accessed 11/28/07].
[2] Limited by available appropriated funds.
[3] Includes change in calculating USGS overhead.
[4] Includes 48% of $1.5 million for C/FIP, a federal initiative for Community/ Federal Information Partnership, to demonstrate how geospatial data and maps can enhance community decision-making on local issues.

Note: STATEMAP grew to well over $7 million in FY 2001.

90's." Thus, the funding levels attained by federal awards increased from $1.2 million in fiscal year 1993 to over $4 million in the late 90's.

Major efforts were commenced in 1994 to promote the reauthorization of the National Geologic Mapping Act. Its initial authorization was only through fiscal year 1996. Success was realized in 1997 when the act was extended to 2000. The upward shift to 20 percent in the proportion of authorized STATEMAP funds was formalized by law and occurred in fiscal year 1998 with the reauthorization of the National Geologic Mapping Act. This percentage increased to 25 percent of the available funds in fiscal year 2000. In 1999, the AASG oversaw the introduction and passage of additional legislation in Congress for a second reauthorization. This reauthorization bill, signed on December 9, 1999, extended the program for another 5 years through fiscal year 2005. Authorization amounts were increased annually from $30 million in fiscal year 2000 to $64 million in 2005. Significantly, the 1999 reauthorization bill also specified that 48 percent of appropriated funds for the program during this 5-year period would be for STATEMAP and 2 percent for EDMAP.

In 1996, additional impetus was given to implementing the original mapping act when the USGS began in earnest to develop a digital geologic map database in cooperation with the AASG. The USGS appointed David Soller to compile the database, with AASG represented by Thomas Berg (Ohio). The AASG Digital Geologic Mapping Committee had its first annual Digital Mapping Techniques workshop in 1997 and formed several subcommittees to pursue the needed activities. This AASG committee and its subcommittees continued to meet with USGS counterparts in the late 90's to aggressively tackle the tasks at hand.

Other highlights for the National Cooperative Geologic Mapping Program in the 90's included the development of a true partnership between the USGS and the AASG. While the relationship was an uneasy one in the early 90's, it blossomed in 1996 and again in 1998, with ongoing efforts and changes in leadership and attitude (see chapter 12). As a result of a workshop between the USGS and the AASG in Washington, D.C., in December 1994, a document was developed, "Geologic Mapping into the 21st Century: Concepts toward a National Plan for the National Geologic Mapping Program." This and the 1994 agreement reached between President Hoskins of AASG and Director Eaton of USGS set the tone for future cooperation, which was further enhanced by a leadership change in the NCGMP in fiscal year 1996 and again in fiscal year 1998.

Throughout the decade, Charles Mankin (Oklahoma) played the lead role in getting legislation drafted and introducing it into and passed by Congress. He was instrumental in seeking and gaining the help and cooperation of the USGS, AASG presidents, the AASG committees (Implementation, Liaison, and Steering), and AASG members. They aided significantly in developing and arguing the case for the program. They provided testimony and recommendations and sought the backing of federal agencies, state legislatures and clientele, the National Governors Association, other national associations, and the public to achieve the ultimate goal.

AASG Activities in the Context of Political Actions in Washington, D.C.

Political actions in Washington, D.C., some affecting federal agencies, had major impacts on AASG's activities in the 90's. Some of these actions are reviewed here to help provide context.

In the fall of 1991, some federal agencies were affected by the lack of funds. The fiscal year 1993 budget, then under consideration, was again going to be tight. Funding for the earth sciences was especially threatened. The general mood in Washington was away from defense and science. In addition, the AASG had noted that impacts on urbanization, buffers around federal lands, wetlands protection, and movements for large land withdrawals from development had failed to consider the location and importance of mineral deposits, including aggregates. As such, the local, state, and national needs for minerals were neglected. In May 1992, budget problems connected with the economy were preoccupying Washington. The growth in mandatory spending, coupled with the recession, had reduced revenues, creating a $400 billion deficit. Downsizing and restructuring affected a number of federal agencies, especially the Minerals Management Service and Bureau of Land Management. The Department of Energy also experienced cuts. During this time, the Bush administration attempted to reduce federal regulations that were not cost-effective.

In view of coming elections in the fall of 1992, considerable legislative activity was left over for the next Congress. In addition, there would be new activity in 1993. Under consideration were major changes in mining-law reform, amendments to federal flood insurance, amendments to the Resource and Conservation Recovery Act concerning mining wastes, the Clean Water Act, wetlands legislation, and the National Earthquake Hazards Reduction Program. So, when Bill Clinton assumed office as president, his administration offered new challenges and new opportunities for the AASG. Policy shifts in the new administration and Congress had impacts on the AASG in mining-law reform, funding to implement the National Geologic Mapping Act of 1992, the Flood Insurance Act, coastal erosion, the Clean Water Act, the Superfund Act, and criteria for siting nuclear power plants.

At the 1993 meeting, AASG outgoing President Morris W. Leighton took note of the vast changes that had occurred during the year with respect to agency budgets, downsizing, the new federal administration, and associated changes in federal agency personnel and direction. Incoming President Donald Hull further recognized that the coming year would be a time of challenge and opportunity because of the change in the Washington administration. With the slow transition that was occurring with the new appointments in the federal government, he recognized that there was much unfinished business.

In June 1994, AASG took note that unfinished federal business still included reauthorization of the Earthquake Hazards Reduction Act, mining-law reform, processes that had an impact on the Clean Water and Clean Air Acts, and implementation of geologic mapping standards. In the fall of 1994, AASG was provided with information on the status of pending legislation regarding reauthorization of the Indoor Radon Abatement Act, the Earthquake Hazards Reduction Act, the Comprehensive Environmental Response, Compensation, and Liability Act (commonly known as Superfund), and the Coastal Zone Management Act, as well as information on legislation affecting mining-law reform, natural hazards reduction, clean drinking water, and salt water. In addition, AASG held downsizing and reorganization discussions with the Bureau of Reclamation, the USGS, and the Bureau of Land Management. Following the national election in November 1994, the Republicans gained majority control in the House.

By the spring of 1995, a recurring theme was heard in Washington from senators, congressmen and women, congressional committees, and subcommittees regarding "devolution" (i.e., the transference of federal programs to the states). A new contact was also established at the President's Office of Environmental Policy. Contacts were continued with the Office of Science and Technology Policy, Office of Management and Budget, Department of Energy, Environmental Protection Agency, and U.S. Geological Survey.

In the fall of 1995, the most important news heard by the AASG Liaison Committee was the demise of the U.S. Bureau of Mines, with parts of their program going to the Department of Energy and the USGS. There were also severe cutbacks in the Bureau of Indian Affairs, a deep reduction in force at the Office of Surface Mining, and transference of the National Biological Services to the USGS. In the spring of 1996, the USGS underwent a reduction in force accompanied by reorganization of the Geological Division and other units. The USGS budget also was faced with substantial cuts. The Association learned that the congressional Committee on Resources had taken over the jurisdiction of the Endangered Species Act, but no longer handled nuclear wastes. In the latter half of 1996, the AASG learned that individual senators had placed a "hold" on all bills from the Energy and Natural Resources Committee, stalling activities for almost all of the 104th Congress.

Smoother political sailing was encountered in 1997. The National Earthquake Hazards Reduction Program was reauthorized. Other issues arose, however, that offered further challenges and opportunities. These issues included climate change and the Kyoto Agreement; air quality, with new standards for particulates and ozone; an Environmental Protection Agency mercury report; increasing gas demand; utility restructuring; and declining research and development budgets. In 1998, Charles Mankin, reporting for the AASG's Energy and Minerals Policy Committee, noted that a proposed 50 percent cut in the Department of Energy's budget for oil-related projects in their fossil energy program would threaten the American Geological Institute's data preservation efforts and the Petroleum Technology Transfer Council. This would have an effect on a number of states.

In 1999, global climate change continued to be a major issue. In the closing years of the decade, treaties on natural gas supplies were under review, as was the increasing instability of foreign energy sources relative to the needs of the U.S. economy. Water-resource availability posed issues, especially in water-short areas, which the AASG was able to address as the 21st century began. Elections in 2000 were looming.

Changing Nature of the Liaison and Other AASG Committees in the 90's, along with the Development of Additional Opportunities for Participation in Federal Programs. This section is intended to convey the magnitude of the effort, the changes made in AASG committees (namely the Liaison Committee), and the large amount of legwork required in the 90's by the AASG to develop viable opportunities for cooperative partnerships with federal agencies.

In the 90's, the Liaison Committee, a standing committee of the AASG, met twice a year in Washington, D.C., to exchange information and ideas with government officials and national organizations (see Tables 3 and 5). Each of the committee members was appointed annually by AASG's president in accordance with the AASG constitution and bylaws. Staggered 3-year terms provided for continuity. During the early 90's, the committee was composed of the Association's Executive Committee and four additional members. Each committee member served as a regional contact for the other state geologists. Generally, a brochure called "Liaison Committee to Federal Agencies" was updated annually in the 90's for use in meetings with officials in Washington. The brochure described the committee and its purpose, gave a brief history of the AASG, and listed the names and addresses of all the state geologists.

At the beginning of the 90's, the committee had as its major objectives to meet new federal department, bureau, and committee heads in Washington to discuss the importance of geologic mapping to the health, safety, welfare, and security of the nation. In the fall of 1990, the objectives were not only focused on geologic mapping, but were broadened to discuss possible new federal initiatives, and to ascertain the directions the federal program would take, given the serious concerns about the 1991 budget priorities.

In 1991, the committee continued its efforts to introduce into Congress a bill to establish a national geologic mapping program and to seek further support for that program from federal agencies and the National Research Council. In an effort to look for other opportunities, it also sought the latest thinking by agencies on possible cooperative programs with state surveys and on developments in natural resources, energy policy, wetlands, coastal erosion, and national seismic programs. It appeared in the spring of 1991 that opportunities were limited and in need of nurturing. In the fall meeting of that year, with many frank and candid discussions on this subject with officials in Washington, the committee identified some possible opportunities for cooperative programs.

Table 5. AASG Liaison Committee members, decade of the 90's.

Program Year	Committee Members
1989–90	Ernest A. Mancini, chair (Alabama), Donald C. Haney (Kentucky), Larry D. Fellows (Arizona), Robert H. Fakundiny (New York), Donald A. Hull (Oregon), Morris W. Leighton (Illinois), Donald M. Hoskins (Pennsylvania), John C. Rold (Colorado), R. Thomas Segall (Michigan)
1990–91	Robert H. Fakundiny, chair (New York), Ernest A. Mancini (Alabama), Donald C. Haney (Kentucky), Morris W. Leighton (Illinois), Donald M. Hoskins (Pennsylvania), Walter Schmidt (Florida), Donald A. Hull (Oregon), Larry D. Woodfork (West Virginia), Perry B. Wigley (Nebraska). Charles J. Mankin (Oklahoma) represented the National Geologic Mapping Initiative.
1991–92	Morris W. Leighton, chair (Illinois), Robert H. Fakundiny (New York), Ernest A. Mancini (Alabama), Donald A. Hull (Oregon), Donald M. Hoskins (Pennsylvania), Earl H. Bennett (Idaho), Walter Schmidt (Florida), Perry B. Wigley (Nebraska), Larry D. Woodfork (West Virginia).
1992–93	Donald A. Hull, chair (Oregon), Morris W. Leighton (Illinois), Robert H. Fakundiny (New York), Donald M. Hoskins (Pennsylvania), Walter Schmidt (Florida), Earl H. Bennett (Idaho), Jonathan G. Price (Nevada), Perry B. Wigley (Nebraska), James H. Williams (Missouri).
1993–94	Donald M. Hoskins, chair (Pennsylvania), Donald A. Hull (Oregon), Morris W. Leighton (Illinois), Norman C. Hester (Indiana), Walter Schmidt (Florida), Earl H. Bennett (Idaho), Charles E. Chapin (New Mexico), James M. Robertson (Wisconsin), James H. Williams (Missouri).
1994–95	Walter Schmidt, chair (Florida), Donald M. Hoskins (Pennsylvania), Donald A. Hull (Oregon), Earl H. Bennett (Idaho), Emery T. Cleaves (Maryland), Diane Conrad (Vermont), Norman C. Hester (Indiana), James M. Robertson (Wisconsin), James H. Williams (Missouri).

Program Year	Committee Members
1995–96	Earl H. Bennett, chair (Idaho), Walter Schmidt (Florida), Donald M. Hoskins (Pennsylvania), Charles H. Gardner (North Carolina), Jonathan G. Price (Nevada), Emery T. Cleaves (Maryland), Perry B. Wigley (Nebraska), James M. Robertson (Wisconsin), Lee C. Gerhard (Kansas).
1996–97	Charles H. Gardner, chair (North Carolina), Earl H. Bennett (Idaho), Walter Schmidt (Florida), Larry D. Woodfork (West Virginia), James M. Robertson (Wisconsin), Jonathan G. Price (Nevada), Emery T. Cleaves (Maryland), Lee C. Gerhard (Kansas), John C. Steinmetz (Montana), Perry B. Wigley (Nebraska), Arthur A. Socolow (honorary members representative).
1997–98	Larry D. Woodfork, chair (West Virginia), Charles H. Gardner (North Carolina), Earl H. Bennett (Idaho), James M. Robertson (Wisconsin), S. Cragin Knox (Mississippi), Jonathan G. Price (Nevada), Emery T. Cleaves (Maryland), Lee C. Gerhard (Kansas), Stanley S. Johnson (Virginia), William W. Shilts (Illinois), John C. Steinmetz (Indiana), Perry B. Wigley (Nebraska), Milton A. Wiltse (Alaska), Kenneth N. Weaver (honorary members representative).
1998–99	James M. Robertson, chair (Wisconsin), Larry D. Woodfork (West Virginia), Charles H. Gardner (North Carolina), Jonathan G. Price (Nevada), S. Cragin Knox (Mississippi), Vicki J. Cowart (Colorado), Emery T. Cleaves (Maryland), Ed G. Deal (Montana), Stanley S. Johnson (Virginia), William W. Shilts (Illinois), John C. Steinmetz (Indiana), David L. Southwick (Minnesota), Milton A. Wiltse (Alaska), Stephen G. Conrad (honorary members representative).
1999–2000	Jonathan G. Price, chair (Nevada), James M. Robertson (Wisconsin), Larry D. Woodfork (West Virginia), Vicki J. Cowart (Colorado), M. Lee Allison (Utah), John C. Steinmetz (Indiana), Emery T. Cleaves (Maryland), Ed G. Deal (Montana), Robert G. Marvinney (Maine), Donald F. Oltz (Alabama), William W. Shilts (Illinois), David L. Southwick (Minnesota), Milton A. Wiltse (Alaska), Stephen G. 0 Conrad (honorary members representative).

As a result of its success in promoting the National Geologic Mapping Act, its growing understanding of the workings in Washington, and the Association's need for funds, the Association undertook in 1992 to (1) establish a greater presence in the coastal erosion research program of the Minerals Management Service, (2) continue its review of the EPA–USGS National Radon Mapping Program, (3) review federal lands policy, (4) participate in national groundwater-protection programs, (5) review national energy strategy, (6) continue to participate in research on offshore mineral resources, and (7) participate in regional seismic-hazard evaluation programs. All were vital to the Association's efforts to build a national and regional presence and programs that relied on the expertise, data, and resources of the state geological surveys. Following the elections in 1992, Bill Clinton assumed the office of president in 1993.

By 1993, the AASG had positioned itself, through its various committees, to provide counsel and advice to numerous federal agencies, members of Congress, and their staffs. The Liaison Committee in particular held meetings with new members of the Clinton administration to begin building bridges for federal-state cooperation and joint participation. Model efforts had already been established by the Continental Margins Committee on offshore resources of sand and gravels, and by the Environmental Affairs Committee in coordinating state radon reports under contract to the EPA. In addition, in 1993, following its major success in obtaining authorization by Congress of the National Cooperative Geologic Mapping Program, the Association rallied additional support for congressional funding for geologic mapping from the states' own clientele, their State Mapping Advisory Committees, professional societies, business associations, members of Congress, and staffers on the Hill, and at the highest levels in Washington. Increased involvement in national issues and in outreach activities were recognized by AASG President Hull. In 1993, a change occurred under Chair Donald Hoskins in the manner of reporting on Liaison Committee meetings. The new report covered the meetings with congressional committees, highlighting their importance and the importance of legislation to the AASG and to the geologic profession. The report then covered federal offices and finally national organizations—all arranged alphabetically within each category.

At the fall 1994 meeting, the committee focused on exchanging ideas on geologic mapping issues, reauthorization procedures and plans, pending legislation, AASG's participation in current and future programs, and government reorganization. It also urged the need for more equitable funding between all four elements of the geologic mapping program. It further noted the failure of the Geological Advisory Committee to meet and the failure of the USGS to match available state funds.

At the spring 1995 Liaison Committee meeting, emphasis was directed to even more congressional contact. Chair Walter Schmidt (Florida) noted that meetings were scheduled directly with senators and representatives from states with members on the Liaison Committee. Emphasis of the committee was on informing, educating, and *influencing* selected congressional members and staff, congressional committees, administration, federal offices and staff, and national organizations. The committee discussed primarily two issues: first, the current congressional budget and program reductions and their impact on geosciences and earth systems, and second, communicating the potential benefits of reauthorization of the National Geologic Mapping Act, a state and federal partnership. Relevancy to hazards and environmental issues was stressed. More congressional contact was reported than had been undertaken previously.

In the fall 1995 Liaison Committee meeting, the committee pursued reauthorization of the National Geologic Mapping Act. The committee met with congressmen and -women as well as others, especially with representatives who served on the Energy and Mineral Resources Subcommittee of the House Resource Committee, and with the Forest and Public Land Management Subcommittee of the Senate Energy and Natural Resources Committee. Earl Bennett (Idaho), chair, noted that the committee found no opposition to the mapping program. They did find, however, a problem in versions of the Budget Reconciliation Act that called for privatization of all mapping functions within the Department of the Interior. The committee acted successfully to have the language in the Senate reconciliation bill dropped. In spring 1996, the Liaison Committee reverted to exchanging information with federal agencies, with less emphasis on congressional visits.

In fall 1996, the Liaison Committee placed special emphasis on efforts toward reauthorization, communications with the USGS, and exploring possible cooperative projects with federal and other national organizations. In spring 1997, the committee talked with over 20 separate federal agencies and other groups, along with making congressional committee and delegation visits. Because the USGS was in the process of reorganization, the most far-reaching in its history, their meeting with the AASG was extended from 2 hours to half a day. Also, the committee arranged to add two workshops at the end of the visit, leading to a rewarding but exhausting 4-day stint in Washington, D.C. It was recognized that the committee had changed from an information-gathering body to one that was influencing issues and legislation.

In 1995 and 1996, various groups within the Association, in addition to the Liaison Committee, continued to seek opportunities for cooperative programs with federal agencies, and several were discussed at the Association's annual meeting. Members continued to point out opportunities with the Federal Emergency Management Agency, especially in their earthquake mitigation program. The National Research Council, in its review of coastal hazards, was encouraged to include geology in its assessment of the needs of this program. In addition, Walter Schmidt (Florida) took the lead on a new program with the Environmental Protection Agency to provide geologic information for their Surf Your Watershed project, noting that the project had the potential to involve other states. In 1996, Donald Hull (Oregon) also pointed out that individual states as well as the Association might find opportunities to create new partnerships. He noted that Oregon had created new partnerships with FEMA, the National Oceanic and Atmospheric Administration, the U.S. Army Corps of Engineers, and the EPA at the federal level and others at the local level. And in 1997, Haig Kasabach (New Jersey) commented on opportunities for state surveys to do geology related to water protection under the reauthorization of the Safe Drinking Water Act.

In 1997, Charles Gardner (North Carolina) added three members to the Liaison Committee, expanding it by presidential decree for the first time in the 1990's. The need was clear to increase AASG contact with a large number of congressional offices, federal executives, and leaders of national associations, therefore, the committee was expanded from 10 to 13 members. Earlier, President Earl Bennett noted at the 1997 annual meeting that it was his dream to have an AASG Liaison Committee made up of 51 state geologists, and that their expenses could be paid by the AASG when called to Washington to testify.

The committee that gathered in September 1997 in Washington had 48 official visits in 3 days. The committee sought support for full National Geologic Mapping Act authorization, for topographic mapping, and for a new director to be appointed to the USGS. Topographic mapping, under the USGS Mapping Division, needed support for continuing their updates of topographic maps and for integrating digital mapping to more fully consider public uses and needs. The committee reported that the AASG had established a strong and respected presence in Washington, D.C. In September 1997 and March 1998, the area of committee focus also included Minerals Management Service funding for geologic studies, natural hazard legislation, environmental geology, stream gaging by the USGS, and cooperative projects with a number of agencies.

The AASG hosted a congressional reception in March 1998, dovetailed with the Liaison Committee meeting in Washington, D.C. The reception was well received by representatives and their staffs. The reception and Liaison Committee effort involved 45 state geologists. They were divided into teams to visit with representatives and their staffs and with federal agency and private association executives. Over the 4-day period, nearly 40 various agencies, representatives and senators, staff, congressional committees, offices, and organizations were visited. The outstanding logistics for this Washington visit were handled by Committee Chair Larry Woodfork and his West Virginia survey staff, especially Carl J. Smith, who received special recognition by the Association for their efforts. Woodfork, in his report to the Association, noted that the various visits ranged from essentially "get acquainted" courtesy calls, "thank you visits" for past and continuing support, "show the flag visits," and information-exchange visits, to visits discussing specific policy positions and exploring funding of cooperative opportunities. A common theme was full funding for the National Geologic Mapping Act. Woodfork noted that the major benefit of the Liaison Committee's efforts was as much in conducting the process as in tangible outcomes. He noted that engendered goodwill, visibility, validation, and general support are often difficult to quantify, but nonetheless important results of the Washington liaison efforts.

At the spring 1999 Liaison Committee meeting in Washington, the committee reported that ecosystem studies were being replaced by land-based study areas. The committee also noted the need to insert a "geological aspect" into new congressional and executive actions. Donald Hull (Oregon) especially noted that the bills before Congress on hazard protection and insurance would need a healthy dose of geologic input. The ensuing fall meeting of 1999 resulted in a number of suggestions from the committee to the Association, to:

- Contact regional offices of the Bureau of Indian Affairs to explore interest in hazard, environmental, and resource work
- Urge the Bureau of Land Management to do hazard assessments prior to land transfers
- Alert the Association members of Department of Energy—Fossil Energy's new solicitation involving grants for possible sequestration and oil and gas projects
- Prepare a response to the Environmental Protection Agency's request for the AASG to be involved in their Futures Forum
- Alert AASG members that the Federal Emergency Management Agency had recognized geologic hazard mapping as an appropriate type of mitigation eligible for funding
- Follow up on a NASA indication of interest in a memorandum of understanding or a memorandum of agreement with the AASG
- Urge that the AASG submit a proposal to renew the National Science Foundation mentors program and support the major equipment initiative by NSF

- Be alert to the considerable opportunities for AASG and individual state geological surveys to work with the Natural Resources Conservation Service
- Be aware of the Office of Surface Mining's expressed interest in developing a memorandum of understanding with the AASG
- Reinforce geology as a basis for ecological systems at the Biological Resources Division of the USGS
- Push for 1:100,000-scale topographic maps, and
- Review a concept for a Washington, D.C.– based Geologic Information Center.

It is obvious that the Liaison Committee continued to find increasing numbers of opportunities to participate with other agencies.

At the end of the decade, the growing list of agencies requesting or requiring AASG assistance was a far cry from the short list of opportunities for involvement noted in the early 90's. Partly as a result of its success in having the National Geologic Mapping Act passed in 1992 and partly with the encouragement of the Liaison Committee and other AASG committees and AASG members, federal agencies appeared to take more notice of the AASG, its data sources, and its potential to make constructive suggestions and changes. The effect of AASG's success was like a double-edged sword. Not only had federal agencies begun to take greater notice of the AASG and become more aware of its effectiveness, but the AASG itself understood that it could be successful in affecting legislation, seeking funds, and implementing cooperative programs. It began to realize the power of 51 state geologists speaking with one voice in Washington, D.C., and to more assertively exert that influence.

Efforts that resulted in successful partnerships are highlighted in the next section.

Introduction of New AASG Income Sources—MOU's and Cooperative Agreements. In 1990, the AASG approved a motion to participate in a federal review of a national radon potential map prepared for the Environmental Protection Agency by the U.S. Geological Survey. This was a source of new income for the AASG. An advance of $10,410 for the analysis was received by the AASG, as reported by its secretary-treasurer. By 1992, the AASG was directly involved in a review of the EPA–USGS radon hazards mapping program and signed an amended grant extending the radon project. In 1993, Walter Schmidt (Florida), chair of the Environmental Affairs Committee, reported that a summary of the AASG–EPA radon project had been delivered to the EPA as the Association's final deliverable. The AASG had developed a national presence on the radon issue.

In 1994, an extra meeting of the Executive Committee with Dr. Lindsay McClelland of the National Park Service was called during the annual meeting by President Hull to discuss a possible memorandum of understanding between the NPS and the AASG. The NPS was initiating a 10-year program to collect information in an inventory of the parks and to undertake a monitoring effort to include both surficial and bedrock geology. They were seeking help in collecting available published geologic data and land-use planning, geologic hazards and minerals assessments, waste clean-up plans, paleontology, and groundwater protection in all the national parks. In 1995, after a series of meetings with the National Park Service, the AASG signed a memorandum of understanding with the NPS for the coordination of mapping, collaborative research, inventories, and data exchange. In 1996, a contract to provide geologic data on selected parks was completed by the AASG. Activities were coordinated by Earl Bennett (Idaho) on behalf of the AASG. Lindsay McClelland, NPS, acknowledged that the contract with the AASG had been successful and that they expected to have the most comprehensive geologic information available. AASG, through the Idaho survey, provided a digital bibliography of all state publications covering national parklands nationwide, resulting in about 3,000 references. Additional assistance was provided to the NPS in succeeding years.

The year 1998 saw the culmination of the AASG–Minerals Management Service cooperative agreement that was initiated in the 80's and that authorized the MMS-funded offshore studies by a number of state geological surveys through the Texas Bureau of Economic Geology. The AASG Continental Margins Committee cosponsored with the MMS the Fourth Symposium on Studies Related to Continental Margins: A Summary of Year-Nine and Year-Ten Activities. AASG's president, Charles Gardner, noted the high productivity of the MMS–AASG partnership. He urged its continuance, which led to further discussions with MMS executives in Washington on the possibilities for a renewed cooperative program. During 1998, the AASG Executive Committee and USGS leadership developed a proposed AASG–USGS memorandum of understanding. Also proposed was a memorandum of understanding between AASG and the EPA.

In 1999, an attempt to develop a memorandum of understanding with the EPA was spurned in favor of agreements for individual programs. Toward the end of the decade, other agencies had suggested a memorandum of understanding or memorandum of agreement with the AASG, including NASA and the Office of Surface Mining, and another with the NPS. President James Robertson concluded at the midyear meeting held in October 1999 that there were a number of new opportunities for memorandums with various federal agencies and that the AASG needed to create new ad hoc committees to handle these emerging opportunities, and quickly did so.

It is obvious that the AASG had built a solid reputation in handling memorandums of understanding and had come a long way in its cooperative partnerships in the 1990's. This is reflected in part in the build-up of its treasury balance from $40,542 in 1989 (including its regular account balance and unspent oil and gas contract monies) to a net of $93,637 in 1999, as reported at the October 26, 1999, midyear meeting—more than double the net assets in 1989. The outlook at the end of the decade of the 90's for improving on this was good.

Trend in Federal Agencies' Efforts to Work with the AASG. While the Liaison Committee observed in 1991 that opportunities for state survey involvement appeared limited, a few agencies began to approach the AASG beginning in 1992 to seek assistance, if not cooperative arrangements. In 1992, President Fakundiny noted that the AASG had been approached to review federal lands policies and national energy strategy, to participate in national groundwater protection efforts, and to participate in regional studies of seismic hazards. The Minerals Management Service had also requested additional efforts in its coastal research program.

In 1994, AASG won a seat on FEMA's Technical Mapping Advisory Council for floodplain mapping, and Donald Hull (Oregon) became the AASG's representative. Also in 1994, besides the National Park Service, the Forest Service had been aware of, and had been influenced by, the Association's success with the National Cooperative Geologic Mapping Program and talked with the Association regarding memorandums of understanding to assist them in their programs. The U.S. Army Corps of Engineers was also prompted by the success of the NCGMP to determine if an expansion of Corps partnerships might be feasible.

In 1996, AASG's Walter Schmidt (Florida) was invited to participate in an intersociety workshop sponsored by the American Geological Institute and the Department of the Interior on the integration of the National Biological Service into the USGS. In addition, Deputy Secretary of the Interior John Garamendi requested AASG's input in assisting the USGS to refine its mission and work plans for the future, and AASG put considerable thought and effort into its response.

Increasing contacts by federal agencies, seeking AASG's assistance and vice versa, continued through the rest of the 90's. In 1999, for example, Emery Cleaves (Maryland) worked on the National Water Quality Assessment Program Council, serving on a committee reviewing stream gaging. The USGS worked with the AASG to develop a national landslide program.

Table 6. AASG honorary members added in the 90's.

Year Accepted	Honorary Member	State Represented
1990	Genevieve Atwood	Utah
	Stephen G. Conrad	North Carolina
	Hugo F. Thomas	Connecticut
	Ralph Bernhagen	Ohio
1991	Frank E. Kottlowski	New Mexico
	Meredith (Buzz) Ostrom	Wisconsin
1992	Robert C. Milici	Virginia
	Norman K. Olson	South Carolina
	Charles A. Ratté	Vermont
	John W. Rold	Colorado
	Merle J. Tipton	South Dakota
	Kenneth N. Weaver	Maryland
1993	Charles (Chip) Groat	Louisiana
	Joseph A. Sinnott	Massachusetts
1994	William L. Fisher	Texas
	Morris W. Leighton	Illinois
1995	Walter Anderson	Maine
1996	Ernest A. Mancini	Alabama
1997	–	–
1998	–	–
1999	Lee C. Gerhard	Kansas
	Gary B. Glass	Wyoming
	Donald C. Haney	Kentucky
	Donald A. Hull	Oregon
	Haig F. Kasabach	New Jersey

This included a grants component. Jonathan Price (Nevada) served on a committee to review the USGS cooperative program. Donald Hull (Oregon) was asked to serve on the National Technical Advisory Council to FEMA. The Environmental Protection Agency requested the AASG to review a report on the Conservation Environmental Response and Compensation Act to be sent to Congress. This was assigned to the AASG's Environmental Affairs Committee. EPA's request to support its Futures Forum was referred to the chair of AASG's Environmental Affairs Committee. In addition, the Liaison Committee noted that plans were under way to have an American Geological Institute academia-corporate associates meeting to follow the next Liaison Committee meeting. Also, FEMA had asked that the state geological surveys work with their offices of emergency management and with state floodplain managers to help set priorities for hazard mitigation.

President Robertson noted at the October 1999 midyear meeting of the AASG that a large number of federal agencies wanted to work with the states and the AASG—again, a major change from the early 90's. Validation of the value of AASG was well under way.

Changes in the Structure, Operations, and Policies of the AASG in the 90's. In parallel with the evolution of AASG's endeavors to better position itself to seek cooperative partnerships and to have a positive influence on federal legislation, the Association undertook changes in its constitution and bylaws, policies, and methods of operation for a more effective organization. In addition, as women geologists grew in stature with various surveys and became state geologists, they were welcomed as members in the AASG. Only one female state geologist (Genevieve Atwood, Utah) had joined the organization in the 1980's, while a total of four joined in the 1990's, reaching a maximum of three at any one time in 1993: Vicki Cowart (Colorado), later to become president of the Association in the next decade, Priscilla Grew (Minnesota), and Diane Conrad (Vermont). The 90's ended with two women state geologists: Cowart and Lisbeth Hyman (Puerto Rico). These additions accompanied a change from an organization perceived by some as a "good old boys society" to one that operated in a more efficient, businesslike, yet collegial manner.

From time to time changes were made to the constitution and bylaws so as to improve clarity and the Association's effectiveness in its operations. They were made in 1990, 1991, 1995, 1996, and 1999. There was a change in the composition of the Nominating Committee for officers in 1990, and sweeping changes in the constitution in 1995 affecting the scope of AASG activities, guidelines for electing honorary members, terms of office for officers, clarification of the duties of senior officers, composition of the Executive Committee and its reporting requirements, timing of notices to members, expansion of those eligible to attend AASG's annual meetings, and clarification of procedures for proposing constitutional amendments. Changes in the bylaws accompanied the changes in the constitution in 1995. Constitutional amendments in 1996 affected the election of honorary members, created separate offices for secretary and treasurer instead of a single secretary-treasurer, with both officers to be on the Executive Committee, and established the timing for submittal of the slate of officers to the Executive Committee prior to the annual meeting. Constitutional amendments in 1999 expanded the membership to include associates, allowed the use of electronic media to expedite official business, and provided the Executive Committee with the authority to enter into appropriate cooperative agreements, contracts, grants, and other covenants with other parties and to receive and distribute income.

Policies and operations were also modified during the course of business as approved by the membership. In 1990 at its annual meeting, the AASG approved a motion to accept responsibility to participate in a committee with the Geological Society of America to provide an award as a part of the GSA Memorial Fund honoring John C. Frye, former Illinois state geologist and executive director of the GSA. The award would honor annually the best paper in environmental geology published either by the GSA or a state geological survey.

Just before the annual meeting in 1992, the Executive Committee agreed that the Association would not continue to collect state geologists' salary information. At the 1992 annual meeting, membership dues were increased from $75 to $150 per year to help defray travel expenses of those members on National Geologic Mapping Act–related committees whose surveys could not support out-of state travel. At the fall meeting in 1992, an Endowment Steering Committee, chaired by Larry Fellows (Arizona), was established. At the annual meeting held in 1994, however, the committee and Association membership concluded that an anticipated small endowment would not be worth the effort, and the committee was subsequently disbanded by the incoming president, Donald Hoskins (Pennsylvania). Also, in 1994, just before the annual meeting, the Association's Executive Committee adopted a policy of operating with a balanced budget and laid out plans to achieve this policy. In addition, the Executive Committee proposed that the annual meeting fee be increased by $75 and the midyear meeting fee by $25. The membership was not in favor and suggested that voluntary contributions be made instead by the members or their organizations and that meeting guests also pay registration fees.

At the 1992 midyear meeting, the Association adopted a policy that professional certification can best be left in professional hands and that Congress should not intrude to authorize the certification of workers. Later, at the annual meeting in 1996, the membership discussed complimentary registrations for guests who were invited to make presentations to the Association. President Walter Schmidt noted that he had received legal opinion from the Department of the Interior that it is appropriate for the AASG to waive registration for meetings, but not for field trips, for those making presentations. This ruling was to become part of the planning for future meetings.

At the 1995 annual meeting, a motion to keep the statistician's financial numbers confidential and to only release trends was narrowly approved by the voting members. This was reemphasized at the 1996 annual meeting by Statistician Haig Kasabach (New Jersey), who noted that the statistician's report is confidential, although the graphs that combine the data to show trends may be released.

At the 1995 midyear meeting, it was announced that at the next annual meeting in Virginia, a room was to be made available for an evening meeting of the assistant or associate state geologists. Later in 1999, with a change in the Association's constitution, the AASG's membership was expanded to include this group of highly productive contributors to the business of the Association.

At the 1996 annual meeting, the Association agreed to be a formal sponsor of part of the Geological Society of America's annual meeting in Salt Lake City. Later in 1999, another motion was passed to enable the AASG to be a cosponsor of the International Survey Program at the GSA, but without financial obligation.

Trends in operations of the state geological surveys and the AASG were noted by Donald Hull (Oregon) at the 1996 annual meeting. He pointed out that the surveys and the Association are: (1) shifting from research to applications of research for public benefits, (2) moving from a mineral resource focus to one on geologic hazards and environmental protection, (3) creating new federal partnerships, and (4) adding staff for nonscientific functions to improve performance. He noted that geologic mapping was moving from rural to urban areas, from federal to private lands, and away from energy and metallic resources into construction aggregates. He added that some new roles for AASG could be technology transfer, multistate partnerships, and recruiting. In 1997, the expanding role of AASG members in environmental geology was highlighted at the midyear meeting.

In 1997, the Executive Committee approved a request for limited expenses so that an honorary member could represent the Association at the 150th anniversary meeting of the American Association for the Advancement of Science, an organization that former state geologists helped to initiate. The Executive Committee also authorized funds in support of the reconstruction of the Rapp Granary in New Harmony, Ind., the birthplace of geology and field mapping in the Midwest under pioneer geologist-educators William Maclure and David Dale Owen.

In March 1998 at the time of the Liaison Committee meeting, the AASG, in gathering momentum, hosted a congressional reception for the first time. The event, held in the Rayburn House Office Building foyer, was the culmination of several months of planning. It was designed to explain and demonstrate with posters the relevance and value of geologic maps and to show the considerable progress made under the National Cooperative Geologic Mapping Program. The reception in combination with the

Liaison Committee's visits were later recognized by the Association as the largest and most complex ever undertaken by the AASG.

At the annual meeting in 1998 and again in 1999 when presenting the historian's report, Emery Cleaves (Maryland) sought clarification on the policy for archiving AASG's reports and correspondence. The Executive Committee undertook to provide this guidance. Also at the 1998 annual meeting, President-elect Larry Woodfork noted that he was forming a committee to look into the incorporation of the Association in one of the states, and another committee to study the issue of a congressional charter for the Association. Then, in the year 1998–99, the Association sought and secured a state charter incorporating the organization as a Delaware corporation, thus providing a legal identity and an appropriate instrument for the responsible conduct of Association business. At the annual meeting in 1999, President Woodfork reviewed the status of his proposal to request that Congress establish a federal charter for the Association. He reported that Rep. Nick Rahall's (D-West Virginia) office had drafted a charter to be reviewed by the Association and was prepared to submit the bill to Congress. The draft charter was made available to the members electronically for their review; however, the novel idea lacked general AASG support and failed. Also at the 1999 annual meeting, it was announced that the Association had signed on to the American Geological Institute statement on global change.

In addition, a policy issue came up in 1999 concerning participation of the AASG with foreign surveys. William Shilts (Illinois) was asked at the annual meeting by President-elect James Robertson to chair a new ad hoc committee on international affairs to address this issue. This was one of several new ad hoc committees formed by Robertson at the close of the 1999 annual meeting. Included were ones on guidelines for the historian, on new opportunities for geoscience information dissemination, and on bylaw revisions concerning associate members.

The Executive Committee, at its September 12, 1999, meeting in Washington, D.C., provided guidance to the ad hoc committee on revision of bylaws to include associate members. The Executive Committee also agreed to review selection criteria for the next Pick and Gavel Awards before accepting suggestions as to who should be considered for the awards. This was completed prior to the midyear meeting.

Other significant changes in the structure and mode of operation of the Association occurred, namely in the nature and composition of its committees. Flexibility was demonstrated in the appointment of additional ad hoc committees to handle the increasing business of the AASG as it expanded its activities in the late 90's. The single most striking change was in the composition of the Liaison Committee, which grew from nine members in the early 90's to 13 in 1997, with a final gesture by President-elect James Robertson at the annual meeting to invite all state geologists to attend the Liaison Committee meeting in Washington, D.C., on September 25, 1999. Also important was the policy adopted by the Executive Committee to include a representative of the honorary members as a nonvoting member of the Executive Committee and the Liaison Committee, as described in the next section.

This discussion of the changes in the structure, operations, and policies of the AASG was not intended to be a complete record, but to give examples only. All in all, from the various reports and minutes, it appears that the Association was functioning well during and at the close of the 90's.

Changes in the Election and Activities of Honorary Members in the 90's. The number of living honorary members grew significantly in the 1990's, from 42 in 1990 to 51 in 1999. For the 3-year period 1995 through 1997, the honorary members outnumbered the active state geologists 53 to 51 (the latter figure included Puerto Rico). Those accepted as honorary members in the 90's are listed by year in Table 6. The Honorary Members Committee, one of the standing committees of AASG, was made up of a number of honorary members and two of the active state geologists, one of whom served as chair of the committee. The committee was responsible for bringing forward eligible nominees to be voted on by the AASG at the annual or midyear meeting.

Guidelines developed by the Association in 1983 for the election of honorary members continued into the 90's, but received additional scrutiny beginning in 1991 at the annual meeting when Larry Fellows, in his Honorary Members Committee report, reiterated those guidelines and referenced the article in the constitution that authorizes honorary membership. The guidelines prepared in 1983 specified that "seven years in office, plus substantial participation and contribution to the affairs of the Association shall be normally considered minimum qualification for election as an Honorary Member...." Discussion centered on the word "normally." The committee report was unanimously adopted, and the guidelines were subsequently appended to the constitution in 1991.

In 1995 and again in 1996, the guidelines were amended for clarity and understanding and were incorporated in the body of the constitution itself. The final version appeared in article III, section 4 and read:

> A former Association member who has served for a substantial period of time, generally more than seven years, as head of a State, Commonwealth, Possession, or Territorial geologic organization is eligible for election to honorary membership in the Association. Honorary membership is to be based on substantial participation in and significant contributions to the affairs of the Association

and is not to be conferred automatically upon retirement or leaving office. Persons eligible should be recommended to the Honorary Members Committee by Association members. Any Association member shall be evaluated by the Honorary Members Committee for election. The Honorary Members Committee shall establish guidelines for honorary membership. These guidelines and amendments to the guidelines should be approved at the Annual Meeting by majority vote of the members. Persons considered eligible for honorary membership are recommended by the Honorary Members Committee, and election is by majority vote of the Members at the Annual Meeting or Special Business Meeting. Honorary Members of the Association are non-voting members.

The constitution was also amended to clarify the eligibility of honorary members to serve on AASG committees.

In addition to the Honorary Members Committee, an Honorary Members Caucus was formed informally in 1995 so that all members could convene for communications and fellowship at the annual meeting. The history of the caucus and of the inclusion of a representative of the honorary members on the Executive and Liaison Committees is provided in chapter 9 of this volume. In appreciation of AASG's efforts to include honorary members to a greater extent in the Association's affairs, Arthur Socolow (Pennsylvania) commended the AASG at the 1997 midyear meeting for drawing on the expertise of the honorary members, citing as examples the selection of Kenneth Weaver (Maryland) to attend the Executive Committee and Liaison Committee meetings and Stephen Conrad (North Carolina) to become the Awards Committee chair. The Honorary Members Caucus, once initiated, provided reports on their activities at the annual meetings.

Robert Jordan (Delaware), an ardent supporter of the honorary members, continued to chair the Honorary Members Committee throughout the 90's. He periodically updated an honorary members directory, a list of deceased honorary members, a list of officers of the AASG since 1941, and a master list of all state geologists. These historical databases proved helpful to the honorary members and to all AASG members as well. The honorary members helped the Association to grow initially, and were encouraged and given new and welcome opportunities in the 90's to do so even after retirement.

AASG Support of Education in the 90's. Over the years, the AASG has strongly supported education in the geosciences, and the 90's were no exception. In 1991, the Association participated throughout the year in numerous symposia, workshops, and panel discussions, culminating in a unanimous resolution at the annual meeting in Saratoga Springs supporting the American Geological Institute's initiative to promote earth science education.

In 1992, the Association voted unanimously to submit a request to AGI to join the Coalition of Earth Science Educators, the first of two coalitions it joined in the 90's. The other was the Federal Emergency Management Agency's NEHRP Coalition. In addition, in 1992, the Association unanimously endorsed support of the National Science Foundation's K-6 Earth Science Sourcebook proposal.

In 1993, a $300 contribution was made to the National Association of Geology Teachers in support of their summer students' geologic mapping program as a nonrecurring expense subject to annual review. The Association participated again in 1994 and in 1995 in a cooperative summer field training program by the NAGT and the USGS. Another $300 scholarship to NAGT was provided in support of a student attending the geologic field camp. In 1994, President Donald Hoskins requested the AASG Earth Science Committee (chair, Robert Fakundiny) to begin work on a sourcebook for educational purposes. In 1995, the Association recognized the New York survey and its staff for their efforts in compiling and releasing the Earth Science Education Sourcebook, compiled under the direction of Robert Fakundiny.

In the later 90's, the Association initiated a new program with the National Science Foundation and the USGS to provide mentoring in geologic field mapping for undergraduate students. In 1999, Jonathan Price (Nevada), treasurer, reported that the AASG had been collecting administrative charges on the NSF mentoring program. The net result was an increase of $13,000 to the AASG treasury. The Association reported that the AASG–NSF mentoring program, then in its second year, had awarded 29 grants to 19 states.

AASG Public Relations and Outreach in the 90's. In 1991, the Association undertook to prepare and set up exhibits illustrating AASG's activities at national meetings of the Geological Society of America or the American Association of Petroleum Geologists, or both, under AASG's vice president. An exhibit was established and has been maintained for AASG displays at two or three major meetings annually since that time. In 1992, the Association members approved a motion to provide provincial and foreign surveys that attended the Canadian sesquicentennial with copies of the AASG history volume. Seeking still greater outreach, the Association in 1993 approved the joint operation of an exhibit booth with the American Institute of Professional Geologists at the National Council of State Legislatures meeting in San Diego and continued to exhibit with NCSL annually thereafter throughout the decade. Also, an updated brochure on the AASG was issued by Secretary-Treasurer Walter Schmidt (Florida), entitled "AASG, an Association of American State Geologists, Representing 50 States and the Commonwealth of Puerto Rico." It briefly described the Association, what it does, the annual meeting, Liaison Committee, publications (including a new Fact Book), and a list of state geologists as of February 20, 1993.

In 1996, the AASG participated in the annual meeting of the Association of Engineering Geologists. The AASG exhibit, which had been in use since 1992, was significantly upgraded. Also in 1996, an AASG Website was finalized by the Kansas Geological Survey under the direction of Lee Gerhard.

In 1997, the AASG passed a resolution to establish Earth Science Week as the second full week in October and supported the position of 39 governors who had signed an Earth Science Week proclamation for 1997 and henceforth. As an expansion of its outreach activities, the AASG extended invitations to heads of foreign surveys who were attending the annual GSA meeting to attend the midyear breakfast meeting of the AASG in Salt Lake City, Utah. Similar invitations were extended to foreign survey representatives in 1998 and 1999 to attend the meetings in Toronto, Canada, and Denver, Colo.

In 1998, AASG exhibited for the first time at a conference for the National Order of Women Legislators/National Foundation for Women Legislators. The meeting was held in Charleston, S.C. Also in 1998, AASG, through Arthur Socolow, honorary member from Pennsylvania, prepared a profile of AASG for the American Association for the Advancement of Science's 150th anniversary annual meeting. In 1999, the AASG was offered free booth space at the Mine Expo in Reno, Nev., and coordinated with the Nevada Bureau of Mines and Geology in exhibiting there.

Changes in AASG Publications in the 90's. In 1990, the Association published a limited quantity of a State Geological Survey Staff Directory, arranged by the Kansas Geological Survey, to support communications between the surveys. It was approved to continue this publication in 1992. Also, in 1990, the Association accepted the Association Fact Book, assembled by James Williams (Missouri) of the Professional Affairs Committee. The Fact Book was subsequently updated periodically in the 90's. In addition, a motion was approved to abolish the AASG's publication list, which had become duplicative of other sources of this information.

In the fall of 1992, the Association accepted Editor Thomas Berg's recommendation to change *The State Geologists Journal* to an 8½ x 11 inch format. In addition, the formal *Association Newsletter* was to come out twice a year. The resolutions passed by the Association at its official meetings were published in the 1994 *The State Geologists Journal* and sporadically in the *Journal* thereafter, namely in 1997 and 1998. In 1997, the content of the *Journal* was changed to include a description of the AASG–GSA John C.

Frye Award and a listing of AASG officers and committee chairs by state. In 1999, a description of the Pick and Gavel Award was added, plus a listing of all of the officers from 1930 to 2000.

In 1995, the inventory of all AASG publications was moved from Lexington, Ky., to Columbus, Ohio, following a flood at the Kentucky survey's warehouse. And in 1996, the Association unanimously agreed to abandon publication of the *Association Newsletter*.

In 1998, the AASG editor developed an outline of the administrative structure of the AASG, and published two newly formatted pocket-size AASG directories. That year, Arthur Socolow (Pennsylvania) also announced that there were still some 200 copies of the hard-bound publication, *The State Geological Surveys, A History*, available through the editor, Thomas Berg, and suggested that any state geologist who had not received a copy should get one.

Other AASG Legislative Activities and Business in the 90's. The Association carried on a number of other activities in the 90's. It tracked federal legislation for flood insurance, riverine and coastal erosion, and for earthquakes and seismicity; it kept up with the Department of Energy's efforts in oil and gas activities; it issued position papers on critical subjects; it tracked the progress made in the United States on registration of professional geologists, while following a policy of neutrality in neither favoring nor opposing registration; it cooperated with and sought affiliation with various professional societies and organizations; it supported various candidates for office; and it supported the budgets, staff, and state geological surveys threatened by state legislation.

Noteworthy were its efforts with FEMA and the House Banking and Finance Committee in supporting amendments dealing with National Flood Insurance and in giving input in the form of ideas and information to these federal groups, successfully securing an amendment to HR 3474, giving the Association a voice in the development of mapping programs for both coastal and riverine erosion. It also worked with FEMA and the USGS on developing programs and strategies for earthquake mitigation and seismicity investigations, and in successfully relating geologic hazards to insurance legislation. The AASG was also involved in issues related to mining-law reform.

Position papers prepared on legislative issues in the 90's by various AASG committees and adopted by the Association included a "Wetlands Statement" in 1992 and one in 1994 on "Ecosystem Management and the Need to Understand Earth Science Systems," both by the Environmental Affairs Committee.

Table 7. AASG memorials and necrologies.

Frederic F. Mellen	1911–1989	Mississippi
Eugene Callaghan	1904–1990	New Mexico
Charles Eugene Doll	1898–1990	Vermont
Edwin G. Koch	1905–1990	Montana
Alvin Thompson	1903–1990	New Mexico
William C. Hayes Jr.	1920–1991	Missouri
J. Robert Van Pelt	1896–1991	Montana
Arthur E. Slaughter	1920–1991	Michigan
James Lewis Calver	1913–1914	Virginia
Wallace B. Howe	1925–1995	Missouri
Don H. Baker Jr.	1924–1996	New Mexico
Robert E. Bergstrom	1923–1996	Illinois
Marshall T. Huntting	1918–1996	Washington
Lincoln R. Page	1911–1996	New Hampshire
John Schilling	1927–1996	Nevada
Glen W. Stewart	1914–1996	New Hampshire
Wallace W. Hagan	1913–1997	Kentucky
Ralph J. Bernhagen	1910–1997	Ohio
Wilson M. Laird	1915–1997	North Dakota
Virgil E. Barnes	1903–1998	Texas
William Paxton Hewitt	1909–1998	Utah
Norman Francis Williams	1916–1998	Arkansas
Robert B. Erwin	1928–1999	West Virginia
Frank J. Markewicz	1921–1999	New Jersey
Kimble Widmer	1913–1999	New Jersey

In 1993, the Association increased its support of the American Geological Institute's Government Affairs Program to $3,000 and continued to support it in the $2,500 to $3,000 per year range. Later in the 90's, AASG became a participant on AGI's Member Society Council, its Government Affairs Committee, and its Ian Campbell Award Committee. In the 90's, the Association was also successful in seeking a number of alliances or associations with other professional organizations, including recognition of the AASG by the American Association for the Advancement of Science as an affiliate and by the GSA as an associated society.

Periodically in the decade, the AASG took positions on behalf of its candidates for public office, informing appropriate government officials of their candidacy and capabilities through letters of support. The Association also provided support to several state geological surveys requesting help in the early 90's as they faced threatened cuts in budgets and staff. Letters from the presidents of the Association were sent to the respective state governors, state legislatures, or state legislative committees as appropriate, pointing out the kind of work state geological surveys do, their value, and the impacts of budget cuts. Association support proved helpful in restoring or partially restoring budgets. For example, the Minnesota legislature restored $1.075 million after intervention by AASG.

AASG Awards and Honors in the 90's. In the 90's, the first awards were made by the AASG under the John C. Frye Award for the best published paper on environmental geology, and the first for the Pick and Gavel Award recognizing significant contributions in public policy. The history of each of these awards is given in chapters 11 and 10, respectively, and also in issues of the *State Geologists Journal* beginning in 1997 for the Frye Award and 1999 for the Pick and Gavel Award.

Recognition and honors were also bestowed from outside sources on AASG members in the 90's. For awards made to AASG members in the 90's, most may be found in a separate publication compiled by Donald C. Haney in 2001 entitled "A Directory of Selected Awards and Medals for the Geosciences." In all, some 28 awards were made to AASG members, either past or present, during the 90's, including the American Association of Petroleum Geologists' highest honor, the Sydney Powers Memorial Medal, to one member, William Fisher (Texas); the American Geological Institute's Ian Campbell Medal to seven distinguished members; AGI's William G. Heroy Jr. Award for Distinguished Service to AGI to one member; the American Institute of Professional Geologists' most distinguished award, the Ben H. Parker Memorial Medal, to three members; AIPG's John T. Galey Sr. Memorial Public Service Award to five members; AIPG's Martin Van Couvering Award to two members; AAPG–Eastern Section's George V. Cohee Public Service Award to five members; and AAPG–Eastern Section's Gordon H. Wood Jr. Memorial Award to one member. In addition, the U.S. Geological Survey's John Wesley Powell Award went to Kenneth Weaver (Maryland) in this period. A number of members also were honored as elected officers to national professional societies and associations or selected for their boards. The AASG itself also formally recognized several who had contributed sig-nificantly to public service, including, for example, Charles Mankin, director of the Oklahoma Geological Survey, for his exceptional, long, and tireless work on the National Cooperative Geologic Mapping Program on behalf of the Association. These awards and offices and efforts brought further honor and distinction to the AASG.

AASG Memorials and Necrologies in the 90's. AASG members who passed away in the 90's were recognized and honored by the Association at its official meetings, or memorials or necrologies were published in the *Journal*. Deceased state geologists and senior geologists honored by the Association in the 90's are listed in Table 7.

USGS Changes in the 90's and Their Impacts on the AASG. A number of significant changes in USGS personnel, programs, and policies occurred in the 90's and had direct impacts on the affairs of the AASG. Among them were changes in leadership when Director Dallas Peck retired in 1993, to be succeeded in 1994 by Gordon Eaton, and when the latter retired in 1997, to be succeeded by Charles Groat in 1998. Also, the USGS leadership in implementing, coordinating, and managing the National Cooperative Geologic Mapping Program changed in 1996 and in 1998, both times resulting in a strengthening of USGS support for the program.

In 1994, under Director Eaton, the USGS was redesigned around four major themes: hazards, resources, environment, and information. In 1995, the USGS underwent a reduction in force that had a significant impact on its Geological Division, its leadership, and personnel. Gordon Eaton agreed with the AASG that the USGS would keep its large core-sample facility in Denver; and in the year 1995–96, the Geological Division was reorganized. At the AASG annual meeting in 1996, Director Eaton noted that the USGS had been developing a strategic plan, stating that "the USGS is an earth-science organization that is recognized worldwide as scientifically credible, objective and demonstrably relevant to societal needs" (Bennett, 1996, p. 12). He discussed the new mission for the USGS and noted that the merger of the National Biological Service into the USGS would be completed in October of that year. He also reported that programmatic directions were changing from single studies in wilderness areas toward multipurpose products, urban corridors, partnerships, regional environmental assessments, assessing federal lands, and geochemical baselines. Major changes in the minerals program included more work on industrial minerals, abandoned mine lands, environmental assessments, minerals information, and issue-driven mapping.

In 1997, the AASG entered into discussions with the USGS concerning the distribution of excess USGS publications in their warehouse in Denver. Arrangements were finalized in 1998 for the transfer of much of the excess USGS materials to the states.

Also in 1997, the USGS was working on a 5-year plan. Later in 1997, Pat Leahy, chief geologist, USGS, mentioned the planning under way by the Geological Division, which placed emphasis on natural hazards, surficial processes and materials, data management, digital standards, and federal-state collaborations. This was followed by invitations from the USGS to the AASG to participate in the development of their strategic plan, which the Association accepted. The western, central, and eastern regions of AASG participated in cluster meetings with USGS leadership over a period of 3 days in March 1998. Panel discussions on the strategic plan were held in Reston, Denver, and Menlo Park. During this period, cooperation between USGS and AASG reached a new high. The Association worked with the USGS Water Resources Division's district chiefs and the chief geologist to clarify the role of USGS regional representatives as facilitators, not "gate-keepers," in communications with state agencies. President Charles Gardner met on a number of occasions with USGS leaders in Raleigh, N.C., and in Reston, Va., regarding improved communications and coordination.

Charles (Chip) Groat was appointed the new director of the USGS in November 1998. Further integration of USGS projects followed. With Groat as director, cooperation between USGS and AASG improved further.

Ongoing Issues at the End of the Decade. At the end of the decade of the 90's, while major strides had been made in funding the National Cooperative Geologic Mapping Program, the Association was still aggressively pursuing adequate and equitable funding for STATEMAP and EDMAP under the amended National Geologic Mapping Act.

Also at the end of the 90's, while considerable progress had been made from 1995 through 1999 in resolving a number of AASG and USGS issues regarding national geologic mapping, there remained some differences of opinion between the AASG and the USGS's National Mapping Division on the National Topographic Mapping Program. The AASG and its Topographic Mapping Subcommittee of the Digital Mapping Committee were working diligently to seek an ultimate resolution.

The AASG was also continuing its efforts to seek productive partnerships and ways of participating with various federal agencies. Efforts with the Department of Energy to support and pursue their program for possible grant solicitations for carbon sequestration studies and for oil and gas projects were continuing. The AASG was also in dialogue with the American Geological Institute on issues that would secure seismic data and core storage facilities. Continuation of the National Science Foundation Mentoring Program was pending, and the Association's position on evolution and creationism was under review. Also under review at the end of the decade was an idea for a cooperative project to establish a Washington, D.C.–based Geologic Information Center, staffed by representatives from the state surveys and the USGS.

Concluding Comments. For the AASG, the decade of the 90's was a period of transition from an organization having narrowly focused interests of restricted value to an integrated Association concentrating on a number of national issues of geologic, economic, and environmental importance. AASG's emphasis in the 90's was on the National Cooperative Geologic Mapping Program and on vital elements that complemented the Association's efforts to build national and regional programs that rely on the expertise, data, and resources of the state geological surveys. AASG was recognized in this period as a uniquely integrated and focused organization with the "geodiversity" needed to work toward a thriving economy and a healthy environment. As a result of its activities in this decade, the AASG had gained stature and placed itself well to influence both federal and state activities.

Acknowledgments. I wish to thank James C. Cobb, state geologist, Kentucky Geological Survey, for his counsel and guidance throughout the preparation of this document and Michael Bograd (Mississippi state geologist), Donald L. Koch (honorary member and former Iowa state geologist), and James H. Williams (honorary member and former Missouri state geologist) for their peer review and helpful comments, most of which have been incorporated.

Main sources of information used in completing the decade of the 90's include the "President's Page" in the *State Geologists Journal* for 1990–2000 and the descriptive text in these journals covering the "Notes" or "Minutes" of the annual and midyear meetings, "Memorials," and the "Honorary Members" during this period. Sources also included AASG's Liaison Committee minutes for 1995–99 and available Executive Committee minutes for 1995–99. AASG correspondence files, available in Illinois State Geological Survey archives for 1990–94 and for 1998, were also utilized.

2000–08

Kenneth B. Taylor *(North Carolina, Associate)*

This summary is more news than history, since AASG's first decade in the 21st century has not been completed, but it has been filled with firsts, including the election of the first female, the first Nevadan, and first person from Maine to lead the Association.

The decade so far has seen a large turnover in the membership, the establishment of the AASG Foundation, the wars in Iraq and Afghanistan with the associated cuts in discretionary federal spending, and the unsuccessful effort (so far) to reauthorize the National Geologic Mapping Act.

2000–01. The decade began in July 2000 with Jonathan Price (Nevada) assuming the presidency of AASG. He had been elected on June 22, 2000, at the annual meeting in St. Louis, Mo. Price was the first Nevada state geologist to serve as AASG president. The other officers in that slate were Vicki Cowart (Colorado) as president-elect, James Robertson (Wisconsin) as past-president, Emery Cleaves (Maryland) as vice president, Lee Allison (Utah) in his second term as secretary, and John Steinmetz (Indiana) in his second term as treasurer.

The year ended with the annual meeting June 23–27, 2001, in Butte, Mont., hosted by the relatively new state geologist, Edmond Deal. That task was laid upon him after John Steinmetz, who had lobbied hard to have the annual meeting in Montana, became the state geologist of Indiana. Later in the decade Steinmetz made amends when his Indiana survey played host to the 2002 annual meeting in New Harmony, Ind.

During the 2001 annual meeting—which included geologic sightseeing, a campy theater show, and the opportunity to pan for sapphires—history was made when Vicki Cowart (Colorado) was elected president of the Association. She was not only the first female AASG president, but she was also the first one from Colorado. The annual meeting was also a watershed for associates—senior staff members in the state surveys who were not the state geologist but were active in support of the Association. At that meeting, the entire class of associates was recognized, and each member was given a certificate attesting to the status.

President Price summarized the year by looking at the Association's achievements under the four objectives outlined in the AASG constitution.

Under the objective "to advance the science and practical application of geology," President Price cited the National Science Foundation awarding AASG two additional years of funding for the grant "Research Experiences in the Field with Mentors from State Geological Surveys." In addition, the AASG Executive Committee approved $1,000 for two competitive scholarships for the National Association of Geoscience Teachers' program to help geology students attend summer field camps. Finally, he noted that the 2000 John C. Frye Award for Environmental Geology was awarded to staff members from the Pennsylvania geological survey for their landslide susceptibility maps.

Under the objective "to improve the effectiveness of state geological surveys," President Price noted the excellent venues for interaction among the state geologists and their staff. In addition, a new Committee on History of AASG and a new External Service and Awards Subcommittee were formed, and the Awards Committee was expanded. Finally, Guam and the Virgin Islands were invited to consider joining AASG, and the ongoing struggle to maintain state geological surveys by writing AASG letters of support to governors, university officials, and state legislators continued.

Under the objective "to improve the methods of assembling and disseminating data and information," Price noted that AASG has worked to increase the federal appropriation for the National Cooperative Geologic Mapping Program and success was measured in 2001 with a healthy increase in funding. Part of that success was due to the creation of one-page fact sheets for most states on the mapping program. Finally, the duties of the AASG vice president were defined to coordinate the set-up and staffing of the AASG booth at professional meetings such as the National Conference of State Legislatures and Geological Society of America.

Under the objective "to effectively coordinate activities with federal and state agencies," Price pointed out that AASG signed letters or memoranda of agreement or understanding with the Office of Surface Mining, the U.S. Geological Survey, and NASA, and another was to be finalized with the National Resources Conservation Service in September 2001. In addition, with only 51 members, AASG continued to be the largest per capita contributor to the Government Affairs Program of the American Geological Institute. Finally, AASG recognized the coordination of the geologic profession and the deliberative process of government with the AASG Pick and Gavel Award. The recipients for 2001 were Rep. Ralph Regula of Ohio and Sen. Joseph Lieberman of Connecticut.

President-elect Cowart, in her remarks at the annual meeting, noted that James Robertson (Wisconsin) was rotating off the Executive Committee after having served five consecutive years on the committee as AASG secretary, vice president, president-elect, president, and past-president.

Three colleagues passed away in 2000–01: Leo W. Hough, former director and state geologist of the Louisiana Geological Survey; Frank E. Kottlowski, former director and state geologist of the New Mexico Bureau of Mines and Mineral Resources; and Daniel N. Miller Jr., the former state geologist and executive director of the Wyoming Geological Survey.

2001–02. When President-elect Cowart received the gavel from President Price at the end of the 2001 annual meeting, no one knew that 3 months later, when the state emergency management directors would also be gathered in Montana at their annual meeting, three hijacked commercial airplanes would be flown into the Twin Towers of the World Trade Center and the Pentagon, and a fourth would crash into a farm field in rural Pennsylvania as passengers struggled to take back the aircraft.

The fall liaison meeting in 2001 was scheduled for the week after 9/11, and President Cowart made many telephone calls and sent e-mails to colleagues to determine if the liaison meeting should take place. The D.C. agency representatives said to come on, since Washington was open for business. The September 2001 liaison meeting went forward with 11 attendees conducting 23 meetings. Many federal agency partners spoke to the AASG representatives about a potential world-changing shift in national priorities.

One major opportunity opened for the first time at that fall liaison meeting. President-elect Cleaves had been successful in scheduling an appointment with the Office of Management and Budget. President Cowart, President-elect Cleaves, and Past-president Price met with Mr. Jason Freihage, the USGS budget examiner. This meeting provided AASG with a great opportunity to talk with a relatively young person, one who did not possess a geologic background, but was given the task of examining and understanding the USGS spending priorities. The meeting was an eye-opener, which allowed AASG leadership to peer into the inner workings of the federal government and see how technical information needs to be presented in a logical and understandable fashion.

The spring liaison meeting had 44 attendees and 33 meetings. Another first at that meeting was an appointment with the Department of Interior science advisor. President Cowart presented the Pick and Gavel Award to Department of Interior Secretary Gale A. Norton.

The year ended in New Harmony, Ind., where John Steinmetz and the Indiana Geological Survey were hosts to the 94th annual meeting. President Cowart recognized one new state geologist, C.R. (Rick) Berquist (Virginia), and two acting state geologists, Val Chandler (Minnesota) and Carl Smith (West Virginia).

Some of the meeting highlights included an oral report from James Cobb (Kentucky) on the status of finding, inventorying, scanning, and archiving the official records of the Association. He said the AASG Website was being updated so that members and honoraries could keep their contact information current as well as participate in Association activities.

President-elect Cleaves related his experiences in dealing with the liaison meeting the week after 9/11. Attendance quadrupled and 50 percent more meetings occurred during the spring liaison meeting compared to the fall meeting. Cleaves also reported that the USGS was struggling with regionalization and the Department of the Interior was developing a top-down strategic plan.

President Cowart was appointed to the National Petroleum Council, the first time a member of AASG had been on that board.

Kenneth Weaver (former state geologist of Maryland) was awarded the 2001 Ian Campbell Medal.

Jonathan Price (Nevada) and James Robertson (Wisconsin) had a work session on STATEMAP issues. Price and Robertson were frank about how to be successful and avoid pitfalls.

Later during the annual meeting, Dr. Charles G. (Chip) Groat, director of the U.S. Geological Survey, acknowledged the role the AASG has in the reauthorization of the National Geologic Mapping Act. Doug Wysocki, a research soil scientist with the National Resources Conservation Service's National Soil Survey Center, discussed with the Association the recently signed memorandum of understanding between AASG and NRCS. One paradigm he spoke of was the fact that most NRCS programs are state-based activities, but the NRCS Soil Survey is organized nationally.

At the conclusion of the 2001–02 year, Jonathan Price (Nevada) left the Executive Committee after having served 7 years as secretary (1995–96), treasurer (1996–98), vice president, president-elect, president, and past-president.

Emery Cleves (Maryland) was elected president and was the fifth Maryland state geologist to serve as AASG president, William B. Clark (1914–16), Edward B. Mathews (1921–24), Joseph T. Singewald (1956), and Kenneth N. Weaver (1973) having previously served.

Two colleagues passed away during 2001–02: Dr. Robert B. Forbes, former state geologist and director of the Alaska Division of Geological and Geophysical Surveys, and Dr. John G. Broughton, former principal scientist and state geologist of New York.

2002–03. The year began with President Cleaves presiding over the September 8, 2002, Executive Committee meeting in Washington, D.C. The fall liaison meeting, which started the next day, had 25 representatives and 40 confirmed appointments with federal agencies.

A new face for AASG would be Dr. Randy Orndorff, the new STATEMAP coordinator. The memorandum of understanding between AASG and the Federal Emergency Management Agency was signed on the next day, with Anthony Lowe signing for FEMA. There was no movement on the reauthorization of the National Geologic Mapping Act.

At the AASG midyear meeting in October in Denver, David Applegate from the American Geological Institute spoke of the 15 percent increase in funding for the U.S. Geological Survey and National Science Foundation. AGI called for a coalition to support the national mission of the USGS. He also said the Homeland Security agency would have a big impact on sciences and geosciences.

The John C. Frye Award was presented to Peggy Johnson, New Mexico Bureau of Geology and Mineral Resources, for the decision-makers field guide, *Water, Watersheds, Santa Fe, New Mexico*.

During the executive session, James Cobb (Kentucky) reported on the need for a permanent archive of AASG records. As part of that effort, President Cleaves wanted to consider funding a project on the history of the AASG at the $10,000 level. President Cleaves also recognized three new state geologists: Carl Smith (Virginia), Steve Macbee (Massachusetts), and Barry "Nick" Tew (Alabama). Jonathan Price (Nevada) was assigned to chair the FEMA memorandum of understanding Implementation Committee.

Donald Hoskins (honorary member from Pennsylvania) presented a draft outline for the history volume. John Steinmetz (Indiana) reported on core sample preservation and summarized the National Research Council's report on the subject. Hoskins proposed that AASG become a funding partner in publication for the American Geological Institute mapping publication. It was moved, seconded, and passed without dissent that $10,000 be committed to the project.

The next gathering of the AASG was preceding the spring liaison meeting, when the AASG Executive Committee met at the Cosmos Club in Washington, D.C., in March 2003.

President Cleaves, in his presidential update, reported that since the annual meeting 9 months earlier, six state geologists had retired or resigned and new ones had been appointed to succeed them. Charles Gardner (North Carolina), Donald Oltz (Alabama), Milton Wiltse (Alaska), and William Bush (Arkansas) retired during the last half of 2002. James Simons (North Carolina), Berry H. (Nick) Tew (Alabama), Rodney Combellick (Alaska, acting), and Mac Woodward (Arkansas) succeeded them. Vicki Cowart (Colorado) had resigned and Ron Cattany was acting state geologist for Colorado. Robert Jordan (Delaware) retired and John Talley was appointed interim director of the Delaware survey. Two other retirements would take place in July 2003: Earl Bennett (Idaho) and James Davis (California).

The Pick and Gavel Awards were presented to Sen. Ted Stevens of Alaska and Sen. Jeff Bingaman of New Mexico. Both received a shark's tooth, *Carcharodon megalodon*, from the Miocene deposits.

President Cleaves reported that the book *Geologic Mapping and Natural Systems* was being prepared by the American Geological Institute, and AASG committed $10,000 toward its publication. Four AASG members—James Robertson (Wisconsin), Peter Scholle (New Mexico), Robert Fakundiny (New York), and Lee Allison (Kansas)—agreed to serve on the book's editorial committee. Five states—Maryland, New Jersey, Kansas, Florida, and Colorado—had sent articles, and four others—Utah, Ohio, Virginia, and New Mexico—had indicated they were preparing articles also.

President Cleaves also reported on attendance at the January 22, 2003, initial meeting of the Coalition for the USGS. Twelve representatives met in Washington, D.C., at the American Geophysical Union Building to hammer out a statement of purpose, and two other working group sessions had occurred.

With the resignation of Vicki Cowart (Colorado), Jonathan Price (Nevada) was called back to duty on the Executive Committee to serve as past-president.

The 2003 spring liaison meeting had 30 representatives from 24 states, and AASG had 39 appointments with D.C. agencies. As president-elect John Steinmetz (Indiana) summarized the meeting later, the war in Iraq and the protesting tobacco farmer in the pond dominated most of the news coverage during the March meeting. The themes for liaison appointments were appropriations, budgets, and the fact that the fiscal year 2003 budget was not approved until February 2003 (5 months into the fiscal year). The president's fiscal year 2004 budget was released at almost the same time. The other issue was the war tax: $90 billion to $100 billion in supplemental requests. Homeland Security was still being sorted out and the AASG heard about the Office of Management and Budget's Program Assessment Rating Tool review.

The Office of Management and Budget uses the PART in its 5-year review of all programs. These unique scores have an impact on budgets. For example, the Fossil Energy program was cut in half in 2002 because it did not score well in PART. The USGS budget was cut 2.6 percent; the budget request for STATEMAP was $4.5 million, which was $1.5 million less than for the previous fiscal year. House Interior Subcommittee staff told AASG there was no money available for increases.

June 16–18, 2003, the AASG gathered in Lincoln, Neb., where Mark Kuzila and the Nebraska Geological Survey were hosts. Harvey Thorliefson (Minnesota) was introduced as the acting but almost official state geologist of Minnesota. President-elect Steinmetz gave a report of opportunities for the state surveys to work with federal agencies such as the Federal Emergency Management Agency on flood map modernization, CO_2 sequestration (a hot topic in the Department of Energy), geoscience data preservation, and predisaster mitigation.

President Cleaves reviewed the year's activities, including the three opportunities for the AASG to provide comment: on the next Interior budget cycle, the landslide interim report, and testimony to the House Appropriations Subcommittee on Interior.

Cleaves also noted the high turnover with the retirement or resignation of 10 state geologists—Davis, Cowart, Bennett, Gardner, Oltz, Jordan, Bush, Beulieau, Lewis, and Wiltse—but welcomed their successors to the work of the Association.

He also briefed the Association on the Coalition for the USGS. A formal vote on AASG participation was scheduled for the midyear meeting (November 2003).

Jonathan Price (Nevada) briefed the group on the implementation of the FEMA memorandum of understanding. He noted the need to convince FEMA about the need for geologic input into the hazard assessment. FEMA's thinking was that mapping was done by USGS, and the AASG was showing FEMA that detailed mapping is not the responsibility of the USGS. Finally, FEMA was reported to be looking at a buy-out program for landslides and there was the possibility of working with surveys to obtain input.

The Monday afternoon session was a "State of the Surveys," facilitated by James Robertson (Wisconsin) along with Earl Bennett (Idaho, honorary) and Walter Schmidt (Florida). Seven states—Wisconsin, Idaho, Florida, Washington, Ohio, Alabama, and Texas—were examined in detail, and there was an excellent discussion.

Next, the STATEMAP review panel—James Robertson (Wisconsin), James Cobb (Kentucky), Richard Allis (Utah), and Mark Kuzila (Nebraska)—gave a frank session on "what to do and not to do" on STATEMAP proposals. Allis stressed the significant role of the advisory committee. Cobb echoed that observation and added the need for a good letter from the State Mapping Advisory Committee. Kuzila said the affiliations of the advisory committee members needed to be included in the application. Cleaves stressed that expenses vary dramatically between states, and the mapping priorities the states select should be clearly spelled out and the review panel should accept them. Randy Orndorff spoke of changes in the requests for proposals. All proposals got an across-the-board cut to meet the reduced funding level; $8.5 million was requested and $6.6 million was available.

On Tuesday, staff from the Kansas Geological Survey gave a 15-minute introduction to digital mapping and an hour-long walking demonstration.

The John Frye Award was given to Ronald K. Churchill, Chris T. Higgins, and Bob Hall for their report, *Areas More Likely to Contain Natural Occurrences of Asbestos in Western El Dorado County, California,* published by the California geological survey in 2000.

John Steinmetz (Indiana) was elected president and was the third Indiana state geologist to serve as president, having been preceded by Charles F. Deiss (1954) and John B. Patton (1966).

During 2002–03, only one colleague died: Dr. Don Halvorson, former state geologist and chair of the University of North Dakota geology department. Dr. Halvorson was the first state geologist of North Dakota who was a native of the state.

2003–04. The year began with President Steinmetz presiding at the Executive Committee meeting on September 14, 2003, at the Cosmos Club, Washington, D.C. As usual, the Executive Committee meeting was on the Sunday before the fall AASG liaison meeting.

Treasurer Scholle reported that the Association was solvent and a significant part of the Association's expenses depended on the National Science Foundation mapping scholarship grant. All 50 states paid dues for the first time since 2000, with a few paying back dues.

President Steinmetz went down a short list of issues and asked several persons to report to the group. He thanked the National Association of Geoscience Teachers for $1,000 for field student support. He asked James Cobb (Kentucky) to report on the American Geological Institute's geologic mapping book. Cobb said there were 35 submittals and about 15 to 16 were used. Because of the Association's $10,000 donation, the state geologists were to have some editorial input. Later, Cobb was also asked to summarize the National Science Foundation field-mentoring proposal. It was submitted on September 11 and was for 3 years. The reviewers had been very critical of the lack of tracking of those who were mentored. The Association addressed this issue with a link on its Website to a student's gallery. Finally, Cobb briefed the Executive Committee on the proposed national map. He said it was no longer a geologic issue since geology was not a theme; instead, themes were topography, roads, subdivisions, industrial parks, etc. James Robertson (Wisconsin) suggested that the National Map Committee go dormant but not be disbanded.

On the topic of National Geologic Mapping Act reauthorization, Robertson was working on appropriations and Peter Scholle (New Mexico) was working on the separate issue of reauthorization. A survey from 47 states indicated that by 2010, $16.5 million would be available for STATEMAP matching. The current authorized level was $64 million, but the current appropriation was less than $7 million.

For geoscience data preservation, $30 million was to be administered by the Secretary of the Interior with the full cooperation of the AASG.

The writing assignments for the AASG history were handed out at the annual meeting in Lincoln. No due dates were made at that time.

The Coalition for the USGS was still getting organized, with the stated goal of raising the USGS appropriation to $1 billion or more. Of all the associations that had signed up, all the others were national, and only AASG was state-oriented.

It was reported that unspent STATEMAP funds of around $500,000 during the lifetime of the program were weakening our position. The information on unspent funds should be available to the STATEMAP review panel, but five to six states were creating most of the problems.

In terms of new business, John Bluemle (North Dakota) announced he was stepping down as editor, and a new editor was needed.

At the AASG midyear meeting in Seattle, Wash., November 2–3, 2003, some of the same issues discussed earlier in the year were still being worked on.

The draft of the AGI geologic mapping book included 15 case studies, and the textbook part had been transformed for a general audience. Treasurer Scholle, also a member of the AASG Editorial Committee, reported that seven case studies were on geologic hazards, two on ecosystems, two on resources, and none on water as a resource. The selections seemed unbalanced, considering the importance of water resources.

For the AASG history, James Cobb (Kentucky) outlined a timetable and table of contents. He said we needed to get moving in order to be ready for the AASG centennial in 2008.

John Kiefer (Kentucky, associate) and Tom Evans (Wisconsin, associate) launched a new division of the Geological Society of America—Geology and Society—at GSA's annual meeting.

During the midyear meeting open session, Jack Hess, executive director of the Geological Society of America, said that year's meeting attendance of approximately 6,600 registrants was second in size only to the centennial meeting, which had 7,500 attendees.

Peter Lyttle, program coordinator for the National Cooperative Geologic Mapping Program at the USGS, reported that Laurel Bybell was a new staff member in the NCGMP office. He confirmed the report made by Peter Scholle (New Mexico) that hearings on National Geologic Mapping Act reauthorization could start in the spring of 2004.

Later, during the business session, President Steinmetz gave his report. He noted that during the Executive Committee meeting the previous night, the recommendation was made to take excerpts from the letters of support in the STATEMAP proposals and include that material as testimony for NGMA reauthorization.

The Liaison Committee reported that 20 states were represented and 34 of 37 meetings were completed at the liaison meeting. A hurricane added extra interest in getting out of town. The $87 billion war bill would strain all budgets. They also reported that the USGS had apparently scored pretty well to that point on the Office of Management and Budget's PART process. There were 26 action items in the report.

The ad hoc Committee on Reauthorization of NCGMP reported that they had met with Capitol Hill staff members, who recommended that AASG go for reauthorization in 2004. Sponsorship was lined up, and letters of support needed to be sent.

James Cobb (Kentucky) reported on the NSF Field Mentoring Program. The proposal was submitted for $500,000, but the Association would get paid only if the slots were used.

Lee Allison (Kansas) reported on an emerging opportunity for a partnership with the Interstate Oil and Gas Compact Commission to increase oil and gas research at the Department of Energy.

The Ian Campbell Medal was awarded to Frank H.T. Rhodes for 2003.

The AASG Executive Committee next met on March 21, 2004, at the Cosmos Club in Washington, D.C. During the session, Treasurer Scholle reported the loss of the National Science Foundation mentoring grant, which translated to a $25,000 reduction in the annual budget. Donald Haney (Kentucky, honorary) confirmed that Ernest Mancini (Alabama, honorary) had been formally nominated to the American Geological Institute for the Ian Campbell Medal. President Steinmetz reported that David Applegate had moved to the USGS hazards program.

On the status of National Geologic Mapping Act reauthorization, President Steinmetz said his testimony was ready, but the hearing had been canceled and would be rescheduled to coincide with the September 2004 liaison meeting.

Another highlight brought out at the meeting was the completion of the American Geological Institute's geologic mapping book, copies of which were available to hand out during the liaison meeting.

James Cobb (Kentucky), Peter Scholle (New Mexico), Jonathan Price (Nevada), and Scott Tinker (Texas) discussed the challenges and successes of the National Science Foundation's Field Mentoring Program. Price probably summarized it best, saying (Deal, 2004)

We chased NSF for several years and they finally suggested getting into the REU program. There was a conscious effort to not make work for AASG and keep it simple. We need to find out what other programs they [NSF] have that we might plug into. Maybe our 5 years had just worn out our welcome.

Lee Allison (Kansas) reported that the geoscience data preservation project had made no progress because the Federal Energy Policy Act was bogged down in Congress.

The AASG annual meeting was at the Skamania Lodge in Stevenson, Wash., from June 13–17, 2004. Ron Teissere and the Washington Division of Geology and Earth Resources were host.

President Steinmetz welcomed representatives from 39 states. Five new AASG members were introduced: Roy Breckenridge (Idaho), Robert Libra (Iowa), Vicki McConnell (Oregon), Vincent Matthews (Colorado), and Harvey Thorleifson (Minnesota).

James Cobb (Kentucky) reported on the conversion of 90 years worth of microfilm to digital files. The conversion was needed for the centennial history project, and the early years were taking much more time than anticipated.

There was a motion that AASG endorse the centennial project and authorize Donald Hoskins (Pennsylvania) and James Cobb (Kentucky) to move ahead with the project. The motion passed without dissent.

John Bluemle's (North Dakota) final report as editor said that 49 states responded to a request for their state input. Pictures of the state geologists were new this year and were also included in the Fact Book.

Treasurer Scholle reported that the National Science Foundation grant was not renewed and the Association was looking at a $9,000 annual deficit for routine expenses. After a discussion, a motion was made to raise the state membership dues to $300. The motion was passed without further discussion or dissent.

The liaison report from President-elect Marvinney noted that the meetings were well attended. The tone was that this was an unusual and unpredictable budget year. As always, some of the representatives the Association meets with seemed bored and disengaged. He asked if we could work toward getting visits at higher levels.

President Steinmetz thanked the Executive Committee and Ron Teissere (Washington) for helping to get meetings planned and getting agendas done. He also called for a committee to advise on the annual meeting, concerning what role honoraries and associates should play, cost containment, if the Association should be more conservative in selecting meeting sites, the appropriate length of meetings and business agenda, and whether committee reports should come out earlier.

Donald Haney (Kentucky, honorary) reported that Ernest Mancini (Alabama, honorary) had been chosen to receive the Ian Campbell Award.

The Nominations Committee recommended the following slate of nominees: President—Robert Marvinney (Maine), President-elect—Peter Scholle (New Mexico), Vice President—Scott Tinker (Texas), Secretary—Edmond Deal (Montana), Historian—James Cobb (Kentucky), Treasurer—Berry (Nick) Tew (Alabama), Editor—Karl Muessig (New Jersey), and Statistician—Walter Schmidt (Florida). Thirty-seven votes were cast and no votes deviated from the slate of nominees. Robert G. Marvinney became the first person from Maine to serve as AASG president.

The meeting ended with resolutions recognizing Ernest Mancini on receiving the Ian Campbell Medal and a resolution that up to $12,500 be provided by the honoraries toward establishing a Geological Society of America endowment for the Ian Campbell Medal and that AASG would commit to a 1:1 match. Both resolutions passed.

Other resolutions passed by the Association at the annual meeting included ones recognizing the outstanding service of John Bluemle (North Dakota) as editor, recognizing the service of Thomas Berg (Ohio) and David Soller for the effort to build the National Geologic Map Database, appreciation to Ron Teissere and the Washington Division of Mines and Geology and for hosting the 96th annual AASG meeting, and recognizing John C. Steinmetz for his outstanding service as AASG president.

Four colleagues died during 2003–04: Robert E. Hershey, former state geologist of Tennessee; Dr. Matt Walton, former director of the Minnesota Geological Survey; Dr. Perry Wigley, former director of the Nebraska Geological Survey; and Don Blackstone, former state geologist of Wyoming.

2004–05. The year began with the Geologic Hazards Policy Committee preparing an AASG position statement on the AASG's support of such programs as the National Earthquake Hazard Reduction Program (by the National Institute of Standards and Technology, U.S. Geological Survey, Federal Emergency Management Agency, and National Science Foundation), the National Tsunami Hazards Mitigation Program (by the National Oceanic and Atmospheric Administration), the National Cooperative Geologic Mapping Program, expanded landslides program and volcano observatories (by the U.S. Geological Survey), Earthscope (by the National Science Foundation), and the modernization of flood insurance rate maps (by the Federal Emergency Management Agency). The AASG Executive Committee adopted the statement in September 2004.

The annual meeting was held June 13–17, 2005, in St. Charles, Ill., and was hosted by William W. Shilts and the Illinois State Geological Survey. Four new AASG members were introduced at the annual meeting: John Parrish (California), Rebecca White (Arkansas), Mark Myers (Alaska), and William Kelly (New York).

Highlights of the AASG meeting minutes and committee reports for the year included a report from Statistician Schmidt, who noted a significant drop in the number of participating states in the statistician's report. For the last 3 years the number has fallen from 44 to 36 to only 32 in 2004.

AASG Historian James Cobb (Kentucky) reported that scanning historical AASG documents was now finished and an index of the documents had been completed. The material was available on CD and would soon be available on the AASG Website.

The match to the funds raised for the Ian Campbell Medal endowment of $12,500 was obligated by AASG.

Vice President Tinker reported that state legislators met in Salt Lake City in 2004. The AASG booth was shared with the American Institute of Professional Geologists and the American Geological Institute. The other booth display for the year was at the Geological Society of America annual meeting in Denver. New booth display materials were used, including posters of the AASG's six position papers, as well as handouts.

President-elect Scholle noted that during the annual liaison meeting, AASG visited 10 to 15 organizations that had not been visited before. Having position papers already prepared gave AASG more to offer when there was a visit. The liaison meetings went well and the 2005 Pick and Gavel Award went to Marcus Milling, executive director of the American Geological Institute.

President Marvinney reported a busy year with continued work to reauthorize the National Geologic Mapping Act and helping Peter Scholle (New Mexico) on a memorandum of understanding with the U.S. Forest Service. He also noted that the position papers provided a concise statement that reflected the opinion of the collective state surveys. He felt they had been highly beneficial.

A work session on STATEMAP suggested several models to distribute the funds. There were several opinions, and President Marvinney asked that state geologists on the STATEMAP Review Panel meet later with the Executive Committee to make some decision about the funding model to be used for the requests for proposals to be issued later in the fall.

President Marvinney chaired an AASG Planning Session on Water and introduced a new AASG initiative: the National Aquifer Characterization and Groundwater Sustainability Assessment Program.

An afternoon field trip to U.S. Silica included dinner at Starved Rock State Park.

Peter Scholle (New Mexico) was elected president, exactly 20 years after Frank Kottlowski, the only other New Mexico state geologist to also serve in that position.

Two colleagues died during 2004–05: William H. Moore, former state geologist and director of the Mississippi Geological Survey, and Joseph A. Sinnott, former state geologist for Massachusetts.

2005–06. During the midyear meeting, Samuel S. Adams was awarded the 2005 Ian Campbell Medal.

The year ended at the annual meeting, held June 3–8, 2006, in Santa Fe, N.M. President Scholle also served as the host for the annual meeting, at which five new AASG members were recognized: Robert Swenson (Alaska), William Harrison (Kansas), Michael Hohn (West Virginia), and Lee Allison (Arizona). Michael Bogard (Mississippi) was also introduced as a new acting state geologist.

Highlights from the business session and committee reports during the year included a report from President-elect Tinker saying that the liaison meeting was "lots of work" and that the meetings worked well with the revised format. Reauthorization of the National Geologic Mapping Act failed, but a new memorandum of understanding with the National Ground Water Association was approved.

Bill Dixon, president-elect of the National Association of State Boards of Geology (ASBOG), chair of the Illinois Board of Licensing for Professional Geologists, and emeritus of the Illinois State Geological Survey, gave a presentation on the process of finalizing the rewording of a memorandum of agreement or memorandum of understanding between ASBOG and AASG.

Thomas Berg (Ohio) and David Soller gave a joint report on the National Geologic Map Database.

Dr. Robert D. Hatcher Jr. was the AASG Ian Campbell Subcommittee nominee for 2006, and the recommendation was forwarded to the AGI Selection Committee.

The AASG Earth Science Education Committee reported that Earthscope hoped to coordinate and cooperate with the American Geological Institute and state geological surveys to act as regional outlets for Earthscope as the array moved across the country. In addition, the committee reported that the post-secondary education pipeline should be the AASG focus. Meetings with the National Science Foundation were planned to determine how the AASG expertise could be molded into the existing NSF diversity programs.

President-elect Tinker (Texas) had asked President Scholle (New Mexico) if he could lead a breakout session on the AASG committee structure. As Tinker reported to the membership during the breakout session, one conclusion was obvious: the committee structure needed to be reorganized.

Scott Tinker was elected president and was the third Texas state geologist to serve in that office, following Peter Flawn (1969) and William Fisher (1981).

On a sad note, Jack A. Simon, former chief of the Illinois survey, and Richard N. Foster, former state geologist of Massachusetts, died during the year.

2006–07. The reorganization of the AASG committee structure began after the annual meeting and was completed by mid-July 2006. President Tinker then gave all committee chairs the task of defining a mission statement and setting goals for their committees. That effort was completed by the end of August 2006.

The fall liaison meeting was attended by representatives from 27 states and involved 38 meetings.

Dr. Robert D. Hatcher Jr. was awarded the 2006 Ian Campbell Medal.

President-elect John postponed his heart surgery to handle the spring liaison meeting, which was a success, with attendance from 32 states and involving 42 meetings. Dr. Frank Press and Rep. Norm Dicks (D-Washington) were awarded the 2007 Pick and Gavel Awards at that meeting.

The year ended at Key Largo, Fla., where Walter Schmidt and his staff of the Florida Geological Survey hosted a wonderful annual meeting June 9–13, 2007. All attendees were told to lose the coats and ties, and everyone was decked out in panama hats and Hawaiian shirts. This was the Florida survey's centennial, and the AASG passed a resolution honoring that landmark achievement.

AASG welcomed three new state geologists: Michael Hohn (West Virginia), Jim Kennedy (Georgia), and Larry Wickstrom (Ohio).

Highlights from the business session and the committee reports were a report from Jonathan Price (Nevada) that the AASG Foundation was under way; many members, honoraries, and associates had made individual contributions. The AASG booth was at the Geological Society of America annual meeting in Philadelphia, and other outreach opportunities were scheduled.

The AASG Ian Campbell Subcommittee selected Arthur A. Socolow, former Pennsylvania state geologist, as the AASG nominee. That recommendation was forwarded to the AGI Ian Campbell Nominating Committee.

President Tinker summarized the previous year and his efforts to increase organizational effectiveness, put the Association on strong financial health, increase its professional relations, and increase internal communications.

During 2006–07, two members passed away: Vince Dreeszen, former Nebraska state geologist, and James Slosson, former California state geologist.

When the gavel was passed to President-elect Chacko John (Louisiana), he said that the current committee structure would stay in place. John was the second Louisiana state geologist to serve as president; Charles (Chip) Groat was elected in 1987.

2007–08. President John called the fall liaison meeting to order in September 2007. That meeting was scheduled by President-elect Berry (Nick) Tew (Alabama) and included a breakout session with the U.S. Geological Survey on geologic data preservation and the AASG–USGS Coordination Committee meeting.

A Capitol Hill reception for the USGS Coalition was attended by most of the AASG liaison attendees, as well as representatives from the Geological Society of America, American Geological Institute, and Incorporated Research Institutions for Seismology.

The midyear meeting was in Denver, where Dr. Socolow was awarded the Ian Campbell Medal for 2007.

At the time of completing this summary, the issue of reauthorization of the National Geologic Mapping Act was not yet settled. The work of the AASG continues in this and many areas.

References Cited

AASG, 1930, Minutes of the meeting of the Association of American State Geologists at Washington, D.C., Feb. 13–14, 1930: AASG scanned archives, www.stategeologists. org/Group/Archive/djvu/1930DCminutes/djvu.

AASG, 1931a, Minutes of the meeting of the Association of American State Geologists at Washington, D.C., February 13–14, 1931: AASG scanned archives, www.stategeologists.org/Group/Archive/djvu/1931DCminutes.djvu.

AASG, 1932, Minutes of the meeting of the Association of American State Geologists at Washington, D.C., February 18–19, 1932: AASG scanned archives, www.stategeologists.org/Group/Archive/djvu/1932DCminutes.djvu.

AASG, 1938, Resolution prepared by a committee of the Association of American State Geologists appointed to prepare a resolution with reference to the need for expediting the Hayden-Ickes plan for mapping of the United States: Journal of the Association of American State Geologists, v. 9, no. 3, p. 11–12.

AASG, 1939a, Correspondence on mapping: Journal of the Association of American State Geologists, v. 10, no. 3, p. 4–11.

AASG, 1939b, Official transcript of joint meeting with U.S. Geological Survey, February 17, 1939: Journal of the Association of American State Geologists, v. 10, no. 2, p. 7–23.

AASG, 1940, Statement of organization: Journal of the Association of American State Geologists, v. 11, no. 2, p. 18–20.

AASG, 1947a, Change in constitution: Journal of the Association of American State Geologists, v. 18, no. 2, p. 20.

AASG, 1947b, Letter to W.E. Wrather, Director, U.S.G.S., from the Executive Committee, November 1, 1946: Journal of the Association of American State Geologists, v. 18, no. 1, p. 22–23.

AASG, 1948, Resolutions: Journal of the Association of American State Geologists, v. 19, no. 2, p. 67–68.

AASG, 1949, Resolutions: Journal of the Association of American State Geologists, v. 20, no. 2, p. 4.

Aldrich, H.R., 1930, The cost of the magnetic survey in Wisconsin: Journal of the Association of American State Geologists, v. 1, no. 4, p. 6–10.

American Engineering Council, 1931, Administrative Board endorses Temple Plan: Journal of the Association of American State Geologists, v. 2, no. 3, p. 26–29.

Bennett, E.H., 1996, Summary minutes, Association of American State Geologists annual meeting, 2–4 June 1996, Omni Hotel, Charlottesville, Virginia: AASG scanned archives, www.stategeologists.org/Group/Archive/djvu/1996VAminutes.djvu.

Bevan, A.C., 1934, Minutes of the annual meeting of the Association of American State Geologists at Washington, D.C., February 22, 1934: AASG scanned archives, www.stategeologists.org/Group/Archive/djvu/1934DCminutes.djvu.

Bevan, A.C., 1935a, Association meetings at Washington: Journal of the Association of American State Geologists, v. 6, no. 2, p. 27–28.

Bevan, A.C., 1935b, Minutes of Rochester meeting: Journal of the Association of American State Geologists, v. 6, no. 1, p. 35.

Bevan, A.C., 1936a, Minutes of New York meeting: Journal of the Association of American State Geologists, v. 7, no. 1, p. 27–28.

Bevan, A.C., 1936b, Minutes of annual Washington meeting: Journal of the Association of American State Geologists, v. 7, no. 2, p. 39–40.

Bevan, A.C., 1937, Minutes of annual Washington meeting: Journal of the Association of American State Geologists, v. 8, no. 2, p. 28–30.

Bevan, A.C., 1939a, Joint meeting with the U.S. Geological Survey, February 17, 1939: Journal of the Association of American State Geologists, v. 10, no. 2, p. 5–7.

Bevan, A.C., 1939b, Minutes of annual meeting, Association of American State Geologists, Thursday, February 16, 1939: Journal of the Association of American State Geologists, v. 10, no. 2, p. 4–5.

Bevan, A., 1940, Public education in geology: Part I: Journal of the Association of American State Geologists, v. 11, no. 3, p. 34–36.

Bevan, A., 1941, Public education in geology: Part II: Journal of the Association of American State Geologists, v. 12, no. 1, p. 19–28.

Bevan, A., 1943, Significant trends in state geological survey work: Journal of the Association of American State Geologists, v. 14, no. 1, p. 7.

Bevan, A.C., Kummel, H.B., and Leighton, M.M., 1933, Report of the meeting of the Committee on Topographic Surveys of the A.A.S.G. with the Administrative Committee of the American Association of State Highway Officials: Journal of the Association of American State Geologists, v. 4, no. 1, p. 26–29.

Birdseye, C.H., 1935, The National Mapping Plan: Report to the Association of American State Geologists: Journal of the Association of American State Geologists, v. 6, no. 2, p. 8–11.

Branner, G.C., 1931a, Article and table submitted to *American Year Book* on "state geological surveys": Journal of the Association of American State Geologists, v. 2, no. 1, p. 3–6.

Branner, G.C., 1931b, History of Association of American State Geologists: Journal of the Association of American State Geologists, v. 2, no. 3, p. 19–25.

Branner, G.C., 1933a, Minutes of the meeting of the Association of American State Geologists at Washington, D.C., Feb. 25, 1933: Journal of the Association of American State Geologists, v. 4, no. 4, p. 18–26.

Branner, G.C., 1933b, Minutes of the meeting of the Association of American State Geologists at Chicago, Illinois, December 29, 1933: AASG scanned archives, www.stategeologists. org/Group/Archive/djvu/1933ILminutes.djvu.

Branner, G.C., 1933c, Table showing income, activities and personnel of state geological surveys for the fiscal year 1932–1933: Journal of the Association of American State Geologists, v. 4, no. 1, p. 1, 12.

Branner, G.C., 1934a, C.W.A. projects being carried on or contemplated under the supervision of the various state geological surveys: Arkansas: Journal of the Association of American State Geologists, v. 5, no. 1, p. 11–12.

Branner, G.C., 1935a, Letter to President Roosevelt, Oct. 25, 1935: Journal of the Association of American State Geologists, v. 6, no. 4, p. 4–5.

Branner, G.C., 1935b, Telegram to President Roosevelt: Journal of the Association of American State Geologists, v. 6, no. 4, p. 3.

Branner, G.C., 1941, Growing import of state geological surveys: Journal of the Association of American State Geologists, v. 12, no. 4, p. 5–8.

Branner, G.C., Bevan, A., and Moore, R.C., 1934, Letter to state geologists: Journal of the Association of American State Geologists, v. 5, no. 4, p. 3–4.

Branner, G.C., Buehler, H.A., and Nixon, E.K., 1940, Military Liaison Committee: Journal of the Association of American State Geologists, v. 11, no. 1, p.12–14.

Calver, J.L., 1975, President's page: The State Geologists Journal, v. 27, no. 1, p. [2].

Clark, E.L., 1945, Progress report, Water Resources Committee, 1945–1946: Journal of the Association of American State Geologists, v. 16, no. 4, p. 14–15.

Committee on Aid to State Geological Surveys, 1942, Report of Committee on Aid to State Geological Surveys: Journal of the Association of American State Geologists, v. 13, no. 3, p. 5–21.

Conrad, S.G., 1981, President's page: The State Geologists Journal, v. 33, no. 1, p. [2].

Daoust, W.L., 1962, President's page: The State Geologists Journal, v. 14, no. 1, p. [3].

Davis, J.F., 1985, President's page: The State Geologists Journal, v. 37, no. 1, p. [2–3].

Deal, E.G., 2004, AASG annual meeting: Business meeting agenda and minutes, Skamania Lodge, Stevenson, Wash.: AASG scanned archives, www.stategeologists.org/Group/Archive/djvu/2004WAminutes.djvu.

Deiss, C., 1951, Association of American State Geologists annual meeting, Rolla, Missouri, February 15–17, 1951: AASG scanned archives, www.stategeologists.org/Group/Archive/djvu/1951MOminutes.djvu.

Dott, R.H., 1941, Executive session minutes, February 21, 1941: p. 12–13.

Dott, R.H., 1943a, Advisory Committee on War Matters: Minutes, Annual Meeting, February 19–20, 1943, Washington, D.C., p. 6.

Dott, R.H., 1943b, Editor's page: Journal of the Association of American State Geologists, v. 14, no. 2, p. 32–38.

Dott, R.H., 1943c, Report of Advisory Committee on War Matters: Journal of the Association of American State Geologists, v. 14, no. 2, p. 17–23.

Dott, R.H., 1944a, Proposed council of geological organizations: Journal of the Association of American State Geologists, v. 15, no. 4, p. 5–11.

Dott, R.H., 1944b, The Washington meeting, February 24, 25, and 26, 1944: Journal of the Association of American State Geologists, v. 15, no. 1, p. 4.

Dott, R.H., and Moore, R.C., 1942, Declarations regarding civilian and military employment of geologists and mining engineers during the present war emergency: Journal of the Association of American State Geologists, v. 13, no. 2, p. 17.

Erwin, R.B., 1979, President's page: The State Geologists Journal, v. 31, no. 1, p. [2].

Fellows, L.D., 1989, President's page: The State Geologists Journal, v. 41, no. 1, p. [2].

Fisher, W.L., 1982, President's page: The State Geologists Journal, v. 34, p. [2].

Flawn, P.T., 1970, President's page: The State Geologists Journal, v. 22, no. 1, p. [2].

Fortas, A., 1944, Letter: Journal of the Association of American State Geologists, v. 15, no. 2, following p. 9.

Groat, C.G., 1988, President's page: The State Geologists Journal, v. 40, p. 1.

Hake, F.F., and Moore, R.C., 1941, Report of conference committee to consider a joint commission on classification and nomenclature of rock units: Journal of the Association of American State Geologists, v. 13, no. 1, p. 10–11.

Hayes, C.W., 1911, The state geological surveys of the United States: U.S. Geological Survey Bulletin 465, 177 p.

Hayes, W.C., 1971, President's page: The State Geologists Journal, v. 23, no. 1.

Hendry, C.W., Jr., 1987, President's page: The State Geologists Journal, v. 39, p. 1.

Johnson, M.E., 1944a, Minutes of the annual meeting, Washington, D.C., February 24–26, 1944: Journal of the Association of American State Geologists, v 15, no. 2, p. 5–9.

Johnson, M.E., 1944b, Report of the retiring editor: Journal of the Association of American State Geologists, v. 15, no. 2, p. 13–14.

Johnson, M.E., 1945a, Annual meeting to be held in Washington, D.C., February 21, 22, and 23, 1945: Journal of the Association of American State Geologists, v. 16, no. 1, p. 5–6.

Johnson, M.E., 1945b, Minutes of the annual meeting, Washington, D.C., February 22–24, 1945: Journal of the Association of American State Geologists, v. 16, no. 2, p. 5–16.

Johnson, M.E., 1946a, Annual meeting of the A.A.S.G. held at Urbana, Ill., February 21–23, 1946, minutes of the meeting: Journal of the Association of American State Geologists, v. 17, no. 2, p. 1–17.

Johnson, M.E., 1946b, Annual meeting to be held in Urbana, Ill., February 21, 22 and 23, 1946: Journal of the Association of American State Geologists, v. 17, no. 1, p. 6–8.

Johnson, M.E., 1946d, Special 40th anniversary number: Journal of the Association of American State Geologists, v. 17, no. 4, p. 3.

Johnson, M.E., 1947, Letter to W.E. Wrather, Director, U.S.G.S., from President Johnson, November 21, 1946: Journal of the Association of American State Geologists, v. 18, no. 1, p. 24.

Jones, W.B., 1947, The election of officers … appointment of Peyton, president-elect: Journal of the Association of American State Geologists, v. 18, no. 2, p. 35.

Jones, W.B., 1948, Minutes of business sessions: Journal of the Association of American State Geologists, v. 19, no. 2, p. 53–68.

Jordan, R.R., 1984, President's page: The State Geologists Journal, v. 36, p. 1.

Journal of the Association of American State Geologists, 1931: Oklahoma: v. 2, no. 3, p. 15.

Journal of the Association of American State Geologists, 1933: v. 1, no. 1, p. 2–3.

Kottlowski, F.E., 1986, President's page: The State Geologists Journal, v. 38, p. 1.

Kummel, H.B., 1941, Early history of the Association: Journal of the Association of American State Geologists, v. 12, no. 3, p. 11–13.

LaMoreaux, P.E., 1972, President's page: An action oriented AASG: The State Geologists Journal, v. 24, no. 1, p. [2].

Landes, K.K., 1933, Minutes of special meeting of Association of American State Geologists, Chicago, Illinois, August 29, 1933: AASG scanned archives, www.stategeologist.org/Group/Archive/djvu/19033ILSpecialMinutes.djvu.

Landes, K.K., 1938, Minutes of annual meeting, Association of American State Geologists, Thursday, Feb. 17, 1938: Journal of the Association of American State Geologists, v. 9, no. 2, p. 22–23.

Leighton, M.M., 1927, Minutes of Association of American State Geologists: AASG scanned archives, www.stategeologists.org.

Leighton, M.M., 1928, Minutes of the Washington, D.C., meeting, April 24, 1928: AASG scanned archives, www.stategeologists.org.

Leighton, M.M., 1929, Minutes of the annual field conference, Oklahoma-Texas, October 5, 1929: AASG scanned archives, www.stategeologists.org.

Leighton, M.M., 1934, The functions of state geological surveys: Journal of the Association of American State Geologists, v. 5, no. 2, p. 4–6.

Leighton, M.M., 1936, The proposed Mineral States Committee: Journal of the Association of American State Geologists, v. 7, no. 4, p. 4–6.

Leighton, M.M., 1949, [Mission statement]: State Geologists Journal, v. 1, no. 1, p. 1.

Leith, C.K., 1941, Strategic minerals, *in* Minutes of annual meeting of Association of American State Geologists, Washington, D.C., February 20–21, 1941: Journal of the Association of American State Geologists, v. 12, no. 2, p. 9.

Lloyd, S.J., 1943, Letter from Lloyd to R.H. Dott, May 3, 1943: Journal of the Association of American State Geologists, v. 14, no. 3, p. 31.

Mankin, C.J., 1969, Minutes of the 61st annual meeting of the Association of American State Geologists, Tucson, Ariz., May 4–8, 1969: AASG scanned archives, www.stategeologists.org/Group/Archive/djvu/1969AZminutes.djvu.

Mankin, C.J., 1976, President's page: The State Geologists Journal, v. 28, no. 1, p. [2].

McGregor, D.J., 1977, President's page: The State Geologists Journal, v. 29, no. 1, p. [2].

Meinzer, O.E., 1940, Ground water surveys, *in* Papers presented at Washington meeting of A.A.S.G., Feb. 1940: Journal of the Association of American State Geologists, v. 11, no. 2, p. 9–12.

Mendenhall, W.C., 1931a, Letter explaining expenses incurred in the cooperative topographic mapping and stream gaging programs: Journal of the Association of American State Geologists, v. 2, no. 2, p. 8–11.

Mendenhall, W.C., 1931b, Letter from acting director of U.S. Geological Survey to Representative H.W. Temple relative to the reinterpretation of the Temple Act: Journal of the Association of American State Geologists, v. 2, no. 4, p. 9–14.

Mendenhall, W.C., 1933, Review of developments since July 23, 1933, incidental to the allotment of federal funds for the use of the U.S. Geological Survey and the U.S. Coast and Geodetic Survey from the funds appropriated for the use of the Federal Administration of Public Works: Journal of the Association of American State Geologists, v. 4, no. 4, p. 17–20.

Miller, D.N., Jr., 1980, President's page: The State Geologists Journal, v. 32, p. 1.

Moore, R.C., 1937a, The annual meeting: Journal of the Association of American State Geologists, v. 8, no. 3, p. 37–38.

Moore, R.C., 1937b, The National Mapping Program: Journal of the Association of American State Geologists, v. 8, no. 4, p. 33–38.

Moore, R.C., 1937c, Time and place of meetings of the association: Journal of the Association of American State Geologists, v. 8, no. 4, p. 29–33.

Moore, R.C., 1938a, Record of the meeting of the American Association of State Geologists held in Washington, D.C., December 30–31, 1937: Journal of the Association of American State Geologists, v. 9, no. 1, p. 33–37.

Moore, R.C., 1938b, War materials: Journal of the Association of American State Geologists, v. 9, no. 3, p. 6–10.

Moore, R.C., 1939, The October issue of the journal: Journal of the Association of American State Geologists, v. 10, no. 1, p. 3–4.

Moore, R.C., 1941, Letter on proposed permanent commission on stratigraphic nomenclature to W.C. Mendenhall, May 21, 1941: Journal of the Association of American State Geologists, v. 12, no. 3, p. 21–25.

Moore, R.C., 1941, Letter on proposed permanent commission on stratigraphic nomenclature to W.C. Mendenhall, July 5, 1941: Journal of the Association of American State Geologists, v. 12, no. 4, p. 18–21.

Moore, R.C., 1941, [President's message]: Journal of the Association of American State Geologists, v. 12, no. 2, p. 4.

New York Times, 1932, A needed map [editorial published in the *New York Times,* May 24, 1932, on topographic mapping]: Journal of the Association of American State Geologists, v. 3, no. 3, p. 14.

Nixon, E.K., 1942, Advisory Committee on War Matters: Journal of the Association of American State Geologists, v. 13, no. 4, p. 17–18.

Nixon, E.K., 1943, National trend inimical to state geological organizations: Journal of the Association of American State Geologists, v. 14, no. 4, p. 7–9.

Ostrom, M.E., 1983, President's page: The State Geologists Journal, v. 35, p. 1.

Price, P.H., 1940, Minutes of annual meeting of Association of American State Geologists, Washington, D.C., February 15, 16, 1940: Journal of the Association of American State Geologists, v. 11, no. 2, p. 5a.

Price, P.H., Dott, R.H., and Moore, R.C., 1947, Amendment to "Outline of Organization," the Association of American State Geologists: Journal of the Association of American State Geologists, v. 18, no. 1, p. 4–7.

Reynolds, H.A., 1932, Letter from secretary of Massachusetts Forestry Association relative to status of organization of Massachusetts land economic survey: Journal of the Association of American State Geologists, v. 3, no. 1, p. 20–21.

Roosevelt, F.D., 1935, Letter to G.C. Branner, Nov. 23, 1935: Journal of the Association of American State Geologists, v. 6, no. 4, p. 6.

Roosevelt, F.D., 1938, Letter to Carl E. Bailey, governor of Arkansas, Feb. 21, 1938: Journal of the Association of American State Geologists, v. 9, no. 2, p. 21.

Sales, R.N., 1934, Government surveys and the mining industry from the view-point of the mining geologist: Journal of the Association of American State Geologists, v. 5, no. 2, p. 8.

Sayers, R.R., 1944, Letter to Association of American State Geologists, March 27, 1944: Journal of the Association of American State Geologists, v. 15, no. 2, p. 10–11.

Sayers, R.R., 1945, Letter to W.C. Broadgate: Journal of the Association of American State Geologists, v. 16, no. 3, p. 9.

Socolow, A.A., 1978, President's page: The State Geologists Journal, v. 30, no. 1, p. [2–3].

Staack, J.G., 1933, Statement regarding status of topographic mapping in the United States, June 30, 1932: Journal of the Association of American State Geologists, v. 4, no. 3, p. 9–12.

Staack, J.G., 1940, Presentation at 1940 AASG annual meeting, *in* Price, P.H., Minutes of annual meeting of Association of American State Geologists, Washington, D.C., February 15, 16, 1940: AASG scanned archives, www.stategeologists.org/Group/ Archive/djvu/1940DCminutes.djvu.

Strauss, M.W., 1945, Letter to T. Millet Hand: Journal of the Association of American State Geologists, v. 16, no. 3, p. 10–11.

Troxell, E.L., 1946, Reactions, recorded and reported: Journal of the Association of American State Geologists, v. 17, no. 4, p. 11.

Weaver, K.N., 1974, President's page: The State Geologists Journal, v. 26, no. 1, p. [2].

White, G., 1947, The role of state surveys in problems of water supply: Journal of the Association of American State Geologists, v. 18, no. 2, p. 16–19.

Wilby, F.B., 1935, Report of the Board of Surveys and Maps: Journal of the Association of American State Geologists, v. 35, no. 1, p. 32–33.

Williams, N.F., 1973, President's page: The State Geologists Journal, v. 25, no. 1, p. [2].

Ian Campbell, an Exemplary State Geologist, and the Ian Campbell Medal

Robert R. Jordan *(Delaware, Honorary)*

T here is much to be learned from the example of Ian Campbell and from the story of how the medal, the American Geological Institute's highest award, was established, sustained, and enhanced. Only a truly outstanding person could possibly have inspired the gratitude, loyalty, emotion, and commitment that comprise this story.

For months in 1978 we quietly passed word about it. There was no e-mail, cell phone network, or text messaging then, but in meetings, telephone calls, and letters, word of Ian Campbell's medical condition was sought. Of course there was concern for Ian and for Kitty, but there was also a sense of disbelief that such a good and valued person could suffer cancer. The group involved was large, vaguely defined, and not exclusively geologists. But it was geologists, especially state geologists, who were touched so meaningfully by Ian Campbell in their definition of themselves and of their subject in a changing world with new fields of endeavor. When his suffering ended on February 11, 1978, there was a spontaneous sense that he must be memorialized and that his example must be held up to benefit geologists and geology of the future.

Perhaps it was Ian's commitment as state geologist of California from 1959 to 1969, in a position where his abilities shined so brilliantly, that made those qualities so particularly appreciated by state geologists with similar responsibilities and evoked a strong, immediate response, that prompted this desire for a memorial. It is unclear who first advanced the idea of a fund; perhaps the need was so obvious that it was one of those rare concepts that appear without specific authorship. It was a simultaneous reaction that spread in our community—a sense that we must seek expression of the honor we owed a dear friend. AASG, with the leadership of President Arthur Socolow and the Executive Committee of State Geologists Erwin, Miller, Jordan, Slaughter, Howe, and Noble, asked for contributions to establish a medal in Ian's memory. The significance of this action lies in the immediate, generous, and heartfelt response. It was my duty as treasurer to receive the contributions, and I am moved to this day by the sincerity with which they were offered. Ian Campbell was clearly a great, beneficial influence on his colleagues, and they responded with affection and gratitude.

Why was Ian Campbell so special? State geologists generally came from scholarship that signaled authenticity and objectivity into conspicuous careers of dedication to service. Moreover, in the 1960's and 70's the science itself was undergoing a revolution, and new heroes were being created. Why was Campbell exceptional in a population of great geologists?

In large part the answer is in his contribution to the profession: He served geologists. And he knew and led others to understand that individually and collectively their support depended on public acceptance of the usefulness of geology. Further, he convinced us that service to the profession and the public is a worthy, noble, and rewarding responsibility. Ian brought uncommon wisdom and judgment and firm, gentle determination to the subject. He was liked, he was appreciated, and his guidance was not only accepted, it was sought. He never seemed too busy to help students, colleagues, organizations, or agencies. "Gentleman," "statesman," and "class" were words used at the mention of Ian Campbell. Former AASG President Norman Williams, a deceptively shrewd judge, said simply: "Ian added class to any company."

Ian Campbell was born in Bismarck, N.D., in 1899. He served in action in World War I. He had memorable adventures exploring the country by motorcycle in the 20's on his way to a B.S. from the University of Oregon. He earned the Sc.D. in geology from Harvard in 1931. Dr. Campbell joined the faculty of the California Institute of Technology in 1931, and continued as a highly respected teacher into 1959. While a Harvard graduate student, Ian married Catherine Chase. It is noteworthy that Catherine (Kitty) Campbell was the first woman to receive a doctorate in geology from Harvard and that she also had a distinguished career in geology and technical writing and editing. Ian moved from Caltech to state geologist of California in 1959, and served in that office until reaching mandatory retirement age in 1969.

A biographical sketch provides some orientation in time and space, but does little to capture the color, the essence, needed to explain the significance of the man and the award. AASG was, of course, not alone in its grief. Moving and informative tributes from other segments of the geologic community testified to Dr. Campbell's scope of involvement and influence;

see memorials by Richard H. Jahns (1982), Gordon B. Oakeshott (1979), Charles W. Chesterman (1979), and Robert P. Sharp (1978). An absolutely remarkable document kindly brought to my attention by the late Marcus Milling of the American Geological Institute is an oral history conducted by Eleanor Swent in 1989, titled "Ian and Catherine Campbell, Geologists: Teaching, Government Service, Editing."

To suggest the unique complexity of Ian Campbell's life, we may note his treasured Scottish heritage, upbringing on a North Dakota sheep ranch and Oregon cherry orchard, volunteered service in World War I, his valued medal from Harley-Davidson, work with the Boy Scouts, oil companies, mining companies, USGS, the World War II draft board, Athenaeum Club, and on and on. There is a common thread: quality service. Throughout this long whirlwind, Catherine supported him in 48 years of marriage. And Dr. Catherine Campbell had a distinguished career of her own, including an award as "Miss Federal Employee 1960."

This hints at the complexity and profundity of the man. More of his essence that will always be important is found in his own words. See especially his foreword to the first edition of AGI's *Glossary of Geology* (Campbell, 1972) and his remarkable GSA presidential address, "Mene, Mene, Tekel, Upharsin" (Campbell, 1969).

AASG found, in the words of the original proposal transmitted by President Robert B. Erwin in 1978, "… the most appropriate recognition of Ian Campbell's illustrious professional career would be … a medal as recognition of singular performance in and contribution to the profession of geology." AASG, to its credit, and despite the almost possessive passion of its members, understood Campbell's scope exceeded even the vast interests of AASG. That medal, therefore, should have the highest pedestal, the most inclusive constituency, that of the American Geological Institute. Moreover, it was recommended that the wide, prominent stage of the Geological Society of America be the place for this highest award.

The AGI Executive Committee approved the AASG proposal, but the Governing Board raised questions at its November 11, 1979, meeting. Colleagues during Dr. Campbell's long teaching career felt the award should specifically benefit students, in keeping with his spirit. The proposal was tabled. It is important to forever remember that the merits of academic, research, and professional contributions were debated and settled at the birth of the AGI Medal in Memory of Ian Campbell. *Service* to the profession emerged as the unique, encompassing quality of Ian Campbell that was to be honored and perpetuated. Teaching and research excellence are essential; they have many established forms of commendation. But broad, generous, overriding service *in addition* defines the unique nature of Campbell and the Campbell Medal.

Jahns's memorial (1982, p. 4) contains the fundamental differentiation of Ian Campbell. After his work on World War II projects and return to full-time teaching at Caltech

> he had by now realized that neither the 24-hour day nor his own remarkable energies could accommodate all the operations that appealed to him. This resulted in a conscious and genuinely humble decision, made with Kitty's help, to shape the remainder of his career along "people-oriented" lines. Thus geology lost a competent researcher, but retained an active scholar, an able teacher, and an increasingly influential statesman.

On June 12, 1980, Meredith Ostrom revived the proposal for the Campbell Medal in the meeting of the AGI Governing Board. As approved, the proposal includes "... Ian's distinguished career would serve as a standard against which nominees for the medal should be measured." Throughout this process, Charles Mankin patiently explained to AGI member societies the merits and unique aspects of the AASG proposal. The first Campbell Medal was presented to Richard H. Jahns at the GSA Awards Banquet of November 4, 1981. AGI has been a responsible, conscientious steward of the Campbell legacy and GSA has continued to lend its broad stage to the award. The commendable attention of those organizations is complemented by the special interest of AASG in the award. Clearly it is *not* an award of or for AASG. It originated there for many deep reasons, most obviously because of the remarkable resonance of Campbell's virtues with the objectives and sensitivities of state geologists. That special interest continues and, as memories dim, is increasingly important. AGI's award is determined by a committee with representation from four of the member societies that Ian led as their president (AASG, AGI, GSA, and Mineralogical Society of America) and from the geologic community at large. Nominations are accepted from member societies; AASG has had an active committee for this purpose, chaired for many years by Donald Haney (Kentucky).

Past Ian Campbell awardees are (AASG members in bold):

1981   Richard H. Jahns
1983   Hollis D. Hedberg
1984   Konrad B. Krauskopf
1985   Robert L. Heller
1986   William B. Heroy Jr.
1987   Charles J. Mankin Jr. (Oklahoma)
1988   John D. Haun
1989   Grover E. Murray
1990   Philip E. LaMoreaux (Alabama)

1991   **William L. Fisher (Texas)**
1992   **Donald C. Haney (Kentucky)**
1993   **Peter T. Flawn (Texas)**
1994   Dallas L. Peck
1995   Gordon P. Eaton
1996   **Robert R. Jordan (Delaware)**
1997   M. Gordon (Reds) Wolman
1998   **Charles G. (Chip) Groat (Louisiana)**
1999   **Priscilla C.P. Grew (Minnesota)**
2000   Luna P. Leopold
2001   **Kenneth N. Weaver (Maryland)**
2002   Frank H.T. Rhodes
2003   Edward C. Roy Jr.
2004   **Ernest A. Mancini (Alabama)**
2005   Samuel S. Adams
2006   Robert D. Hatcher Jr.
2007   **Arthur A. Socolow (Pennsylvania)**

With the passage of time, we have lost many of those who directly, personally felt the touch of Ian Campbell. The purpose of honoring Ian is as valid as ever, but of growing importance is the need to illuminate the example of Campbell as an inspiration to future generations of geologists. The torch has inevitably passed. Ian Campbell has been a personal hero, but time shifts growing importance to the symbolism of his example. That symbol is a gift that can inspire and reward those who accept it and understand its deep significance. During its 2004 annual meeting at Stevenson, Wash., AASG's Campbell Medal Subcommittee (Donald Haney, chair) and the Honorary Members Committee (Robert Jordan, chair) considered concerns that memories of the intent and the procedures inherent in the AGI Medal in Memory of Ian Campbell had faded and that AASG should bring renewed attention to the cherished award.

AASG received and approved a resolution to create a fund to restore and enhance the Campbell Medal. The honorary members undertook to raise $12,500, to be matched by AASG. Under Haney's leadership, the goal was accomplished and exceeded. AASG graciously met its obligation. The institutional values rose to complement personal affection in commendable fashion. History was repeated—after a quarter century, the indelible appreciation and generosity of the original memorial effort resurfaced. A committee of Haney, Ernest Mancini, and Jordan recommended a home for the new funds at the GSA Foundation, and this action was agreed to March 21, 2005, with the signatures of David A. Stephenson, president of the GSA Foundation, John W. Hess, executive director of GSA, and Robert G. Marvinney, president of AASG.

The minutes and archives of AASG, AGI, GSA, and GSAF should be consulted whenever guidance is needed about the purpose or administration of AGI's Medal in Memory of Ian Campbell, GSAF's Ian Campbell Endowed Fund, and AASG's Campbell Medal Subcommittee. The fund management agreement exists between AASG, GSAF, and GSA:

> The purpose of the Fund is to support reasonable costs to [AGI, GSA, AASG, and MSA]...in the award of the AGI Medal in Memory of Ian Campbell as one of the most prestigious awards presented during the Presidential Address and Awards Ceremony at the Annual Meeting of GSA; and to support reasonable costs to AGI, GSA, AASG, and MSA in recognition of the Campbell Medalist in their respective publications and meetings.... Disbursements of the income from this fund will be directed by the Executive Director of AGI.

It has been the intention of AASG to sustain the memory of Ian Campbell in order to honor him and hold forth his example for all geologists. This is to be accomplished in his generous spirit, together with AGI, GSA, and, indeed, the geologic community he served uniquely well. Ian Campbell's cancer was diagnosed in 1965. Some of his greatest achievements occurred during a long remission while carrying a burden most could not suspect. Contemplate Mount Ian Campbell in the Sierra Nevada, consider a taste of Laphroaig Islay malt, and take some comfort in Catherine's words: "Our last trip to the East Coast was to an Association of American State Geologists meeting in Newark, Delaware. As always, the State Geologists meetings were great fun" (Campbell, 1989).

References Cited

Campbell, C.C., 1989, Ian and Catherine Campbell geologists: Teaching, government service, editing: An oral history conducted by Eleanor Swent, Regional Oral History Office, The Bancroft Library, University of California, Berkeley.

Campbell, I., 1969, Mene, mene, tekel, upharsin: Geological Society of American Bulletin, v. 80, p. 553–560.

Campbell, I., 1972, Forward, in Gary, M.G., McAfee, R., Jr., and Wolf, C.L., eds, Glossary of geology: Washington, D.C., American Geological Institute, p. vii–ix.

Chesterman, C.W., 1979, Memorial of Ian Campbell: American Mineralogist, v. 64, p. 669–670.

Jahns, R.H., 1982, Memorial to Ian Campbell 1899–1978: Geological Society of America Memorials, p. 1–9.

Oakeshott, G.B., 1979, Ian Campbell (1899–1978): American Association of Petroleum Geologists Bulletin, v. 63, p. 150–152.

Sharp, R.B., 1978, Recollections of Ian Campbell: California Institute of Technology Journal, March-April, p. 32–34.

Genevieve Atwood,
the First Woman State Geologist

Adapted and expanded from a 1996 interview for the Governor's Commission on
Women and Families in celebration of Utah's Statehood Centennial

(womenscommission.utah.gov/Atwood.pdf)

In 1981, Gov. Scott Matheson appointed Genevieve Atwood as the first woman geologist to head Utah's geological survey. Geology at that time was almost completely the province of men. Genevieve was the first woman to head a state geological survey in the United States and perhaps the world. Her appointment surprised some observers not only because she was a woman but because she was young, had served in the legislature, came from an engineering firm rather than a mining background, was non-Mormon although a fifth-generation Utahan, and had a reputation as a champion for social justice.

As a woman in her scientific profession, Genevieve faced many challenges. Entry-level jobs in her male-dominated field went mainly to men. Awkward situations developed on required field trips. A man-woman field team was still not accepted as appropriate by many organizations. Regulations did not allow her to work in underground mines.

Genevieve's first geology job was at the National Academy of Sciences in Washington, D.C., where she worked on environmental and resource issues. "We saw suggestions from our reports become law so fast, it almost made you blink. You said, 'This system is not too slow; this system is almost too fast!' At the NAS I saw the scientist's power as a policy maker."

In 1974, Genevieve was elected to the Utah State Legislature at age 28. She was an anomaly in Utah politics, holding a position of political power while young, female, and non-Mormon. Her colleagues needed support and votes, and Genevieve was willing to listen. She gained credibility for her knowledge. While serving in the House from 1974–80, she successfully sponsored major legislation, including Utah's Surface Mining Reclamation Act, the Utah Seismic Safety Advisory Council Act, and Utah's Open and Public Meetings Law ("sunshine law"). "There are a tremendous number of public policy issues that involve science. When you are a legislator and have a scientific background and connections, you can make a difference the minute you place a phone call from the floor."

The state legislature is a part-time position in Utah. During her years in the legislature, Genevieve worked as a geologist for an engineering firm, its first woman professional.

> Gradually, my salary and responsibilities went up. I had originally been willing to work for what they paid the rodman on the survey team. Working with engineers was another eye-opener for me. Geologists want to know why something happens. Engineers want to know what's going to happen.

> How did I become state geologist of Utah? Gov. Scott M. Matheson wanted women heads of agencies, he knew me from working together on neighborhood issues, he wanted the Utah Geological and Mineral Survey to provide information about natural hazards, and he knew I was gutsy and relatively non-partisan because I had crossed party lines to support some of his legislation such as a hike in gasoline taxes. I had lost an election bid for State Senate and I leapt at the opportunity.

> Allen Agnew, former state geologist of South Dakota, cautioned me that heading a survey would be more than providing timely advice to the executive branch, that it would take all my time and all my management skills, that I would have to learn fast, hire good people, and call on the AASG for advice. Eugene Callaghan, who had retired from Utah after serving as state geologist of New Mexico, became a personal coach, as did an ad hoc Nurturing Committee of the AASG comprised of Ken Weaver (Maryland), John Rold (Colorado), and Jack Simon (Illinois). I'd get these phone calls from John with his good natured "How's it going" and then we'd talk over some major or minor matter. Don McMillan, the previous Utah Geological Survey director, graciously shared his time and never interfered. Bill Williams of Arkansas taught me some culture and eventually figured I was OK. Soon Priscilla Grew (Minnesota) joined the ranks of state geologists and Vicki Cowart (Colorado), a buddy of mine in the Association for Women Geoscientists, became the Colorado state geologist and an AASG stalwart.

> I was appointed state geologist in 1981. At first it was a bit rough. Even before I arrived, a staff member retired because she "wouldn't work for a woman" and within the first month four more staff left in response to conflicts in management style. My vision for the survey was expansionist during the 1980's times of contraction. The survey budget and staff doubled. Our funding base changed from federal grants to state general funds and from mineral and energy resource studies to quadrangle geologic mapping. A timely earthquake and USGS collaboration led to a major program to better understand seismic hazards along the Wasatch Front. The flooding of Great Salt Lake and

landslides of 1982–87 showed the value of hazards identification. I argued that the best approach was to respect the earth, to avoid problems rather than to solve them later, to understand the flooding of Great Salt Lake rather than attempt to control it. Sometimes I was heard and sometimes not. I left the survey in 1989. I had promised myself to stay at least 5 years and not more than 10. It was hard to leave.

What mattered most at the survey was the staff. I worked as the "outside person," always ready to give timely earth science advice to local and state agencies. Don Mabey, formerly an administrator and distinguished geophysicist with the USGS, was the "inside person," always there for the staff. Geologists of the Utah Geological Survey are self-motivated, dedicated, professional. My job was to get them funding and focus on mission. The staff figured out how best to get the work done well. Utah is safer, richer, and better understood geologically for their work.

I'm a smattering of the many things you can do as an earth scientist. You can work for a not-for-profit, private industry, or government. You can be a policy-maker or a grunt worker. You can make a difference at every level.

Following Genevieve Atwood were Priscilla C. Grew (Minnesota, 1986–93), Vicki J. Cowart (Colorado, 1992–2003), Diane Conrad (Vermont, 1991–95), Lisbeth Hyman (Puerto Rico), Vicki S. McConnell (Oregon, 2003–present), Rebecca C. White (Arkansas, 2005–present), and Margaret A. Thomas (Connecticut, 2006–present). Though not a state geologist, Winifred Goldring served as the New York state paleontologist from 1939 to 1954, and was the first woman to hold that position in the United States. Vicki Cowart served as vice president, president-elect, president, and past-president of the Association from 1999 to 2003. Vicki McConnell was elected secretary of AASG in 2007.

Raymond C. Moore Portrait Sketches

Rex Buchanan *(Kansas, Associate)*

Raymond C. Moore (1892–1974) was the director of the Kansas Geological Survey and state geologist of Kansas from 1916 to 1954. He was also, at various times, the chair of the geology department at the University of Kansas (KU). In 1958, he was named the Solon E. Summerfield Distinguished Professor of Geology at KU. He was the founder of the *Treatise on Invertebrate Paleontology*, published by the Geological Society of America and KU. He was the author or co-author of the widely used books *Invertebrate Fossils*, *Historical Geology*, and *Introduction to Historical Geology*, all published by McGraw-Hill. He was closely identified with the concept of cyclic deposition of rock units in the Midcontinent, and credited with an almost-encyclopedic knowledge of invertebrate fossils. He edited various journals, won scientific awards and medals, and headed several geological societies, including serving as president of the Association of American State Geologists in 1941–42.

But Moore had other talents. Among the more notable and developed was drawing. His early field work resulted in numerous sketches of the geology where he was working. In 1923, for example, Moore was part of a U.S. Geological Survey expedition that was studying the geology of, and looking for dam sites in, the Grand Canyon. While that expedition resulted in numerous photographs of the canyon, Moore also generated a number of sketches of the rock units, faults, unconformities, and other geologic features that he saw.

In some respects, it is almost as if Moore grew up in an earlier time in terms of the practice of geology. Before the advent of photography, drawing geologic features was standard operating procedure, and artists were often a part of geologic field parties. While photography had largely replaced drawing by the time Moore came of age in the early 20th century,

Moore continued to draw and sketch throughout his career (though he did not eschew photography; Moore regularly took photographs of roadcuts and other features, often marking on them with ink to highlight the features that he particularly wanted viewers to notice). Drawing may have provided Moore with another way of looking at the world. To draw something, an artist must look at it deliberately—study it carefully with the eye—in ways that are unnecessary when you simply point a camera at the outcrop and push a button. The result of drawing may be that geologists see outcrops more carefully, and thus learn things about the rocks that they do not learn by a cursory glance through a camera viewfinder.

Throughout his career, Moore also drew many of the figures used in his books. He drew maps and block diagrams of the land. He sketched the world in the geologic past, as he envisioned it, particularly focusing on the appearance of the Kansas landscape during the Pennsylvanian and Permian Periods. My favorite Moore sketch depicts nothing but sky and a featureless ocean, his representation of Kansas covered by a Pennsylvanian sea.

But Moore drew more than geology. He drew people. In his Grand Canyon field notes, for example, is a sketch of a member of the Navajo tribe that he encountered at Lees Ferry, Ariz. He was soon drawing colleagues from throughout the geologic community. In 1929 he painted a large oil portrait of Erasmus Haworth, a previous director of the Kansas Geological Survey who died in 1932, that remains in the Survey's archives.

In the 1940's, his pencil sketches of other state geologists began showing up on the cover of *The State Geologists Journal*. These are sketches done with soft pencil on a textured paper. The drawings nearly always depict their subjects in a formal pose, from the shoulders up. The subjects generally look directly out at the viewer, though in some cases they look to the side or off into the distance. Some of these drawings were likely based on photographs, and thus the subjects often display the same sort of pose and attitude that they would in photos. The background of the portraits is generally left white or blank, again giving the sketches a certain formality, though at least one portrait has a dark background that gives it a more casual feel. The style does not change dramatically over time, though it does appear that the more sketches he drew, the more assured he became.

At least 18 portraits of state geologists sketched by Raymond C. Moore appeared on covers of the *AASG Journal* from 1941 to 1948 (Figs. 4–5). For a journal produced by mimeograph technology of the day, the *Journal* was adorned by skillful and elegant artwork at least for a time. The list below gives the names of the state geologists whose portrait sketches appeared on the cover of the *Journal*. The appearance of the portrait usually indicates that the *Journal* also printed a biographical sketch of that person.

Chief Buehler (Missouri)	v. 12, no. 3	7/15/41
George H. Ashley (Pennsylvania)	v. 12, no. 4	10/15/41
Henry B. Kummel (New Jersey)	v. 13, no. 1	1/15/42
Morris M. Leighton (Illinois),	v. 13, no. 1	1/15/42
Frank W. De Wolf (Illinois),	v. 13, no. 1	1/15/42
H. Foster Bain (Illinois)	v. 13, no. 2	4/15/42
Edward B. Mathews (Maryland)	v. 13, no. 3	7/15/42
Richard A. Smith (Michigan)	v. 14, no. 4	10/15/43
George F. Kay (Iowa)	v. 15, no. 1	1/15/44
Arthur C. Bevan (Virginia)	v. 15, no. 2	4/15/44
Elias H. Sellards (Florida, Texas)	v. 15, no. 4	10/15/44
William H. Emmons (Minnesota)	v. 16, no. 1	1/15/45
Walter W. Bradley (California)	v. 16, no. 2	4/15/45
Francis A. Thomson (Montana)	v. 16, no. 3	7/15/45
Herman Gunter (Florida)	v. 17, no. 1	1/15/46
Edgar P. Rothrock (South Dakota)	v. 17, no. 4	10/15/46
Ernest F. Bean (Wisconsin)	v. 18, no. 2	4/15/47
Edward L. Troxell (Connecticut)	v. 19, no. 2	4/15/48

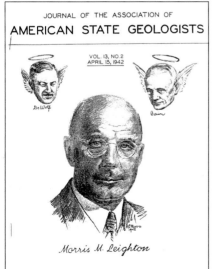

Figure 4. Moore's cover portrait of Morris M. Leighton (Illinois), with Frank De Wolf (Illinois; upper left) and H. Foster Bain (Illinois; upper right).

Figure 5. Moore's cover portrait of Edward B. Mathews (Maryland).

In all, these sketches provide a different way of looking at people, almost as if he was using art to reveal things about and help understand his subjects, the way he used sketches to help him see new things about geology. In some sense, they could be viewed as an expression of affection on Moore's part. Moore was not an easy person to deal with. He could be domineering and demanding. He had scientific and personal conflicts with colleagues that sometimes endured for decades. Yet he drew portraits of many of these same colleagues, portraits that must serve as some token of regard (though Moore's name is nearly always signed prominently, as if he wants to make sure that the subject of the portrait did not receive all the attention).

Certainly, at least some of the subjects of the sketches felt that a Moore portrait was a compliment. If nothing else, it meant that Moore was willing to take time away from professional projects and devote it to a colleague. More than likely, other members of the geologic community depicted in these sketches were pleased with the result too, regardless of their scientific differences with Moore. More than a half century later, these portraits provide another way, one that will probably not be repeated, of viewing some of the major players in the geologic community in the middle of the 1900's.

Some of the information presented here is based on Maples and Buchanan (1989), Buchanan and Maples (1992), and personal conversations with William W. Hambleton.

References Cited

Buchanan, R., and Maples, C.G., 1992, R.C. Moore and the concepts of sea-level change in the Midcontinent, *in* Dott, R.H., Jr., ed., Eustasy: The historical ups and downs of a major geological concept: Geological Society of America, Memoir 180, p. 73–82.

Maples, C.G., and Buchanan, R., 1989, Raymond Cecil Moore (1892–1974): Memorial and bibliography, *in* Celebration of the 100th anniversary of the Kansas Geological Survey: Journal of Paleontology, Memoir 25, 29 p.

The Honorary Members Caucus

Morris W. (Brud) Leighton *(Illinois, Honorary)*

No doubt, the Honorary Members Caucus came about as a result of continued references to encourage the utilization of this group's talents and expertise by both the honorary members and regular members of the AASG over a period of time. In his June 1993 report of the AASG Honorary Members Committee at Coeur d'Alene, Idaho, Robert Jordan (Delaware) recommended that the AASG continue "to utilize this outstanding pool of talent in the conduct of the Association's business when appropriate" (Jordan, 1993). When he was president, Donald Hoskins (Pennsylvania) wrote Morris Leighton (Illinois) on December 24, 1994, that

> following the 1994 AASG Annual meeting, Allen Agnew on behalf of Honorary Members, suggested that a specific time period be dedicated during future AASG meetings so that Honorary Members can convene for communications and fellowship (Hoskins, 1994).

Hoskins stated that he planned to provide such a time and location during the 1995 AASG meeting in Reno, Nev., and asked Leighton to contact fellow honorary members to make arrangements with them, including the development of an agenda for discussion. This was to be a meeting coordinated with but separate from the Honorary Members Committee chaired by Robert Jordan, which had been meeting at least annually to provide the Executive Committee and AASG membership its recommendations regarding eligibility and qualifications of those nominated as honorary members. This appears to be the beginning of the Honorary Members Caucus as separate from the Honorary Members Committee. The latter committee was composed of honorary members appointed by the president, while the former was to include all honorary members attending the annual meeting.

During the June 12, 1995, caucus meeting in Reno, an agenda item was added under "Other Items" and identified as "Honorary Members as a Resource Base." Leighton, in his June 12 report on the caucus to those in attendance at the annual meeting wrote, "We encourage the members to continue to consider us as a resource base. As Bill Fisher put it, help is available and it's fairly cheap" (Leighton, 1995). Then at the midyear meeting (fall of 1995), the honorary members recommended that there be a more formal involvement of honorary members in the activities of the AASG (Jordan, 1996). On January 31, 1996, Walter Schmidt (Florida) wrote to the honorary members indicating that any increase in the Executive Committee's ability to expand honorary members' participation and involvement was clearly a win-win situation. He noted that Past-president Hoskins and he had invited honorary members to participate with the Liaison Committee's activities. He wrote, "Based on a recent discussion with Art Socolow, I anticipate a proposal to the membership to formalize Honorary Member participation/membership on our Executive Committee" (Schmidt, 1996). Schmidt solicited thoughts and suggestions in this regard from other honorary members before the end of February.

In a follow-up, as noted by Jordan in his report of the Honorary Members Committee at the 1996 annual meeting in Virginia, "the Executive Committee recommended that there be an Honorary Members Spokesperson, chosen by the Honorary Members, as an advisor to the Executive Committee" (Jordan, 1996). The spokesperson would have a voice but no vote. The Honorary Members Committee endorsed the Executive Committee's proposal, and the honorary members implemented the proposal at the 1996 meeting by electing Arthur Socolow (Pennsylvania) to serve as the first spokesperson for the honorary members on the Executive Committee. As an advisory member of the Executive Committee, the spokesperson would also serve in that capacity on the Liaison Committee. Socolow was succeeded by Kenneth Weaver (Maryland) at the 1997 annual meeting during the caucus of honorary members, and served from 1997 to 1998. At the caucus of honorary members at the next annual meeting, held in June 1998 in Portland, Maine, and again at the annual meeting in Alaska in June 1999, Stephen Conrad (North Carolina) was elected as the honorary members' representative to the Executive Committee. He served from 1998 to 2000. Donald Haney (Kentucky) was elected to succeed Conrad in June 2000 at the caucus of honorary members, and remained as the elected representative from 2000 to 2007.

In 2006 at the midyear meeting in Philadelphia, the Association's bylaws were changed so that the Honorary Members Committee was expanded to include all honorary members, and the Honorary Members Caucus was disbanded. Its business was to be handled by the re-formed Honorary Members Committee. At the annual meeting in 2007 in Florida, the Honorary Members Committee, under the new system established by the bylaws, submitted to the Executive Committee their list of candidates for spokesperson to serve on the AASG Executive Committee. Emery Cleaves (Maryland) was selected by the Executive Committee to be that person.

Both the Honorary Members Committee and the Honorary Members Caucus, while in existence, made it a general practice to submit separate reports to the membership at the annual meeting for a number of years, and the expanded Honorary Members Committee continues to do so.

References Cited

Hoskins, D.M., 1994, Letter of December 29, 1994, from Donald M. Hoskins, president AASG, to Morris Leighton, emeritus state geologist, Illinois: Illinois State Geological Survey Archives.

Jordan, R.R., 1993, Report of the AASG Honorary Members Committee: Submitted to the AASG secretary and Honorary Members Committee: AASG annual meeting, June 5–8, 1993, Coeur d'Alene, Idaho: Illinois State Geological Survey Archives.

Jordan, R.R., 1996, Report of the AASG Honorary Members Committee: AASG annual meeting, Charlottesville, Va., June 2–4, 1996.

Leighton, M.W., 1995, Report of Honorary Members Caucus, December 12, 1995: Submitted to the AASG secretary and delivered orally to meeting attendees: Illinois State Geological Survey Archives.

Schmidt, W., 1996, Memo on "formal role" of our honorary members written to honorary members of AASG on January 31, 1996: Illinois State Geological Survey Archives.

The Pick and Gavel Award

Larry D. Woodfork *(West Virginia, Honorary)*

The 100th anniversary in 2008 of the founding of the Association of American State Geologists is a propitious event, an occasion to celebrate and reflect on our history. That is the purpose of this centennial volume. When its coordinator and editor, James Cobb (Kentucky), asked me to provide a personal account of the history of our Pick and Gavel Award, I considered the opportunity to be a privilege and honor, because the award has now become arguably the most widely received legacy of my presidency (1998-99) of AASG.

The history of the Pick and Gavel Award is best understood in context. The award itself was but one element—albeit now proven to be a very important one—in a much broader and more comprehensive strategy and agenda that I proposed to enhance and elevate AASG's image, recognition, and general public visibility, and improve its internal organizational operation and provide opportunity for greater involvement of its members and their staff in its affairs.

When I assumed the presidency in 1998 following our annual meeting in Portland, Maine, I presented the membership with a point-by-point agenda of what I hoped to accomplish during my term. At that time, our organization already had a 90-year history of substantial accomplishment and significant influence—a very solid platform for additional progress. Much of the agenda that I proposed to enhance and elevate our public image, internal operations, and opportunity for greater participation of the membership and their staff in Association activities was accomplished. AASG was incorporated as a not-for-profit corporation in the state of Delaware, with Robert Jordan as its registered agent there, thus providing the Association with legal identity and indemnifying its officers. Our constitution and bylaws were amended to allow the use of modern electronic communication to conduct our business in an orderly, timely, year-round basis; thus, in essence, allowing a continuous, ongoing "virtual annual meeting." A new, officially recognized category of affiliation, associates, was created to recognize the contributions of state geological survey staff members to AASG's activities. Unfortunately, a major initiative that I proposed and pursued—a congressional charter for AASG—was not accomplished. Although a bill to provide AASG with a federal congressional charter was introduced in the House of Representatives by Rep. Nick Rahall (D-West Virginia) and cosponsored by Rep. Jim Gibbons (R-Nevada), the potential importance of this initiative to the future of AASG was never well understood nor widely supported by our membership and therefore never gained traction and failed.

In contrast, although as with all new initiatives, there was some initial skepticism concerning the Pick and Gavel Award within the membership when I presented the concept, it proved to have a greater destiny. The Pick and Gavel Award was commissioned by the Executive Committee and endorsed by most of the membership. The award itself was intended to provide an appropriate, long-needed mechanism for AASG to officially reach out to recognize and honor outstanding meritorious persons outside of AASG who supported our mission and activities or made significant contributions to advancing or facilitating the role of the geosciences in the public-policy arena. An additional benefit of recognizing and honoring meritorious persons of high stature with a prestigious award, presented in a highly visible and widely publicized ceremony held in an appropriate venue, is that AASG would bask in the reflected honor cast by the event and thus promote, enhance, and elevate its own public image.

The nature and form of the award as conceived was meant to convey a message relating the earth sciences to public policy. Rather than the usual plaque or certificate, the Pick and Gavel Award would consist of a unique museum-quality mineral, fossil, or rock specimen, suitably mounted or framed, with an inscribed image of a geologist's pick crossed by a gavel and overlain by an outline of the nation's Capitol. The geologist's pick is a traditional symbol of geologic enterprise, the gavel symbolizes deliberative process, and the nation's Capitol represents the arena where the earth sciences converge with deliberative process and play a key role in formulating enlightened public policy.

The event chosen for the presentation of the Pick and Gavel Award was AASG's annual spring liaison meeting in Washington, D.C. The venue chosen for the award presentation ceremony and banquet was the prestigious and venerable Cosmos Club. Its long history is steeped in geology; one of its founders and first presidents was John Wesley Powell, famous explorer of the Grand Canyon, and its membership has included many renowned geologists throughout the years.

Making the Pick and Gavel Award a major focus of the spring liaison meeting was also intended to enhance the internal reputation of the Association by providing additional opportunity for greater participation of a larger number of its members in its Washington liaison activities. For most of its history, those activities were carried out by a standing committee of the organization—the Liaison Committee—along with a small number of members. In recent years, however, beginning around the time of Earl Bennett's (Idaho) presidency, a more egalitarian impulse emerged within the organization, expanding the opportunity of the membership to participate in its Washington liaison activities. Although a formal Liaison Committee continues to exist, the de facto Liaison Committee now consists of any and all AASG members and their staff members who come to the Washington liaison activities. Although there is greater opportunity for involvement, some AASG members are still restrained in their ability to participate in Washington liaison activities because their own states' administrative rules do not allow them to go to Washington without specific permission to meet with congressional representatives, committees, or federal agencies. It was hoped that attendance at an AASG meeting with major focus on an official prestigious awards ceremony would allow those members with more restrictions on their Washington, D.C., travel to present additional justification for their participation in the Washington spring liaison meeting.

I am, of course, very pleased that the Pick and Gavel Award is now widely recognized to have accomplished over the past 10 years what it was originally intended to do. It is a great success story in which AASG can justifiably take great pride. A search of the Internet will document how widely it is publicized now. A review of the published biography of Dr. Frank Press, a recipient of the 2007 Pick and Gavel Award, contained in Wikipedia, illustrates the current prestige that the Pick and Gavel Award enjoys. Dr. Press, among the most renowned geologists of our time, is the recipient of 60 honorary degrees and countless awards, of which only six are listed in his Wikipedia biography: namely, the U.S. National Medal of Science, the Vannevar Bush Award, the Pupin Medal from Columbia University, the Japan Prize from the Emperor of Japan, the Lomonosov Gold Medal, and the Pick and Gavel Award from AASG. Dear readers, I suggest that our award is in pretty "tall cotton" to be listed along with such lofty company!

1999	Sen. Larry E. Craig (R-Idaho), Rep. Barbara Cubin (R-Wyoming), Rep. Nick Rahall (D-West Virginia), Gen. Richard L. Lawson (president, National Mining Association)
2000	Rep. Jim Gibbons (R-Nevada) and Dr. Rita Colwell (director, National Science Foundation)
2001	Sen. Joseph Lieberman (D-Connecticut) and Rep. Ralph Regula (R-Ohio)

2002	Gale A. Norton (secretary, U.S. Department of the Interior)
2003	Sen. Ted Stevens (R-Alaska), Sen. Jeff Bingaman (D-New Mexico)
2004	Sen. Harry Reid (D-Nevada), Sen. Pete Domenici (R-New Mexico)
2005	Marcus Milling (executive director, American Geological Institute)
2006	Rep. Ron Kind (D-Wisconsin)
2007	Dr. Frank Press (president, National Academy of Sciences; chair, National Research Council; science advisor to the president), Rep. Norm Dicks (D-Washington)
2008	Sen. Harrison H. Schmitt (R-New Mexico; Apollo program astronaut; only geologist to do field work on the moon)

The John C. Frye Memorial Award

Revised from www.stategeologists.org/frye.html

The John C. Frye Memorial Award is given each year to the best environmental geology paper published either by the Geological Society of America or by one of the state geological surveys. Papers published during the preceding three calendar years are judged. The award, consisting of $1,000 and a certificate, is presented at the AASG breakfast meeting during the annual GSA meeting.

The award began during an evening session at the 1989 GSA meeting in St. Louis, when Robert L. Fuchs (president, GSA Foundation), F. Michael Wahl (GSA executive director), and Frank E. Kottlowski (New Mexico) discussed a proper award to be made of the income from the John C. Frye Memorial Fund, which at that time had a balance of $8,100. After conferring with John W. Hawley (another close friend of John Frye), it was decided that an annual award for the best environmental geology paper, published by either the GSA or one of the state geological surveys, would be most appropriate.

John C. Frye was state geologist of Kansas and Illinois before serving as executive director of the Geological Society of America. He is credited with creating the phrase and field of investigation of "environmental geology."

John Frye was very active in the Association of American State Geologists, serving as president (1958–59), and represented AASG on many national committees, particularly related to the National Academy of Sciences. John began his geologic career with the USGS Ground Water Division in 1938. He joined the Kansas Geological Survey in 1942, and in 3 years became its director, serving there until 1954. That year, he was appointed chief of the Illinois State Geological Survey and served in that position for 20 years. When he retired in 1974, John had a second career as the executive director of GSA. He retired from GSA in 1982 and shortly thereafter, passed away. The excellence of both the Kansas and Illinois surveys is in part a credit to John's leadership. When he took over as executive director of GSA, the organization was in a precarious financial condition. John put GSA back on a firm financial and scientific foundation. While at Boulder with the GSA, he spent his vacation time partly in Illinois and partly in New Mexico working on Quaternary geology.

John's major scientific interests were in Quaternary geology and environmental geology. He was one of the first to bring attention to the interrelationship of man and the environment, as viewed through the science of geology. The term "environmental geology" had its origin at the Illinois State Geological Survey during his tenure as chief. Environmental geology provided a means of focusing public and professional interest on the application of geology to society. This subdiscipline of geology now enjoys wide acceptance as the public becomes more aware of and shows more concern for its natural surroundings. Today, most geological surveys, both in this country and elsewhere, place strong emphasis on environmental geology.

At the 75th anniversary of the Illinois State Geological Survey in 1980, John Frye said,

> In the next few decades, geologic data and advisory input will be needed more urgently than has ever been the case…. When we view an exponentially increasing population set in apposition to finite mineral and land resources, the urgency of the situation becomes apparent.

John Frye extended his environmental activities and interests well beyond the boundaries of his state survey. He served on many national committees dealing with radioactive waste management, environmental sciences, and problems of the environment.

"Environmental geology" (as defined by John Frye) means an attitude of mind, an orientation, the application of the best and most sophisticated scientific work we are capable of doing to the problem of accommodating a rapidly shrinking living space and resource base to the needs of man.

Nominations for the Award

Nominations may be made by anyone. The nominated paper must have been published by a state geological survey or in Geological Society of America publications. It must have been published during the preceding three calendar years. The deadline for receipt of nominations is March 31 of each year. Nominations should include a letter stating the pertinence of the paper. Three copies of the paper or book must be supplied.

Send nominations to:
Program Officer—Grants, Awards, and Recognition
Geological Society of America
P.O. Box 9140
Boulder, CO 80301-9140
(303) 357-1028
awards@geosociety.org

Criteria for Nominations

The nominated paper or book must identify or recognize a geologically based environmental problem or issue. It must provide technically sound substantive information on the basic geology or geologic process pertinent to the problem, and relate the geology to the problem or issue. The information must be presented in a manner that is understandable and directly usable by geologists and other professionals such as land-use planners and engineers. It is highly desirable that the paper or book be easily understood by informed laypersons.

Basis of Selection

The winning entry must meet the criteria for nomination and have been judged as best of those nominated, based on uniqueness or significance as a model of its type of work and report, and its overall worthiness for the award.

Committee

The John C. Frye Memorial Award in Environmental Geology is selected by a three-person committee. One committee member is appointed for a period of 3 years by the Geological Society of America and the other two members are appointed by the president of AASG. The Frye Committee reviews the papers nominated and makes a recommendation for the award, preferably by mid-June of each year.

The 1989–90, 1990–91, and 1991–92 committee was Earl Bennett (Idaho), chair, John Kempton (GSA representative), and Frank Kottlowski (New Mexico). The 1992–93 and 1993–94 committee was Kempton, Diane Conrad (Vermont), and Kottlowski, chair. In 1993, AASG President Donald Hull appointed Conrad and Kottlowski for terms ending in November 1996 and John Kempton was reappointed by GSA to a 3-year term ending in 1997. When Conrad was promoted to deputy director of the Vermont Agency on Natural Resources, Larry Becker (acting director, Vermont Geological Survey) served in 1995 with Kempton and Kottlowski. James Robertson

(Wisconsin) was appointed to Becker's position by AASG President Walter Schmidt. AASG President Earl Bennett appointed Larry Fellows (Arizona) and Kottlowski to serve during 1996–97. AASG President Charles Gardner continued Fellows and Kottlowski for 1997–98. Richard Berg (Illinois) was appointed as GSA representative from 1997–2000. AASG President Larry Woodfork continued Fellows and Kottlowski for 1998–99. The 2001 committee was Fellows, chair, Robert Marvinney (Maine), and Orrin Pilkey (GSA representative). Fellows and Marvinney continued in 2002; Berg was the GSA appointee. For 2003–04, the AASG members were Walter Schmidt (Florida), chair, and John Bluemle (North Dakota).

Recipients

| 1990 (Dallas) | Linda L. Noson, Anthony Qamar, and Gerald W. Thorsen, 1988, Washington state earthquake hazards: Washington Division of Geology and Earth Resources, Information Circular 85. |

1991 (San Diego)   Richard C. Berg, H. Allen Wehnnann, and John M. Shafer, 1989, Geological and hydrological factors for siting hazardous or low-level radioactive waste disposal facilities: Illinois State Geological Survey, Circular 546.

1992 (Cincinnati)   Edwin J. Hartke and Henry H. Gray, 1989, Geology for environmental planning in Monroe County, Indiana: Indiana Geological Survey, Special Report 47.

1993 (Boston)   Robert F. Walters, 1991, Gorham Oil Field, Russell County, Kansas: Kansas Geological Survey, Bulletin 228.

1994 (Seattle)   Ronald W. Hoenstine and Ed Lane, 1991, Environmental geology and hydrogeology of the Gainesville area, Florida: Florida Geological Survey, Special Publication 33.

1995 (New Orleans)   Mike Lowe, Bill D. Black, Kimm M. Harty, Jeffrey R. Keaton, William E. Mulvey, E. Fred Pashley Jr., and Scott R. Williams, 1992, Geological hazards of the Ogden area, Utah, *in* Field guide to geologic excursions in Utah and adjacent areas of Nevada, Idaho, and Wyoming: Utah Geological Survey, Miscellaneous Publication 92–3, p. 231–285.

1996 (Denver)   Steven Slaff, 1993, Land subsidence and earth fissures in Arizona: Arizona Geological Survey, Down-to-Earth Series 3.

1997 (Salt Lake City)   Michael J. Chrzastowski, Myra M. Killey, Robert A. Bauer, Paul B. DelMontelle, Anne L. Erdmann, Beverly L. Herzog, John M. Masters, and Lisa R. Smith, 1994, The Great Flood of 1993: Geologic perspectives on the flooding along the Mississippi River and its tributaries in Illinois: Illinois State Geological Survey, Special Report 2.

1998 (Toronto)   David C. Noe, Candace L. Jochim, and William P. Rogers, 1997, A guide to swelling soils for Colorado homebuyers and homeowners: Colorado Geological Survey, Special Publication 43.

1999 (Denver)   Ed Lane and Frank Rupert, 1998, Earth systems: The foundation of Florida's ecosystems: Florida Geological Survey, poster.

2000 (Reno)   Helen L. Dalano and Peter J. Wilshusen, 1999, Landslide susceptibility in the Williamsport 1- by 2-degree quadrangle: Pennsylvania Department of Conservation and Natural Resources, Environmental Geology Report 9.

2001 (Boston)   Julie A. LeFever, John P. Bluemle, and Ryan P. Waldkirch, 1999, Flooding in the Grand Forks–East Grand Forks North Dakota and Minnesota area: North Dakota Geological Survey, Educational Series 25.

2002 (Denver)   Peggy S. Johnson, 2001, Decision-makers field guide 1— Water, watersheds, and land use in New Mexico: Impacts of population growth on natural resources—Santa Fe region: New Mexico Bureau of Geology and Mineral Resources, Decision-Makers Field Guide.

2003 (Seattle)   Ron Churchill, Chris Higgins, and Bob Hill, 2000, Areas more likely to contain natural occurrences of asbestos in western El Dorado County, California: California Geological Survey, Open-File Report 2000–02.

2004 (Denver)   Raymond C. Harris and Philip A. Pearthree, 2002, A home buyer's guide to geologic hazards in Arizona: Arizona Geological Survey, Down-to-Earth Series 13.

2005 (Salt Lake City) Carol L. Ruthven, John D. Kiefer, Stephen F. Greb, and William M. Andrews Jr., 2003, Geologic maps and geologic issues in Kentucky: A citizen's guide: Kentucky Geological Survey, Special Publication 3.

2006 (Philadelphia) Ralf Topper, Karen L. Spray, William H. Bellis, Judith L. Hamilton, and Peter E. Barkmann, 2003, Ground water atlas of Colorado: Colorado Geological Survey, Special Publication 53.

2007 (Denver) David K. Brezinski, 2004, Stratigraphy of the Frederick Valley and its relationship to karst development: Maryland Geological Survey, Report of Investigations 75.

The National Geologic Mapping Act

Donald C. Haney *(Kentucky, Honorary),*
Larry D. Fellows *(Arizona, Honorary),*
and Earl H. Bennett *(Idaho, Honorary)*

The well-being of any nation is based, in large part, on its ability to locate and prudently use its mineral and water resources, to assess potential harm to its citizens from natural hazards, and to provide for safe disposal of its waste material. These tasks require detailed knowledge of the character and distribution of geologic materials at or near the surface of the earth; geologic maps are the principal source of this type of information. Geologic maps provide essential information regarding the assessment of mineral, energy, and water resources; locating potential sites for the safe disposal of hazardous and nonhazardous waste; land-use planning; earthquake reduction; predicting volcanic hazards; reducing losses from landslides and other ground failures; mitigating effects of coastal and stream erosion; siting of critical facilities; and basic earth-science research. Geologic maps are the primary source of geologic information for nearly all decision-making related to our habitation of the earth's surface and our use of its resources. Although available maps are in continuous use by federal agencies, state and local government, private industries, and the general public, large areas of the United States remain unmapped, or were mapped at scales too general to be of use.

The need for such information dates back to the early history of our country. During the relatively peaceful period following the Revolutionary War, the westward movement toward the frontier beyond the Blue Ridge Mountains was revived by people in search of opportunities that were not apparent in the crowded East Coast of the new nation. This movement led to an increased demand for information about the frontier, especially information concerning transportation routes, water, and mineral resources needed for survival in the wilderness. Though the first organized geological survey is credited to S.L. Mitchell during this era, one of the most experienced and thorough field geologists was William Maclure of Philadelphia, who included a geologic map of the United States with his *Observations on the Geology of the United States,* published in 1809 and revised in 1817. Between 1824 and 1858, more than 30 individual state geological surveys were organized for the purpose of mapping water, mineral, and energy resources to support the growth of the emerging nation. Most of those state "surveys" resulted in the publication of small-scale reconnaissance maps, but gradually more detailed large-scale maps became available through the efforts of state geological surveys such as the North Carolina survey, which was formed in 1823. During the early to middle 20th century, more detailed mapping took place in response to the need for mineral and energy resources to drive the United States industrial machine, especially during the two world wars. Most of that mapping was provided by state geological surveys and the U.S. Geological Survey.

Perhaps the most ambitious detailed state geologic mapping project took place in Kentucky between 1960 and 1978, when the state was mapped under a cooperative geologic mapping program between the Kentucky Geological Survey and the U.S. Geological Survey. The program was launched by Dr. Wallace Hagan, who became the 10th state geologist of Kentucky in 1958. He led the charge to begin a cooperative geologic mapping program in Kentucky that would result in total coverage of the state at a scale of 1:24,000. He enlisted the assistance of numerous groups in Kentucky, including the Chamber of Commerce, the coal and mineral industries, agriculture, education, and state government. He also solicited assistance from many federal agencies, asking them to be participants in his far-reaching and visionary efforts to establish a national geologic mapping program. In his view, the Kentucky program would be the pilot program for the United States. In direct response to Dr. Hagan's efforts, the USGS, in cooperation with KGS, initiated the program in 1960. They completed and published 707 geologic quadrangle maps (7.5-minute, 1:24,000-scale) during the 18-year period. Though most of the mapping was conducted by USGS geologists, several quadrangles were mapped by KGS geologists and university professors. In addition to the 707 published maps, the project resulted in the publication of approximately 150 professional articles and reports (McGrain, 1979).

McGrain further reported that agriculture benefited from information related to design and location of farm ponds, groundwater supplies, and the relationship of bedrock to classification of soils. From the urban viewpoint, the new maps provided information for industrial-site locations, urban master plans, sanitary-landfill sites, and reservoir locations, and provided much information needed for the expanding Interstate highway programs. Conversely, the lack of detailed geologic maps in other areas has led to poor design of such structures as dams and waste-disposal facilities. The cost in tax dollars and human health relative to the migration and cleanup of one Superfund site further demonstrates the utility of knowing the detailed nature of earth as is provided by geologic maps. Estimated benefits far exceeded the cost of data collection and compilation of geologic mapping products. Even though geologic studies in Kentucky appeared to have reached their zenith prior to completion of the project, it became evident that the mapping program stimulated ever-increasing geologic activity related to coal, oil and gas, industrial minerals, geologic hazards, and urban planning. Considering the many obvious benefits of high-quality geologic maps to the nation, it was imperative that a national geologic mapping program be initiated. McGrain's analysis of the benefits of the availability of detailed geologic maps to the nation was further documented by a National Research Council report in 1988, which stated that users who benefited from geologic maps ranged from private industry to federal, state, and local governments, to the general public.

The Kentucky maps have been well received by the public, based upon the record of map sales showing 81,000 maps sold as of 1999. Further research has indicated the actual number could be closer to 150,000 copies sold or distributed. This volume of sales is a measure of how highly valued these maps are, but there had been no quantitative estimate of their economic value until a study by S. Bhagwat and V. Ipe of the Illinois State Geological Survey in 2000. The Kentucky maps were an ideal case study because they had been in circulation for more than 25 years, long enough for a meaningful influence on construction, roads, mining, and water projects. Geologic maps were viewed in Bhagwat and Ipe's (2000) study as public goods, in the same way as roads, bridges, reservoirs, and other things of value to the public created at public expense, rather than as commodities such as cars, bicycles, radios, and televisions that are consumer products bought by private citizens. Funding for the mapping program was a 50-50 cost share between the U.S. Geological Survey and the Kentucky Geological Survey.

The economic analysis by Bhagwat and Ipe (2000) showed, among other things, that the dollar amount saved on projects because detailed geologic maps were available ranged from $27,776 to $43,527 per 7.5-minute quadrangle. The amount users would voluntarily pay for a 7.5-minute geologic quadrangle map was $342. Based upon user estimates and on map sales volumes, the value of the geologic quadrangle maps to Kentucky was at least $2.25 billion and as much as $3.53 billion in 1999 dollars. The return on investment to the taxpayers was from 25 to 39 times the cost, a remarkable return on the taxpayers' investment!

With the exception of the Kentucky project, efforts in geologic mapping had significantly diminished during the 1960's and 70's, as geologic research in the United States shifted from a pragmatic approach to more fundamental research. Thus, geologic mapping became the victim, especially at the federal level. The combined capacities of the state, federal, and academic groups to produce geologic maps were not sufficient to meet the present or future needs of the nation. This was recognized by state geological surveys, and in spite of efforts to turn the tide at the national level, the trend continued, and production of detailed geologic maps decreased. The availability of detailed, accurate geologic maps, which are vital to national security, environmental protection, energy demands, and for finding raw materials needed by industry, was totally inadequate.

In response to this and other disturbing trends in the geological sciences, representatives from the Mississippi Valley state geological surveys held a conference May 11, 1982, at the Illinois State Geological Survey in Champaign-Urbana, Ill., to consider what could be done to reverse what was considered a move toward a national crisis in the collection, preservation, and publication of basic geologic data about water supplies, mineral resources, energy resources, geologic hazards, and land-use planning. The group unanimously agreed that those topics were crucial to the states and the nation, and that large-scale detailed geologic map data are the foundation for all solid-earth endeavors. Furthermore, the group agreed to pursue the subject as the top priority at both the state and federal level and use the Kentucky project as a model.

Over the next 2 years, representatives of the Association of American State Geologists had several discussions with federal officials, particularly at the USGS, concerning the need for a comprehensive national geologic mapping initiative involving state and federal agencies. It was suggested that the program be patterned after the USGS Water Resources Cooperative, in which federal funds would be matched by states and mapping would be conducted by state geological surveys. In April 1984, USGS announced that a Cooperative Geologic Mapping (COGEOMAP) initiative would be introduced as a line item in the Geologic Division budget; it would be funded at $1 million, to be matched by the states. Although the program would include basic geologic mapping and geophysical mapping, it actually involved nothing more than renaming a line in the regular Geologic Division budget document and allocating $1 million identified as Cooperative Geologic Mapping. At the 1984 AASG annual meeting in Duluth, Minn., President-elect James Davis established a COGEOMAP Committee, intended to last 1 year, to report findings at the AASG fall liaison meeting in Washington, D.C. The report was to include a poll of the states, conducted after August 15, to determine the content of proposals submitted to USGS. The AASG committee would also advise the Liaison Committee on implications of COGEOMAP and make comments on the program. Committee members were Edward Bingler (Montana), chair, Walter Anderson (Maine), Charles Mankin (Oklahoma), Matt Walton (Minnesota), Robert Milici (Virginia), and Larry Fellows (Arizona). In November 1984, USGS announced that $1 million had indeed been authorized and that 18 states would receive funding for the new Cooperative Geologic Mapping program, at $22,000 per state. This marked the beginning of a state-federal geologic mapping initiative. Though modest in scope, it was progress.

The COGEOMAP program continued with this modest budget into the latter part of the 1980's. It was determined that only a small percentage of the United States had been mapped at a scale necessary to meet the needs of the user community. At the current funding level it would take decades to make significant progress. A major effort would be needed to correct the situation. AASG decided to take the lead role. Committee Chair Edward Bingler (Montana) reported in 1985 that COGEOMAP funding was too small and reinforced the notion that at current funding levels decades would be needed to make significant progress. Chairman Bingler also questioned whether the effort would ever become a major program and suggested that it would likely be an exercise in futility.

A forum, "Regional Geologic Mapping: State and Federal Roles: COGEOMAP Roles," was conducted at the AASG annual meeting in 1985. Participants included state and USGS representatives. An AASG resolution was passed at the meeting that "endorses concept of COGEOMAP and urges the USGS to increase the program" (Segall, 1985, p. 10). In response, the USGS reorganized the Land Resources Surveys and designated Geologic Framework and Processes as the principal budget line and broke it down into two programs titled "National Geologic Mapping" and "Geologic Framework." No significant additional funding was forthcoming, however. COGEOMAP was continued at essentially level funding as an activity under Geologic Framework. Even though the AASG urged the USGS to establish a meaningful cooperative national geologic mapping program, state geologists remained disenfranchised in the planning process.

President-elect Frank Kottlowski (New Mexico) continued the COGEOMAP Committee for an additional year and added Ross Schaff (Alaska). The COGEOMAP Committee, along with AASG members of the western states, held discussions in October 1985 with USGS officials at Lake Tahoe, Nev., and expressed concerns similar to those presented at the annual meeting in June. Further discussions were held the following year, including a panel discussion at the June 1986 AASG annual meeting in Long Beach, Calif., where commitments were made by USGS to increase funding for the program and to convene a session later in the year to discuss a cooperative and jointly planned national geologic mapping program. Such a meeting was held during a western states cluster meeting in Portland, Ore., in October 1986 to discuss COGEOMAP and the new USGS national mapping initiative. The proposed new initiative, described by Gene Rosenboom of the USGS, would fund mapping directly through university geology departments. The role of states in administering or overseeing such a program was not defined. This was not an initiative expected by state geologists; "a heated and animated" discussion followed. Again state geologists were thwarted in their effort to establish a state-federal national cooperative geologic mapping program. In February 1987, Charles Mankin (Oklahoma) testified before the Subcommittee on Interior and Related Agencies, House Committee on Appropriations, during a hearing on the National Geologic Mapping Act of 1987. Little response came from that testimony.

During the 1987 AASG annual meeting in Traverse City, Mich., a resolution to USGS was adopted that included language in support of geologic mapping, COGEOMAP, a national geologic mapping plan, increased support for COGEOMAP, and a request for a response from USGS, because past requests had fallen on deaf ears. At the October 1987 midyear meeting in Phoenix, Ariz., AASG President Charles Groat reported on the progress that had been made during the year and stated that if the nation was to have a national geologic mapping program, the effort must have national significance and scale. In his opinion, neither the COGEOMAP program nor the present mapping efforts of the USGS and other agencies would accomplish the goal of having a comprehensive and effective national geologic mapping program.

Because of budget constraints and Department of Interior priorities, President Groat felt that the chances of the USGS achieving a national geologic mapping program that was adequately funded were not very high. To develop a truly national geologic mapping program that would be the underpinning for resource assessment and environmental planning in this country, the AASG would have to take the lead in the effort. Although other state and federal agencies were beginning to recognize the need for sound geologic mapping, the state surveys were still the ones who would have to initiate the effort and draft a strong strategic plan. The plan would need to reflect the perspective of the states in order to achieve a geologic mapping program that has national purpose and scale. It was not intended that state surveys undertake this task alone; cooperation from other state and federal agencies would be welcome. Furthermore, the state surveys would not be the sole vehicle for accomplishing this goal, but neither would it be their objective to channel the effort solely through the USGS. President Groat reiterated that AASG would welcome the USGS and other federal agencies as an integral part of the process, saying that the Association must decide whether to pursue a national legislative or appropriation route to achieve its goal.To begin the effort, President Groat appointed an ad hoc organizing committee. The committee was charged with formulating strategies to accomplish a comprehensive and effective national geologic mapping program that would be truly national in significance and scope. The committee consisted of Chair Robert Milici (Virginia), Ernest Mancini (Alabama), Robert Fakundiny (New York), Norman Hester (Indiana), Thomas Segall (Michigan), Meredith Ostrom (Wisconsin), Frank Kottlowski (New Mexico), Larry Fellows (Arizona), and Genevieve Atwood (Utah). The AASG membership concurred with President Groat's assessment and urged moving forward. Other discussions were held at various meetings from 1987 to 1989.

On June 18, 1988, at the AASG annual meeting in Lexington, Ky., Ernest Mancini (Alabama), chair of the ad hoc Organization Committee for National Geologic Mapping, recommended that (1) the committee prepare a position paper and pursue the legislative route, (2) drafts be prepared and circulated to AASG members, and (3) AASG be prepared to act at the midyear meeting. Association members voted to carry out these recommendations.

President Larry Fellows appointed Donald Haney (Kentucky) to chair a National Geologic Mapping Committee charged with moving forward in a national effort to develop a geologic mapping initiative with or without the cooperation of the USGS. Fellows also established a subcommittee, chaired by Frank Kottlowski (New Mexico), to develop a position paper written in layman's language to be used to promote the initiative in congressional and executive branches of the U.S. government and the public. In addition, Fellows established a Legislation Subcommittee, chaired by Ernest Mancini (Alabama), to draft legislation to establish a national geologic mapping program by statute and to circulate the draft throughout government to find a suitable and willing cooperator. The Legislation Subcommittee took advantage of an opportunity to use and modify a draft document that Earl Bennett and Robert Bartlett (Idaho) had developed in 1987 to reflect more detailed concerns that AASG members had previously identified as a result of many conferences and panel discussions. The draft reports of the National Geologic Mapping Committee were approved at the

AASG annual meeting in Oklahoma City in 1989 and ordered to be printed for national circulation.

On behalf of Frank Kottlowski, who could not attend the Oklahoma City meeting in May 1989, Donald Haney (Kentucky) reviewed the 1988 October position paper developed by Kottlowski and his subcommittee and presented it to the Association for ratification. The position paper highlighted in layman's terms most of the points presented by McGrain (1979) and the National Research Council (1988). The Legislative Subcommittee report was also considered and submitted for ratification. Both reports were accepted by the Association, and a National Geologic Mapping Program was approved, in principal, by unanimous vote of the Association. During late summer and early fall of 1989, the Implementation Committee, led by Charles Mankin (Oklahoma), developed a plan for a congressionally authorized National Geologic Mapping Program for the United States and began the process for introducing the legislation to Congress for action.

In 1989, a committee composed of Ernest Mancini (Alabama), Charles Groat (Louisiana), Earl Bennett (Idaho), Donald Hoskins (Pennsylvania), Charles Mankin (Oklahoma), Robert Forbes (Alaska), and Chair Frank Kottlowski (New Mexico) was asked to draft a position paper on such an act.

In 1989, an Implementation Committee was appointed, including Mankin as chair, Donald Haney (Kentucky) as an ex officio member, William Fisher (Texas), Donald Hoskins (Pennsylvania), Ernest Mancini (Alabama), and Jonathan Price (Nevada). This committee's formidable task was to develop a plan for a National Geologic Mapping Program and prepare and introduce legislation to Congress. A possible source of initial funding for the new mapping initiative was the COGEOMAP program started by the U.S. Geological Survey in 1984 in part to map large sections of the United States as a cooperative effort between the USGS and the state surveys.

A forum on geologic mapping was held in 1990. Mitch Reynolds (USGS) stressed the need to retain the COGEOMAP program while pursuing the new mapping initiative. He noted that USGS was the federal lead agency for all geologic mapping via Office of Management and Budget Circular A-16 and that OMB would require a rigorous cost-benefit analysis of the proposed program. The American Mining Congress pledged support for the program and the Environmental Protection Agency also noted that they supported the program. Charles Mankin (Oklahoma) anticipated that federal legislation could be introduced as early as July 1990, with possible hearings held that fall.

As a result of the implementation committee's work, Senate Bill 1179, "The National Geologic Mapping Act," was introduced in 1991, sponsored by Sen. J. Bennett Johnston (D-Louisiana), Sen. Jeff Bingaman (D-New

Mexico), and Sen. Larry Craig (R-Idaho). The initial hearing before the Subcommittee on Public Lands and Forests of the Senate Committee on Energy and Natural Resources, chaired by Sen. Craig, was supposed to be a well-orchestrated dance between USGS Director Dallas Peck and the AASG. The Association members were shocked when the USGS spoke against the legislation at the hearing. Supposedly, the Department of the Interior had told Director Peck in the 11th hour that he was not to support the bill. Funding was the major concern. After the hearing, another hurdle was raised when Sen. Johnston asked that a section be included in the bill to cover the use of radar mapping. The use of radar images was added to the possible list of potential factors that could be used by mappers. The National Governors Association endorsed the act in August. In spite of the initial teething problems, the National Geologic Mapping Act was passed unanimously by both houses of the 102nd Congress with 23 senators and 49 representatives as co-sponsors. The bill was signed into law (PL 102-258) on May 18, 1992, by President George H.W. Bush (see chapter 5, 1990–99).

It is important to note that the original act states what was to be done, but not exactly how it would be done. There were four key elements in the act. All of the geologic mapping by the U.S. Geological Survey was included in the FEDMAP element, other geologic data (paleontologic, geochronologic, geochemical, and geophysical) were under SUPPORTMAP, and state mapping efforts would be under STATEMAP; a fourth element (for training future mappers) was in the EDMAP provision. The program would be administered by the U.S. Geological Survey, and funding levels for the first 5 years of the program were recommended by program element. The USGS was also charged with putting together a national geologic map database in a standardized format. Under STATEMAP, the states would match federal funds dollar for dollar, and each state would establish in-state priorities via a multirepresentational state panel (this would develop into the State Mapping Advisory Committees). The entire program would be overseen by a 16-member advisory committee with representatives from federal agencies (including the USGS), universities, state surveys, and the private sector. How the elements and other provisions in the act would be accomplished would be detailed in an implementation plan submitted to the Committee on Natural Resources of the House of Representatives and the Committee on Energy and Natural Resources of the Senate within 800 days after May 18, 1992. An annual report would also be submitted to Congress within 90 days of the close of the fiscal year.

The euphoria of successfully passing federal legislation was quickly replaced by the sobering reality that although the act called for a $37.5 million appropriation for fiscal year 1993, there was only $23.2 million in the president's budget for the USGS's entire geologic mapping program, and not a nickel specifically authorized for the National Cooperative Geologic Mapping Program. Of course, an authorization act only suggests funding levels, but does not appropriate any money. That process is done by the 13 "cardinals" who chair the appropriations subcommittees in the House and Senate, as well as the full Appropriations Committee. AASG would now have to launch a major campaign to increase the funding levels for the program. To get the NCGMP started, the USGS allocated $1.2 million from their mapping budget for the STATEMAP component of the act in fiscal year 1993 (about the same amount as they were investing in COGEOMAP), and there was no funding for the EDMAP component.

A somewhat less critical, but still daunting task was the actual implementation of the act. As required in the law, a new Implementation Committee was appointed by AASG President Robert Fakundiny at the Alabama annual meeting. There would be six representatives on the committee: three chosen by the regional clusters and three (including the AASG president as an ex officio member) selected by the AASG Executive Committee. The cluster representatives were Thomas Berg (eastern region), Charles Mankin (central region), and Jonathan Price (western region). The Executive Committee asked Earl Bennett and Donald Haney to serve at large. In addition, Berg, Price, and Haney were asked to serve on the Federal Advisory Committee, although the committee would not meet until 1994, as federal appointments were stalled in Congress.

The new Implementation Committee met several times in the next year in Cincinnati, Reno, Nev., Annapolis, Md., and Washington, D.C. Work began on a requirements analysis. Debate continued on establishing a fair overhead rate for the USGS for administering the program (it would eventually be 18 percent) and to the state surveys as part of the proposal process.

In response to a program opportunity notice, 43 states were funded to do geologic mapping out of 55 proposals. The total request was for $3.1 million, but only $1.2 million was available. The implementation plan called for establishing a Peer Panel to review the proposals and make awards. The first Peer Panel consisted of Earl Bennett (Idaho), Robert Fakundiny (New York), Norman Hester (Indiana), Charles Mankin (Oklahoma), Perry Wigley (Nebraska), and James Williams (Nebraska) as an alternate to Wigley. Most of the first year's meeting was spent hammering out how the Peer Panel would function and what criteria would be used to evaluate proposals. As expected, without good guidelines, the first proposals were a real potpourri of styles and formats. It would take several years to develop formatting and procedures for the proposals, with feedback provided by the Peer Panel to other AASG members. One recommendation of the first panel was to encourage the surveys to map areas with strong societal needs, usually in urban areas. As a result of several years of Peer Panel deliberations and fine-tuning, today's proposals are so well written that it is difficult for the panel to match up requested dollars with available funds. Another problem in the early days was the late notification of awards to the successful states by USGS. Some did not get contracts until well into the next field season. This would also improve markedly over the next few years.

EDMAP representatives included Lehigh Hintze (Utah) and Thomas Smith (Alaska), although the committee did not meet because there was no funding in the program yet. The Federal Advisory Committee (whose first meeting would be held in 1996) included members from the EPA, DOA, DOE, Office of Science and Technology Policy, and USGS. Representatives from the AASG were Charles Mankin (Oklahoma), Thomas Berg (Ohio), Donald Haney (Kentucky), and Jonathan Price (Nevada). As might be expected, the early years of the NCGMP were hampered by low funding and the basic ponderous nature of federal bureaucracies. In spite of frustration on all sides, the program slowly began to gel and take form.

Because of the time and effort required to reauthorize a federal act, work began in earnest in 1993–94 on reauthorization of the NCGMP, which had to be completed by 1998. The early start would prove justified, as reauthorization would not happen until 1997. The Senate bill was submitted by Sen. Larry Craig (R-Idaho) and the House bill was introduced in the Energy and Mineral Resources Subcommittee (Rep. Barbara Cubin, R-Wyoming, chair). Problems arose when the executive director of the Management Association for Private Photogrammetric Surveyors, John Palatiello, raised objections on the House side about a conflict of interest with the private sector. Charles Mankin (Oklahoma) was successful in convincing MAPPS (interested primarily in the acquisition of aerial photography) that the use of remote imaging as a key tool for geologic mapping was included in the bill. The AASG effort was greatly assisted by the thoughtful advice of Bill Condit (professional staff on the House Subcommittee on Energy and Mineral Resources), who, as a geologist, understood the importance of the act. A few years later, John Rishel (chief of staff for the full House Committee on Resources) would also make valuable contributions to the successful progress of the mapping program.

The Peer Panel of 1993–94 distributed some $1.65 million to 37 states. The program opportunity notice was greatly improved, and a marked improvement in the quality and format of the proposals was noted.

In 1994 and 1995 the NCGMP would come into its own. While seemingly unrelated, it is important to note that at the time the U.S. Bureau of Mines was in serious trouble with Congress and the president's office. Questions were asked about the agency's research mission. Under the congressionally driven "Contract with America," budgets would be cut, including that of the Department of the Interior, and it eventually came down to who would go, the Bureau of Mines or the U.S. Geological Survey. AASG supported both agencies, including reluctant approval of a series of controversial fact sheets prepared for each state by the USGS. In the end, the U.S. Bureau of Mines was eliminated as a federal agency in 1995.

In the midst of the controversy over the survival of USBM and USGS, a National Geologic Mapping Workshop was held in Washington, D.C., in December 1994. One result of the meeting was a draft document, "Geologic Mapping into the 21st Century: Concepts toward a National Plan for the National Cooperative Geologic Mapping Program." Following the workshop, AASG President Donald Hoskins reached an agreement with USGS Director Gordon Eaton that in the future, STATEMAP would be funded at 20 percent of the available NCGMP funds and would also absorb 20 percent of any funding cuts. This important agreement would increase STATEMAP funding from $1.34 million to $4.4 million.

Work continued on reauthorization of the NCGMP. Sen. Larry Craig (R-Idaho) and Rep. Ken Calvert (R-California) agreed to sponsor the reauthorization bills.

In fiscal year 1996, the USGS leadership of the NCGMP changed, and John Sutter and Art Schultz were appointed as program and assistant program coordinators. While relationships between the USGS and AASG had improved over the past few years, the new leadership brought with it a true spirit of cooperation, and the general attitude toward the program moved from "let's get this working" to "how do we improve this program and where do we go from here." The welcome shift in direction was immediately apparent.

After 3 years of STATEMAP funding, the Peer Panel in 1995 approved a new option for the next fiscal year's proposals. States could now submit two proposals, one for new mapping (with several parts) and a second for digital mapping, including digital compilations. This digital mapping provision would allow Kentucky (with completed 7.5-minute, 1:24,000-scale geologic maps) to begin 1:100,000-scale compilations. The western states could also begin modern compilations in areas with little or no consistent mapping. There was still some dissatisfaction with the Peer Panel process, but out of 40 states receiving awards totaling some $4 million, only five had registered complaints.

In 1995–96 (fiscal year 1996), $3.7 million was awarded to 41 states under STATEMAP. The FEDMAP part of the program began to take shape, and Earl Bennett (Idaho) and Vicki Cowart (Colorado) were asked to help select and review FEDMAP projects for fiscal year 1997. State geologists have been invited to help guide FEDMAP ever since.

EDMAP was fully implemented in fiscal year 1996. This important segment of the NCGMP was intended to provide the nation with future geologic mappers. University professors would sponsor and mentor students via a peer-reviewed proposal process similar to that of STATEMAP. As with STATEMAP, the participating universities would match federal funds dollar for dollar. The proposals had to be signed off on by the state geologist and USGS as being within the framework of the program guidelines and expectations. By 2000, 74 students from 40 schools were active in the program, and over 240 undergraduate and graduate students have participated in EDMAP since 1995.

Reauthorization of the NCGMP failed in October 1996 when Sen. Tom Daschle (D-South Dakota) placed a hold on hundreds of bills that were finally released in the final hours of the 104th Congress. In the waning hours of the last day, and after passing several large batches of bills, the Senate ran out of time and the last bundle of bills containing the NCGMP reauthorization was not considered. One important provision of the reauthorization was an increase in STATEMAP funding from 20 percent to 25 percent of the total available for the NCGMP in 2000. As would happen repeatedly, AASG was successful in having Congress replace $1.7 million that had been removed from NCGMP funding for 1997–98 in the president's budget.

The Peer Panel awarded some $3.7 million to 41 states for fiscal year 1997. Over 700 new geologic maps had been produced since the program started in 1992. The proposal process was broadened to allow federal agencies and the private sector to participate in STATEMAP via cooperative proposals.

The Federal Advisory Committee finally met in 1995–96 after the Department of the Interior finally approved federal representation. AASG was able to get continued support for reauthorization of the NCGMP from the National Governors Council and added support from the Environmental Council of the States. The Biological Resources Division (formerly the National Biological Survey) was added to the USGS as a major new program.

Jonathan Price (Nevada) was convinced that the way the USGS calculated overhead charges on the STATEMAP component was in error. Because of the error, the USGS added an additional $120,000 to STATEMAP for fiscal year 1998, for a total of $4.44 million.

Another important change in program administration occurred in fiscal year 1998. John Pallister was appointed as program coordinator and Peter Lyttle as assistant coordinator. The "attitude adjustment" on both sides was complete, and the new team would not only continue the Sutter/Schultz philosophy of strong support for the NCGMP within the USGS, but would become true champions for the program. Cooperation between USGS and AASG would reach an all-time high. Although the State Mapping Advisory Committees were up and running in each state, there was little conformity in the makeup or responsibilities of these committees. With the nuts and bolts of how STATEMAP proposals needed to be prepared now well understood by all of the states, a tightening up of the requirements for what actually constituted a SMAC began. Geologic mapping priorities for each state are set with the advice of its SMAC, which includes representatives from private industry, geotechnical firms, federal, state, and county officials, and academia. Current customer needs for geologic maps are considered, and priorities are set for mapping areas where geologic maps are lacking or need improvement. Each state uses this information to determine the geologic mapping that will be conducted by its state geological survey and the projects that will be proposed to STATEMAP.

The National Geologic Mapping Reauthorization Act was passed by the 105th Congress and signed into law by President Bill Clinton on August 5, 1997 (Public Law 105-36). The reauthorization included some new provisions over the original act, including ramping up the STATEMAP share of the federal allocation to 25 percent by the year 2000. EDMAP would be funded at 2 percent, and the remaining 73 percent would go to FEDMAP/SUPPORTMAP. In March, AASG President Charles Gardner (North Carolina) testified before the House Appropriations Interior Subcommittee, recommending full $28 million funding for the entire NCGMP or at least the authorized $6.7 million for STATEMAP and $0.6 million for EDMAP.

One of the requirements from the original act was that the USGS establish a national geologic map database with a consistent format. As all of the new geologic maps produced under the NCGMP would be digital, there was an immediate need for digital standards for all of the new maps that would be stored in the database. There was also the question of what to do with all of the older pre-digital geologic maps.

The formation of the National Geologic Map Database began in 1996. The process accelerated when the USGS appointed David Soller to compile the database in cooperation with AASG (represented by Dick Berg of Illinois). At the annual meeting of AASG in Portland, Maine, in 1997, Soller stressed the need for digital mapping standards. He described plans to build a digital archive for not only all geologic maps, but other geodata as well. Thomas Berg followed by asking for representatives from each state to begin the process. Berg would work with Soller over the ensuing years to build the digital library that we enjoy today. The Digital Geologic Mapping Committee, which represents all of the state geological surveys and works with the NCGMP to establish digital geologic map standards for the National Geologic Map Database, had its first annual Digital Mapping Techniques Workshop in 1997 and has met annually ever since.

Also at the Maine meeting, John Pallister explained that the NCGMP Advisory Committee would have to conform to the requirements of the Federal Advisory Committee Act of 1972.

On March 18, 1998, AASG hosted a congressional reception in the foyer of the Rayburn House Office Building to show off and promote the use of geologic maps and the great progress that had been made under NCGMP. Forty-five state geologists participated, and the foyer was filled with colorful geologic maps, almost all of them done with digital cartographic methods.

By spring 1999, the Reauthorization Committee chaired by Robert Fakundiny (New York) reported that bills had been introduced in the House and Senate to once again reauthorize the NCGMP. AASG members were asked to contact delegations to support the proposed funding increase. Vicki Cowart (Colorado) asked that the state geologists solicit letters of support to Congress from their governors, business leaders, and other influential sources.

By the time of the annual meeting in Fairbanks, Alaska, in June, the reauthorization bill was out of Senate committee and on its way to the floor. The House hearing was scheduled for June 17 in Rep. Barbara Cubin's (R-Wyoming) committee. Nonvoting delegates from the U.S. protectorates, including Puerto Rico and Guam, were on this committee. It was noted that AASG needed to talk to staff for these delegates to avoid any surprises at the hearing. Once again, AASG's Hill workhorse, Charles Mankin from Oklahoma, used his many years of experience in dealing with Congress to smooth the way for reauthorization.

A third category was added to STATEMAP in 1999 to populate map catalogs, establish metadata, provide support for data model technology teams, digitize maps, etc. STATEMAP would also receive 48 percent of about $1.5 million in new funding from the Community-Federal Information Partnership. There were questions about whether these new categories would be mandated or optional and if they might displace or dilute the other STATEMAP options. There were also concerns that qualifiers, such as the Great Lakes coalition, might restrict use of STATEMAP funds.

An important agreement was reached in Reno, Nev., with Paul Beauchemin of the USGS, and Jonathan Price (Nevada) and Earl Bennett (Idaho) representing AASG. Beauchemin suggested that all future increases in funding as well as any cuts to the program would be split 50-50 between

FEDMAP and STATEMAP/EDMAP. This was promptly accepted and would be very important for STATEMAP in fiscal year 2001.

Under President Larry Woodfork, AASG implemented the Pick and Gavel Award, presented at the spring liaison banquet in the Cosmos Club in Washington, D.C. The award recognizes those who have been of service to AASG. The first awards were presented to Sen. Larry Craig (R-Idaho), Rep. Barbara Cubin (R-Wyoming), Gen. Richard Lawson (president of the National Mining Association), and Rep. Nick Rahall (D-West Virginia) for their outstanding support of the NCGMP. The Pick and Gavel tradition continues today and is a highlight of the spring liaison meeting.

Strategic planning came into vogue as we welcomed in the new millennium. Charles Groat, director of the USGS, announced that all programs in the federal survey would prepare 5-year strategic plans. The first plan for the NCGMP was released in 2000.

By October 1999, both versions of the reauthorization bill were alive in the House and Senate. Sen. Jeff Bingaman (D-New Mexico) had a hold on bills over a conflict with Alaska on a fishing issue. It was likely that reauthorization would be delayed until the second session of the 106th Congress and that the House would likely accede to the Senate bill. As predicted, reauthorization occurred on December 9, 1999 (Public Law 106-48), when signed by President Clinton.

Progress in compiling the National Geologic Map Database was rapid. By June 2000, about 24,000 USGS maps were listed in the database. About 10 percent of the maps produced by the states were also in the database, and many more had been cataloged. Dave Soller noted that he expected to have all state maps in the system by September 2000. Map symbolization standards were mailed to all state geologists in June 2000.

The Data Capture Working Group discovered that no one agency had it all figured out, and this led to a series of digital mapping workshops (Digital Mapping Techniques), with the next meeting in Alabama in May 2001. The Data Model Working Group completed a report on how to manage data in a computer. This group was superseded by the Data Model Steering Committee.

Following past practice, the Peer Panel—James Williams (Missouri), John Steinmetz (Indiana), William Shilts (Illinois), Larry Fellows (Arizona), Larry Woodfork (West Virginia), and Peter Lyttle (USGS)—offered suggestions for improving STATEMAP proposals at the annual meeting in St. Louis, Mo. The committee emphasized the importance of the makeup and mission of the SMAC's, and noted these advisory committees needed to be a balanced group that met regularly and discussed mapping priorities for STATEMAP under a long-term plan. There would also be more scrutiny of product quality.

Reflecting the common enthusiasm for the NCGMP, Paul Beauchemin noted that the USGS would testify in support of NCGMP reauthorization; this was definitely a change in the attitude of the administration, since Dallas Peck was required to oppose the initial act in 1992.

In June 2000, the USGS and AASG released a flier, "National Geologic Mapping Act, a Decade of Success," that described the program and noted many examples of the application of the new maps across the nation.

In fiscal year 2001, $6.6 million was awarded to 47 states for STATEMAP projects, the best funding ever. The increase was the result of the Community-Federal Information Partnership addition of $5 million in one-time funding. AASG would of course begin to try and change "one time" to "permanent."

Lee Allison (Kansas) offered to work with USGS to produce fact sheets for each state's STATEMAP program. They would be sent to Congress and other decision-makers. James Robertson (Wisconsin) prepared a prototype sheet. Jonathan Price (Nevada) suggested the sheets show all the geologic mapping in each state. Some 45 states completed the fact sheets, which were posted on the NCGMP Website.

President Vicki Cowart (Colorado) reported at the annual meeting in 2002 in New Harmony, Ind., that NCGMP reauthorization was successful because of persistence, proaction, and general pestering. At least 19 states wrote to Congress about NCGMP, and this had real benefit.

As had happened with the other parts of STATEMAP, and as reported by Derrick Iles (South Dakota) at the annual meeting in 2002, the EDMAP proposals were increasing in number and the quality was improving. Ranking the proposals and making awards was more challenging. Iles noted that support letters from state geological surveys were a critical part of the EDMAP proposals and that preplanning and early discussions with state surveys were weighed very heavily.

Charles Mankin and James Robertson noted that the Federal Advisory Committee meeting would be in September and that the committee would meet once every 2 years. The transition of the NCGMP program coordinators from the USGS had slowed the process, and the expectation was that the committee would meet every year in the near future.

Robertson said that money from sources other than state surveys may be used as part of the nonfederal match. He provided guidance, that it must be verified and needed to be extremely well documented.

Peter Lyttle, coordinator of the National Cooperative Geologic Mapping Program, reported that the new associate director for STATEMAP and EDMAP should be selected by the next month.

An early draft of a report to Congress was circulating, and it would be a document we would all be happy with. It celebrated accomplishments and was not process-oriented. A second draft, with graphics and outcomes, would be submitted to the Federal Advisory Committee. Much of the committee's work would revolve around the report, and they would write the preface. Hearings on the Hill would follow submission of the report.

The sum of $20,000 had been given to the American Geological Institute for a book on geologic mapping. It was to be published in their environmental book series. Bill Thomas, professor at the University of Kentucky, would work on the book. Lyttle said he wanted to work with AASG to show some real outcomes in the form of geologic maps, and hoped that the book would be out before reauthorization. AGI was to handle the book's graphics.

At the 2003 meeting in Omaha, Neb., Peter Scholle (New Mexico) noted that the 50-50 split for new moneys through reauthorization was unacceptable and proposed a 60-40 split. This idea was discussed at length with the membership and the USGS.

The AGI book on geologic mapping was moving forward, with contributions from 30 states.

A questionnaire assessing progress and looking at the future of the program had been sent to all state geologists, but only 27 responses had been received so far. The impression at the time was that it was critical to get 100 percent participation. AASG wanted a comprehensive listing of map production, and state geologists needed to estimate how much money their states could provide for matching funds in the program. This information was needed for the fiscal year 2005 cycle.

It was reported that some funding might be available for derivative maps if they were linked to new mapping and their funding was only a small percentage of the total funding. These types of maps can be very useful in demonstrating societal relevance, but there was still a need to protect base funding. State geologists were urged to remember that the reason we had this program was that no one was making geologic maps, but making derivatives from old data. There was a continuing concern about letting derivative mapping take over. Also, funds for derivatives were often more easily generated from other sources.

The STATEMAP Review Panel—James Cobb (Kentucky), Mark Kuzila (Nebraska), and James Robertson (Wisconsin)—noted that the proposals were all good and that there was continuing scrutiny of the State Mapping Advisory Committees' involvement.

In the Executive Committee meeting held before the 2004 meeting in Stevenson, Wash., President John Steinmetz (Indiana) noted that his testimony for reauthorizing NCGMP was ready, but that hearings had been canceled because a senior House staffer had changed jobs. The hearing would be rescheduled to coincide with the September liaison meeting.

The Federal Advisory Committee had suggested cutting USGS's new money by 2 percent and giving EDMAP 4 percent; STATEMAP funding would stay at 50 percent. James Robertson (Wisconsin) pointed out that these were two separate issues: reauthorization and annual budget.

During the annual meeting, Stephen Mabee (Massachusetts) reported that the EDMAP Review Panel reviewed 61 proposals, of which 36 were funded, including 60 students from 30 universities. Since the program had started, some 150 students from 118 universities had benefited. The panel awarded $490,000 out of a total request of $958,000. Mabee noted that there was a need to clarify mentor time, and also that some state geologists had signed off on proposals that were not good, mostly because of poorly written proposals. There was a need for better relationships between surveys and principal investigators. Mabee suggested having EDMAP meetings at GSA sectional meetings.

The STATEMAP Review Panel—Richard Allis (Utah), David Wunsch (New Hampshire), James Robertson (Wisconsin), and Emery Cleaves (Maryland)— described a point system for evaluating proposals that placed more emphasis on products than in the past. The new system was based on SMAC (10 points), purpose of mapping (15 points), technical quality (30 points), budget (15 points), and products (30 points). Randy Orndorff (USGS) noted that 47 proposals, including 137 projects (44 with urban themes), had been submitted. The new Program Assessment Rating Tool would emphasize productivity, quality, and relevance of the program and products.

David Soller (USGS) and Thomas Berg (Ohio) reported that the Geologic Mapping Database now contained some 65,000 products, more than 3,000 of which were in digital format. Thirty-two states had more than 100 maps each in the database, and the Website received from 17,000 to 20,000 hits each month. Regarding standards for maps and databases, they noted that this involved various committees and that many standards would be adopted nationally. One of the final goals of the online geologic map database was to design it so that it would end up as a seamless national geologic map.

Peter Lyttle (USGS) noted that there were five or six co-sponsors of the reauthorization bill in the House and 13 or 14 in the Senate. The American Congress on Surveying and Mapping had asked to present testimony in support of the bill. There was some discussion about allowing AASG to charge some overhead to STATEMAP.

At the Executive Committee meeting in Denver, Colo., in March 2005, James Robertson (Wisconsin) and Peter Scholle (New Mexico) noted that the reauthorization bill had been reintroduced in the Senate and that hearings went well. They thought the House would hear the bill soon. The Senate and House language was different because the Environmental Protection Agency member on the Federal Advisory Committee had been dropped over lack of attendance at meetings. There were other minor and innocuous changes that had caused friction over control of the bill language. President Robert Marvinney (Maine) reported at the annual meeting in St. Charles, Ill., in 2005 that reauthorization had again failed, because of this slight difference in language between the House and Senate, but would be reintroduced in 2005–06.

According to the USGS Website, after passage of the National Geologic Mapping Act in 1992 (Public Law 102-285), Congress reauthorized the act in 1997 and 1999 (Public Laws 105-36 and 106-148), and a third reauthorization was scheduled to occur in 2006.

In response to the act, the following events have occurred:

1. The matching-funds program component with state geological surveys (STATEMAP) was fully implemented in fiscal year 1996, although a limited amount of funding was distributed earlier.

2. The EDMAP matching-funds cooperative with universities was implemented in fiscal year 1996.

3. The NCGMP Federal Advisory Committee first met in 1996.

4. The National Geologic Map Database was implemented as a digital database in 1996.

5. The Digital Geologic Mapping Committee, which represents all of the state geological surveys and works with the NCGMP to establish digital geologic map standards for the National Geologic Map Database, had its first annual Digital Mapping Techniques Workshop in 1997.

6. The first NCGMP 5-year strategic plan was released in 2000.

The Website added that the efficiency and effectiveness of the NCGMP is monitored and evaluated regularly by several methods, including the Federal Advisory Committee Act, the White House Office of Management and Budget's Program Assessment Rating Tool, and the Government Performance and Results Act.

STATEMAP has evolved to the point that a national evaluation panel, which has three USGS representatives and five state geologists, meets each December to integrate state mapping priorities with NCGMP priorities and to evaluate STATEMAP proposals. Each proposal is given a numerical score based on scientific and technical quality, consistency with SMAC priorities, project justification, budget, and past performance. The amount of funding is tied directly to this score.

References Cited

Bhagwat, S., and Ipe, V., 2000, Economic benefits of detailed geologic mapping to Kentucky: Illinois State Geological Survey Special Report 3, 39 p.

Maclure, W., 1817, Observations on the geology of the United States; Philadelphia, printed for the author by A. Small, 127 p.

McGrain, P., 1979, An economic evaluation of the Kentucky geologic mapping program: Kentucky Geological Survey, 12 p.

National Research Council, Committee on Geologic Mapping, 1988, Geologic mapping: Future needs: Washington, D.C., National Academy Press, 84 p.

Segall, R.T., 1985, Minutes of the 77th annual meeting of the Association of American State Geologists: AASG scanned archives, www.stategeologists.org/Group/Archive/djvu/1985CTminutes.djvu.

The AASG–AGI Connection

James C. Cobb *(Kentucky; AASG Historian)*

T he American Geological Institute developed out of a need to unify the geological sciences. This need was articulated by Dr. Carey Croneis of Rice University, who saw the value of closer relations and cooperation between the geological sciences and for geologists to take a more active role in science in service to the nation. Dr. Croneis was professor of geology, acting president, and chancellor of Rice University. It took geoscientists 6 years to create AGI. The formal organization of AGI took place on November 15, 1948, in Washington, D.C. The National Academy of Sciences–National Research Council provided assistance and office space for the fledgling AGI (Beebe, 1967; Landon, 1998).

AASG began discussing the need for public outreach and education for geology and public policy from 1911 to 1919. This topic occurred frequently at annual meetings throughout the 1910's, 20's, 30's, and 40's. Therefore, when AGI extended an invitation to join, a majority of the members were enthusiastic about doing so, but some were skeptical about the uncertain future and direction of AGI. Some state geologists had experience with AGI in their roles with other societies, such as Raymond C. Moore (Kansas), as a representative to AGI as president of the Paleontological Society, and Arthur C. Bevan (Virginia), as a representative to AGI as a member of the National Research Council. These state geologists were on the first board of directors for AGI in 1948. It can safely be assumed that networking in support of AGI in its early years had a positive affect on AASG's position to join.

In 1950, AASG member and Past-president Paul Price (West Virginia) invited Dr. William B. Heroy Sr., president of AGI, and Dr. David M. Delo, executive director of AGI, to the AASG meeting in Washington, D.C., to inform the membership about its programs. These men expressed the desire for an official connection between AGI and AASG, such as an affiliated membership for the purposes of public education. A motion was made at this meeting for AASG to join AGI, but that motion was tabled. At the 1951 annual meeting in Rolla, Mo., Dr. Robert Dott (Oklahoma) moved and George Condra (Nebraska) seconded the motion to join AGI. An amendment to the motion was made and seconded that AASG should not join. Charles Deiss (Indiana) spoke at length on the positive aspects and opportunities AGI created to help shape national policy. Morris Leighton (Illinois) also spoke in support of joining, giving these reasons:

1. AASG would be represented on committees with other scientific organizations and included in hearings on important issues such as the use of technical and scientific personnel in the armed forces.

2. AASG needed representation in the field of public education and AGI would provide this.

Following proper parliamentary procedure, the amendment that would have changed the original motion to be against joining AGI was defeated 14 to 5. Then the original motion to join was brought to the floor and passed. Leighton moved that the AASG president be the representative for 1 year and the president-elect for 2, and that this become a permanent policy. It was seconded by Condra and passed. President Wilson M. Laird (North Dakota) and President-elect Edgar P. Rothrock (South Dakota) thus became the first AASG representatives to AGI. AASG became the 12th affiliated society to join AGI.

AASG and AGI have had a close and mutually supporting relationship ever since this inauspicious beginning in 1951. AGI coordinates the Ian Campbell Medal together with AASG and the Geological Society of America (see chapter 6). As of 2007, at least 12 state geologists have been president of AGI, and scores of other state geologists have served in all capacities for AGI and its Executive Committee. Charles G. (Chip) Groat (Louisiana) was executive director of AGI from 1990–92. AASG members who served as president of AGI:

1956–57: Morris M. Leighton (Illinois)
1960–61: Raymond C. Moore (Kansas)
1961–62: Ian Campbell (California)
1966–67: John C. Frye (Illinois)
1972–73: Philip E. LaMoreaux (Alabama)
1978–79: Charles J. Mankin (Oklahoma)
1987–88: James F. Davis Jr. (California)
1988–89: Peter T. Flawn (Texas)
1991–92: William L. Fisher (Texas)
1993–94: Donald C. Haney (Kentucky)
2001–02: Larry D. Woodfork (West Virginia)
2006–07: Ernest A. Mancini (Alabama)

References Cited

Beebe, B.W., 1967, Quest for unity in the geological sciences: Geotimes, May–June 1967.

Landon, S.M., 1998, President's message in celebrating 50 years of federation and service: American Geological Institute, 16 p.

Workings of AASG in 2007

Scott W. Tinker *(Texas; AASG President 2006–07)*

President's Final Report
June 30, 2007

The AASG is a relevant, thriving, and unique association. Each state geologist serves as the chief executive in his or her state and, as such, represents both an individual state survey and a larger state constituency. Taken together, the 50 state surveys and their combined constituencies represent a significant component of the applied-geosciences impact network in the United States.

It is with recognition of that network and its impact that, when asked, I was honored and humbled to take the reins as your president on July 1, 2006. I was supported this past year by an outstanding Executive Committee, including Peter Scholle (past president, New Mexico), Chacko John (president-elect, Louisiana), David Wunsch (vice president, New Hampshire), Berry (Nick) Tew (treasurer, Alabama), Ron Teissere (secretary, Washington), and Donald Haney (honorary members representative, Kentucky).

I began the year guided by four overriding focus areas:

- Organizational efficiency
- Financial health
- Professional relations
- Internal communication.

Organizational Efficiency. Because the AASG has no permanent staff, all of the work is done by elected and appointed volunteers from the membership at large (members, honorary members, associates, and survey staff). As such, I believe that the committee structure represents the working arm of the organization, and chairs must be empowered to act and be expected to deliver.

When I took over as president, the AASG had

- Six elected committees
- Four standing committees
- Three bylaws committees
- Twelve affiliations committees
- Four annual meetings committees
- Eighteen appointed committees and subcommittees
- Twelve ad hoc committees and subcommittees.

The average member served on six committees, and some members on as many as 17 committees. Many committees had 15 members, and several had over 20 members. On the basis of a very thoughtful letter from Harvey Thorleifson (Minnesota), I asked then-President Scholle if I could lead a breakout session at the annual meeting in Santa Fe on committee structure. Results of the breakout session were conclusive: the AASG committee structure needed to be reorganized. The goal of the reorganization process was efficiency and a refocusing on existing AASG priorities. Results of the reorganization, completed in mid-July 2006, were reported in a memo from me to all members, honorary members, and associates (Attachment I).

I am pleased to report that each committee, working under the leadership of its respective chair, took on the task of defining a mission statement and setting goals with great vigor, and the process was complete by the end of August 2006. This procedure allowed each committee to report four times during the year: fall liaison meeting in D.C., midyear at GSA in Philadelphia, spring liaison meeting in D.C., and the annual meeting in Key Largo, Fla.

Although no reorganization is perfect or permanent—fine-tuning will always be needed—in my judgment, the new structure has worked very well, with only a few necessary modifications throughout the year. I was pleased when incoming President John announced at the annual meeting in Key Largo that he planned to keep the same committee structure in place.

I want to thank all of the committee chairs and members. You were outstanding in your work this year, and the organization as a whole was the beneficiary.

Financial Health. The AASG lives on the edge of being in "the red" year to year. In the early 90's, the concept of a foundation was first discussed, and a committee was set up to consider the idea. In the end, it was decided not to pursue such a foundation.

Under the leadership of President Peter Scholle and Nick Tew in 2006, however, the AASG Foundation concept finally took shape, whose purpose is to provide support to the AASG. Trustees of the foundation will disburse funds in a fashion that they deem to be in the best interests of AASG, including financial support for activities such as operations, education, and research.

This year, we made tremendous progress. We put in place a board of trustees (Attachment II, October/November), had our first trustees meeting (spring liaison), and submitted all paperwork for formal approval for a separate incorporated entity. It was a tremendous amount of work, and for the formational effort, thanks go largely to Nick Tew. Jonathan Price (Nevada) will serve as the first president of the foundation.

I dedicated much of my effort this year to raising money, and our broad membership has come through in grand style—both the number of contributors and size of contributions continue to grow. Jonathan Price suggested the creative idea of "buying a beer or whiskey" for the foundation at the annual meeting, and each trustee and ex officio trustee was charged with soliciting contributions. It was a great success!

As president-elect, I worked with Tim Brittan, president of Infinity Oil and Gas, to establish a lead contribution to the foundation ($25,000) at the annual meeting in Santa Fe. Tim was subsequently named external trustee on the board and contributed another $25,000 gift at the annual meeting in 2007. In addition, Tim sponsored the hospitality events at the 2007 annual meeting for an additional $5,000. The importance of Tim's early support cannot be underestimated.

I made two visits to Denver, one to speak at a luncheon of the Explorers Club and one to meet with leading independent oil and gas producers in the area. These visits resulted in $2,000 and $10,000 gifts, respectively. My efforts in this area will continue.

In the end, when formally approved, the AASG Foundation will have nearly $100,000 in endowment and will be well on its way to its initial goal of $300,000. I recommend limited disbursement of funds until the initial goal is reached. When the goal is reached, the foundation will have on the order of $15,000 annually with which to invest in worthy projects and programs. We will go from being in the red to being in the black.

Professional Relations. The AASG interacts with a broad array of federal and state agencies, professional associations, academic institutions, and legislative bodies. The reach of the organization is limited only by the limitations of human capacity. We are but 51 members—with honorary members, associates, and staff.

It is vital that we take an impartial, science-based, ethical, and professional approach in all of our actions as an association, because by so doing, the potential of the AASG to have true impact is substantial.

I was pleased and impressed with all of our members and the leadership each and every one of you displayed. I heard back from many of the people with whom we interact who said, in so many words, that "the AASG has really become an entity with impact and one that must be considered."

An example of our becoming "an entity with impact" was our deliberations regarding joining the USGS Coalition, which was in response to a direct request by USGS Director Mark Myers.

Although discussions were largely electronic, many members and honoraries weighed in with thoughtful, historical, and present-day perspectives. The interchange provided the exact, fact-based input required for the membership to make a considered decision. At the end of the day, the vote was strong and in favor of joining, with

- Forty in favor of joining (80 percent of total membership, 87 percent of those who voted)
- Four opposing
- Two abstaining
- Four not voting.

I wrote a letter to Director Myers outlining the basis of our decision and the context under which it would be considered in subsequent years (Attachment III).

Internal Communications and Fabric. The root cause of many issues (if it can be exposed) is inadequate, incomplete, or misunderstood communication. In an electronic world in which much is done by e-mail, without the benefit of voice or tone and context (or even grammar and punctuation), it is easy for communication to fail. And failed communication has the potential to tear the fabric of an organization.

I did my best to

- Solicit and consider broad input from members, honorary members, and associates on issues of importance, such as the constitutional change to term limits for Executive Committee members, joining the USGS Coalition, content for the annual meeting, etc.
- Set agendas for the four Executive Committee meetings early and to include broad input.
- Work with committee chairs to define clear goals, provide a forum for each committee in which to report results often, and then let the committees do their jobs.
- Pick up the phone and talk with members when e-mail was failing.
- Set and engage in monthly phone calls with USGS Director Myers.
- Provide periodic written documentation and updates of Association activities and decisions to the broad membership.

My effort was far from perfect. But I feel that, as a result, the fabric of the AASG today is strong. Most of the places showing signs of wear in that fabric—which is inevitable in anything approaching its 100th birthday—have been patched, and we are weaving new cloth in many areas. I think that we have made, and will continue to make, a great impact on our science and on our country.

The Future. The Association is in capable hands with incoming President John, President-elect Tew, and the many other elected officers, chairs, and volunteers.

We are poised to exert tremendous influence on national and global issues, such as water quality and quantity, energy resource use and policy, mineral resource use and policy, environmental impact of resource decisions, geologic hazard prediction and mitigation, geoscience data preservation, and, of course, geologic mapping.

It has been an honor and privilege to serve you all. Thanks to each of you for your input, support, and confidence this past year. If we keep our eye on the horizon and boots on the ground, the AASG will flourish!

Attachment I: Committee Reorganization, July 26, 2006

To: State Geologists, Associates, and Honorary Members
From: Scott W. Tinker, President, AASG
Re: AASG Officers and Committee Assignments for 2006–07

Colleagues,

Thank you for your feedback, committee requests, and patience the past 6 weeks. I hope the results are worth the considerable effort. I anticipate these committees will evolve with time.

Some facts and observations:

- I heard back from 40 state geologists, 15 honoraries, and five associates with requests.
- I believe that everyone who responded got his or her first choice for a committee.
- In addition to those who made requests, I assigned several associates, honoraries, and state geologists to committees.
- Total number in each committee is somewhat higher than I wanted, ranging from a low of seven to a high of 15. Subcommittees are kept pretty small, but combined, make for the larger coordinating committees.
- Some of you were worried that a subcommittee means lower stature. It does not. It is simply a means of organizing committees with similar functions under a coordinating chair, with the goal of improving communication across subcommittees. Each coordinating committee comprises all members from its subcommittees.
- The Honorary Members Committee is a committee "of the whole," as recommended at the annual meeting by the Honorary Members Caucus. Several important functions and goals of this committee have been suggested to me during this process, and subcommittees may be required. I will forward these to committee co-chairs Jonathan Price and Larry Fellows.
- The Liaison Committee is chaired by the president-elect. It has only a few members, who will help the president-elect arrange liaison meetings and logistics. All members of the Executive Committee are ex officio of the Liaison Committee. *Liaison attendance in the spring and fall is open to all members, honoraries, and associates.*
- As discussed in Santa Fe, everyone is on considerably fewer committees than in the past. The intent is for each committee member to be actively engaged. I tracked the total counts for elected offices and committee assignments combined, as shown in the table below (i.e., 14 state geologists have one assignment, 16 have two, etc.). This is good representation across state geologists, associates, and honoraries. It does not overburden anyone.

Committees and Elected Positions

	1	2	3	4	5
State geologists	14	16	9	2	2
Associates	11	3			
Honoraries	12	7			

- I will use the standing committees extensively to conduct the business of the Association.
- Committee chairs will be vital to committee success. In some cases, co-chairs made sense and are so assigned. Three committees are chaired or co-chaired by honorary members.
- Committee members should be willing to be fully engaged.
- The first item of business is for each committee chair to organize his/her committee and define the mission and a few goals for the year. Members of the EC are happy to be engaged in these discussions as needed. I sent out the mission statements from prior years' committees a few weeks ago as a starting point. I will send thoughts that I have received from various members to chairs under separate cover. *Chairs, I would like to have committee missions finished and sent.*

Each of the 12 committees should report twice a year: once at the GSA midyear meeting and once at the annual meeting in Florida. Reports should be brief (one-page highlights) and include subcommittee reports as required.

Each committee should make it a top priority to develop/update the fact sheet/issue statement for our Washington visits. Committee assignments follow. Let me know soon whether you do not wish to or cannot serve on a committee or as chair or you did not get on a committee and are burning to be a member.

Attachment II: Monthly Actions of the President

June/July

- Letters with Energy Committee Chair Tew supporting energy research to federal legislature.
- Established ad hoc Constitution and Bylaws Committee to update.
- Set up new AASG committee structure.
- Transferred Website from Kansas to Alaska.

August

- Secured key gifts for AASG Foundation.
- Finalized all committee mission/responsibilities/goals.
- Identified foundation trustees.
- Proposed term limits constitutional amendment.
- EC meeting: Liaison.

October/November

- Named Foundation trustees and acceptance.

		Term Ends		
2007	**2008**	**2009**	**2010**	**2011**
Tinker		Price	Robertson	Marvinney
Tew		Tim Brittan		
		LaMoreaux		

- Letter to Marcus Milling on behalf of AASG.
- Finalized term limits constitutional amendment.
- EC midyear meeting.

December/January

- Marcus Milling resolution plaques.
- Supported Scholle nomination for AGI president (with Tew).
- Established links with AASG/USGS/NSF Data Preservation and Geoinformatics.
- Approved workshop attendance for AASG/ USGS Data Presentation Workshop.
- Letter to Jan Boon for retirement from GSC of Canada (with Bluemle).
- Finalized Pick and Gavel awardees and letters to each.

February/March

- Coordinated updates of fact sheets and produced.
- Worked with Patty Benecke on proposal for renaming NGMA to the Thor Kulsgaard NGMA.
- Set procedures for supporting the centennial volume.
- Set agenda for liaison, EC, and annual meeting in Florida (Jon Arthur).
- Designated AASG representative for USGS Mineral Resources External Research Program panel.
- AASG Foundation fundraiser in Colorado.
- AASG ad hoc committee for MAPPS (Management Association for Private Photogrammetric Surveyors) action, chaired by Harvey Thorleifson.
- AASG formal support for COPUS (Coalition on the Public Understanding of Science).
- AASG formal support of Interstate Council on Water Policy.
- Established and ran process for AASG consideration of USGS Coalition.
- Letter of support for Paleontological Research Institution.

April/May

- AASG vote of approval to join USGS Coalition and letter to Mark Myers.
- Letter on Minerals Program cuts to Mark Myers.
- Decision to support SB 240 (NGMA) as amendment to pending Energy Bill 2007.
- Prepared all program agendas for annual meeting and invited external guests.
- Continued to lead AASG Foundation fundraising.
- Updated duties of officers and distributed.
- Recommended and helped draft AASG resolutions for Tim Brittan, Donald Haney, Charles Groat, Donald Hoskins, and Pat Leahy.
- Finalized $10,000 gift to Foundation from Bud Scherr.

June

- Ran AASG meeting in Key Largo, Fla.
- Transitioned leadership to fiscal year 2008 Executive Committee.
- Considered Coordination Subcommittee of the AASG to facilitate communication with USGS.
- Developed and presented Florida Geological Survey with plaque thanking them for hosting 99th meeting of the AASG and recognizing them for their 100th year of service as the FGS.
- Finalized $25,000 gift to Foundation from Infinity Oil and Gas (Tim Brittan).

Attachment III: Letter to Director Mark Myers about USGS Coalition, April 20, 2007

Dear Mark,

At our March liaison meeting, you asked the AASG to join the USGS Coalition. On its face, this is a straightforward request. However, many feel the implications of joining the coalition are significant.

As you know, the AASG and USGS enjoy a unique relationship. We are at once partners and competitors, collaborators and subcontractors. We share a mission of geoscience excellence, with the USGS nationally focused and the state surveys more locally focused. The USGS cannot advocate federally; the AASG educates on the Hill and thus benefits all geoscience and specifically USGS programs.

I will not elaborate on the AASG/USGS history, a history we both know reasonably well. Suffice it to say it has been, at times, rocky. As a result, there is considerable caution on the part of many AASG members and honoraries and a healthy skepticism by several.

All believe a strong relationship between the USGS and the AASG in key areas would benefit both organizations. Several do not believe that AASG joining the USGS coalition would serve to further the relationship. I believe a relationship will develop only if we take positive steps forward. The jointly hosted AASG–USGS centennial meeting is one such step. The AASG joining the USGS Coalition is another.

With the foregoing as background, I am pleased to report that AASG active members, after extensive and healthy discussion and debate, voted in favor of joining the USGS Coalition. This vote was made with careful thought and consideration and carries with it my duty to report to you the following hopes, expectations, and caveats.

1) We hope our membership on the coalition roster fosters a continued spirit of improved collaboration, transparency, and trust and adds further legitimacy to the USGS and its mission. Federal and state surveys will stand together, or fall apart. NCGMP and Data Preservation represent two programs in which collaboration benefits both organizations. As we have discussed, we each have different roles and should each reap benefits accordingly and proportionally.

2) We reserve the right to leave the coalition if we feel that such collaboration, transparency, and trust are not being achieved. We will plan, as a matter of course, to re-vote USGS Coalition membership on an annual basis.

3) The goals of the coalition are largely to "…support increased federal investment in the USGS…" and as you stated in a note to me, the coalition "prefers to indicate its support for the entirety of the USGS." We support the broad USGS mission; however, we will focus our education efforts on specific programs of mutual interest and do not intend, and in fact cannot, lobby broadly for the USGS.

4) AASG independence and objectivity are a hallmark of our reputation. There may be cases where the AASG opposes certain USGS programs, and we reserve the right to so indicate when necessary in Washington or at the state level.

5) Although the coalition was not organized as a mechanism for its members to provide policy input, it is our expectation that the AASG will continue to have growing policy input at several levels within the USGS. We hope that by joining the coalition, this direct input will improve and increase. For example, our "monthly" telephone calls have proved very useful, and I hope the same would continue between you and subsequent AASG presidents.

6) The USGS has a national mission and the state surveys have a state mission. We hope and expect that unhealthy competition between the state surveys and the USGS at the state and local level will decrease under your leadership. The business model of the Water Resources Division best represents this. The direct competition with WRD for state funds and paucity of associated funding from the WRD for the state surveys makes the relationship one-sided and divisive. There must be a way to bring the Geologic and Water Resource Divisions into alignment and create a healthy collaboration with the states. It needs your direct and considered attention.

7) Improved communication between AASG and USGS is vital. It is a two-way street. We need a mechanism to coordinate state and federal research efforts so that they fully utilize the strengths of both. As an initial suggestion, AASG participation early in several key state-related USGS program decision-making processes would serve to better the USGS and broaden its state support. It could also create new opportunities for collaboration. As you know, historical efforts along these lines, often formalized, have been considerable, but largely unsuccessful. Positive actions could include USGS appointments of key state geologists to USGS review panels, FAQ's and the like in the *early* phases of planning, and communications from district directors to state geologists regarding annual projects being considered *before* they are too far down the road. This could be tried in one or two key programs as a pilot test.

Mark, I am pleased by your leadership and, without exception, our members have expressed their pleasure with how you are handling the early days of your position and their desire to support your efforts. We recognize that the USGS is a "big ship" and the captain can only do so much.

It is my sincere hope as president of the AASG that this action is both symbolic and substantive and represents another step along the way to an improved AASG/USGS relationship and increased scientific collaborations between the USGS and state geological surveys.

Warmest regards,
Scott

History of the AASG Foundation

Jonathan G. Price *(Nevada),* Berry H. (Nick) Tew Jr. *(Alabama),*
Scott W. Tinker *(Texas),* and Larry D. Fellows *(Arizona, Honorary)*

The Association of American State Geologists Foundation was incorporated in 2007 as a nonprofit corporation in the state of Alabama. The sole purpose of the AASG Foundation is to support AASG, including operational, educational, and research activities.

The concept of forming an AASG Foundation developed during the tenure of Peter Scholle (New Mexico) as AASG president and continued during the term of Scott Tinker (Texas). Tinker and Berry (Nick) Tew (Alabama), then AASG treasurer, received encouragement to move forward with establishing the foundation from the AASG membership during the 2006 annual meeting in Santa Fe, N.M. Tew, with legal assistance from his office in Alabama, furthered the concept by drafting articles of incorporation and bylaws and by arranging the organizational meeting of the board of trustees of the foundation on March 5, 2007, in the Main Interior Building in Washington, D.C., during the AASG Liaison Committee meeting. Tew acted as chair and Tinker acted as secretary of that meeting. Other trustees who attended the organizational meeting, and were encouraged to volunteer by Tinker, included Robert Marvinney (Maine), Jonathan Price (Nevada), James Robertson (Wisconsin), and, by telephone, Tim Brittan (Infinity Oil and Gas). The trustees adopted bylaws at the initial meeting; these were later modified and ratified at the June 10, 2007, meeting of the foundation in Key Largo, Fla. The trustees elected the following seven persons to serve initial terms as follows:

Active AASG Members

Robert G. Marvinney (through June 30, 2011)

James M. Robertson, secretary/treasurer (through June 30, 2010)

Jonathan G. Price, president (through June 30, 2009)

Honorary AASG Member

Phillip E. LaMoreaux (through June 30, 2009)

At-Large Trustee

Tim Brittan (through June 30, 2009)

Ex Officio, Nonvoting Trustees

AASG president (Scott Tinker, through June 30, 2007)

AASG treasurer (Berry (Nick) Tew, through June 30, 2007).

Thanks largely to the efforts of Scott Tinker, the foundation got off to a strong start with donations from corporations, active state geologists, and AASG honorary members that totaled $36,100 at the time of the organizational meeting.

As a nonprofit, tax-exempt 501(c)(3) corporation, the foundation has certain restrictions on how it can spend its funds. The trustees set an initial goal to build an endowment and use part of the annual investment income to support AASG activities. The foundation invests funds such that the remaining investment income keeps the endowment rising at least with inflation. At its organizational meeting, the trustees identified several items of high priority for use of the investment income. These include, with proper application and approval each year, support for:

1. Costs of the annual Pick and Gavel Award and banquet, at which AASG honors generally one or two persons who have contributed to the geosciences through high-profile activities at the national level (approximately $10,000 per year).

2. Some of the costs of the AASG annual meeting, in particular to cover the registration fees for honorary members and to help pay for hospitality (approximately $12,000 per year).

3. Costs of special projects (such as the centennial publication), selected AASG publications (for example, brochures and booklets, such as the AGI booklet, "Meeting Challenges with Geologic Maps," and *The State Geologists Journal*), and possibly geologic map postcards, if a small state survey can't afford to provide postcards, which are quite popular at the AASG booth (approximately $21,000 per year).

4. Exhibit costs (approximately $2,000 per year).

5. Travel costs for key state geologists to attend key meetings, particularly the Liaison Committee meetings at which the presence of those state geologists would be of special benefit to AASG, and if they are unable to attend because of budget restrictions (approximately $5,000 per year).

These five items sum to $50,000 per year. The trustees set the following goals for the endowment:

- $300,000 by June 30, 2009 (generating $15,000 per year)
- $600,000 by June 30, 2011 (generating $30,000 per year)
- $1 million by June 30, 2014 (generating $50,000 per year).

The trustees plan to periodically review the fundraising goals and the priorities, and they welcome suggestions from AASG members, honorary members, and associates. The trustees have developed a strategy to reach corporate, foundation, and individual donors, many of whom are more likely to donate for specific good causes than for a long-term endowment. They also encourage each state geologist and each AASG honorary member to contribute.

Although the AASG Foundation was formed in 2007, the underlying concept went back several years. In June 1991, Larry Fellows (Arizona) proposed to President Robert Fakundiny (New York) that the AASG establish an endowment fund. In 1992, President Morris Leighton (Illinois) asked Fellows to chair an ad hoc Endowment Fund Committee to investigate and report on whether an endowment fund should be established on behalf of the AASG, and, if so, the manner in which it should be set up. The committee was also asked to identify the problems, opportunities, and mechanisms for implementing and operating such a fund. Allen Agnew (South Dakota), William Fisher (Texas), Peter Flawn (Texas), and Philip LaMoreaux (Alabama) served on the committee. The committee recommended at the annual meeting in Coeur d'Alene, Idaho, in 1993, with some reservation, that the AASG should establish an endowment fund. AASG members were, in general, supportive of the concept, but concluded that additional details were needed before they could make a final decision.

President Donald Hull asked the Endowment Fund Committee to continue its work, and added Kenneth Weaver (Maryland) to replace Agnew. At the 1994 annual meeting in Maumee Bay, Ohio, the committee presented two alternatives for members to consider:

1. Encourage members to contribute or make bequests to the AASG to carry out their specific objectives, but do not establish an endowment fund.

2. Establish an endowment fund, determine a minimum funding level to be sought, and aggressively solicit funds from members, honorary members, corporations, foundations, and others.

The committee pointed out that if an endowment fund was established, a money manager would have to be selected to make investments, monitor progress of the fund, and account for contributions and earnings. An AASG committee would have to be created to determine which activities would be supported each year, solicit funding, and oversee the work of the money manager. The committee further noted that the need to incorporate to protect officers of the Association from liability related to fund activities would have to be reviewed. The committee felt that, because the AASG has few members, and because there is so much competition for dollars from other funds, the AASG endowment fund may never be large.

The Endowment Fund Committee then recommended that an endowment fund not be established unless there was a strong commitment from AASG members, because a lot of time and effort would be required by them. After substantial discussion, members voted in 1994 not to establish an endowment fund at that time.

The foundation trustees met on June 10, 2007, during the AASG annual meeting in Key Largo, Fla., to discuss fundraising and investment strategies. Over the next couple of days, attendees in Florida enthusiastically contributed. By the end of the annual meeting, the foundation had secured donations and pledges from 33 AASG members, 15 honorary members, 10 associates, and 12 individuals and corporations, totaling $85,000.

Appendix 1:
Officers of the AASG

President

Year	President (referred to as chairman until 1908, then president)
1906	Ernest R. Buckley (Missouri) (temporary)
1907–08	Willis S. Blatchley (Indiana)
1908–09	Henry B. Kummel (New Jersey)
1909–10	Henry B. Kummel (New Jersey)
1910–11	Henry B. Kummel (New Jersey)
1911–12	Henry B. Kummel (New Jersey)
1912–13	Israel C. White (West Virginia)
1913–14	Israel C. White (West Virginia)
1914–15	William B. Clark (Maryland)
1915–16	William B. Clark (Maryland)
1916–17	Frank W. De Wolf (Illinois)
1917–18	Frank W. De Wolf (Illinois)
1918–19	William O. Hotchkiss (Wisconsin)
1919–20	William O. Hotchkiss (Wisconsin)
1920–21	George H. Ashley (Pennsylvania)
1921–22	Edward B. Mathews (Maryland)
1922–23	Edward B. Mathews (Maryland)
1923–24	Edward B. Mathews (Maryland)
1924–25	Wilbur A. Nelson (Tennessee, Virginia)
1925–26	Wilbur A. Nelson (Tennessee, Virginia)
1926–27	Henry A. Buehler (Missouri)
1927–28	Ernest F. Bean (Wisconsin)
1928–29	Ernest F. Bean (Wisconsin)
1929–30	Ernest F. Bean (Wisconsin)

Year	President (referred to as chairman until 1908, then president)
1930–31	Ernest F. Bean (Wisconsin)
1931–32	Morris M. Leighton (Illinois)
1932–33	Morris M. Leighton (Illinois)
1933–34	Morris M. Leighton (Illinois)
1934–35	George C. Branner (Arkansas)
1935–36	George C. Branner (Arkansas)
1936–37	George C. Branner (Arkansas)
1937–38	Arthur C. Bevan (Virginia)
1938–39	Walter F. Pond (Tennessee)
1939–40	George E. Condra (Nebraska)
1940–41	R.A. Smith (Michigan)
1941–42	Raymond C. Moore (Kansas)
1942–43	Paul H. Price (West Virginia)
1943–44	Paul H. Price (West Virginia)/Earl K. Nixon (Oregon) (acting, 6/43)
1944–45	Earl K. Nixon (Oregon)/Robert H. Dott (Oklahoma) (acting 5/44)
1945–46	Robert H. Dott (Oklahoma)
1946–47	Meredith E. Johnson (New Jersey)
1947–48	Edward L. Troxell (Connecticut)
1948–49	Garland Peyton (Georgia)
1949–50	Walter B. Jones (Alabama)
1950–51	Wilson M. Laird (North Dakota)
1951–52	Edgar P. Rothrock (South Dakota)
1952–53	E.L. Clark (Missouri)
1953–54	Herman Gunter (Florida)
1954–55	Charles F. Deiss (Indiana)
1955–56	Daniel J. Jones (Kentucky)
1956–57	Joseph T. Singewald Jr. (Maryland)
1957–58	Olaf P. Jenkins (California)
1958–59	Jasper L. Stuckey (North Carolina)
1959–60	H. Garland Hershey (Iowa)
1960–61	John C. Frye (Illinois)
1961–62	William L. Daoust (Michigan)
1962–63	Carl C. Branson (Oklahoma)
1963–64	Earl F. Cook (Idaho)
1964–65	Frank C. Foley (Kansas)
1965–66	Ian Campbell (California)
1966–67	John B. Patton (Indiana)
1967–68	Robert O. Vernon (Florida)
1968–69	Wallace W. Hagan (Kentucky)

Year	President (referred to as chairman until 1908, then president)
1969–70	Peter T. Flawn (Texas)
1970–71	William C. Hayes (Missouri)
1971–72	Philip E. LaMoreaux (Alabama)
1972–73	Norman F. Williams (Arkansas)
1973–74	Kenneth N. Weaver (Maryland)
1974–75	James L. Calver (Virginia)
1975–76	Charles J. Mankin (Oklahoma)
1976–77	Duncan J. McGregor (South Dakota)
1977–78	Arthur A. Socolow (Pennsylvania)
1978–79	Robert B. Erwin (West Virginia)
1979–80	Daniel N. Miller Jr. (Wyoming)
1980–81	Stephen G. Conrad (North Carolina)
1981–82	William L. Fisher (Texas)
1982–83	Meredith E. Ostrom (Wisconsin)
1983–84	Robert R. Jordan (Delaware)
1984–85	James F. Davis (California)
1985–86	Frank E. Kottlowski (New Mexico)
1986–87	Charles W. Hendry Jr. (Florida)
1987–88	Charles G. Groat (Louisiana)
1988–89	Larry D. Fellows (Arizona)
1989–90	Donald C. Haney (Kentucky)
1990–91	Ernest A. Mancini (Alabama)
1991–92	Robert H. Fakundiny (New York)
1992–93	Morris W. Leighton (Illinois)
1993–94	Donald A. Hull (Oregon)
1994–95	Donald M. Hoskins (Pennsylvania)
1995–96	Walter Schmidt (Florida)
1996–97	Earl H. Bennett (Idaho)
1997–98	Charles H. Gardner (North Carolina)
1998–99	Larry D. Woodfork (West Virginia)
1999–2000	James M. Robertson (Wisconsin)
2000–01	Jonathan G. Price (Nevada)
2001–02	Vicki J. Cowart (Colorado)
2002–03	Emery T. Cleaves (Maryland)
2003–04	John C. Steinmetz (Indiana)
2004–05	Robert G. Marvinney (Maine)
2005–06	Peter A. Scholle (New Mexico)
2006–07	Scott W. Tinker (Texas)
2007–08	Chacko J. John (Louisiana)

Past–president (Position Created in 1928)

Year	Past–President
1928–29	Henry A. Buehler (Missouri)
1929–30	Henry A. Buehler (Missouri)
1930–31	Henry A. Buehler (Missouri)
1931–32	Ernest F. Bean (Wisconsin)
1932–33	Ernest F. Bean (Wisconsin)
1933–34	Morris M. Leighton (Illinois)
1934–35	Morris M. Leighton (Illinois)
1935–36	Morris M. Leighton (Illinois)
1936–37	George C. Branner (Arkansas)
1937–38	George C. Branner (Arkansas)
1938–39	Arthur C. Bevan (Virginia)
1939–40	Walter F. Pond (Tennessee)
1940–41	George E. Condra (Nebraska)
1941–42	R.A. Smith (Michigan)
1942–43	Raymond C. Moore (Kansas)
1943–44	Paul H. Price (West Virginia)
1944–45	Earl K. Nixon (Oregon)
1945–46	Robert H. Dott (Oklahoma)
1946–47	Robert H. Dott (Oklahoma)
1947–48	Meredith E. Johnson (New Jersey)
1948–49	Edward L. Troxell (Connecticut)
1949–50	Garland Peyton (Georgia)
1950–51	W.B. Jones (Alabama)
1951–52	Wiilson M. Laird (North Dakota)
1952–53	Edgar P. Rothrock (South Dakota)
1953–54	E.L. Clark (Missouri)
1954–55	Herman Gunter (Florida)
1955–56	Charles F. Deiss (Indiana)
1956–57	Daniel J. Jones (Kentucky)
1957–58	Joseph T. Singewald Jr. (Maryland)
1958–59	Olaf P. Jenkins (California)
1959–60	Jasper L. Stuckey (North Carolina)
1960–61	H. Garland Hershey (Iowa)
1961–62	John C. Frye (Illinois)
1962–63	W.L. Daoust (Michigan)
1963–64	Carl C. Branson (Oklahoma)
1964–65	Earl F. Cook (Idaho)

Year	Past–President
1965–66	Frank C. Foley (Kansas)
1966–67	Ian Campbell (California)
1967–68	John B. Patton (Indiana)
1968–69	Robert O. Vernon (Florida)
1969–70	Wallace W. Hagan (Kentucky)
1970–71	Peter T. Flawn (Texas)
1971–72	William C. Hayes (Missouri)
1972–73	Philip E. LaMoreaux (Alabama)
1973–74	Norman F. Williams (Arkansas)
1974–75	Kenneth N. Weaver (Maryland)
1975–76	James L. Calver (Virginia)
1976–77	Charles J. Mankin (Oklahoma)
1977–78	Duncan J. McGregor (South Dakota)
1978–79	Arthur A. Socolow (Pennsylvania)
1979–80	Robert B. Erwin (West Virginia)
1980–81	Daniel N. Miller Jr. (Wyoming)
1981–82	Stephen G. Conrad (North Carolina)
1982–83	William L. Fisher (Texas)
1983–84	Meredith E. Ostrom (Wisconsin)
1984–85	Robert R. Jordan (Delaware)
1985–86	James F. Davis (California)
1986–87	Frank E. Kottlowski (New Mexico)
1987–88	Charles W. Hendry Jr. (Florida)
1988–89	Charles G. Groat (Louisiana)
1989–90	Larry D. Fellows (Arizona)
1990–91	Donald C. Haney (Kentucky)
1991–92	Ernest A. Mancini (Alabama)
1992–93	Robert H. Fakundiny (New York)
1993–94	Morris W. Leighton (Illinois)
1994–95	Donald A. Hull (Oregon)
1995–96	Donald M. Hoskins (Pennsylvania)
1996–97	Walter Schmidt (Florida)
1997–98	Earl H. Bennett (Idaho)
1998–99	Charles H. Gardner (North Carolina)
1999–2000	Larry D. Woodfork (West Virginia)
2000–2001	James M. Robertson (Wisconsin)
2001–2002	Jonathan G. Price (Nevada)
2002–2003	Jonathan G. Price (Nevada)
2003–2004	Emery T. Cleaves (Maryland)

Year	Past–President
2004–2005	John C. Steinmetz (Indiana)
2005–2006	Robert G. Marvinney (Maine)
2006–2007	Peter A. Scholle (New Mexico)
2007–2008	Scott W. Tinker (Texas)

President–elect (Position Created in 1948)

Year	President–Elect
1947–48	Garland Peyton (Georgia)
1948–49	Walter B. Jones (Alabama)
1949–50	Wilson M. Laird (North Dakota)
1950–51	Edgar P. Rothrock (South Dakota)
1951–52	E.L. Clark (Missouri)
1952–53	Herman Gunter (Florida)
1953–54	Charles F. Deiss (Indiana)
1954–55	Daniel J. Jones (Kentucky)
1955–56	Joseph T. Singewald Jr. (Maryland)
1956–57	Olaf P. Jenkins (California)
1957–58	Jasper L. Stuckey (North Carolina)
1958–59	H. Garland Hershey (Iowa)
1959–60	John C. Frye (Illinois)
1960–61	John T. Lonsdale (Texas) (died)
1961–62	Carl C. Branson (Oklahoma)
1962–63	Earl F. Cook (Idaho)
1963–64	Frank C. Foley (Kansas)
1964–65	Ian Campbell (California)
1965–66	John B. Patton (Indiana)
1966–67	Robert O. Vernon (Florida)
1967–68	Wallace W. Hagan (Kentucky)
1968–69	Peter T. Flawn (Texas)
1969–70	William C. Hayes (Missouri)
1970–71	Philip E. LaMoreaux (Alabama)
1971–72	Norman F. Williams (Arkansas)
1972–73	Kenneth N. Weaver (Maryland)
1973–74	James L. Calver (Virginia)
1974–75	Charles J. Mankin (Oklahoma)
1975–76	Duncan J. McGregor (South Dakota)
1976–77	Arthur A. Socolow (Pennsylvania)
1977–78	Robert B. Erwin (West Virginia)
1978–79	Daniel N. Miller Jr. (Wyoming)

Year	President–Elect
1979–80	Stephen G. Conrad (North Carolina)
1980–81	William L. Fisher (Texas)
1981–82	Meredith E. Ostrom (Wisconsin)
1982–83	Robert R. Jordan (Delaware)
1983–84	James F. Davis (California)
1984–85	Frank E. Kottlowski (New Mexico)
1985–86	Charles W. Hendry Jr. (Florida)
1986–87	Charles G. Groat (Louisiana)
1987–88	Larry D. Fellows (Arizona)
1988–89	Donald C. Haney (Kentucky)
1989–90	Ernest A. Mancini (Alabama)
1990–91	Robert H. Fakundiny (New York)
1991–92	Morris W. Leighton (Illinois)
1992–93	Donald A. Hull (Oregon)
1993–94	Donald M. Hoskins (Pennsylvania)
1994–95	Walter Schmidt (Florida)
1995–96	Earl H. Bennett (Idaho)
1996–97	Charles H. Gardner (North Carolina)
1997–98	Larry D. Woodfork (West Virginia)
1998–99	James M. Robertson (Wisconsin)
1999–2000	Jonathan G. Price (Nevada)
2000–01	Vicki J. Cowart (Colorado)
2001–02	Emery T. Cleaves (Maryland)
2002–03	John C. Steinmetz (Indiana)
2003–04	Robert G. Marvinney (Maine)
2004–05	Peter A. Scholle (New Mexico)
2005–06	Scott W. Tinker (Texas)
2006–07	Chacko J. John (Louisiana)
2007–08	Berry H. (Nick) Tew (Alabama)

Vice President (Executive Committeeman until 1937, Then Vice President)

Year	Vice President
1907–08	Alfred C. Lane (Michigan)
1908–09	Joseph H. Pratt (North Carolina)
1909–10	Israel C. White (West Virginia)
1910–11	Israel C. White (West Virginia)
1911–12	Israel C. White (West Virginia)
1912–13	Henry B. Kummel (New Jersey)

Year	Vice President
1913–14	Henry B. Kummel (New Jersey)
1914–15	Joseph H. Pratt (North Carolina)
1915–16	Joseph H. Pratt (North Carolina)
1916–17	Joseph H. Pratt (North Carolina)
1917–18	Joseph H. Pratt (North Carolina)
1918–19	Edward B. Mathews (Maryland)
1919–20	Edward B. Mathews (Maryland)
1920–21	Edward B. Mathews (Maryland)
1921–22	Henry A. Buehler (Missouri)
1922–23	Henry A. Buehler (Missouri)
1923–24	Henry A. Buehler (Missouri)
1924–25	Edward B. Mathews (Maryland)
1925–26	Edward B. Mathews (Maryland)
1926–27	Wilbur A. Nelson (Tennessee, Virginia)
1927–28	Henry A. Buehler (Missouri)/Wilbur A. Nelson (Tennessee, Virginia)
1928–29	Henry A. Buehler (Missouri)/Edward B. Mathews (Maryland)
1929–30	Henry A. Buehler (Missouri)/Edward B. Mathews (Maryland)
1930–31	Edward B. Mathews (Maryland)
1931–32	Arthur C. Bevan (Virginia)
1932–33	Arthur C. Bevan (Virginia)
1933–34	Arthur C. Bevan (Virginia)
1934–35	Raymond C. Moore (Kansas)
1935–36	Raymond C. Moore (Kansas)
1936–37	Raymond C. Moore (Kansas)
1937–38	Walter F. Pond (Tennessee)
1938–39	George E. Condra (Nebraska)
1939–40	Raymond C. Moore (Kansas)
1940–41	Raymond C. Moore (Kansas)
1941–42	Raymond C. Moore (Kansas)
1942–43	Earl K. Nixon (Oregon)
1943–44	Earl K. Nixon (Oregon)
1944–45	Robert H. Dott (Oklahoma)/Garland Peyton (Georgia) (acting)
1945–46	Edward L. Troxell (Connecticut)
1946–47	Arthur C. Trowbridge (Iowa)
1947–48	Arthur C. Trowbridge (Iowa)
1948–49	Wilson M. Laird (North Dakota)
1949–50	Edgar P. Rothrock (South Dakota)
1950–51	E.L. Clark (Missouri)
1951–52	Herman Gunter (Florida)

Year	Vice President
1952–53	Charles F. Deiss (Indiana)
1953–54	Daniel J. Jones (Kentucky)
1954–55	Joseph T. Singewald Jr. (Maryland)
1955–56	Olaf P. Jenkins (California)
1956–57	John H. Melvin (Ohio)
1957–58	H. Garland Hershey (Iowa)
1958–59	John C. Frye (Illinois)
1959–60	John T. Lonsdale (Texas)
1960–61	William L. Daoust (Michigan)
1961–62	Earl F. Cook (Idaho)
1962–63	Frank C. Foley (Kansas)
1963–64	Ian Campbell (California)
1964–65	John B. Patton (Indiana)
1965–66	Robert O. Vernon (Florida)
1966–67	Wallace W. Hagan (Kentucky)
1967–68	Peter T. Flawn (Texas)
1968–69	William C. Hayes (Missouri)
1969–70	Gerald E. Eddy (Michigan)
1970–71	Norman F. Williams (Arkansas)
1971–72	Kenneth N. Weaver (Maryland)
1972–73	James L. Calver (Virginia)
1973–74	Charles J. Mankin (Oklahoma)
1974–75	William L. Fisher (Texas)
1975–76	Arthur A. Socolow (Pennsylvania)
1976–77	Robert B. Erwin (West Virginia)
1977–78	Daniel N. Miller Jr. (Wyoming)
1978–79	Stephen G. Conrad (North Carolina)
1979–80	William L. Fisher (Texas)
1980–81	Meredith E. Ostrom (Wisconsin)
1981–82	Robert R. Jordan (Delaware)
1982–83	James F. Davis (California)
1983–84	Frank E. Kottlowski (New Mexico)
1984–85	Charles W. Hendry Jr. (Florida)
1985–86	Wallace B. Howe (Missouri)
1986–87	Larry D. Fellows (Arizona)
1987–88	Donald C. Haney (Kentucky)
1988–89	Ernest A. Mancini (Alabama)
1989–90	Robert H. Fakundiny (New York)
1990–91	Morris W. Leighton (Illinois)

Year	Vice President
1991–92	Donald A. Hull (Pennsylvania)
1992–93	Donald M. Hoskins (Pennsylvania)
1993–94	Norman C. Hester (Indiana)
1994–95	Norman C. Hester (Indiana)
1995–96	Charles H. Gardner (North Carolina)
1996–97	Larry D. Woodfork (West Virginia)
1997–98	James M. Robertson (Wisconsin)
1998–99	Jonathan G. Price (Nevada)
1999–2000	Vicki J. Cowart (Colorado)
2000–01	Emery T. Cleaves (Maryland)
2001–02	M. Lee Allison (Utah)
2002–03	S. Cragin Knox (Mississippi)
2003–04	S. Cragin Knox (Mississippi)
2004–05	Scott W. Tinker (Texas)
2005–06	Chacko J. John (Louisiana)
2006–07	David R. Wunsch (New Hampshire)
2007–08	David R. Wunsch (New Hampshire)

Secretary (Secretary–Treasurer until 1996; Secretary Thereafter)

Year	Secretary–Treasurer
1906	H. Foster Bain (Illinois) (temporary)
1907–08	H. Foster Bain (Illinois)
1908–09	H. Foster Bain (Illinois)
1909–10	H. Foster Bain (Illinois)
1910–11	Frank W. De Wolf (Illinois)
1911–12	Frank W. De Wolf (Illinois)
1912–13	Frank W. De Wolf (Illinois)
1913–14	Frank W. De Wolf (Illinois)
1914–15	Frank W. De Wolf (Illinois)
1915–16	Frank W. De Wolf (Illinois)/William O. Hotchkiss (Wisconsin)
1916–17	William O. Hotchkiss (Wisconsin)
1917–18	William O. Hotchkiss (Wisconsin)
1918–19	Thomas L. Watson (Virginia)
1919–20	Thomas L. Watson (Virginia)
1920–21	Wilbur A. Nelson (Tennessee, Virginia)
1921–22	Wilbur A. Nelson (Tennessee, Virginia)
1922–23	Wilbur A. Nelson (Tennessee, Virginia)
1923–24	Wilbur A. Nelson (Tennessee, Virginia)
1924–25	Morris M. Leighton (Illinois)

Year	Secretary–Treasurer
1925–26	Morris M. Leighton (Illinois)
1926–27	Morris M. Leighton (Illinois)
1927–28	Morris M. Leighton (Illinois)
1928–29	Morris M. Leighton (Illinois)
1929–30	Morris M. Leighton (Illinois)/George C. Branner (Arkansas)
1930–31	George C. Branner (Arkansas)
1931–32	George C. Branner (Arkansas)
1932–33	George C. Branner (Arkansas)
1933–34	George C. Branner (Arkansas)
1934–35	Arthur C. Bevan (Virginia)
1935–36	Arthur C. Bevan (Virginia)
1936–37	Arthur C. Bevan (Virginia)
1937–38	Raymond C. Moore (Kansas)
1938–39	Raymond C. Moore (Kansas)
1939–40	Paul H. Price (West Virginia)
1940–41	Paul H. Price (West Virginia)
1941–42	Robert H. Dott (Oklahoma)
1942–43	Robert H. Dott (Oklahoma)
1943–44	Robert H. Dott (Oklahoma)
1944–45	Meredith E. Johnson (New Jersey)
1945–46	Meredith E. Johnson (New Jersey)
1946–47	Edward L. Troxell (Connecticut)
1947–48	Walter B. Jones (Alabama)
1948–49	E.L. Clark (Missouri)
1949–50	E.L. Clark (Missouri)
1950–51	Charles F. Deiss (Indiana)
1951–52	Charles F. Deiss (Indiana)
1952–53	Daniel J. Jones (Kentucky)
1953–54	Olaf P. Jenkins (California)
1954–55	Olaf P. Jenkins (California)
1955–56	John H. Melvin (Ohio)
1956–57	Eugene Callaghan (New Mexico)
1957–58	John C. Frye (Illinois)
1958–59	Carlyle Gray (Pennsylvania)
1959–60	Carlyle Gray (Pennsylvania)
1960–61	Carlyle Gray (Pennsylvania)
1961–62	Carlyle Gray (Pennsylvania)/John B. Patton (Indiana) (acting)
1962–63	John B. Patton (Indiana)
1963–64	John B. Patton (Indiana)

Year	Secretary–Treasurer
1964–65	Thomas R. Beveridge/William C. Hayes (Missouri)
1965–66	William C. Hayes (Missouri)
1966–67	William C. Hayes (Missouri)
1967–68	William C. Hayes (Missouri)
1968–69	Hollis M. Dole (Oregon)
1969–70	Charles J. Mankin (Oklahoma)
1970–71	Charles J. Mankin (Oklahoma)
1971–72	Charles J. Mankin (Oklahoma)
1972–73	Charles J. Mankin (Oklahoma)
1973–74	Daniel N. Miller Jr. (Wyoming)
1974–75	Daniel N. Miller Jr. (Wyoming)
1975–76	Daniel N. Miller Jr. (Wyoming)
1976–77	Daniel N. Miller Jr. (Wyoming)
1977–78	Robert R. Jordan (Delaware)
1978–79	Robert R. Jordan (Delaware)
1979–80	Robert R. Jordan (Delaware)
1980–81	Robert R. Jordan (Delaware)
1981–82	Charles W. Hendry Jr. (Florida)
1982–83	Charles W. Hendry Jr. (Florida)
1983–84	Charles W. Hendry Jr. (Florida)
1984–85	Robert T. Segall (Michigan)
1985–86	Robert T. Segall (Michigan)
1986–87	Ernest A. Mancini (Alabama)
1987–88	Ernest A. Mancini (Alabama)
1988–89	Donald A. Hull (Oregon)
1989–90	Donald A. Hull (Oregon)
1990–91	Donald M. Hoskins (Pennsylvania)
1991–92	Donald M. Hoskins (Pennsylvania)
1992–93	Walter Schmidt (Florida)
1993–94	Walter Schmidt (Florida)
1994–95	Earl H. Bennett (Idaho)
1995–96	Jonathan G. Price (Nevada)
1996–97	James M. Robertson (Wisconsin)
1997–98	S. Cragin Knox (Mississippi)
1998–99	S. Cragin Knox (Mississippi)
1999–2000	M. Lee Allison (Utah)
2000–01	M. Lee Allison (Utah)
2001–02	Robert G. Marvinney (Maine)
2002–03	Robert G. Marvinney (Maine)

Year	Secretary–Treasurer
2003–04	Edmond G. Deal (Montana)
2004–05	Edmond G. Deal (Montana)
2005–06	Ron Tiessere (Washington)
2006–07	Ron Tiessere (Washington)
2007–08	Vicki S. McConnell (Oregon)

Treasurer (Position Created 1996)

Year	Treasurer
1996–97	Jonathan G. Price (Nevada)
1997–98	Jonathan G. Price (Nevada)
1998–99	Jonathan G. Price (Nevada)
1999–2000	Vicki J. Cowart (Colorado)
2000–01	John C. Steinmetz (Indiana)
2001–02	John C. Steinmetz (Indiana)
2002–03	Peter A. Scholle (New Mexico)
2003–04	Peter A. Scholle (New Mexico)
2004–05	Berry H. (Nick) Tew Jr. (Alabama)
2005–06	Berry H. (Nick) Tew Jr. (Alabama)
2006–07	Berry H. (Nick) Tew Jr. (Alabama)
2007–08	Vince Matthews (Colorado)

Historian

Year	Historian
1951–52	John H. Melvin (Ohio)
1952–53	John H. Melvin (Ohio)
1953–54	John H. Melvin (Ohio)
1954–55	H. Garland Hershey (Iowa)
1955–56	H. Garland Hershey (Iowa)
1956–57	Carl C. Branson (Oklahoma)
1957–58	Carl C. Branson (Oklahoma)
1958–59	Carl C. Branson (Oklahoma)
1959–60	Carl C. Branson (Oklahoma)
1960–61	George F. Hanson (Wisconsin)
1961–62	George F. Hanson (Wisconsin)
1962–63	George F. Hanson (Wisconsin)
1963–64	George F. Hanson (Wisconsin)
1964–65	George F. Hanson (Wisconsin)
1965–66	George F. Hanson (Wisconsin)

Year	Historian
1966–67	George F. Hanson (Wisconsin)
1967–68	George F. Hanson (Wisconsin)
1968–69	George F. Hanson (Wisconsin)
1969–70	George F. Hanson (Wisconsin)
1970–71	George F. Hanson (Wisconsin)
1971–72	George F. Hanson (Wisconsin)
1972–73	Charles G. Doll (Vermont)
1973–74	Charles G. Doll (Vermont)
1974–75	Charles G. Doll (Vermont)
1975–76	Charles G. Doll (Vermont)
1976–77	Charles G. Doll (Vermont)
1977–78	Arthur E. Slaughter (Michigan)
1978–79	Arthur E. Slaughter (Michigan)
1979–80	Arthur E. Slaughter (Michigan)
1980–81	Arthur E. Slaughter (Michigan)
1981–82	Robert E. Hershey (Tennessee)
1982–83	Robert E. Hershey (Tennessee)
1983–84	Robert E. Hershey (Tennessee)
1984–85	Robert E. Hershey (Tennessee)
1985–86	John B. Patton (Indiana)
1986–87	John H. Schilling (Nevada)
1987–88	John H. Schilling (Nevada)
1988–89	Norman K. Olson (South Carolina)
1989–90	Norman K. Olson (South Carolina)
1990–91	Norman K. Olson (South Carolina)
1991–92	Norman K. Olson (South Carolina)
1992–93	Donald L. Koch (Iowa)
1993–94	Donald L. Koch (Iowa)
1994–95	Donald L. Koch (Iowa)
1995–96	Donald L. Koch (Iowa)
1996–97	Emery T. Cleaves (Maryland)
1997–98	Emery T. Cleaves (Maryland)
1998–99	Emery T. Cleaves (Maryland)
1999–2000	Emery T. Cleaves (Maryland)
2000–01	David L. Southwick (Minnesota)
2001–02	David L. Southwick (Minnesota)
2002–03	James C. Cobb (Kentucky)
2003–04	James C. Cobb (Kentucky)

Year	Historian
2004–05	James C. Cobb (Kentucky)
2005–06	James C. Cobb (Kentucky)
2006–07	James C. Cobb (Kentucky)
2007–08	James C. Cobb (Kentucky)

Editor

Year	Editor
1929–30	George C. Branner (Arkansas)
1930–31	George C. Branner (Arkansas)
1931–32	George C. Branner (Arkansas)
1932–33	George C. Branner (Arkansas)
1933–34	Arthur C. Bevan (Virginia)
1934–35	Arthur C. Bevan (Virginia)
1935–36	Arthur C. Bevan (Virginia)
1936–37	Raymond C. Moore, Kenneth K. Landes (Kansas)
1937–38	Raymond C. Moore, Kenneth K. Landes (Kansas)
1938–39	Paul H. Price (West Virginia)
1939–40	Paul H. Price (West Virginia)
1940–41	Robert H. Dott (Oklahoma)
1941–42	Robert H. Dott (Oklahoma)
1942–43	Robert H. Dott (Oklahoma)
1943–44	Meredith E. Johnson (New Jersey)
1944–45	Meredith E. Johnson (New Jersey)
1945–46	Edward L. Troxell (Connecticut)
1946–47	Walter B. Jones (Alabama)
1947–48	E.L. Clark (Missouri)
1948–49	E.L. Clark (Missouri)
1949–50	Morris M. Leighton (Illinois)
1950–51	Morris M. Leighton (Illinois)
1951–52	E.L. Clark (Missouri)
1952–53	E.L. Clark (Missouri)
1953–54	E.L. Clark (Missouri)
1954–55	Thomas R. Beveridge (Missouri)
1955–56	Thomas R. Beveridge (Missouri)
1956–57	Thomas R. Beveridge (Missouri)
1957–58	Thomas R. Beveridge (Missouri)
1958–59	Thomas R. Beveridge (Missouri)
1959–60	Ian Campbell (California)

Year	Editor
1960–61	Ian Campbell (California)
1961–62	Ian Campbell (California)
1962–63	Robert O. Vernon (Florida)
1963–64	Robert O. Vernon (Florida)
1964–65	James L. Calver (Virginia)
1965–66	James L. Calver (Virginia)
1966–67	James L. Calver (Virginia)
1967–68	James L. Calver (Virginia)
1968–69	James L. Calver (Virginia)
1969–70	James L. Calver (Virginia)
1970–71	James L. Calver (Virginia)
1971–72	Edwin A. Noble (North Dakota)
1972–73	Edwin A. Noble (North Dakota)
1973–74	Edwin A. Noble (North Dakota)
1974–75	Edwin A. Noble (North Dakota)
1975–76	Edwin A. Noble (North Dakota)
1976–77	Edwin A. Noble (North Dakota)
1977–78	Edwin A. Noble (North Dakota)
1978–79	Vincent H. Dreeszen (Nebraska)
1979–80	Vincent H. Dreeszen (Nebraska)
1980–81	Vincent H. Dreeszen (Nebraska)
1981–82	Vincent H. Dreeszen (Nebraska)
1982–83	Vincent H. Dreeszen (Nebraska)
1983–84	Vincent H. Dreeszen (Nebraska)
1984–85	Ernest A. Mancini (Alabama)
1985–86	Ernest A. Mancini (Alabama)
1986–87	Robert C. Milici (Virginia)
1987–88	Robert C. Milici (Virginia)
1988–89	Robert C. Milici (Virginia)
1989–90	Robert C. Milici (Virginia)
1990–91	Robert C. Milici (Virginia)
1991–92	Thomas M. Berg (Ohio)
1992–93	Thomas M. Berg (Ohio)
1993–94	Thomas M. Berg (Ohio)
1994–95	Thomas M. Berg (Ohio)
1995–96	Thomas M. Berg (Ohio)
1996–97	John P. Bluemle (North Dakota)
1997–98	John P. Bluemle (North Dakota)
1998–99	John P. Bluemle (North Dakota)

Year	Editor
1999–2000	John P. Bluemle (North Dakota)
2000–01	John P. Bluemle (North Dakota)
2001–02	John P. Bleumle (North Dakota)
2002–03	John P. Bleumle (North Dakota)
2003–04	John P. Bleumle (North Dakota)
2004–05	Karl W. Muessig (New Jersey)
2005–06	Karl W. Muessig (New Jersey)
2006–07	Karl W. Muessig (New Jersey)
2007–08	Karl W. Muessig (New Jersey)

Statistician

Year	Statistician
1943–44	Wilson M. Laird (North Dakota)
1944–45	Theodore R. Meyers (New Hampshire)
1945–46	Wilson M. Laird (North Dakota)
1946–47	Wilson M. Laird (North Dakota)
1947–48	Wilson M. Laird (North Dakota)
1948–49	Wilson M. Laird (North Dakota)
1949–50	John H. Melvin (Ohio)
1950–51	John H. Melvin (Ohio)
1951–52	John H. Melvin (Ohio)
1952–53	John H. Melvin (Ohio)
1953–54	Eugene Callaghan (New Mexico)
1954–55	Eugene Callaghan (New Mexico)
1955–56	Carlyle Gray (Pennsylvania)
1956–57	Carlyle Gray (Pennsylvania)
1957–58	Frank C. Foley (Kansas)
1958–59	Frank C. Foley (Kansas)
1959–60	Frank C. Foley (Kansas)
1960–61	Frank C. Foley (Kansas)
1961–62	Robert O. Vernon (Florida)
1962–63	Wallace W. Hagan (Kentucky)
1963–64	Wallace W. Hagan (Kentucky)
1964–65	Wallace W. Hagan (Kentucky)
1965–66	Wallace W. Hagan (Kentucky)
1966–67	Philip E. LaMoreaux (Alabama)
1967–68	Philip E. LaMoreaux (Alabama)
1968–69	Philip E. LaMoreaux (Alabama)

Year	Statistician
1969–70	Philip E. LaMoreaux (Alabama)
1970–71	Arthur A. Socolow (Pennsylvania)
1971–72	Arthur A. Socolow (Pennsylvania)
1972–73	Robert R. Jordan (Delaware)
1973–74	Robert R. Jordan (Delaware)
1974–75	Robert R. Jordan (Delaware)
1975–76	Robert R. Jordan (Delaware)
1976–77	Robert R. Jordan (Delaware)
1977–78	Wallace B. Howe (Missouri)
1978–79	Wallace B. Howe (Missouri)
1979–80	Wallace B. Howe (Missouri)
1980–81	Wallace B. Howe (Missouri)
1981–82	Wallace B. Howe (Missouri)
1982–83	Wallace B. Howe (Missouri)
1983–84	Wallace B. Howe (Missouri)
1984–85	Larry D. Fellows (Arizona)
1985–86	Larry D. Fellows (Arizona)
1986–87	Morris W. Leighton (Illinois)
1987–88	Morris W. Leighton (Illinois)
1988–89	Morris W. Leighton (Illinois)
1989–90	Morris W. Leighton (Illinois)
1990–91	Haig F. Kasabach (New Jersey)
1991–92	Haig F. Kasabach (New Jersey)
1992–93	Haig F. Kasabach (New Jersey)
1993–94	Haig F. Kasabach (New Jersey)
1994–95	Haig F. Kasabach (New Jersey)
1995–96	Haig F. Kasabach (New Jersey)
1996–97	Vicki J. Cowart (Colorado)
1997–98	Vicki J. Cowart (Colorado)
1998–99	Vicki J. Cowart (Colorado)
1999–2000	Laurence R. Becker (Vermont)
2000–01	Laurence R. Becker (Vermont)
2001–02	Laurence R. Becker (Vermont)
2002–03	David R. Wunsch (New Hampshire)
2003–04	David R. Wunsch (New Hampshire)
2004–05	Walter Schmidt (Florida)
2005–06	Walter Schmidt (Florida)

Appendix 2:
Summaries of Annual Meetings, 1906–98

Compiled in 1977 by Charles G. Doll
(Vermont State Geologist, Retired; AASG Historian, 1972–77)

updated in 2007 by Richard A. Smath
(Kentucky Geological Survey)

and James C. Cobb
(Kentucky State Geologist; AASG Historian)

Introduction (from Charles G. Doll's 1977 manuscript)

As newly elected historian of the AASG, I [Charles Doll] felt an urgency to embark upon a project that would result in a contribution of interest to the members of the Association; hence, during a conversation with my good friend and colleague from Kentucky, Wallace Hagan, he made a suggestion that was adopted and pursued and which resulted in a chronological compilation of annual meetings of the Association from 1906 through 1976, contained in the following pages.

With one exception, the historian's incomplete files were the sole source of the needed information; the files consisted primarily of minutes, *The State Geologists Journal* (and its predecessor, *Journal of the Association of American State Geologists*), and correspondence. The one exception was the response to his appeal through the secretary for assistance in locating equivalents of the following missing minutes for the years 1907, 1909, 1913, 1914, 1916, 1917, and 1919–1925, inclusive. It now appears almost a certainty that they no longer exist. The source of the meager information for those years is indicated at the bottom of the entries for each of those years. Where information regarding the place of meeting is uncertain, it is indicated by a question mark, and where not known, the space is left blank.

Attention is called to the facts involving changes in and creation of offices as, it appears, the workload of the secretary became increasingly burdensome. With the founding of *Journal of the Association of American State Geologists* in 1930, the secretary was appointed editor and held this additional duty until 1950, when the editor became a separate entity. The secretary was also treasurer, which continues to the present day. There were two editors in 1935 and 1937. The office of vice president was established in 1937, replacing the executive committeemen (third and fourth members of the Executive Committee from 1927 to 1937). The position of third member of the Executive Committee (executive committeeman) existed from 1908 to 1927. The position of president-elect dates from 1948.

The office of statistician, actually established in 1944, is the continuation of the secretary's annual activities questionnaire and chart of the state geological surveys, the latter first appearing in the *Journal* in 1931. The records indicate that the secretary acted, in addition to his several other duties, as statistician from 1930 to 1944, when the work became separate. It appears that the term "statistician" was first employed in 1954, but is used in this compilation prior to this date as a matter of convenience. The office of historian was created in 1952, as an additional duty of the statistician until 1954.

The term "chairman" was used from 1906 to 1909, when the title was replaced by president.

The average attendance at annual meetings from 1906 to 1940 was 13 members, and from 1940 through 1976 was 31, more than double that of the previous period. The 1972 and 1975 annual meetings at Moab and Asheville, respectively, share the highest attendance records to that date of 33 state geologists. Attendance increased appreciably from 1940 through 1976, partly because assistants began attending meetings as well. Prior to 1927, six of the annual meetings took place in Washington, D.C., but from 1927 through 1945, all annual meetings were held there, the U.S. Geological Survey acting as host. The last annual meeting in the nation's capital was in 1950. Practically all meetings subsequent to 1950 were hosted by state geological organizations.

In 1920, a proposal was made to levy dues, but it seems that dues were indirectly paid in an assessment for defraying expenses of the *Journal* in 1930. The first mention of dues as such was in the treasurer's report in 1936.

The steady increase in the volume and diversity of the business of the Association through the years has necessitated the establishment of new offices and the appointment of special committees. Other agencies and organizations and federal agencies have been yearly participants almost from the beginning, and they have played an important role in the increase of business topics at the annual meetings. In the list below, the order of business in "Business Session" is in the same order as was presented in the minutes, and might therefore serve as a topical outline of the business conducted.

Acknowledgment and thanks are hereby expressed to members who responded to my requests for help. I enjoyed this research project and am grateful for the opportunity to serve the Association as its historian.

Note: The effort begun by Charles Doll to summarize the annual meetings was resumed by the Kentucky Geological Survey in 2004. The summaries for 1977 to 1998 were done using scanned images of the minutes and optical character recognition software.

Summaries of Annual Meetings of the AASG

1906, March 31, Chicago, Ill.,
Association of State Geologists of the Mississippi Valley
Host: H. Foster Bain, University of Chicago
Officers:

> Chairman: Ernest R. Buckley (temporary chair, Willis S. Blatchley)
> Secretary: H. Foster Bain

Members Present:

> H. Foster Bain, Illinois
> Willis S. Blatchley, Indiana
> Erasmus Haworth, Kansas
> Charles J. Norwood, Kentucky
> Alfred C. Lane, Michigan
> Ernest R. Buckley, Missouri
> Alfred C. Lane (Michigan)
> John A. Bownocker, Ohio

Business Session:

- Stated that the object of the meeting was to form an organization of Mississippi Valley state geologists for mutual benefit.
- Named organization Association of State Geologists of the Mississippi Valley.
- Named Willis S. Blatchley chairman.
- Named H. Foster Bain secretary.
- Informally discussed methods of testing and sampling materials.
- Discussed generally the need for an organization of geologists of the Mississippi Valley.

- Proposed annual spring conferences to which other geologists of the Mississippi Valley would be invited. Intention was conferences to bring about closer acquaintance and discussion rather than reading of papers.
- Discussed the relation of state surveys to the federal survey, of members of state surveys to private professional work, of the form and character of state publications, and other subjects (not mentioned in minutes).

1907, Washington, D.C.

Host: U.S. Geological Survey

Officers:

Chairman: Willis S. Blatchley

Secretary: H. Foster Bain

Executive Committeeman: Alfred C. Lane

Reference: *Journal of the Association of American State Geologists,* v. 2, no. 3, p. 19–25.

1908, May 12, Washington, D.C.

Host: U.S. Geological Survey

Officers:

Chairman: Henry B. Kummel

Secretary: H. Foster Bain

Executive Committeeman: Joseph H. Pratt

Members Present:

Eugene A. Smith, Alabama

Albert H. Purdue, Arkansas

Elias H. Sellards, Florida

Samuel W. McCallie, Georgia

H. Foster Bain, Illinois

Samuel Calvin, Iowa

Erasmus Haworth, Kansas

Gilbert D. Harris, Louisiana

William B. Clark, Maryland

Alfred C. Lane, Michigan

Albert F. Crider, Mississippi

Henry A. Buehler, Missouri

Erwin H. Barbour, Nebraska

Henry B. Kummel, New Jersey

John H. Clarke, New York

Joseph H. Pratt, North Carolina

Arthur G. Leonard, North Dakota

John A. Bownocker, Ohio

Richard H. Hice, Pennsylvania

Earle Sloan, South Carolina

George H. Perkins, Vermont

Israel C. White, West Virginia

William O. Hotchkiss, Wisconsin

Business Session:

- Discussed desirability of an organization of state geologists and its aim.
- Committee of chairman and secretary appointed to draft set of bylaws based upon suggestions made during discussion.
- Committee report. Name of organization: Association of American State Geologists. Officers: President, secretary, and a third member comprise Executive Committee. Elections: Annual elections of officers, who serve 1 year. Committees: Additional committees appointed. Transaction of business: Any proposition by a member given in brief form to the secretary, who circulates it among members for comment and discussion. Amendments: Bylaws amendments or changes by majority vote.
- Discussed obtaining franking privileges for the state surveys.
- Made resolution regarding appropriations for topographic work.
- Made motion to extend invitations to state geological surveys and similar organizations not represented at this meeting.

1909, December 28–31, Cambridge, Mass.

Host: Harvard University; met in conjunction with Geological Society of America

Officers:

President: Henry B. Kummel

Secretary: H. Foster Bain

Executive Committeeman: Israel C. White

Business Session:

- Urged passing of National Bureau of Mines bill.

Reference: *Journal of the Association of American State Geologists,* v. 2, no. 3, p. 19–25.

1910, May, Washington, D.C.

Host: U.S. Geological Survey

Officers:

President: Henry B. Kummel

Secretary: Frank W. De Wolf

Executive Committeeman: Israel C. White

Members Present:

Eugene A. Smith, Alabama
William N. Rice, Connecticut
Samuel W. McCallie, Georgia
Frank W. De Wolf, Illinois
Erasmus Haworth, Kansas
Edward B. Mathews, Maryland
Rollan C. Allen, Michigan
Ephraim N. Lowe, Mississippi
Henry A. Buehler, Missouri
Erwin H. Barbour, Nebraska
Henry B. Kummel, New Jersey
Joseph H. Pratt, North Carolina
Arthur G. Leonard, North Dakota
John A. Bownocker, Ohio
Charles N. Gould, Oklahoma
Thomas L. Watson, Virginia
Israel C. White, West Virginia
William O. Hotchkiss, Wisconsin

Business Session:

- Approved plan for cooperative bulletin on geological surveys.
- Committee appointed to collect and compile information regarding organization and work of the various surveys, with a view to its publication as a handbook of geologic and hydrographic surveys in the United States.

1911, April 20, Washington, D.C.
Host: U.S. Geological Survey
Officers:

President: Henry B. Kummel
Secretary: Frank W. De Wolf
Executive Committeeman: Israel C. White

Members Present:

Eugene A. Smith, Alabama
William N. Rice, Connecticut
Samuel W. McCallie, Georgia
Frank W. De Wolf, Illinois
Erasmus Haworth, Kansas
Edward B. Mathews, Maryland
Rollan C. Allen, Michigan
Ephraim N Lowe, Mississippi

Henry A. Buehler, Missouri

Erwin H. Barbour, Nebraska

Henry B. Kummel, New Jersey

Joseph H. Pratt, North Carolina

John A. Bownocker, Ohio

Charles N. Gould, Oklahoma

Charles W. Brown, Rhode Island

Thomas L. Watson, Virginia

Israel C. White, West Virginia

William O. Hotchkiss, Wisconsin

Business Session:

- Resolved that state geologists cooperating with Mineral Resources Division, U.S. Geological Survey, have right to publish lists of mineral producers in their states.

- Resolved that due credit for cooperation of state surveys be given in USGS publications.

1912, December 27–30, New Haven, Conn.

Host: Yale University; met in conjunction with Geological Society of America

Officers:

President: Israel C. White

Secretary: Frank W. De Wolf

Executive Committeeman: Henry B. Kummel

Members Present:

Eugene A. Smith, Alabama

Albert H. Purdue, Arkansas

William N. Rice, Connecticut

Elias H. Sellards, Florida

Frank W. De Wolf, Illinois

George F. Kay, Iowa

William B. Clark, Maryland

William H. Emmons, Minnesota

Henry B. Kummel, New Jersey

Joseph H. Pratt, North Carolina

George H. Perkins, Vermont

Israel C. White, West Virginia

Business Session:

- Resolved to elect officers annually at winter instead of at spring meetings.
- Discussed exchange of geologists employed by various state surveys.
- Discussed care of oil and gas wells to safeguard coal and water supplies.

- Discussed "blue sky law" and enforcement of the law by a state survey in regard to examining and reporting on mining corporations offering stock for sale within a state. Opinion was that such a function by a state would be "exceedingly dangerous."
- Discussed that mere acknowledgments in publications of the U.S. Geological Survey for cooperative work was not sufficient. Credit should be given in press bulletins for cooperation statistics; acknowledgments of cooperation in topography in press bulletins and key maps to show progress of topographic mapping.

1913, December 30–31, Princeton, N.J.

Host: Princeton University; met in conjunction with Geological Society of America

Officers:

President: Israel C. White

Secretary: Frank W. De Wolf

Executive Committeeman: Henry B. Kummel

Reference: *Journal of the Association of American State Geologists*, v. 2, no. 3, p. 19–25.

1914, December, Philadelphia, Pa.

Host:

Officers:

President: William B. Clark

Secretary: Frank W. De Wolf

Executive Committeeman: Joseph H. Pratt

Business Session:

- Kern-Foster Bill (selection of location of mining experiment stations and mine safety stations under U.S. Bureau of Mines) approved.

Reference: *Journal of the Association of American State Geologists*, v. 2, no. 3, p. 19–25.

1915, December 27, Washington, D.C.

Host: U.S. Geological Survey

Officers:

President: William B. Clark

Secretary: Frank W. De Wolf

Executive Committeeman:

Members Present:

Eugene A. Smith, Alabama

William N. Rice, Connecticut

Samuel W. McCallie, Georgia

Frank W. De Wolf, Illinois

William B. Clark, Maryland

Henry A. Buehler, Missouri

Henry B. Kummel, New Jersey

Johan A. Udden, Texas

George H. Perkins, Vermont

Israel C. White, West Virginia

William O. Hotchkiss, Wisconsin

Loyal W. Trumbull, Wyoming

Business Session:

- Exhibited new maps and reports.
- Urged that U.S. Bureau of Mines not act without recommendation of state geologists in locating experiment stations.
- Voted that state surveys assist in war time by locating deposits of pyrite, platinum, fluorite, iron, tin, tungsten, etc.
- Reported on and discussed allotting federal funds for topographic surveys.
- Elected officers of Association. "Old" officers continued for another term.
- Issued invitation to hold a field meeting in Oklahoma in fall of 1916.
- Discussed and reviewed California laws governing drilling of oil and gas wells.
- Discussed function of state surveys in appraising mining property and mineral land for taxation.
- Discussed expenses of motorcycles and automobiles in survey work.
- Discussed maintenance of museums.
- Discussed relation of official employees to private work in their own states or in other states; a variety of policies were in place.
- Discussed distribution of oil reports to operators, landowners, and the press.
- Discussed exhibits of high school collections and publicity movements.
- Discussed master "key" maps as guides to field notebooks and detailed office files.
- Discussed care of sample drillings from wells.
- Resolved to request that director of U.S. Geological Survey notify state geologists regarding hearings of Committee on Formation Names; also solicited and offered advice about each season's geologic program in the several states.
- Expressed that it was a lean year for congressional appropriations for the U.S. Geological Survey and the U.S. Bureau of Mines; suggested that state geologists help through their delegations in Congress.

1916, December 27–29, Albany, N.Y.

Host: Office of Geology and Paleontology;
met in conjunction with Geological Society of America

Officers:

President: Frank W. De Wolf

Secretary: William O. Hotchkiss

Executive Committeeman: Joseph H. Pratt

Reference: *Journal of the Association of American State Geologists,*
v. 2, no. 3, p. 19–25.

1917, December 27–29, St. Louis, Mo.

Host: Washington University; met in conjunction with
Geological Society of America

Officers:

President: Frank W. De Wolf

Secretary: William O. Hotchkiss

Executive Committeeman: Joseph H. Pratt

Reference: *Journal of the Association of*
American State Geologists,
v. 2, no. 3, p. 19–25.

1918, December 28–29, Baltimore, Md.

Host: Edward B. Mathews, Maryland Geological Survey;
met in conjunction with Geological Society of America

Officers:

President: William O. Hotchkiss

Secretary: Thomas L. Watson

Executive Committeeman: Edward B. Mathews

Members Present:

William N. Rice, Connecticut

Samuel W. McCallie, Georgia

Frank W. De Wolf, Illinois

George F. Kay, Iowa

Edward B. Mathews, Maryland

Rollan C. Allen, Michigan

William H. Emmons, Minnesota

Henry A. Buehler, Missouri

Henry B. Kummel, New Jersey

John H. Clarke, New York

John A. Bownocker, Ohio

Charles W. Shannon, Oklahoma

Wilbur A. Nelson, Tennessee

Johan A. Udden, Texas

George H. Perkins, Vermont

Thomas L. Watson, Virginia

Israel C. White, West Virginia

William O. Hotchkiss, Wisconsin

Loyal W. Trumbull, Wyoming

Business Session:

- Discussed war minerals.
- Announced that Mineral Administration Bill was approved.
- Called for closer cooperation with the U.S. Bureau of Mines.
- Discussed cooperative topographic mapping.
- Discussed cooperation between state geological surveys and university research.
- Discussed War Minerals Bill; need for it had passed.
- Discussed topographic mapping, costs and allotments.
- Passed motion to secure from each state a statement as to the amount of cooperative topographic funds asked from their legislature.
- Passed motion to appoint committee to act with committee from state highway and other organizations to secure sufficient appropriations for topographic maps.
- Passed motion to encourage those states without surveys to establish one.
- Passed motion to appoint committee to consider correlation problems between states.
- Discussed cooperative studies of formations extending into other states.
- Passed motion that question of summer meeting in 1919 be left to Executive Committee, with power to set.
- Passed motion that president of the Association be on National Research Council.
- Discussed budget systems, state surveys connected with other state departments, salaries paid by state surveys.

1919, September 1–6, Birmingham, Ala.

Host: Thomas L. Watson, Geological Survey of Alabama

Officers:

President: William O. Hotchkiss

Secretary: Thomas L. Watson

Executive Committeeman: Edward B. Mathews

Reference: *Journal of the Association of American State Geologists,* v. 2, no. 3, p. 19–25.

1920, December 28, Chicago, Ill.

Host: University of Chicago; met in conjunction with Geological Society of America

Officers:

> President: George H. Ashley
>
> Secretary: Wilbur A. Nelson
>
> Executive Committeeman: Edward B. Mathews

Business Session:

- Voted that the Executive Committee propose a permanent organization with levying dues.

Reference: *Journal of the Association of American State Geologists,* v. 2, no. 3, p. 19–25.

1921, December 28–30, Amherst, Mass.

Host: Amherst College; met in conjunction with Geological Society of America

Officers:

> President: Edward B. Mathews
>
> Secretary: Wilbur A. Nelson
>
> Executive Committeeman: Henry A. Buehler

Members Present:

> Frank W. De Wolf, Illinois
>
> George F. Kay, Iowa
>
> Raymond C. Moore, Kansas
>
> Edward B. Mathews, Maryland
>
> Henry B. Kummel, New Jersey
>
> John M. Clarke, New York
>
> Chris A. Hartnagel, New York
>
> Charles W. Honess, Oklahoma
>
> George H. Ashley, Pennsylvania
>
> Wilbur A. Nelson, Tennessee
>
> Johan A. Udden, Texas
>
> George H. Perkins, Vermont
>
> Thomas L. Watson, Virginia
>
> Israel C. White, West Virginia

Business Session:

- Discussed topographic mapping costs and appropriations.
- Discussed molding sands.
- Elected officers.

Reference: *Journal of the Association of American State Geologists,* v. 2, no. 3, p. 19–25.

1922, December 28–30, Ann Arbor, Mich.

Host: University of Michigan; met in conjunction with
Geological Society of America

Officers:

> President: Edward B. Mathews
>
> Secretary: Wilbur A. Nelson
>
> Executive Committeeman: Henry A. Buehler

Reference: *Journal of the Association of American State Geologists,*
v. 2, no. 3, p. 19–25.

1923, December 27–29, Washington, D.C.

Host: U.S. Geological Survey

Officers:

> President: Edward B. Mathews
>
> Secretary: Wilbur A. Nelson
>
> Executive Committeeman: Henry A. Buehler

Business Session:

- Discussed the Temple Bill.
- Reviewed clay products statistics.
- Discussed molding sands investigations.

Reference: *Journal of the Association of American State Geologists,*
v. 2, no. 3, p. 19–25.

1924, December 29–30, Ithaca, N.Y.

Host: Cornell University; met in conjunction with
Geological Society of America

Officers:

> President: Wilbur A. Nelson
>
> Secretary: Morris M. Leighton
>
> Executive Committeeman: Edward B. Mathews

Business Session:

- Reported on molding sand surveys.
- Voted to write the president of the United States
  requesting liberal support for scientific work.

Reference: *Journal of the Association of American State Geologists,*
v. 2, no. 3, p. 19–25.

1925, December, New Haven, Conn.

Host: Yale University; met in conjunction with Geological Society of America

Officers:

> President: Wilbur A. Nelson
> Secretary: Morris M. Leighton
> Executive Committeeman: Edward B. Mathews

Business Session:

- Voted to oppose proposed cut of the budget of the Secretary of the Interior.
- Voted to support proposed bill of American Engineering Council to commit Congress to a program for the completion of a nationwide survey of water resources.

Reference: *Journal of the Association of American State Geologists,* v. 2, no. 3, p. 19–25.

1926, December 28–29, Madison, Wis.

Host: Ernest F. Bean, Wisconsin Geological Survey; met in conjunction with Geological Society of America

Officers:

> President: Henry A. Buehler
> Secretary: Morris M. Leighton
> Executive Committeeman: Wilbur A. Nelson

Members Present:

> Morris M. Leighton, Illinois
> George F. Kay, Iowa
> Kenneth K. Landes, Kansas
> Edward B. Mathews, Maryland
> William H. Emmons, Minnesota
> Henry A. Buehler, Missouri
> Henry B. Kummel, New Jersey
> John A. Bownocker, Ohio
> Charles N. Gould, Oklahoma
> Edgar P. Rothrock, South Dakota
> Wilbur A. Nelson, Tennessee
> Elias H. Sellards, Texas
> Harold E. Culver, Washington
> Ernest F. Bean, Wisconsin

Business Session:

- Discussed Temple Bill and status of topographic survey appropriations by Congress.

- Discussed Newton Bill for increasing appropriations for water resource investigations. Motion carried unanimously that the Newton Bill be enthusiastically endorsed.
- Appointed member to Highway Research Board.
- Discussed standard scales for topographic mapping.
- Launched projects for securing better well records, samples, and cores.
- Discussed the formation of well drillers' associations.
- Agreed to cooperate with the National Research Council relative to salvaging well records.
- Elected officers.
- Discussed invitation by U.S. Geological Survey to meet in Washington early in April. Passed motion to accept invitation.

1927, April 25–26, Washington, D.C.

Host: U.S. Geological Survey

Officers:

> President: Ernest F. Bean
>
> Secretary: Morris M. Leighton
>
> Executive Committeemen: Henry A. Buehler, Wilbur A. Nelson

Members Present:

> Herman Gunter, Florida
>
> Samuel W. McCallie, Georgia
>
> Morris M. Leighton, Illinois
>
> Raymond C. Moore, Kansas
>
> Edward B. Mathews, Maryland
>
> Henry A. Buehler, Missouri
>
> Henry B. Kummel, New Jersey
>
> Chris A. Hartnagel, New York
>
> John A. Bownocker, Ohio
>
> Charles N. Gould, Oklahoma
>
> Ralph W. Stone, Pennsylvania
>
> Wilbur A. Nelson, Tennessee
>
> Walter F. Pond, Tennessee
>
> Israel C. White, West Virginia
>
> Ernest F. Bean, Wisconsin

Business Session:

- Discussed cooperation with the U.S. Coast and Geodetic Survey.
- Voted that the Association oppose transfer of work of U.S. Coast and Geodetic Survey from the Department of Commerce to the Department of the Interior.
- Voted that immediate past president be member of Executive Committee for 1 year.

- Discussed appointment of advisory boards from each state to act with U.S. Geographic Board of Names.
- Appointed committee of three to be on Coal Classification Committee of American Society for Testing and Materials.
- Discussed geologic names and U.S. Geological Survey Committee on Geologic Names.
- Discussed appropriate field scales in topographic mapping and method of making primary traverses to reduce cost.
- Discussed publishing of county topographic maps for use of the public.
- Discussed the Temple Bill.
- Discussed accelerated topographic mapping in Maine.
- Discussed the Newton Bill.
- Addressed by state geologist of New South Wales, Australia.
- Discussed relations of U.S. Geological Survey to state geological surveys in regard to federal parties doing geologic work in states without contacting state geologists, etc.
- Discussed relations of state surveys to geology departments doing graduate work.
- Discussed relations with U.S. Board of Geographic Names.
- Federal agencies made presentations.
- Memorialized the following senior state geologists of the Association:
  Dr. Eugene A. Smith, Alabama
  Dr. Israel C. White, West Virginia
  Dr. George H. Perkins, Vermont
  Dr. Samuel W. McCallie, Georgia
- Statements made concerning the activities and contributions of these gentlemen were made in the order given above by:
  Dr. Edward B. Mathews, Maryland
  Dr. John A. Bownocker, Ohio
  Dr. Henry B. Kummel, New Jersey
  Dr. Wilbur A. Nelson, Virginia

1928, April 24–25, Washington, D.C.

Host: U.S. Geological Survey

Officers:

>President: Ernest F. Bean
>Secretary: Morris M. Leighton
>Executive Committeemen: Henry A. Buehler, Edward B. Mathews

Members Present:

>George C. Branner, Arkansas
>Samuel W. McCallie, Georgia
>Morris M. Leighton, Illinois

George F. Kay, Iowa

Edward B. Mathews, Maryland

Richard A. Smith, Michigan

Henry A. Buehler, Missouri

George E. Condra, Nebraska

Charles N. Gould, Oklahoma

George H. Ashley, Pennsylvania

Walter F. Pond, Tennessee

David B. Reger, West Virginia

Ernest F. Bean, Wisconsin

Business Session:

- Discussed status of legislation regarding flood-control problem in relation to topographic mapping.
- Discussed Temple Bill to accelerate topographic mapping in the United States.
- Discussed Newton Bill.
- Discussed aerial photographic mapping.
- Discussed U.S. Coast and Geodetic Survey as serving cooperative topographic mapping.
- Discussed use of aerial photographs.
- Discussed financial basis of cooperation between state and federal agencies, especially topographic mapping and water-resources study.
- Discussed coordination of work of federal and state engineering; duplication of effort.
- Discussed standard scales and specifications for topographic mapping.
- Discussed kind of paper used for engraving topographic maps.
- Discussed "Relations of the Geological Work of the State and Federal Surveys."
- Suggested placing type specimens in fossil collections in the national museum.
- Continued discussion on paper for topographic maps.
- Discussed cooperation between federal and state surveys.
- Discussed methods for drilling and finishing water wells in cooperation with state well drillers' associations.
- Listened to brief address on control work, leveling, and triangulation.
- Discussed administration of state geological surveys, popularization of geology, legislative tendencies, organization of state departments and their effect on state geological surveys, representation of the Association on proposed commission to study flood control, field training to students majoring in geology and remuneration, and size of editions and distribution of geologic reports.
- Held personal conferences with cooperating officials of the U.S. Geological Survey and congressmen.

1929, February 15–16, Washington, D.C.

Host: U.S. Geological Survey

Officers:

> President: Ernest F. Bean
> Secretary: Morris M. Leighton
> Executive Committeemen: Edward B. Mathews, Henry A. Buehler

Members Present:

> Samuel W. McCallie, Georgia
> Raymond C. Moore, Kansas
> Edward B. Mathews, Maryland
> Henry A. Buehler, Missouri
> Henry B. Kummel, New Jersey
> Charles N. Gould, Oklahoma
> George H. Ashley, Pennsylvania
> Walter F. Pond, Tennessee
> William M. McGill, Virginia
> David B. Reger, West Virginia
> Ernest F. Bean, Wisconsin

Business Session:

- Discussed cooperative topographic mapping, costs of strip mapping, state maps.
- Discussed increases in appropriations for topographic mapping and in budget of U.S. Coast and Geodetic Survey for horizontal and vertical surveys.
- Discussed interstate physiographic correlations: physiographic levels; relations of U.S. Geological Survey with state surveys in this matter. Representatives of the Association and U.S. Geological Survey were to meet on broad correlation of physiographic features to develop a program for cooperative study and correlation of physiographic units.
- Discussed how state geological surveys may serve towns and villages with regard to deep water supplies.
- Discussed problem of combating unscrupulous oil and gas promoters.
- Heard report of Coal Classification Committee.
- Discussed and listened to presentations on topographic mapping: engraving of topographic maps.
- Compared costs of using 1:48,000 and 1:24,000 field scales, and value of recognizing physiographic forms in topographic field mapping.
- Discussed state geologic maps.
- Discussed extension and reorganization of state geological surveys, establishment of new surveys and revival of old.
- Discussed interstate correlations.
- Discussed popularization of geology and publicity on geologic survey work.

1930, February 13–14, Washington, D.C.

Host: U.S. Geological Survey

Officers:

> President: Ernest F. Bean
>
> Secretary: George C. Branner
>
> Executive Committeemen: Edward B. Mathews, Henry A. Buehler
>
> Editor: George C. Branner

Present:

> George C. Branner, Arkansas
>
> Walter H. Bradley, California
>
> Herman Gunther, Florida
>
> Samuel W. McCallie, Georgia
>
> Morris M. Leighton, Illinois
>
> Edward B. Mathews, Maryland
>
> Richard A. Smith, Michigan
>
> Henry A. Buehler, Missouri
>
> Francis A. Thomson, Montana
>
> Henry B. Kummel, New Jersey
>
> Wilbur Stout, Ohio
>
> Charles N. Gould, Oklahoma
>
> George H. Ashley, Pennsylvania
>
> Walter F. Pond, Tennessee
>
> Arthur C. Bevan, Virginia
>
> Ernest F. Bean, Wisconsin

Business Session:

- Discussed air route maps and aerial mapping, cooperative topographic mapping, coal standards, and water-resources investigation.
- Adopted statement of organization of the Association.
- Discussed plans for summer field trip and 1932 meeting of International Geological Congress.
- Discussed new move to cause state to share printing cost of topographic maps and stream gaging reports.
- Discussed issuing *Journal of the Association of American State Geologists:* cost of materials, labor, and expense of publishing. Voted to regard material in *Journal* as confidential and not for public release.
- Heard report of Joint Committee on Physiographic Correlations.
- Discussed federal appropriations for geology for the coming year.
- Discussed progress in the preparation of state geologic maps.
- Heard report of Joint Committee on Geologic Correlation: coal classification report.

- Stated that official name of Association is "The Association of American State Geologists."
- Discussed membership: Ex officio and confined to heads of state geological surveys or organizations performing similar functions. Assistant state geologists had membership privileges. Members had power to appoint temporary alternates to represent them. One vote to a survey.
- Stated terms of office: 1 year. Incumbents were eligible for reelection.
- Discussed meetings: Executive Committee, publication, and U.S. Bureau of Mines conference.

1931, February 13–14, Washington, D.C.
Host: U.S. Geological Survey
Officers:

> President: Morris M. Leighton
> Secretary: George C. Branner
> Executive Committeemen: Arthur C. Bevan, Ernest F. Bean
> Editor: George C. Branner

Present:

> George C. Branner, Arkansas
> Herman Gunter, Florida
> Samuel W. McCallie, Georgia
> John W. Finch, Idaho
> Morris M. Leighton, Illinois
> George F. Kay, Iowa
> Edward B. Mathews, Maryland
> Richard A. Smith, Michigan
> Henry A. Buehler, Missouri
> Wilbur Stout, Ohio
> Walter F. Pond, Tennessee
> Arthur C. Bevan, Virginia
> James D. Sisler, West Virginia

Business Session:

- Voted for officers.
- Discussed expenses of *Journal* and secretary.
- Amended statement of organization.
- Heard reports of representatives on National Research Council.
- Celebrated 200th anniversary of birth of George Washington.
- Discussed excursion rates, convention railway rates.
- Discussed summer field meeting.
- Discussed filing of geologic maps.
- Discussed overhead costs of cooperative topographic mapping and stream gaging.

- Discussed International Geological Congress.
- Discussed status of state-federal cooperation.
- Discussed airplane mapping.
- Discussed cooperative agreements on stream gaging.
- Discussed cooperative geologic mapping.
- Discussed U.S. Coast and Geodetic Survey control surveys.
- Discussed new requirement providing for state sharing printing costs of topographic maps and stream gaging reports.
- Discussed reduction of Interior Department appropriations for 1933.
- Discussed magnetometer and electrical resistivity.
- Discussed methods of financing state geological surveys.
- Discussed reinterpretation of the Temple Act.
- Discussed topographic mapping allocations.
- Discussed water resources.
- Discussed U.S. Coast and Geodetic Survey levels.
- Discussed status of International Geological Congress.

1932, February 18–19, Washington, D.C.
Host: U.S. Geological Survey
Officers:

> President: Morris M. Leighton
> Secretary: George C. Branner
> Executive Committeemen: Arthur C. Bevan, Ernest F. Bean
> Editor: George C. Branner

Members Present:

> Gurdon M. Butler, Arizona
> George C. Branner, Arkansas
> Walter H. Bradley, California
> Herman Gunter, Florida
> John W. Finch, Idaho
> Morris M. Leighton, Illinois
> Raymond C. Moore, Kansas
> Richard A. Smith, Michigan
> Henry A. Buehler, Missouri
> Francis A. Thomson, Montana
> Henry B. Kummel, New Jersey
> George H. Ashley, Pennsylvania
> Walter F. Pond, Tennessee
> Arthur C. Bevan, Virginia
> William M. McGill, Virginia
> James D. Sisler, West Virginia

Business Session:
- Voted for officers.
- Discussed expenses of *Journal* and secretary.
- Heard reports of committees:
  - National Research Council.
  - International Geological Congress.
- Discussed summer field meeting.
- Discussed library of the U.S. Geological Survey.
- Discussed statement of organization.
- Discussed cooperation with American Association of State Highway Engineers in regard to topographic mapping.
- Elected committee members.
- Discussed political contacts and public relations of members.
- Discussed reduction of Department of the Interior appropriations for 1933.
- Discussed magnetometer and electrical resistivity.
- Discussed methods of financing state geological surveys.
- Discussed reinterpretation of the Temple Act.
- Discussed topographic mapping allocations.
- Discussed water resources.
- Discussed U.S. Coast and Geodetic Survey levels.
- Discussed status of International Geological Congress.

1933, February 23–24, Washington, D.C.

Host: U.S. Geological Survey

Officers:

President: Morris M. Leighton
Secretary: George C. Branner
Executive Committeemen: Arthur C. Bevan, Ernest F. Bean
Editor: George C. Branner

Members Present:

Edward B. Mathews, Maryland
Francis A. Thomson, Montana
George H. Ashley, Pennsylvania
Walter F. Pond, Tennessee
Arthur C. Bevan, Virginia
Harold E. Culver, Washington
James D. Sisler, West Virginia

Business Session:
- Voted for officers.
- Heard secretary's report.

- Discussed legislative action affecting various state surveys. Surveys and budgets were in danger.
- Discussed policies regarding analyses of specimens.
- Discussed talks before civic organizations.
- Discussed status of state surveys.
- Heard presentations of U.S. Geological Survey. Proof of new geologic map of the United States displayed.
- Discussed topographic mapping for employment of engineers.
- Discussed highway mapping.
- Discussed publication of water resource papers.
- Discussed topographic mapping appropriations.
- Discussed International Geological Congress.
- Discussed Century of Progress Exposition in Chicago.
- Noted change in names of surveys.
- Expressed appreciation of *Journal*.

1934, February 22–23, Washington, D.C.

Host: U.S. Geological Survey

Officers:

George C. Branner, Arkansas
Richard W. Smith, Georgia
John W. Finch, Idaho
Morris M. Leighton, Illinois
Francis A. Thomson, Montana
Henry B. Kummel, New Jersey
Herman J. Bryson, North Carolina
Harold E. Simpson, North Dakota
Walter F. Pond, Tennessee
Arthur C. Bevan, Virginia
James D. Sisler, West Virginia

President: George C. Branner
Secretary: Arthur C. Bevan
Executive Committeemen: Raymond C. Moore, Morris M. Leighton
Editor: Arthur C. Bevan

Members Present:

George C. Branner, Arkansas
Richard W. Smith, Georgia
John W. Finch, Idaho
Morris M. Leighton, Illinois
Francis A. Thomson, Montana
Henry B. Kummel, New Jersey
Herman J. Bryson, North Carolina
Harold E. Simpson, North Dakota
Walter F. Pond, Tennessee
Arthur C. Bevan, Virginia
James D. Sisler, West Virginia

Business Session:

- Elected officers.
- Presented financial statement.
- Held symposium on state geological surveys.
- Discussed Civil Works Administration projects.

- Discussed Public Works Administration projects.
- Discussed national planning.
- Discussed mineral resources surveys carried on with Public Works Administration funds.
- Discussed progress of topographic mapping by the U.S. Geological Survey.
- Discussed topographic mapping with Public Works funds.
- Discussed Photo-mapping under Civil Works Administration.
- Discussed Commodities Division of the U.S. Army.
- Discussed water resources work of U.S. Geological Survey.
- Discussed other finances of the U.S. Geological Survey.

1935, February 21, Washington, D.C.

Host: U.S. Geological Survey

Officers:

George C. Branner
President: George C. Branner
Secretary: Arthur C. Bevan
Executive Committeemen: Raymond C. Moore, Morris M. Leighton
Editor: Arthur C. Bevan

Members Present:

George C. Branner, Arkansas
Walter H. Bradley, California
Melville F. Coolbaugh, Colorado
Richard W. Smith, Georgia
Morris M. Leighton, Illinois
Arthur C. Trowbridge, Iowa
Edward B. Mathews, Maryland
Richard A. Smith, Michigan
Henry A. Buehler, Missouri
George H. Ashley, Pennsylvania
Walter F. Pond, Tennessee
Arthur C. Bevan, Virginia
Paul H. Price, West Virginia

Business Session:

- Made committee appointments.
- Discussed statement chart showing appropriations of geological surveys and their allocations to types of projects.
- Discussed popularization of geology.
- Discussed topics submitted by various state geologists: publicity, state planning, relations of state geological surveys to public works projects relative to natural resources.

1936, February 20–22, Washington, D.C.

Host: U.S. Geological Survey

Officers:

> President: George C. Branner
>
> Secretary: Arthur C. Bevan
>
> Executive Committeemen: Raymond C. Moore, Morris M. Leighton
>
> Editor: Arthur C. Bevan

Members Present:

> George C. Branner, Arkansas
>
> Morris M. Leighton, Illinois
>
> Arthur C. Trowbridge, Iowa
>
> Kenneth K. Landes, Kansas
>
> Richard A. Smith, Michigan
>
> A.M. Gaudin, Montana
>
> Henry B. Kummel, New Jersey
>
> Robert H. Dott, Oklahoma
>
> George H. Ashley, Pennsylvania
>
> Arthur C. Bevan, Virginia

Business Session:

- Heard secretary's report
- Heard summary of net funds available to state geological surveys and of projects undertaken.
- Reported on and discussed activities of state geological surveys.
- Discussed formation of National Defense Committee of the Association.
- Requested suggestions in regard to "Report of the Planning Committee for Mineral Policy."
- Discussed mapping agencies and obtaining funds for accelerating topographic mapping.
- Discussed work of American Mining Congress.
- Went into executive session pertaining to uncompleted work of U.S. Coast and Geodetic Survey.
- Participated in annual conference with federal officials: U.S. Geological Survey, U.S. Bureau of Mines, U.S. Coast and Geodetic Survey, National Resources Committee, National Park Service, American Engineering Council.

1937, February 18–20, Washington, D.C.

Host: U.S. Geological Survey

Officers:

> President: Arthur C. Bevan
>
> Secretary: Raymond C. Moore
>
> Vice President: Walter F. Pond
>
> Editors: Raymond C. Moore, Kenneth K. Landes

Members Present:

> George C. Branner, Arkansas
>
> Morris M. Leighton, Illinois
>
> Arthur C. Trowbridge, Iowa
>
> Raymond C. Moore, Kansas
>
> Edward B. Mathews, Maryland
>
> Richard A. Smith, Michigan
>
> Henry A. Buehler, Missouri
>
> Henry B. Kummel, New Jersey
>
> George H. Ashley, Pennsylvania
>
> Arthur C. Bevan, Virginia
>
> Paul H. Price, West Virginia

Business Session:

- Heard report of secretary.
- Passed motion that title of "third member of Executive Committee" be changed to "vice president."
- Discussed publicizing geology.
- Discussed cost and printing of geologic maps.
- Discussed geophysical benchmarks, their locations to be determined in consultation with state geologists.
- Discussed acceleration of topographic mapping.
- Suggested that U.S. Geological Survey act as connecting link between states in problems of interstate correlation, stratigraphy, and other broad geologic problems.
- Discussed problem of prompt collection of mineral production statistics.
- Reported on exhibits of American Mining Congress.
- Summarized programs of state surveys:
- Discussed groundwater, Works Progress Administration projects, natural gas and brines, new state geologic maps, topographic mapping, areal mapping, new publications, exhibits, educational activities, elevations, work on coal, oil and gas, clays, rock products, state museum work, materials to schools, road materials, stratigraphic problems.
- Heard report of annual conference with federal officials.
- Discussed topographic mapping program further.

1938, February 17–18, Washington, D.C.
Host: U.S. Geological Survey
Officers:
> President: Arthur C. Bevan
>
> Secretary: Raymond C. Moore
>
> Vice President: George E. Condra
>
> Editors: Raymond C. Moore, Kenneth K. Landes

Members Present:
> George C. Branner, Arkansas
>
> Morris M. Leighton, Illinois
>
> Kenneth K. Landes, Kansas
>
> Edward B. Mathews, Maryland
>
> Franklin G. Pardee, Michigan
>
> Henry A. Buehler, Missouri
>
> Francis A.Thomson, Montana
>
> George E. Condra, Nebraska
>
> Robert H. Dott, Oklahoma
>
> George H. Ashley, Pennsylvania
>
> Walter F. Pond, Tennessee
>
> Arthur C. Bevan, Virginia
>
> Paul H. Price, West Virginia

Business Session:
- Approved minutes of special December meeting in Washington.
- Heard treasurer's report.
- Moved and approved regular assessment of $7 as dues for the membership.
- Read communication from President Franklin D. Roosevelt relating to general mapping program.
- Appointed committee to draft resolution reaffirming support of Hayden-Ickes Bill.
- Reported on activities of Nominating Committee.
- Reported on activities of the Geological Society of America Committee on Public Education in Geology.
- Reported on methods of geologic illustrations.
- Reported on use and cost of planographing geological survey publications.
- Reported on conference with federal officials:
  - Review of work of U.S. Geological Survey related to states.
  - Status and progress of geologic folios: "have died a natural death."
  - Report on United States iron work.
  - Report on fuels and economic studies of fuel resources.

   – Lexicon of geologic names has been prepared.
   – Report on water resources.
   – Report on topographic mapping.
   – Availability of aerial photographs for the states.
   – Report on selecting a repository for aerial maps.
   – Recommendations of state geologists on whether
    or not to show individual houses on topographic
    maps in large cities, and how to accomplish.
   – Report of U.S. Coast and Geodetic Survey.
   – Report of Division of Terrestrial Magnetism and Seismology.
   – Committee appointed to prepare resolution on topographic mapping.
   – Proposal for strip topographic mapping along federal highways.
 • Reviewed activities of state surveys.

1939, February 16–17, Washington, D.C.

Host: U.S. Geological Survey

Officers:
  President: Walter F. Pond
  Secretary: Paul H. Price
  Vice President: Raymond C. Moore
  Editor: Paul H. Price

Members Present:
  Morris M. Leighton, Illinois
  Edward B. Mathews, Maryland
  Francis A. Thomson, Montana
  George E. Condra, Nebraska
  Meredith E. Johnson, New Jersey
  Earl K. Nixon, Oregon
  George H. Ashley, Pennsylvania
  Walter F. Pond, Tennessee
  Arthur C. Bevan, Virginia
  Paul H. Price, West Virginia

Business Session:
 • Reported on meeting of Nominating Committee.
 • Discussed multigraph duplicator process in publication of maps.
 • Directed secretary to provide for honorary membership without dues.
 • Discussed methods of distribution of state geological survey publications.
 • Discussed water facilities program and its relation to state surveys.
 • Discussed state reports in regard to educational usefulness.
 • Proposed having annual meetings jointly with
  Geological Society of America.

- Discussed participation by state geological surveys in forthcoming XVIII International Geological Congress in England.
- Reported on activities of Nominating Committee.
- Presentations made by federal agencies:
    - U.S. Geological Survey on topographic mapping, groundwater study, and study of strategic minerals.
    - Report on magnetic surveys.
    - U.S. Department of Agriculture discussed preparation and publication of reports on natural resources, including minerals, and data on the different states.
    - Questions and discussions on a number of topics related to those mentioned above with federal officials.
    - Report of U.S. Coast and Geodetic Survey.

1940, February 15–16, Washington, D.C.

Host: U.S. Geological Survey

Officers:

President: George E. Condra

Secretary: Paul H. Price

Vice President: Raymond C. Moore

Editor: Paul H. Price

Members Present:

S.J. Lloyd, Alabama

George C. Branner, Arkansas

Melville F. Coolbaugh, Colorado

Edward L. Troxell, Connecticut

Aurelius S. Furcron, Georgia

Garland Peyton, Georgia

Morris M. Leighton, Illinois

Arthur C. Trowbridge, Iowa

Frank C. Foley, Kansas

Raymond C. Moore, Kansas

Henry A. Buehler, Missouri

Francis A. Thomson, Montana

George E. Condra, Nebraska

Meredith E. Johnson, New Jersey

Earl K. Nixon, Oregon

George H. Ashley, Pennsylvania

Walter F. Pond, Tennessee

Arthur C. Bevan, Virginia

Paul H. Price, West Virginia

Business Session:

- Discussed relations of public geological surveys to commercial consultants and laboratories.
- Discussed feasibility of meeting of the Association at annual meeting of the Geological Society of America.
- Discussed relation of geological surveys to regional meetings of geologists.
- Discussed public relations of geological surveys.
- Reported on deficiency minerals.
- Heard report of Committee on Reorganization.
- Heard reports of federal agencies: U.S. Geological Survey, U.S. Bureau of Mines, U.S. Department of Agriculture.
- Reviewed Works Progress Administration work.
- Discussed cooperative statewide mineral survey.
- Heard report on taxation of mineral deposits.
- Discussed laboratory studies of industrial materials.
- Discussed content of well-studied survey programs.
- Discussed possible methods of public education in geology.
- Heard report of the treasurer.
- Discussed distribution of the *Journal*.
- Heard report of committee on reorganization of certain federal departments.
- Gave expressions of appreciation and thanks.

1941, February 20–21, Washington, D.C.

Host: U.S. Geological Survey

Officers:

> President: Raymond C. Moore
> Secretary: Robert H. Dott
> Vice President: Paul H. Price
> Editor: Robert H. Dott

Members Present:

> S.J. Lloyd, Alabama
> Thomas G. Chapman, Arizona
> George C. Branner, Arkansas
> Edward L. Troxell, Connecticut
> Garland Peyton, Georgia
> Morris M. Leighton, Illinois
> Arthur C. Trowbridge, Iowa
> Raymond C. Moore, Kansas
> Richard A. Smith, Michigan
> Henry A. Buehler, Missouri

Francis A. Thomson, Montana

George E. Condra, Nebraska

Meredith E. Johnson, New Jersey

Chris A. Hartnagel, New York

Thomas G. Murdock, North Carolina

Jasper L. Stuckey, North Carolina

Robert H. Dott, Oklahoma

Malcolm C. Oakes, Oklahoma

George H. Ashley, Pennsylvania

Walter F. Pond, Tennessee

Arthur C. Bevan, Virginia

Paul H. Price, West Virginia

Business Session:

- Discussed defense minerals in Georgia.
- Discussed bulletins, their cost and financial return.
- Discussed Federal Stock Piling Act.
- Discussed Interstate Oil Compact program.
- Discussed federal oil and gas control versus state control through Interstate Oil Compact.
- Discussed using national needs for obtaining state appropriations.
- Presented results obtained by state geological surveys in their programs of public education in geology.
- Discussed the *Journal* and state geologists' part in the activities of the Association.
- Discussed mineral supply problems.
- Discussed strategic minerals.
- Discussed position of state geological surveys in national defense program.
- Discussed groundwater legislation, federal mapping program.

1942, February 13–14, Washington, D.C.
Host: U.S. Geological Survey
Officers:

President: Paul H. Price

Secretary: Robert H. Dott

Vice President: Earl K. Nixon

Editor: Robert H. Dott

Members Present:

S.J. Lloyd, Alabama

George C. Branner, Arkansas

Edward L. Troxell, Connecticut

Garland Peyton, Georgia

Morris M. Leighton, Illinois

Ralph E. Esarey, Indiana

Arthur C. Trowbridge, Iowa

Raymond C. Moore, Kansas

Edward B. Mathews, Maryland

Richard A. Smith, Michigan

Henry A. Buehler, Missouri

Francis A. Thomson, Montana

George E. Condra, Nebraska

Jay A. Carpenter, Nevada

Meredith E. Johnson, New Jersey

Henry B. Kummel, New Jersey

Chris A. Hartnagel, New York

Jasper L. Stuckey, North Carolina

Wilson M. Laird, North Dakota

Robert H. Dott, Oklahoma

Earl K. Nixon, Oregon

George H. Ashley, Pennsylvania

Edgar P. Rothrock, South Dakota

Walter F. Pond, Tennessee

Elbridge C. Jacobs, Vermont

Arthur C. Bevan, Virginia

Harold E. Culver, Washington

Paul H. Price, West Virginia

Ernest F. Bean, Wisconsin

Business Session:

- Discussed propriety of holding this meeting in Washington, D.C., because of hotel situation.
- Heard reports from Association committees on:
  - Aids to geological surveys, survey publications, liaison with agencies in Washington.
  - State survey war activities, state survey organization.
  - State survey programs and policies, as emphasis on field studies, groundwater investigations, beneficiation of minerals, administration of state conservation regulations, etc.
- Discussed part state surveys can play in the national effort.
- Discussed status of war minerals and mapping programs.
- Heard report of Committee on Stratigraphic Classification and Nomenclature.
- Heard report of New England Committee on Mineral Resources.
- Summarized war work problems.
- Heard reports on state survey control.
- Heard presentations by federal agencies: U.S. Geological Survey, U.S. Bureau of Mines.

- Heard report of Auditing Committee.
- Heard report of Balloting Committee.
- Heard report of Resolutions Committee.
- Heard report of secretary.

1943, February 19–20, Washington, D.C.
Host: U.S. Geological Survey
Officers:

President: Paul H. Price
Secretary: Robert H. Dott
Vice President: Earl K. Nixon
Editor: Robert H. Dott

Members Present:

S.J. Lloyd, Alabama
Bert S. Butler, Arizona
Richard J. Anderson, Arkansas
Edward L. Troxell, Connecticut
Morris M. Leighton, Illinois
Ralph E. Esarey, Indiana
Arthur C. Trowbridge, Iowa
John C. Frye, Kansas
Richard A. Smith, Michigan
Frank F. Grout, Minnesota
Henry A. Buehler, Missouri
George E. Condra, Nebraska
Theodore R. Meyers, New Hampshire
Chris A. Hartnagel, New York
Jasper L. Stuckey, North Carolina
Robert H. Dott, Oklahoma
Earl K. Nixon, Oregon
George H. Ashley, Pennsylvania
Walter F. Pond, Tennessee
Arthur C. Bevan, Virginia
Harold E. Culver, Washington
Paul H. Price, West Virginia
Ernest F. Bean, Wisconsin

Business Session:

- Heard report of Committee on Public Education in Geology.
- Heard report of Committee on Aids to Geological Surveys.
- Heard report and summary of Advisory Committee on War Matters.
- Discussed paper on geophysical methods in groundwater studies.

- Heard report on national situation in minerals.
- Heard presentation on and discussed foreign sources of minerals.
- Discussed minerals in Alaska.
- Discussed role of geological surveys during war.
- Heard report on activities of the U.S. Geological Survey.
- Heard report on activities of the U.S. Bureau of Mines.

1944, February 24–26, Washington, D.C.
Host: U.S. Geological Survey
Officers:
President: Earl K. Nixon
Secretary: Meredith E. Johnson
Vice President: Robert H. Dott
Editor: Meredith E. Johnson
Statistician: Wilson M. Laird

Members Present:
S.J. Lloyd, Alabama
Olaf P. Jenkins, California
Edward L. Troxell, Connecticut
Garland Peyton, Georgia
Morris M. Leighton, Illinois
Ralph E. Esarey, Indiana
Arthur C. Trowbridge, Iowa
John C. Frye, Kansas
Daniel J. Jones, Kentucky
Joseph T. Singewald Jr., Maryland
Richard A. Smith, Michigan
Henry A. Buehler, Missouri
George E. Condra, Nebraska
Theodore R. Meyers, New Hampshire
Meredith E. Johnson, New Jersey
Chris A. Hartnagel, New York
Jasper L. Stuckey, North Carolina
Wilson M. Laird, North Dakota
Robert H. Dott, Oklahoma
Earl K. Nixon, Oregon
George H. Ashley, Pennsylvania
Edgar P. Rothrock, South Dakota
Walter F. Pond, Tennessee
Arthur C. Bevan, Virginia
Harold E. Culver, Washington
Ernest F. Bean, Wisconsin

Business Session:

- Discussed work of U.S. Geological Survey in the different states.
- Discussed work on mineral deposits by U.S. Geological Survey in the different states; also work of U.S. Bureau of Mines, and state geological surveys as cooperating agencies.
- Discussed present situation of mineral supplies in the United States.
- Discussed cooperative groundwater studies.
- Heard report of retiring editor.

1945, February 21–23, Washington, D.C.

Host: U.S. Geological Survey

Officers:

Ｐresident: Robert H. Dott
Secretary: Meredith E. Johnson
Vice President: Edward L. Troxell
Editor: Meredith E. Johnson
Statistician: Theodore R. Meyers

Members Present:

Walter B. Jones, Alabama
Walter W. Bradley, California
Edward L. Troxell, Connecticut
Garland Peyton, Georgia
Morris M. Leighton, Illinois
Arthur C. Trowbridge, Iowa
John C. Frye, Kansas
Daniel J. Jones, Kentucky
Joseph T. Singewald Jr., Maryland
Franklin G. Pardee, Michigan
Frank F. Grout, Minnesota
William C. Morse, Mississippi
E.L. Clark, Missouri
George E. Condra, Nebraska
Jay A. Carpenter, Nevada
Meredith E. Johnson, New Jersey
Jasper L. Stuckey, North Carolina
Robert H. Dott, Oklahoma
George H. Ashley, Pennsylvania
Walter F. Pond, Tennessee
Arthur C. Bevan, Virginia
Harold E. Culver, Washington
Ernest F. Bean, Wisconsin
Arthur F. Hagner, Wyoming

Business Session:

- Met with Ground Water Committee; conference on groundwater cooperation.
- Met at Cosmos Club with U.S. Geological Survey and U.S. Bureau of Mines: "food and drink in bountiful amount, one half keg of beer, pretzels, popcorn, doughnuts in quantity, and 3 gallons of cider."
- Heard reports of committees.
- Heard report on election of officers.
- Discussed cooperation with U.S. Geological Survey and U.S. Bureau of Mines.
- Discussed experience in use of aerial photographs; value and uses.
- Discussed publication problems.
- Discussed public relations, including radio.
- Held roundtable discussion of geologic programs for 1945 and post-war planning.
- State geologists reported on highlights of problems in 1945, and how they were solved.
- Discussed geology for Boy Scouts and other groups.
- Discussed public education in geology for lower age levels. Better public understanding and appreciation for the future.
- Held individual conferences with federal officials.
- Discussed need for coordinated mapping and topographic mapping accelerated under supervision of U.S. Geological Survey.
- Heard report on formation of an "American Geological Institute."
- Heard report of Ground Water Committee.
- Heard report of Committee on Regional Correlations.
- Heard report of secretary.
- Heard report of editor.
- Heard report of Balloting Committee.
- Heard report of Auditing Committee.
- Heard report of Resolutions Committee.
- Heard report of Publicity Committee.

1946, February 21–23, Urbana, Ill.

Host: Morris M. Leighton, Illinois State Geological Survey

Officers:

President: Meredith E. Johnson
Secretary: Edward L. Troxell
Vice President: Arthur C. Trowbridge
Editor: Edward L. Troxell
Statistician: Wilson M. Laird

Members Present:

Walter B. Jones, Alabama
Harold B. Foxhall, Arkansas
Walter W. Bradley, California
Edward L. Troxell, Connecticut
Garland Peyton, Georgia
Morris M. Leighton, Illinois
Charles F. Deiss, Indiana
Arthur C. Trowbridge, Iowa
John C. Frye, Kansas
Daniel J. Jones, Kentucky
Joseph T. Singewald Jr., Maryland
Richard A. Smith, Michigan
Frank F. Grout, Minnesota
William C. Morse, Mississippi
E.L. Clark, Missouri
Francis A. Thomson, Montana
George E. Condra, Nebraska
Theodore R. Meyers, New Hampshire
Meredith E. Johnson, New Jersey
Jasper L. Stuckey, North Carolina
Wilson M. Laird, North Dakota
Robert H. Dott, Oklahoma
Fay W. Libbey, Oregon
George H. Ashley, Pennsylvania
John T. Lonsdale, Texas
Arthur C. Bevan, Virginia
Sheldon L. Glover, Washington
Paul H. Price, West Virginia
Ernest F. Bean, Wisconsin

Business Session:

- Made committee appointments.
- Heard reports of officers and committees, elected new officers, etc.
- Heard report of Water Resources Committee.
- Heard report of Correlations Committee.
- Made 40th anniversary plans.
- Discussed federal surplus property.
- Heard report of secretary-treasurer.
- Summarized research programs of Geological Resources Section, Geochemical Section, and Minerals Section of USGS.
- Discussed Illinois survey's educational extension program.
- Discussed current geologic activities of the U.S. Geological Survey.

- Discussed current topographic work of U.S. Geological Survey and future plans.
- Discussed current activities of U.S. Bureau of Mines.
- Discussed future of petroleum.
- Discussed conservation of groundwater through state control.
- Discussed resolutions, news releases, etc.

1947, March 24–26, Washington, D.C.
Host: U.S. Geological Survey
Officers:
> President: Edward L. Troxell
> Secretary: Walter B. Jones
> Vice President: Arthur C. Trowbridge
> Editor: Walter B. Jones
> Statistician: Wilson M. Laird

Members Present:
> Walter B. Jones, Alabama
> Harold B. Foxhall, Arkansas
> Ben H. Parker, Colorado
> Edward L. Troxell, Connecticut
> Herman Gunter, Florida
> Robert O. Vernon, Florida
> Morris M. Leighton, Illinois
> Eugene Callaghan, Indiana
> Arthur C. Trowbridge, Iowa
> Raymond C. Moore, Kansas
> Daniel J. Jones, Kentucky
> Joseph T. Singewald Jr., Maryland
> Gerald E. Eddy, Michigan
> George M. Schwartz, Minnesota
> E.L. Clark, Missouri
> George E. Condra, Nebraska
> Jay A. Carpenter, Nevada
> Theodore R. Meyers, New Hampshire
> Meredith E. Johnson, New Jersey
> George W. White, Ohio
> Stanley H. Carthcart, Pennsylvania
> Edgar P. Rothrock, South Dakota
> John T. Lonsdale, Texas
> Arthur C. Bevan, Virginia
> Paul H. Price, West Virginia
> Ernest F. Bean, Wisconsin

Business Session:
- Heard report of the president.
- Heard report of the secretary-editor.
- Heard report of the treasurer.
- Heard report of Water Resources Committee.
- Heard report of Committee on Nomenclature.
- Heard report of Color Chart Committee.
- Heard report of Research Committee of the American Association of Petroleum Geologists.
- Heard report of Committee on Aid to State Geological Surveys.
- Discussed post-war role of geology in the national economy.
- Discussed progress in geologic techniques.
- Discussed minerals in a new market and an expanding demand.
- Discussed the role of state surveys in problems of water supply.
- Discussed change in constitution.
- Discussed current projects and plans of the U.S. Geological Survey.
- Discussed topographic mapping in the country.
- Discussed the activities of the U.S. Bureau of Mines.
- Discussed work of the U.S. Coast and Geodetic Survey.
- Discussed ways in which a survey can extend its service to the public.
- Discussed programs of basic geologic studies.
- Discussed the *Journal* in general:
  - Left unchanged restricted distribution.
  - Voted to increase annual subscription from $7 to $15.
- Heard report of Resolutions Committee.

1948, March 31–April 4, Tuscaloosa, Ala.

Host: Walter B. Jones, Alabama Geological Survey 100th anniversary

Officers:
> President: Garland Peyton
> President-elect: Walter B. Jones
> Vice President: Wilson M. Laird
> Secretary-Treasurer: E.L. Clark
> Editor: E.L. Clark
> Statistician: Wilson M. Laird

Members Present:
> Olaf P. Jenkins, California
> Edward L. Troxell, Connecticut
> Herman Gunter, Florida
> Robert O. Vernon, Florida
> Garland Peyton, Georgia

Morris M. Leighton, Illinois

Charles F. Deiss, Indiana

John B. Patton, Indiana

H. Garland Hershey, Iowa

John C. Frye, Kansas

Raymond C. Moore, Kansas

Daniel J. Jones, Kentucky

Leo W. Hough, Louisiana

Gerald E. Eddy, Michigan

George M. Schwartz, Minnesota

William C. Morse, Mississippi

E.L. Clark, Missouri

George E. Condra, Nebraska

Theodore R. Meyers, New Hampshire

Meredith E. Johnson, New Jersey

E.C. Anderson, New Mexico

Wilson M. Laird, North Dakota

John H. Melvin, Ohio

Robert H. Dott, Oklahoma

Hugh D. Miser, Oklahoma

Fay W. Libbey, Oregon

Stanley H. Carthcart, Pennsylvania

Edgar P. Rothrock, South Dakota

John T. Lonsdale, Texas

Arthur L. Crawford, Utah

Arthur C. Bevan, Virginia

Sheldon L. Glover, Washington

Paul H. Price, West Virginia

Ernest F. Bean, Wisconsin

Business Session:

- Heard report of Water Resources Committee:
    - Discussed well drillers' attack on whole U.S. Geological Survey in Minnesota, especially the Ground Water Division.
- Heard report of *Journal* Committee.
- Heard report of Committee on Public Education.
- Discussed newspaper publicity.
- Heard report of Color Chart Committee.
- Heard report of Correlations Committee.
- Heard reports on American Commission on Stratigraphic Nomenclature.
- Discussed:

- Matter of sending out lists of state geologists.
- Group preference that financial summaries be held within the Association.
- Difficulty in preparing questionnaire for activity summary.
- Relation of government bureaus such as the U.S. Bureau of Mines and U.S. Geological Survey.
- Appointment of director of U.S. Bureau of Mines.
- Topographic mapping in the United States.
- Geology and our national welfare.
- Uniform well-construction standards.
- Final action of American Petroleum Institute.
- Interstate relations and boundary-line geology.
- Release of information from U.S. Bureau of Mines and U.S. Geological Survey.
- Made committee appointments.

1949, February 11–12, San Francisco, Calif.

Host: Olaf P. Jenkins, California Division of Mines

Officers:

President: Walter B. Jones
President-elect: Wilson M. Laird
Vice President: Edgar P. Rothrock
Secretary-Treasurer: E.L. Clark
Editor: E.L. Clark
Statistician: Wilson M. Laird

Members Present:

Walter B. Jones, Alabama
Harold B. Foxhall, Arkansas
Olaf P. Jenkins, California
Ben H. Parker, Colorado
Chester R. Longwell, Connecticut
Garland Peyton, Georgia
Morris M. Leighton, Illinois
Charles F. Deiss, Indiana
Leo W. Hough, Louisiana
Joseph T. Singewald Jr., Maryland
Gerald E. Eddy, Michigan
George M. Schwartz, Minnesota
E.L. Clark, Missouri
Francis A. Thomson, Montana
Jay A. Carpenter, Nevada

  Meredith E. Johnson, New Jersey
  Wilson M. Laird, North Dakota
  John H. Melvin, Ohio
  Fay W. Libbey, Oregon
  Stanley H. Carthcart, Pennsylvania
  Sheldon L. Glover, Washington

Business Session:

- Discussed rock color chart.
- Discussed topographic maps.
- Heard report on International Geological Congress, London, 1948.
- Created position of editor of *Journal*; new series of *Journal* to begin.
- Discussed water resources and water-well construction standards.
- Discussed role of state geological surveys in public education.
- Discussed U.S. Geological Survey programming of state needs.
- Discussed oil and gas publications.
- Discussed extent of chemical analyses by state surveys.
- Discussed cooperation with university and college research programs.

1950, February 10–11, Washington, D.C.

Host: U.S. Geological Survey

Officers:

  President: Wilson M. Laird
  President-elect: Edgar P. Rothrock
  Vice President: E.L. Clark
  Secretary-Treasurer: Charles F. Deiss
  Editor: Morris M. Leighton
  Statistician: John H. Melvin

Members Present:

  Walter B. Jones, Alabama
  Harold B. Foxhall, Arkansas
  Olaf P. Jenkins, California
  Edward L. Troxell, Connecticut
  Herman Gunter, Florida
  Morris M. Leighton, Illinois
  Charles F. Deiss, Indiana
  H. Garland Hershey, Iowa
  John C. Frye, Kansas
  Daniel J. Jones, Kentucky
  Joseph T. Singewald Jr., Maryland
  Gerald E. Eddy, Michigan

George M. Schwartz, Minnesota
E.L. Clark, Missouri
Donald W. McGlashan, Montana
George E. Condra, Nebraska
Meredith E. Johnson, New Jersey
Eugene Callaghan, New Mexico
John G. Broughton, New York
Jasper L. Stuckey, North Carolina
John H. Melvin, Ohio
Robert H. Dott, Oklahoma
Stanley H. Carthcart, Pennsylvania
L.L. Smith, South Carolina
Edgar P. Rothrock, South Dakota
John T. Lonsdale, Texas
Arthur L. Crawford, Utah
Paul H. Price, West Virginia
Ernest F. Bean, Wisconsin

Business Session:

- Heard presentations by federal agencies: U.S. Geological Survey, U.S. Bureau of Mines.
- Discussed water problems and pending legislation.
- Discussed request for cooperation by National Water Well Association.
- Saw and described eolian map of the United States; its importance to the study of soils.
- Discussed cooperation with National Water Well Association.
- Heard report of secretary-treasurer.
- Discussed activities chart.
- Discussed distribution of state survey publications to members of the Association.
- Discussed Tennessee Valley Authority.
- Discussed cooperation with American Geological Institute.
- Discussed *Journal* business.
- Discussed types of state geological survey organizations.
- Discussed changes in mining laws as proposed by Bureau of Land Management.
- Discussed groundwater studies and legislation covering conservation of groundwaters.
- Discussed federal and state relationships in geologic investigations.
- Heard report of Resolutions Committee.
- Heard report of Elections Committee.
- Discussed future meetings.

1951, February 15–17, Rolla, Mo.

Host: E.L. Clark, Missouri Geological Survey

Officers:

> President: Edgar P. Rothrock
> President-elect: E.L. Clark
> Vice President: Herman Gunter
> Secretary: Charles F. Deiss
> Editor: Morris M. Leighton
> Statistician: John H. Melvin

Members Present:

> Walter B. Jones, Alabama
> Norman F. Williams, Arkansas
> Olaf P. Jenkins, California
> Edward L. Troxell, Connecticut
> Herman Gunter, Florida
> Garland Peyton, Georgia
> Morris M. Leighton, Illinois
> Charles F. Deiss, Indiana
> John C. Frye, Kansas
> Daniel J. Jones, Kentucky
> Leo W. Hough, Louisiana
> Joseph T. Singewald Jr., Maryland
> Gerald E. Eddy, Michigan
> George M. Schwartz, Minnesota
> William C. Morse, Mississippi
> E.L. Clark, Missouri
> George E. Condra, Nebraska
> Theodore R. Meyers, New Hampshire
> Eugene Callaghan, New Mexico
> Wilson M. Laird, North Dakota
> John H. Melvin, Ohio
> Robert H. Dott, Oklahoma
> Fay W. Libbey, Oregon
> Edgar P. Rothrock, South Dakota
> John T. Lonsdale, Texas
> Sheldon L. Glover, Washington

Business Session:

- Discussed *The State Geologists Journal*. Editor's note: Time for receipt of items for publication.
  - Purpose of *Journal,* price, and number of copies.
- Discussed cooperative projects between state surveys.

- Discussed problem of inducting of state survey personnel into armed forces.
- Summarized report of President's Water Policy Commission.
- Discussed relations of state surveys to U.S. Geological Survey and U.S. Bureau of Mines.
- Discussed importance and influence of state surveys.
- Discussed American Geological Institute affiliation.
- Discussed again importance and influence of state surveys.
- Heard reports of committees.
- Discussed application of geophysics to the solution of geologic problems.
- Discussed advertising survey publications.

1952, April 16–17, Tallahassee, Fla.

Host: Herman Gunter, Florida State Geological Survey

Officers:

 President: E.L. Clark
 President-elect: Herman Gunter
 Vice President: Charles F. Deiss
 Secretary: Daniel J. Jones
 Editor: E.L. Clark
 Statistician: John H. Melvin
 Historian: John H. Melvin

Members Present:

 Walter B. Jones, Alabama
 Norman F. Williams, Arkansas
 Olaf P. Jenkins, California
 Edward L. Troxell, Connecticut
 Johan J. Groot, Delaware
 Herman Gunter, Florida
 Garland Peyton, Georgia
 Morris M. Leighton, Illinois
 Charles F. Deiss, Indiana
 John C. Frye, Kansas
 Daniel J. Jones, Kentucky
 Leo W. Hough, Louisiana
 Joseph T. Singewald Jr., Maryland
 Franklin G. Pardee, Michigan
 William C. Morse, Mississippi
 E.L. Clark, Missouri
 J. Robert Van Pelt, Montana
 George E. Condra, Nebraska
 Eugene Callaghan, New Mexico

Jasper L. Stuckey, North Carolina

John H. Melvin, Ohio

Stanley H. Carthcart, Pennsylvania

Edgar P. Rothrock, South Dakota

Herman W. Ferguson, Tennessee

Arthur L. Crawford, Utah

Sheldon L. Glover, Washington

Paul H. Price, West Virginia

Business Session:

- Heard committee reports.
- Discussed equipment and personnel questionnaires.
- Discussed study of President's Water Policy Commission.
- Discussed aims and objectives of the Association.
- Discussed American Geological Institute.
- Discussed definition of duties of state surveys by law.
- Discussed intrusion in work that is properly the province of state geological surveys.
- Discussed cooperation for regional studies.
- Discussed public relations.
- Discussed popular publications.
- Discussed printing and publication problems.
- Held joint session with federal agencies.

1953, February 13–14, Los Angeles, Calif.

Host:

Officers:

President: Herman Gunter

President-elect: Charles F. Deiss

Vice President: Daniel J. Jones

Secretary: Olaf P. Jenkins

Editor: E.L. Clark

Statistician: John H. Melvin

Historian: John H. Melvin

Members Present:

Olaf P. Jenkins, California

Edward L. Troxell, Connecticut

Herman Gunter, Florida

Garland Peyton, Georgia

Morris M. Leighton, Illinois

John B. Patton, Indiana

Raymond C. Moore, Kansas

Daniel J. Jones, Kentucky
Leo W. Hough, Louisiana
Joseph M. Trefethen, Maine
George M. Schwartz, Minnesota
E.L. Clark, Missouri
George E. Condra, Nebraska
Vernon E. Scheid, Nevada
Eugene Callaghan, New Mexico
John H. Melvin, Ohio
William E. Ham, Oklahoma
Fay W. Libbey, Oregon
Sheldon L. Glover, Washington

Business Session:

- Discussed the *Journal:* its purpose, contents, distribution, etc.
- Heard report of historian: functions, etc.
- Discussed American Commission on Stratigraphic Nomenclature.
- Heard report of Glossary Committee.
- Heard report of Committee on Aims and Objectives.
- Revised personnel and equipment lists.
- Discussed policy to govern annual meetings in the future.
- Discussed White House Conference on Resources for the Future.
- Discussed cooperative projects with the U.S. Geological Survey.
- Discussed authority and organization of a state geological survey as related to state universities.
- Discussed core and sample libraries.
- Restated and revised statement of organization.
- Discussed honorary membership due to retirement.
- Discussed abstracts and bibliographic citations.
- Met with federal agencies.

1954, February 19–20, Baltimore, Md.

Host: Joseph T. Singewald Jr., Maryland Geological Survey

Officers:

President: Charles F. Deiss
President-elect: Daniel J. Jones
Vice President: Joseph T. Singewald Jr.
Secretary-Treasurer: Olaf P. Jenkins
Historian: John H. Melvin
Editor: E.L. Clark
Statistician: Eugene Callaghan

Members Present:

Walter B. Jones, Alabama
Olaf P. Jenkins, California
Edward L. Troxell, Connecticut
Johan J. Groot, Delaware
Herman Gunter, Florida
Garland Peyton, Georgia
Morris M. Leighton, Illinois
Charles F. Deiss, Indiana
H. Garland Hershey, Iowa
Daniel J. Jones, Kentucky
Joseph M. Trefethen, Maine
Joseph T. Singewald Jr., Maryland
William L. Daoust, Michigan
E.L. Clark, Missouri
Walter S. March Jr., Montana
Vernon E. Scheid, Nevada
Meredith E. Johnson, New Jersey
Eugene Callaghan, New Mexico
Jasper L. Stuckey, North Carolina
Wilson M. Laird, North Dakota
John H. Melvin, Ohio
William E. Ham, Oklahoma
Carlyle Gray, Pennsylvania
John T. Lonsdale, Texas
Charles G. Doll, Vermont
William M. McGill, Virginia
Sheldon L. Glover, Washington
Paul H. Price, West Virginia
George F. Hanson, Wisconsin

Business Session:

- Introduced new members.
- Distributed minutes of Hartford and Los Angeles meetings and approved as written.
- Appointed committees.
- Heard report of Committee on Stratigraphic Nomenclature.
- Discussed relationship of the Association to the American Geological Institute.
- Discussed American Geological Institute glossary.
- Discussed Association delegates to AGI meetings.
- Discussed contributions for support of AGI.

- Heard report of Committee on Specialized Equipment, Personnel, and Services.
- Heard report on chart of income activities and personnel of state geological surveys.
- Heard report of Committee on Publications.
- Heard report on *The State Geologists Journal.*
- Heard report on annual meetings.
- Appointed committee to select honorary members.
- Discussed constitution and bylaws.
- Discussed ownership of property purchased under U.S. Geological Survey cooperative agreement.
- Discussed White House Conference on Resources for the Future.
- Heard treasurer's report.
- Heard report of Nominating Committee.
- Heard report of Auditing Committee.
- Heard report of Honorary Membership Committee.
- Heard presentations of federal agencies: U.S. Geological Survey, U.S. Bureau of Mines.
- Heard report of Resolutions Committee.

1955, March 10–12, Socorro, N.M.

Host: Eugene Callaghan, New Mexico Institute of Mining and Technology

Officers:

> President: Daniel J. Jones
> President-elect: Joseph T. Singewald Jr.
> Vice President: Olaf P. Jenkins
> Secretary-Treasurer: John H. Melvin
> Historian: H. Garland Hershey
> Editor: Thomas R. Beveridge
> Statistician: Eugene Callaghan

Members Present:

> Olaf P. Jenkins, California
> John B. Lucke, Connecticut
> Robert O. Vernon, Florida
> Garland Peyton, Georgia
> Lewis S. Prater, Idaho
> John C. Frye, Illinois
> Charles F. Deiss, Indiana
> F. Garland Hershey, Iowa
> Frank C. Foley, Kansas
> Daniel J. Jones, Kentucky

Clarence O. Durham, Louisiana

Joseph M. Trefethen, Maine

Joseph T. Singewald Jr., Maryland

William L. Daoust, Michigan

George M. Schwartz, Minnesota

Garrett A. Muilenburg, Missouri

Theodore R. Meyers, New Hampshire

Meredith E. Johnson, New Jersey

Eugene Callaghan, New Mexico

Wilson M. Laird, North Dakota

John H. Melvin, Ohio

Carl C. Branson, Oklahoma

Carlyle Gray, Pennsylvania

Edgar P. Rothrock, South Dakota

John T. Lonsdale, Texas

Arthur L. Crawford, Utah

Charles G. Doll, Vermont

William M. McGill, Virginia

Sheldon L. Glover, Washington

Paul H. Price, West Virginia

George F. Hanson, Wisconsin

W.H. Wilson, Wyoming

Business Session:

- Approved minutes of last meeting.
- Appointed committees.
- Heard treasurer's report.
- Heard statistician's report.
- Heard editor's report.
- Heard historian's report.
- Heard report of Committee on Specialized Equipment, Personnel, and Services.
- Heard report of committee on AGI Board of Directors.
- Heard report of committee on ownership status of property purchased under USGS cooperative agreement.
- Heard report of committee on AGI glossary.
- Heard report of committee on contracts for cooperative collection of mineral statistics with USBM.
- Replaced member on AGI Board of Directors.
- Elected Puerto Rico to Association membership.
- Studied eligibility of Alaska and Hawaii for membership.
- Discussed policy memoranda to USGS relative to USGS's attitude toward state geological surveys.

- Discussed invitation from AGI for state survey articles in *AGI Newsletter*.
- Discussed survey replies to requests for minerals, rocks, books, maps, etc. Should there be a common form in answering these requests?
- Discussed role of surveys in public education.
- Discussed policies of surveys regarding distribution of publications.
- Discussed uniformity of publications by USGS for all cooperative programs with state geological surveys.
- Discussed expediting reports on groundwater studies by USGS–state cooperative work.
- Discussed relationships of state geological surveys to conservation activities in the respective states.
- Discussed state geological surveys in educational programs for Boy Scouts.
- Discussed state geological survey relationships to accelerated superhighway programs.
- Discussed effective methods of presenting accomplishments of state surveys to citizens of the state.
- Discussed exchanging data on cost, printing methods of publication and map producing, and suitability of printing houses.
- Discussed geophysical methods used by the various surveys and results.
- Discussed organization, programs, and plans of new survey of Puerto Rico.
- Discussed state geological survey cooperation with other departments within the respective states.
- Heard report of Committee on Stratigraphic Nomenclature.
- Heard report of Auditing Committee.
- Heard report of Balloting Committee.
- Heard report of Resolutions Committee.
- Discussed place of next annual meeting.
- Heard report of Committee on Honorary Membership.
- Heard presentations of federal agencies: U.S. Geological Survey, U.S. Bureau of Mines.

1956, April 18–22, Hardin, Ky.
Host: Daniel J. Jones, Kentucky Geological Survey
Officers:

    President: Joseph T. Singewald Jr.

    President-elect: Olaf P. Jenkins

    Vice President: John H. Melvin

    Secretary-Treasurer: Eugene Callaghan

    Historian: H. Garland Hershey

    Editor: Thomas R. Beveridge

    Statistician: Carlyle Gray

Members Present:

    Walter B. Jones, Alabama

Norman F. Williams, Arkansas
Olaf P. Jenkins, California
John B. Lucke, Connecticut
Johan J. Groot, Delaware
Herman Gunter, Florida
Garland Peyton, Georgia
John C. Frye, Illinois
Charles F. Deiss, Indiana
Maurice Biggs, Indiana
H. Garland Hershey, Iowa
Frank C. Foley, Kansas
William H. Hambleton, Kansas
Daniel J. Jones, Kentucky
Arthur C. McFarlan, Kentucky
Clarence Durham, Louisiana
John R. Rand, Maine
Joseph T. Singewald Jr., Maryland
William L. Daoust, Michigan
George M. Schwartz, Minnesota
William C. Morse, Mississippi
Thomas R. Beveridge, Missouri
Meredith E. Johnson, New Jersey
Eugene Callaghan, New Mexico
Jasper L. Stuckey, North Carolina
Wilson M. Laird, North Dakota
John H. Melvin, Ohio
Carl C. Branson, Oklahoma
Carlyle Gray, Pennsylvania
Edgar P. Rothrock, South Dakota
F.M. Alexander, Tennessee
John T. Lonsdale, Texas
Charles G. Doll, Vermont
William M. McGill, Virginia
Paul H. Price, West Virginia
George F. Hanson, Wisconsin

Business Session:
- Appointed committees.
- Discussed AGI Glossary Committee.
- Discussed cooperative water programs with USGS.
- Discussed state employment of professional personnel from civil service rosters.

- Discussed scope and limitation of services furnished by state surveys.
- Discussed licensing of professional geologists.
- Met with representatives of Atomic Energy Commission.
- Heard presentations of federal agencies; U.S. Geological Survey and U.S. Bureau of Mines.
- Heard report of Resolutions Committee.

1957, August 19–25, Houghton, Mich.

Host: William L. Daoust, Michigan Geological Survey Division

Officers:

President: Olaf P. Jenkins

President-elect: Jasper L. Stuckey

Vice President: H. Garland Hershey

Secretary-Treasurer: John C. Frye

Historian: Carl C. Branson

Editor: Thomas R. Beveridge

Statistician: Carlyle Gray

Members Present:

Norman F. Williams, Arkansas

Olaf P. Jenkins, California

John B. Lucke, Connecticut

Johan J. Groot, Delaware

Aurelius S. Furcron, Georgia

Earl F. Cook, Idaho

William L. Daoust, Michigan

George M. Schwartz, Minnesota

Thomas R. Beveridge, Missouri

Meredith E. Johnson, New Jersey

Alvin J. Thompson, New Mexico

Jasper L. Stuckey, North Carolina

Wilson M. Laird, North Dakota

Ralph J. Bernhagen, Ohio

Carl C. Branson, Oklahoma

Carlyle Gray, Pennsylvania

Allen F. Agnew, South Dakota

John T. Lonsdale, Texas

Arthur L. Crawford, Utah

Charles G. Doll, Vermont

Paul H. Price, West Virginia

George F. Hanson, Wisconsin

Business Session:

- Introduced new state geologists.
- Approved minutes of last meeting.
- Appointed committees.
- Heard report of Balloting Committee
- Heard report of treasurer.
- Heard report of statistician.
- Heard report of editor.
- Heard report of historian.
- Heard report of Honorary Members Committee.
- Heard report on American Geological Institute.
- Heard report on American Commission on Stratigraphic Nomenclature.
- Heard report of AGI Glossary Committee.
- Heard report of Auditing Committee.

1958, March 30–April 2, Austin, Tex.

Host: John T. Lonsdale, Texas Bureau of Economic Geology

Officials:

President: Jasper L. Stuckey
President-elect: H. Garland Hershey
Vice President: John C. Frye
Secretary-Treasurer: Carlyle Gray
Historian: Carl C. Branson
Editor: Thomas R. Beveridge
Statistician: Frank C. Foley

Members Present:

Walter B. Jones, Alabama
James D. Forrester, Arizona
Norman F. Williams, Arkansas
Gordon B. Oakeshott, California
John B. Lucke, Connecticut
Johan J. Groot, Delaware
Robert O. Vernon, Florida
Garland Peyton, Georgia
Aurelius S. Furcron, Georgia
Earl F. Cook, Idaho
John C. Frye, Illinois
Morris M. Leighton, Illinois
Charles F. Deiss, Indiana
John B. Patton, Indiana

H. Garland Hershey, Iowa

Frank C. Foley, Kansas

William W. Hambleton, Kansas

Daniel J. Jones, Kentucky

Joseph T. Singewald Jr., Maryland

William L. Daoust, Michigan

Thomas R. Beveridge, Missouri

Eugene C. Reed, Nebraska

Meredith E. Johnson, New Jersey

Alvin J. Thompson, New Mexico

Jasper L. Stuckey, North Carolina

Ralph J. Bernhagen, Ohio

Carl C. Branson, Oklahoma

Carlyle Gray, Pennsylvania

Allen F. Agnew, South Dakota

Edgar P. Rothrock, South Dakota

John T. Lonsdale, Texas

Elias H. Sellards, Texas

Virgil E. Barnes, Texas

Peter T. Flawn, Texas

Charles G. Doll, Vermont

James L. Calver, Virginia

Marshall T. Huntting, Washington

Paul H. Price, West Virginia

George F. Hanson, Wisconsin

W.H. Wilson, Wyoming

Business Session:

- Approved minutes of last meeting.
- Appointed committees.
- Heard report of treasurer.
- Heard report of statistician.
- Heard report of editor.
- Heard report of historian.
- Heard report on American Geological Institute.
- Discussed AGI Glossary Committee.
- Heard report of representatives on American Commission on Stratigraphic Nomenclature.
- Discussed future meetings.
- Discussed American Association of Petroleum Geologists basement rock project.
- Heard report of Balloting Committee.

- Heard report of Auditing Committee.
- Heard report of Honorary Membership Committee.
- Discussed foreign exchanges, exchange of mailing lists, and publication distribution policies.
- Reviewed Association objectives.
- Discussed monthly or regular magazines published by various surveys.
- Discussed new state geologic maps.
- Discussed exchange of personnel.
- Discussed consulting work by staff members.
- Heard presentations by federal agencies: U.S. Geological Survey and U.S. Bureau of Mines.
- Appointed AGI Study Committee.
- Heard report of Resolutions Committee.

1959, April 12–16, Lawrence, Kan.

Host: Frank C. Foley, State Geological Survey of Kansas

Officers:

President: Jasper L. Stuckey
President-elect: H. Garland Hershey
Vice President: John C. Frye
Secretary-Treasurer: Carlyle Gray
Historian: Carl C. Branson
Editor: Thomas R. Beveridge
Statistician: Frank C. Foley

Members Present:

Norman F. Williams, Arkansas
Ian Campbell, California
John B. Lucke, Connecticut
Robert O. Vernon, Florida
Earl F. Cook, Idaho
John C. Frye, Illinois
Charles F. Deiss, Indiana
H. Garland Hershey, Iowa
Frank C. Foley, Kansas
William W. Hambleton, Kansas
Wallace W. Hagan, Kentucky
Joseph T. Singewald Jr., Maryland
William L. Daoust, Michigan
George M. Schwartz, Minnesota
Tracy W. Lusk, Mississippi
Thomas R. Beveridge, Missouri

Eugene C. Reed, Nebraska

Kemble Widmer, New Jersey

John G. Broughton, New York

Jasper L. Stuckey, North Carolina

M. Hansen, North Dakota

Ralph J. Bernhagen, Ohio

Carl C. Branson, Oklahoma

William E. Ham, Oklahoma

Carlyle Gray, Pennsylvania

Allen F. Agnew, South Dakota

John T. Lonsdale, Texas

Arthur L. Crawford, Utah

Charles G. Doll, Vermont

James L. Calver, Virginia

Marshall T. Huntting, Washington

Paul H. Price, West Virginia

George F. Hanson, Wisconsin

Business Session:

- Approved minutes of last meeting.
- Appointed committees.
- Heard treasurer's report.
- Heard historian's report.
- Heard report on American Geological Institute.
- Discussed contribution to AGI.
- Appointed member to AGI Glossary Committee.
- Discussed American Committee on Stratigraphic Nomenclature.
- Heard statistician's report.
- Discussed future meetings.
- Suggested longer meeting and shorter field trip.
- Discussed experiences in getting budget support.
- Inquired regarding storage of cores and cuttings.
- Discussed revision of stratigraphic code.
- Discussed state surveys writing papers on geology for soil surveys.
- Discussed geology for highway engineering.
- Discussed ethics of state geological survey geologists.
- Discussed custom of surveys relative to sale of publications in bulk.
- Discussed distribution of specimens.
- Discussed AGI abstracts.
- Discussed raising money directly from industry for large programs.
- Heard presentations by federal agencies: U.S. Geological Survey, U.S. Bureau of Mines.

- Summarized organization and activities of National Science Foundation, Earth Sciences Program.
- Discussed Aero Service Corp. on airborne geophysical surveys.
- Heard report on American Association of Petroleum Geologists program to publish uniform roadlogs of geology for popular use with state geologists' cooperation.
- Proposed inviting U.S. Army Corps of Engineers and the Bureau of Reclamation to future meetings of the Association.
- Heard report of Auditing Committee.
- Heard report of Balloting Committee.
- Heard report of Resolutions Committee.

1960, April 22–23, Harrisburg, Pa.

Host: Carlyle Gray, Pennsylvania Bureau of Topographic and Geological Survey

Officers:

 President: H. Garland Hershey
 President-elect: John C. Frye
 Vice President: John T. Lonsdale
 Secretary-Treasurer: Carlyle Gray
 Historian: Carl C. Branson
 Editor: Ian Campbell
 Statistician: Frank C. Foley

Members Present:

 Walter B. Jones, Alabama
 Norman F. Williams, Arkansas
 Ian Campbell, California
 John B. Lucke, Connecticut
 Johan J. Groot, Delaware
 Garland Peyton, Georgia
 Earl F. Cook, Idaho
 M.L. Thompson, Illinois
 John B. Patton, Indiana
 H. Garland Hershey, Iowa
 Frank C. Foley, Kansas
 William H. Hambleton, Kansas
 Wallace W. Hagan, Kentucky
 Joseph T. Singewald Jr., Maryland
 William L. Daoust, Michigan
 George M. Schwartz, Minnesota
 Tracy W. Lusk, Mississippi

Thomas R. Beveridge, Missouri

John G. Broughton, New York

Donald W. Fisher, New York

Jasper L. Stuckey, North Carolina

Carl C. Branson, Oklahoma

Carlyle Gray, Pennsylvania

Allen F. Agnew, South Dakota

John T. Lonsdale, Texas

Arthur L. Crawford, Utah

James L. Calver, Virginia

Paul H. Price, West Virginia

George F. Hanson, Wisconsin

Business Session:
- Appointed committees.
- Approved minutes of previous meeting.
- Heard presentations of federal agencies: U.S. Geological Survey, U.S. Bureau of Mines, U.S. Army Corps of Engineers (Geology Branch).
- Heard treasurer's report.
- Heard historian's report.
- Heard editor's report.
- Heard statistician's report.
- Heard report of the AGI Glossary Committee.
- Heard report on American Geological Institute.
- Heard report of American Committee on Stratigraphic Nomenclature.
- Heard report on geology as applied to highway engineering.
- Heard committee reports: Auditing, Future Meetings, Honorary Membership, Necrology.
- Distributed reprints policy.
- Heard committee report on statistics.
- Discussed open-file reports.
- Discussed costs borne by state cooperation in topographic mapping.
- Discussed professional licensing of geologists.
- Heard committee reports: Resolutions Committee, Balloting Committee.

1961, April 19–21, Moscow, Idaho
Host: Earl F. Cook, Idaho Bureau of Mines and Geology
Officers:

President: John C. Frye

President-elect: Carl C. Branson

Vice President: Earl F. Cook

Secretary-Treasurer: John B. Patton

Historian: George F. Hanson

Editor: Ian Campbell

Statistician: Frank C. Foley

Members Present:

Eldred D. Wilson, Arizona

Ian Campbell, California

Joe Webb Peoples, Connecticut

Garland Peyton, Georgia

Earl F. Cook, Idaho

John C. Frye, Illinois

John B. Patton, Indiana

Frank C. Foley, Kansas

Wallace W. Hagan, Kentucky

Turbit H. Slaughter, Maryland

Tracy W. Lusk, Mississippi

William C. Hayes, Missouri

Uuno M. Sahinen, Montana

Eugene C. Reed, Nebraska

Kemble Widmer, New Jersey

Alvin J. Thompson, New Mexico

Wilson M. Laird, North Dakota

Ralph J. Bernhagen, Ohio

Carl C. Branson, Oklahoma

Carlyle Gray, Pennsylvania

Allen F. Agnew, South Dakota

Arthur L. Crawford, Utah

Charles G. Doll, Vermont

James L. Calver, Virginia

Marshall T. Huntting, Washington

Paul H. Price, West Virginia

George F. Hanson, Wisconsin

Business Session:

- Appointed committees.
- Heard treasurer's report.
- Heard editor's report.
- Heard historian's report.
- Heard statistician's report.
- Heard report on American Geological Institute.
- Heard report of American Commission on Stratigraphic Nomenclature.
- Heard report of Committee on Future Meetings.
- Heard report of Honorary Membership Committee.

- Discussed:
  - – USGS cooperative geologic mapping programs.
  - – Political pressure within various state surveys.
  - – Cooperative programs with U.S. Bureau of Mines.
  - – How much help state surveys should give to private industry.
- Discussed public relations programs.
- Heard presentations of federal agencies: U.S. Geological Survey, U.S. Bureau of Mines, U.S. Bureau of Reclamation.
- Heard report of Resolutions Committee.

1962, May 21–22, Albany, N.Y.
Host: John G. Broughton, New York State Museum and Science Service
Officers:

> President: William L. Daoust
> Vice President: Frank C. Foley
> President-elect: Earl F. Cook
> Secretary-Treasurer: John B. Patton
> Historian: George F. Hanson
> Editor: Ian Campbell
> Statistician: Robert O. Vernon

Members Present:

> Norman F. Williams, Arkansas
> Ian Campbell, California
> Joe Webb Peoples, Connecticut
> Robert C. Vernon, Florida
> Garland Peyton, Georgia
> Earl F. Cook, Idaho
> H.B. Risser, Illinois
> John B. Patton, Indiana
> H. Garland Hershey, Iowa
> Frank C. Foley, Kansas
> Wallace W. Hagan, Kentucky
> Turbit H. Slaughter, Maryland
> Paul K. Sims, Minnesota
> Thomas R. Beveridge, Missouri
> Theodore R. Meyers, New Hampshire
> Kemble Widmer, New Jersey
> John G. Broughton, New York
> Ralph J. Bernhagen, Ohio
> Carl C. Branson, Oklahoma
> Arthur A. Socolow, Pennsylvania

Allen F. Agnew, South Dakota
Peter T. Flawn, Texas
Charles G. Doll, Vermont
James L. Calver, Virginia
Paul H. Price, West Virginia
George F. Hanson, Wisconsin
Robert S. Houston, Wyoming

Business Session:
- Heard report of treasurer.
- Heard report of editor.
- Heard report of historian.
- Heard report of statistician.
- Heard report of Association's representative on American Geological Institute Board.
- Heard report of Association's representative on American Commission on Stratigraphic Nomenclature.
- Appointed committees: Auditing, Balloting, Resolutions, Future Meetings, Honorary Membership.
- Voted to ratify proposed new constitution of American Geological Institute.
- Approved AASG constitutional changes.
- Discussed problems of interest or concern to various surveys.
- Heard presentations by federal agencies: U.S. Geological Survey, U.S. Bureau of Mines.
- Discussed atomic waste disposal.
- Heard report of Balloting Committee.
- Heard report of Resolutions Committee.

1963, May 6–7, Morgantown, W.Va.
Host: Paul H. Price, West Virginia Geological and Economic Survey. West Virginia's centennial year.
Officers:
President: Carl C. Branson
President-elect: Frank C. Foley
Vice President: Ian Campbell
Historian: George F. Hanson
Secretary-Treasurer: John B. Patton
Editor: Robert O. Vernon
Statistician: Wallace W. Hagan
Members Present:
Philip E. LaMoreaux, Alabama

Eldred D. Wilson, Arizona

Norman F. Williams, Arkansas

Ian Campbell, California

Johan J. Groot, Delaware

Robert C. Vernon, Florida

Garland Peyton, Georgia

Earl F. Cook, Idaho

John C. Frye, Illinois

John B. Patton, Indiana

Frank C. Foley, Kansas

Wallace W. Hagan, Kentucky

Leo W. Hough, Louisiana

Robert G. Doyle, Maine

Ernst Cloos, Maryland

H.J. Hardenberg, Michigan

Thomas R. Beveridge, Missouri

Eugene C. Reed, Nebraska

Kemble Widmer, New Jersey

John G. Broughton, New York

Jasper L. Stuckey, North Carolina

Wilson M. Laird, North Dakota

Carl C. Branson, Oklahoma

Arthur A. Socolow, Pennsylvania

Allen F. Agnew, South Dakota

Virgil E. Barnes, Texas

Charles G. Doll, Vermont

James L. Calver, Virginia

Paul H. Price, West Virginia

George F. Hanson, Wisconsin

Business Session:

- Appointed committees.
- Heard treasurer's report.
- Heard editor's report.
- Heard historian's report.
- Heard Liaison Committee report.
- Heard Stratigraphic Nomenclature Committee report.
- Heard Honorary Members Committee report.
- Heard Future Meetings Committee report.
- Heard reports of ad hoc committees: Communication with Federal Agencies, Water Resources Projects, Topographic Mapping.
- Discussed environmental matters (surface- and groundwater problems). Lengthy discussion of Anderson Bill.

- Amended constitution.
- Recommended a permanent depository for back issues of the *Journal*.
- Discussed policy regarding dissemination of information to the public.
- Discussed radioactive waste disposal.
- Discussed Wilderness Bill.
- Heard presentations by federal agencies:
    - U.S. Geological Survey (various divisions).
    - U.S. Bureau of Mines:
- Mineral Statistics and Technology.
- Minerals Yearbook.
- Oil and Gas and Coal.
- Heard Resolutions Committee report.
- Heard statistician's report: confidential or public information? Some states keep such information confidential and others public.
- Discussed previous topics.

1964, April 20–21, Norman, Okla.

Host: Carl C. Branson, Oklahoma Geological Survey

Officers:

President: Earl F. Cook
President-elect: Ian Campbell
Vice President: John B. Patton
Secretary-Treasurer: William C. Hayes
Historian: George F. Hanson
Editor: Robert O. Vernon
Statistician: Wallace W. Hagan

Members Present:

James D. Forrester, Arizona
Norman F. Williams, Arkansas
Ian Campbell, California
Joe Webb Peoples, Connecticut
Robert C. Vernon, Florida
Aurelius S. Furcron, Georgia
Earl F. Cook, Idaho
John C. Frye, Illinois
John B. Patton, Indiana
H. Garland Hershey, Iowa
Frank C. Foley, Kansas
Wallace W. Hagan, Kentucky
Leo W. Hough, Louisiana
Kenneth N. Weaver, Maryland

Gerald E. Eddy, Michigan
Thomas R. Beveridge, Missouri
Eugene C. Reed, Nebraska
Glenn W. Stewart, New Hampshire
Miller Hansen, North Dakota
Carl C. Branson, Oklahoma
Arthur A. Socolow, Pennsylvania
Duncan J. McGregor, South Dakota
Peter T. Flawn, Texas
Robert Cohenour, Utah
Charles G. Doll, Vermont
Paul H. Price, West Virginia
James L. Calver, Virginia
George F. Hanson, Wisconsin

Business Session:

- Appointed committees.
- Heard treasurer's report.
- Heard editor's report.
- Heard historian's report.
- Heard statistician's report.
- Heard report on American Geological Institute.
- Heard report on American Commission on Stratigraphic Nomenclature.
- Approved amendment to constitution.
- Discussed Smithsonian Institution proposal to list research projects of AASG members with Science Information Exchange.
- Heard report of Liaison Committee.
- Commented on establishment of water resources research institutes.
- Discussed Earth Science Curriculum Project.
- Discussed certification and registration of geologists.
- Inquired about work in urban geology by state surveys.
- Heard report of Future Meetings Committee.
- Suggested complete lists of state survey publications.
- Discussed requests for rock and mineral specimens.
- Discussed requests from U.S. senators for mineral reports prepared by U.S. Geological Survey in cooperation with state surveys.
- Heard Auditing Committee report.
- Heard presentations by federal agencies: U.S. Geological Survey, U.S. Bureau of Mines.
- Discussed Honorary Members Committee's proposal to amend constitution.
- Heard report of Resolutions Committee.
- Heard report of Balloting Committee.

1965, May 10–11, San Francisco, Calif.

Host: Ian Campbell, California Division of Mines and Geology

Officers:

> President: Frank C. Foley
> President-elect: Ian Campbell
> Vice President: Robert C. Vernon
> Secretary-Treasurer: William C. Hayes
> Historian: George F. Hanson
> Editor: James L. Calver
> Statistician: Wallace W. Hagan

Members Present:

> Philip E. LaMoreaux, Alabama
> Norman F. Williams, Arkansas
> Ian Campbell, California
> Joe Webb Peoples, Connecticut
> Johan J. Groot, Delaware
> Robert O. Vernon, Florida
> John C. Frye, Illinois
> John B. Patton, Indiana
> William W. Hambleton, Kansas
> Wallace W. Hagan, Kentucky
> Leo W. Hough, Louisiana
> Robert G. Doyle, Maine
> Kenneth N. Weaver, Maryland
> Gerald E. Eddy, Michigan
> Paul K. Sims, Minnesota
> William C. Hayes, Missouri
> Eugene C. Reed, Nebraska
> Vernon E. Scheid, Nevada
> Glenn W. Stewart, New Hampshire
> Kemble Widmer, New Jersey
> Alvin J. Thompson, New Mexico
> John G. Broughton, New York
> Carl C. Branson, Oklahoma
> Hollis M. Dole, Oregon
> Arthur A. Socolow, Pennsylvania
> Duncan J. McGregor, South Dakota
> William D. Hardeman, Tennessee
> Peter T. Flawn, Texas
> William P. Hewitt, Utah
> Charles G. Doll, Vermont

James L. Calver, Virginia

Paul H. Price, West Virginia

George F. Hanson, Wisconsin

Business Session:

- President-elect Campbell explained that President Foley had been called to Saudi Arabia for 3 months.
- Introduced new members and guests.
- Approved minutes of 1964 annual meeting.
- Clarified differences between ad hoc and standing committees and made appointments to standing committees.
- Heard treasurer's report.
- Heard editor's report.
- Historian reported that *Geotimes* would publish history of Association in early issue.
- Heard statistician's report.
- Heard report on AGI House of Representatives.
- Discussed certification of geologists and accreditation of schools.
- Heard report on Society of Independent Professional Earth Scientists.
- Amended 1964 minutes.
- Changed term of AASG representative to AGI from 2 years to 3 years. Passed motion that AASG secretary is automatic representative.
- Voted to approve $100 contribution to AGI.
- Heard report of AGI Advisory Board representative.
- Heard report on American Commission on Stratigraphic Nomenclature annual meeting.
- Discussed relationships between federal and state surveys.
- Discussed SB 2.
- Appointed Weaver (Maryland) to Committee on Scientific and Technical Information and Foley (Kansas) to Advisory Committee to the Department of the Interior on Water Data for Public Use.
- Amended article III, section 4 of constitution.
- Heard Laurence B. James's "Highlights of the Geology of the California Water Plan."
- Heard presentation of USGS.
- Heard presentations of USGS divisions: Topographic, Geologic, Water Resources, Conservation, Publication.
- Withdrew proposed amendment to article III, section 1 of constitution.
- Added new article VIII to constitution.
- Heard report of Smithsonian Institution.
- Heard report of U.S. Bureau of Mines.
- Discussed encroachment of Soil Conservation Service into geological studies in Texas; passed motion to notify American Institute of Professional Geologists of situation.

- Agreed to draft resolution requesting needed action for preserving gravity base stations.
- Discussed state survey policies on out-of-state travel.
- Passed proposal that Liaison Committee draw up guidelines for cooperative credit to state surveys on each map bound or folded in a report where state was a contributing agency, or on any revised topographic quadrangle where original mapping was on cooperative agreement.
- Heard report of Resolutions Committee.
- Heard report of Future Meetings Committee.
- Heard report of Auditing Committee.
- Conferred honorary status on Jasper Stucke (North Carolina) and Arthur Crawford (Utah), upon recommendation of Honorary Members Committee.
- Elected slate of officers for 1965–66.
- Heard memorials for Ralph Stone (Pennsylvania) and Garland Peyton (Georgia).
- Elected Peter Flawn (Texas) as new representative to AGI House of Society Representatives.
- Discussed mineral lands to be incorporated into national park areas.

1966, May 9–12, Bloomington, Ind.

Host: John B. Patton, Indiana Geological Survey

Officers:

> President: Ian Campbell
> President-elect: John B. Patton
> Vice President: Robert O. Vernon
> Secretary-Treasurer: William C. Hayes
> Historian: George F. Hanson
> Editor: James L. Calver
> Statistician: Wallace W. Hagan

Members Present:

> Philip E. LaMoreaux, Alabama
> Richard Moore, Arizona
> Norman F. Williams, Arkansas
> Ian Campbell, California
> Joe Webb Peoples, Connecticut
> Robert R. Jordan, Delaware
> Robert O. Vernon, Florida
> A.S. Furcron, Florida
> Lewis Prater, Idaho
> John C. Frye, Illinois
> John B. Patton, Indiana

Frank C. Foley, Kansas

Wallace W. Hagan, Kentucky

Leo W. Hough, Louisiana

Robert G. Doyle, Maine

Kenneth N. Weaver, Maryland

Gerald E. Eddy, Michigan

Paul K. Sims, Minnesota

William H. Moore, Mississippi

William C. Hayes, Missouri

Uuno M. Sahinen, Montana

Eugene C. Reed, Nebraska

Glenn W. Stewart, New Hampshire

Frank E. Kottlowski, New Mexico

John G. Broughton, New York

Stephen G. Conrad, North Carolina

Ralph J. Bernhagen, Ohio

Carl C. Branson, Oklahoma

Hollis M. Dole, Oregon

Arthur A. Socolow, Pennsylvania

Duncan J. McGregor, South Dakota

Peter T. Flawn, Texas

William P. Hewitt, Utah

Charles G. Doll, Vermont

James L. Calver, Virginia

Paul H. Price, West Virginia

George F. Hanson, Wisconsin

Business Session:

- Introduced and welcomed new state geologists.
- Announced appointment of Foley as parliamentarian.
- Announced that meetings with federal agencies would be closed.
- Approved minutes of 1965 annual meeting.
- Announced committee appointments.
- Announced representatives to: American Commission on Stratigraphic Nomenclature, AGI House of Representatives, AGI Advisory Committee, AGI Committee for Coordination for Certification, Committee on Scientific and Technical Information, AAPG Public Information Committee.
- Heard treasurer's report.
- Heard editor's report.
- Heard historian's report.
- Heard statistician's report.
- Heard report on AGI House of Representatives.
- Heard report on AGI Advisory Board.

- Heard report on AGI Commission on Stratigraphic Nomenclature.
- Distributed written report of Liaison Committee.
- Passed motion to accept the invitation for closer cooperation with the Geologic Names Committee of the U.S. Geological Survey.
- Discussed problems with U.S. Department of Agriculture.
- Heard report of the Committee on Scientific and Technical Information.
- Heard report on meeting on Water for Public Use.
- Made suggestions to improve U.S. Bureau of Mines.
- Met with USGS representatives to discuss programs of interest to Association: Earthquake Program, Inter-Agency Solid Earth Science Committee, Heavy Metals Exploration Program, cooperative programs with states.
- Discussed International Water for Peace Conference.
- Met with representative from Soil Conservation Service.
- Met with director of U.S. Bureau of Mines.
- Discussed:
  - Naming delegate to International Geological Congress.
  - Representation on National Academy of Sciences–National Research Council Division of Earth Sciences.
  - Federal subsidy for geologic conservation projects.
  - Soil Conservation Service and possible encroachment upon other agencies' work.
  - Interstate Mining Compact.
  - Bureau of Census questionnaire on research funding.
  - Library of Congress National Referral Center for Science and Technology.
  - U.S. Bureau of Mines mineral production statistics.
  - Confidentiality of statistician's report.
  - Efforts to reestablish state surveys in Massachusetts and Colorado.
  - Practices for release of research material before completion and publication.
- Heard committee reports:
  - Auditing.
    - Honorary Members.
    - Resolutions: Passed resolutions expressing appreciation to the Indiana Geological Survey and Indiana University; thanking participants from outside agencies; memorializing Dan Jones; thanking Bloomington Crushed Stone Co., Ayrshire Collieries Corp., Indiana Limestone Co., and Meshberger Stone Co. for allowing visits to their plants, quarries, and mines during the meeting.
    - Balloting: The slate of officers was elected unanimously.
    - Future Meetings.

- Passed motion to contribute $100 to American Geological Institute.
- Suggested setting dates of future meetings early to avoid conflicts with scheduling other meetings.
- Discussed difficulty of mailing bulletins with maps in pockets.
- Discussed retirement funding at surveys affiliated with universities.
- Discussed certification of geologists.

1967, May 15–18, Lincoln, Neb.

Host: Eugene C. Reed and University of Nebraska Conservation and Survey Division

Officers:

> President: John B. Patton
>
> President-elect: Robert O. Vernon
>
> Vice President: Wallace W. Hagan
>
> Secretary-Treasurer: William C. Hayes
>
> Historian: George F. Hanson
>
> Editor: James L. Calver
>
> Statistician: Philip E. LaMoreaux

Members Present:

> Philip E. LaMoreaux, Alabama
>
> Richard Moore, Arizona
>
> Norman F. Williams, Arkansas
>
> Ian Campbell, California
>
> Joe Webb Peoples, Connecticut
>
> Johan J. Groot, Delaware
>
> Robert O. Vernon, Florida
>
> A.S. Furcron, Georgia
>
> Hubert Risser, Illinois
>
> John B. Patton, Indiana
>
> Frank C. Foley, Kansas
>
> Wallace W. Hagan, Kentucky
>
> Kenneth N. Weaver, Maryland
>
> Gerald E. Eddy, Michigan
>
> Paul K. Sims, Minnesota
>
> William H. Moore, Mississippi
>
> William C. Hayes, Missouri
>
> Uuno M. Sahinen, Montana
>
> Eugene C. Reed, Nebraska
>
> Glenn W. Stewart, New Hampshire
>
> Stephen G. Conrad, North Carolina

Wilson M. Laird, North Dakota

Charles J. Mankin, Oklahoma

Hollis M. Dole, Oregon

Arthur A. Socolow, Pennsylvania

Jose F. Cadilla, Puerto Rico

Merlin J. Tipton, South Dakota

Peter T. Flawn, Texas

William P. Hewitt, Utah

Charles G. Doll, Vermont

James L. Calver, Virginia

Marshall T. Huntting, Washington

Paul H. Price, West Virginia

George F. Hanson, Wisconsin

Business Session:

- Introduced guests.
- Welcomed new state geologist from Oklahoma and honorary member Walter F. Pond (Tennessee).
- Approved minutes of 1966 annual meeting.
- Appointed meeting committees: Auditing, Balloting, Resolutions, Honorary Members, Future Meetings.
- Heard reports of: treasurer, editor, historian, statistician, American Geological Institute House of Representatives, American Commission on Stratigraphic Nomenclature, Advisory Committee on Water Data for Public Use, Committee on Scientific and Technical Information.
- Discussed representation on AGI's Committee on Foreign Bibliographies.
- Appointed Robert Vernon delegate to International Geological Congress.
- Heard Liaison Committee report.
- Met with assistant secretary for Fish and Wildlife and Parks, Department of the Interior, who discussed Wilderness Act of 1964.
- Passed motion in support of International Commission on History of Geology.
- Heard reports from staff of U.S. Geological Survey.
- Heard report from director of Office of Water Resources Research, Department of the Interior.
- Heard report on the Comprehensive Framework Study of the Missouri River Basin.
- Heard report from the U.S. Bureau of Mines.
- Heard report from the assistant to the science advisor to the Secretary of the Interior.
- Discussed state publications.
- Announced the death of Horace D. Thomas (Wyoming).

- Discussed state survey policies regarding out-of-state requests for mineral specimens.
- Discussed statutes governing state surveys.
- Recommended that state geologists attend Public Land Law Review Commission hearings.
- Discussed activities of the Soil Conservation Service.
- Discussed laws and rules relating to disposal of oil-field brines.
- Announced availability of back issues of the *Journal*.
- Discussed printing costs of the *Journal*.
- Suggested submitting list of members to *Geotimes*.
- Discussed use of computers in survey activities.
- Discussed cost-benefit ratios.
- Discussed status of interstate mining control laws.
- Discussed proposal by American Commission on Stratigraphic Nomenclature that the Association define valid publication of a new stratigraphic name.
- Expressed concern about U.S. Army Corps of Engineers publishing floodplain maps.
- Continued discussion on Liaison Committee report.
- President made appointments to Liaison Committee, American Commission on Stratigraphic Nomenclature, AGI House of Representatives.
- Heard report of Auditing Committee and accepted its recommendation that the treasurer's report be accepted.
- Accepted nomination of Ralph Esarey (Indiana) and Arthur McFarlan (Kentucky) for honorary membership.
- Heard report of Resolutions Committee. Passed resolutions to:
  - Express appreciation to Eugene Reed and Nebraska survey.
  - Thank representatives from outside organizations for participating in meeting.
  - Recognize the death of Horace Thomas and express condolences to his widow.
- Heard report of Future Meetings Committee.
- Passed a motion to donate $100 to AGI.
- Accepted slate of Nominations Committee.
- Heard report that a new Colorado geological survey had been authorized.
- Received invitation for state geologists to attend dedication of new facilities in Texas.
- Discussed changes to bylaws of American Geological Institute.

1968, May 5–8, Tuscaloosa, Ala.
Host: Philip E. LaMoreaux and Geological Survey of Alabama
Officers:

President: Robert O. Vernon
President-elect: Wallace W. Hagan
Vice President: Peter T. Flawn
Secretary-Treasurer: William C. Hayes
Historian: George F. Hanson
Editor: James L. Calver
Statistician: Philip E. LaMoreaux

Members Present:

Philip E. LaMoreaux, Alabama
Richard T. Moore, Arizona
Norman F. Williams, Arkansas
Ian Campbell, California
Robert Jordan, Delaware
Robert O. Vernon, Florida
A.S. Furcron, Georgia
John C. Frye, Illinois
John B. Patton, Indiana
H. Garland Hershey, Iowa
Frank C. Foley, Kansas
Wallace W. Hagan, Kentucky
Leo W. Hough, Louisiana
Kenneth N. Weaver, Maryland
Gerald E. Eddy, Michigan
R.K. Hogbert, Minnesota
William H. Moore, Mississippi
William C. Hayes, Missouri
Uuno M. Sahinen, Montana
Vincent H. Dreeszen, Nebraska
Glenn W. Stewart, New Hampshire
John C. Broughton, New York
Stephen G. Conrad, North Carolina
Wilson M. Laird, North Dakota
Charles J. Mankin, Oklahoma
Hollis M. Dole, Oregon
Arthur A. Socolow, Pennsylvania
Jose F. Cadilla, Puerto Rico
Duncan J. McGregor, South Dakota

William D. Hardeman, Tennessee

Peter T. Flawn, Texas

William P. Hewitt, Utah

Charles G. Doll, Vermont

James L. Calver, Virginia

Robert B. Erwin, West Virginia

George F. Hanson, Wisconsin

Business Session:

- Host Philip LaMoreaux welcomed attendees and introduced Alabama survey staff.
- Welcomed honorary members.
- Approved as amended the minutes of the 1967 annual meeting.
- Dr. Peter Fenner of the American Geological Institute led discussion on page-size geologic maps.
- Heard report of AGI.
- Heard report of Plant-Pest Control Division of the U.S. Department of Agriculture on soil quarantines.
- Appointed committees: Future Meetings, Balloting, Resolutions, Auditing, Honorary Members, Liaison.
- Heard treasurer's report.
- Heard editor's report.
- Heard historian's report.
- Heard statistician's report.
- Heard Liaison Committee report.
- Heard report of U.S. Geological Survey.
- Heard report of Soil Conservation Service.
- Heard report of Environmental Science Services Administration.
- Heard report of U.S. Bureau of Mines.
- Heard report of Federal Water Pollution Control Association.
- Heard report of Office of Water Resource Research.
- Heard report of Appalachian Regional Commission.
- Discussed Earth Science Curriculum Project.
- Heard report of National Petroleum Council on revision of "Possible Future Petroleum Provinces of North America."
- Expressed sympathy to Alabama Gov. George Wallace on the death of his wife and former Gov. Lurleen Wallace.
- Discussed Liaison Committee report.
- Heard report on the American Commission on Stratigraphic Nomenclature.
- Accepted report of the Auditing Committee.
- Conferred honorary membership on Eugene C. Reed (Nebraska).
- Accepted guidelines for honorary membership recommended by Honorary Members Committee.

- Adopted resolutions recommended by Resolutions Committee:
  - Extended good wishes to Paul Price (West Virginia) upon his retirement.
  - Expressed sympathy to the widow of Arthur Bevan upon his death.
  - Expressed appreciation to Philip LaMoreaux, the Alabama Geological Survey and Gulf States Paper Corp. for hosting the meeting.
- Accepted report of Future Meetings Committee.
- Discussed informal meeting on environmental geology held at recent South-Central Geological Society of America meeting.
- Heard report of Balloting Committee.
- Appointed Environmental Geology Committee, charged with working with federal agencies to advise and assist in planning the role of geology in environmental and urban programs.
- Appointed Personnel Committee, charged with studying personnel problems in the United States regarding salaries, employment, and to maintain a file on vacancies and available personnel.
- Appointed Nominating Committee.
- Contributed $200 to American Geological Institute.
- Announced second annual meeting of the Association of Earth Science Editors May 14–15 in Norman, Okla.

1969, May 4–8, Tucson, Ariz.

Host: James D. Forrestor and Arizona Bureau of Mines

Officers:

President: Wallace W. Hagan
President-elect: Peter T. Flawn
Vice President: William C. Hayes
Secretary-Treasurer: Hollis M. Dole
Historian: George F. Hanson
Editor: James L. Calver
Statistician: Philip E. LaMoreaux

Members Present:

Philip E. LaMoreaux, Alabama
James D. Forrester, Arizona
Norman F. Williams, Arkansas
Ian Campbell, California
John W. Rold, Colorado
Joe Webb Peoples, Connecticut
Robert R. Jordan, Delaware
Robert O. Vernon, Florida
Jesse H. Auvil, Georgia

John C. Frye, Illinois
John B. Patton, Indiana
H. Garland Hershey, Iowa
Frank C. Foley, Kansas
Wallace W. Hagan, Kentucky
Leo W. Hough, Louisiana
Robert G. Doyle, Maine
Kenneth N. Weaver, Maryland
Gerald E. Eddy, Michigan
Rudolph K. Hogbert, Minnesota
William H. Moore, Mississippi
William C. Hayes, Missouri
Uuno M. Sahinen, Montana
Vincent H. Dreeszen, Nebraska
Vernon E. Scheid, Nevada
Glenn W. Stewart, New Hampshire
Kemble Widmer, New Jersey
Frank E. Kottlowski, New Mexico
James F. Davis, New York
Stephen G. Conrad, North Carolina
Wilson M. Laird, North Dakota
Charles J. Mankin, Oklahoma
Raymond E. Corcoran, Oregon
Arthur A. Socolow, Pennsylvania
Henry S. Johnson Jr., South Carolina
Duncan J. McGregor, South Dakota
Peter T. Flawn, Texas
William P. Hewitt, Utah
Charles G. Doll, Vermont
James L. Calver, Virginia
Paul H. Price, West Virginia
George F. Hanson, Wisconsin
D.L. Blackstone, Wyoming

Business Session:

- Recognized staff members from state surveys.
- Recognized honorary members.
- Introduced new state geologists (Rold, Jordan, Collins, Corcoran, Davis).
- Introduced guests.
- Approved minutes of 1968 annual meeting.
- Appointed meeting committees: Auditing, Balloting, Resolutions, Future Meetings, Honorary Members.

- Contributed $200 to American Geological Institute.
- Heard treasurer's report.
- Heard Liaison Committee's report.
- Heard report of the AGI House of Representatives.
- Heard U.S. Geological Survey report.
- Heard U.S. Bureau of Mines report.
- Heard reports from standing committees: Environmental Geology, National Research Council, American Commission on Stratigraphic Nomenclature, Personnel.
- Heard the editor's report.
- Heard report on the International Geological Congress.
- Heard the historian's report.
- Heard the statistician's report.
- Heard report of the Advisory Committee on Water Data for Public Use.
- Discontinued the Committee on Scientific and Technical Information, Committee on Foreign Bibliographies (AGI), and AGI Committee for Coordination for Certification.
- Discussed expanding to a 3-day business meeting.
- Heard meeting committee reports: Auditing, Honorary Members, Resolutions, Future Meetings.
- Discussed the status of the Vermont Geological Survey and the Colorado Geological Survey.
- Voted to support the establishment of a center of environmental geology.
- Discussed problems related to environmental geology and mineral resources investigations unique to coastal states.
- Discussed establishment of the Interstate Mining Compact.
- Discussed use of computers in survey operations.
- Heard report of the Balloting Committee.
- Appointed a self-study committee to review Association activities; evaluate the constitution, bylaws, and committee structure, as well as the *Journal* and annual meetings; make recommendation on whether to have special committees on federal performance.

1970, April 26–30, Rolla, Mo.

Host: William C. Hayes and Missouri Geological Survey

Officers:

President: Peter T. Flawn

President-elect: William C. Hayes

Vice President: Gerald E. Eddy

Secretary-Treasurer: Charles J. Mankin

Historian: George F. Hanson

Editor: James L. Calver

Statistician: Philip E. LaMoreaux

Members Present:

Philip E. LaMoreaux, Alabama
James D. Forrestor, Arizona
Norman F. Williams, Arkansas
Wesley G. Bruer, California
John W. Rold, Colorado
Robert R. Jordan, Delaware
Robert O. Vernon, Florida
Jesse H. Auvil, Georgia
John C. Frye, Illinois
Maurice Biggs, Indiana
Samuel J. Tuthill, Iowa
Frank C. Foley, Kansas
Wallace W. Hagan, Kentucky
Walter A. Anderson, Maine
Kenneth N. Weaver, Maryland
Gerald E. Eddy, Michigan
Paul K. Sims, Minnesota
William H. Moore, Mississippi
William C. Hayes, Missouri
Uuno M. Sahinen, Montana
Vincent H. Dreezen, Nebraska
Vernon E. Scheid, Nevada
Glenn W. Stewart, New Hampshire
Don H. Baker Jr., New Mexico
James F. Davis, New York
Stephen G. Conrad, North Carolina
Edwin A. Noble, North Dakota
Horace R. Collins, Ohio
Charles J. Mankin, Oklahoma
Arthur A. Socolow, Pennsylvania
Eduardo Aguilar-Cortes, Puerto Rico
Norman K. Olson, South Carolina
Duncan J. McGregor, South Dakota
Robert E. Hershey, Tennessee
Peter T. Flawn, Texas
William P. Hewitt, Utah
Charles G. Doll, Vermont
James L. Calver, Virginia
Robert B. Erwin, West Virginia
George F. Hanson, Wisconsin
Daniel N. Miller, Wyoming

Business Session:
- Introduced staff of state surveys, honorary members, and guests.
- Announced committees: Auditing, Balloting, Resolutions, Future Meetings.
- Heard treasurer's report.
- Heard committee reports: Liaison, Environmental Geology, Review of the State of the Association.
- Heard U.S. Geological Survey report.
- Governor of Iowa conferred title of state geologist emeritus on H. Garland Hershey.
- Heard presentation by U.S. Bureau of Mines.
- Heard report of Advisory Committee on Water Data for Public Use.
- Heard report of Stratigraphic Nomenclature Committee.
- Heard report of Personnel Committee.
- Heard report of Mineral Policy Committee.
- Heard report of executive director of American Geological Institute.
- Raised dues to $50.
- Heard statistician's report.
- Heard editor's report.
- Appointed committees and representatives: Liaison Committee, AGI House of Representatives, American Commission on Stratigraphic Nomenclature, National Research Council, AAPG Public Information Committee, Honorary Members Committee, Environmental Geology Committee, Personnel Committee.
- Passed motion supporting accelerated topographic mapping program by the U.S. Geological Survey.
- Contributed $200 to American Geological Institute.
- Heard Auditing Committee report.
- Accepted recommendation of Honorary Members Committee to confer honorary membership on Eugene Callaghan, Hollis Dole, Wilson Laird, H. Garland Hershey, Johan J. Groot, John Broughton, Frank Foley.
- Approved resolutions submitted by Resolutions Committee:
  - Expressed appreciation to Missouri Geological Survey.
  - Expressed appreciation to J.D. Vineyard, J.H. Williams, and L.D. Fellows for special contributions to the success of the annual meeting.
  - Expressed appreciation to Pilot Knob Pellet Co., Missouri Lead Operating Co., Cominco American Inc., Dresser Ind. Inc., American Zinc, A.P. Green Refractories Co., Arch Mineral Corp., Harbison-Walker Refractories Co., Manley Sand Div. Martin Marietta, Meramec Mining Co., Milchem Inc., Missouri Portland Cement Co., Ozark Lead Co., Peabody Coal Co., Pittsburg & Midway Coal Mining Co., St. Joseph Lead Co., Walsh Refractories, Wellsville Fire Brick Co.
  - Expressed appreciation to H.M. Wharton and J.A. Martin.
  - Expressed appreciation to N.A. "Bud" McDonald.
- Heard report of Future Meetings Committee.
- Accepted slate of Balloting Committee.
- Appointed committees: Finances and Publication, Constitution and Official State.

1971, May 10–14, Kennebunkport, Maine
Host: Robert G. Doyle
Officers:

>President: William C. Hayes
>President-elect: Philip E. LaMoreaux
>Vice President: Norman F. Williams
>Secretary-Treasurer: Charles J. Mankin
>Historian: George F. Hanson
>Editor: James L. Calver
>Statistician: Arthur A. Socolow

Members Present:

>Philip E. LaMoreaux, Alabama
>Richard M. Moore, Arizona
>Norman F. Williams, Arkansas
>John W. Rold, Colorado
>Robert R. Jordan, Delaware
>Robert O. Vernon, Florida
>Jesse H. Auvil Jr., Georgia
>Donald Bishop, Idaho
>John C. Frye, Illinois
>John B. Patton, Indiana
>William B. Hambleton, Kansas
>Wallace W. Hagan, Kentucky
>Leo W. Hough, Louisiana
>Robert G. Doyle, Maine
>Kenneth N. Weaver, Maryland
>Arthur E. Slaughter, Michigan
>William H. Moore, Mississippi
>William C. Hayes, Missouri
>Vincent H. Dreeszen, Nebraska
>Vernon E. Scheid, Nevada
>Glenn W. Stewart, New Hampshire
>Kemble Widmer, New Jersey,
>Don H. Baker Jr., New Mexico
>James F. Davis, New York
>Stephen G. Conrad, North Carolina
>Edwin A. Noble, North Dakota
>Horace R. Collins, Ohio
>Charles J. Mankin, Oklahoma
>Raymond E. Corcoran, Oregon
>Arthur A. Socolow, Pennsylvania
>Eduardo Aguilar-Cortes, Puerto Rico

Duncan J. McGregor, South Dakota

William L. Fisher, Texas

William P. Hewitt, Utah

Charles G. Doll, Vermont

James L. Calver, Virginia

Robert B. Erwin, West Virginia

George F. Hanson, Wisconsin

Daniel Miller Jr., Wyoming

Business Session:

- Introduced new state geologists.
- Welcomed honorary members.
- Introduced staff from state surveys and guests.
- Appointed committees: Auditing, Balloting, Future Meetings, Resolutions.
- Heard treasurer's report.
- Heard Liaison Committee report.
- Heard report on American Institute of Professional Geologists' conference on "Planning a New Town."
- Heard report on formation of Interstate Mining Compact.
- Heard report of U.S. Department of the Interior.
- Heard report of the Office of Water Resources Research.
- Heard report of the U.S. Geological Survey.
- Heard report of the U.S. Bureau of Mines.
- Heard report on the American Geological Institute.
- Heard report of the Personnel Committee.
- Heard report of the Honorary Members Committee; approved honorary membership for Gerald Eddy, Peter Flawn, Donald Forrester.
- Heard report of the statistician.
- Heard report on the American Commission on Stratigraphic Nomenclature.
- Heard report on the AGI House of Society Representatives.
- Heard report on Water Data for Public Use.
- Heard report on the National Research Council.
- Heard report of the Auditing Committee.
- Heard report of the Resolutions Committee.
- Heard report of the Future Meetings Committee.
- Appointed committees and representatives: Honorary Members, Liaison, Environmental Geology, National Research Council, AGI House of Representatives, AAPG Public Relations, Water Data for Public Use, Personnel, American Commission on Stratigraphic Nomenclature.
- Heard and discussed report of ad hoc committee on Finance and Publication. Approved the following recommendations:
  - Maintain dues at $50 per year per state.
  - Reduce the *Journal* to one issue per year.

    – Provide the Liaison Committee with up to $500 per year for expenses, but require a budget to be submitted to the Executive Committee.
- Accepted invitation to have an exhibit at the International Geological Congress in Montreal.
- Established committee to present a list of names to the National Academy of Sciences for consideration as director of the U.S. Geological Survey.
- Established a committee to examine the *Journal*.
- Heard report of the Ballot Committee.

1972, May 15–17, Moab, Utah

Host:

Officers:

President: Philip E. LaMoreaux
President-elect: Norman F. Williams
Vice President: Kenneth N. Weaver
Secretary-Treasurer: Charles J. Mankin
Historian: George F. Hanson
Editor: Edwin A. Noble
Statistician: Arthur A. Socolow

Members Present:

Philip E. LaMoreaux, Alabama
William C. Fackler, Alaska
William H. Dresher, Arizona
Norman F. Williams, Arkansas
Wesley G. Bruer, California
John W. Rold, Colorado
Robert R. Jordan, Delaware
Charles W. Hendry Jr., Florida
Sam M. Pickering Jr., Georgia
Jack Simon, Illinois
John B. Patton, Indiana
Samuel J. Tuthill, Iowa
William B. Hambleton, Kansas
Wallace W. Hagan, Kentucky
Leo W. Hough, Louisiana
Robert G. Doyle, Maine
Kenneth N. Weaver, Maryland
Joseph Sinnott, Massachusetts
Arthur E. Slaughter, Michigan
Paul K. Sims, Minnesota

William H. Moore, Mississippi

Wallace B. Howe, Missouri

Ralph King, Montana

Vincent H. Dreeszen, Nebraska

Vernon E. Scheid, Nevada

Glenn W. Stewart, New Hampshire

Kemble Widmer, New Jersey

Don H. Baker Jr., New Mexico

James F. Davis, New York

Stephen G. Conrad, North Carolina

Edwin A. Noble, North Dakota

Horace R. Collins, Ohio

Charles J. Mankin, Oklahoma

Raymond E. Corcoran, Oregon

Arthur A. Socolow, Pennsylvania

Duncan J. McGregor, South Dakota

William L. Fisher, Texas

William P. Hewitt, Utah

James L. Calver, Virginia

Vaughan E. Livingston Jr., Washington

Robert B. Erwin, West Virginia

George F. Hanson, Wisconsin

Daniel N. Miller, Wyoming

Business Session:

- Recognized new state geologists (Fackler, Dresher, Hendry, Pickering, Sinnott, Howe, Livingston).
- Recognized honorary members (Callaghan, Campbell, Foley, Hershey, Laird).
- Introduced staff from state surveys.
- Appointed committees: Auditing, Balloting, Future Meetings, Honorary Members.
- Heard reports from standing committees: National Research Council, American Geological Institute, AAPG Public Relations, Water Data for Public Use, Personnel, American Commission on Stratigraphic Nomenclature, AASG *Journal*.
- Heard reports of secretary-treasurer, historian.
- Discussed registration; formed ad hoc committee to study the issue.
- Heard statistician's report.
- Heard Liaison Committee's report.
- Heard report of deputy assistant secretary of Interior.
- Heard report of U.S. Geological Survey.

- Heard report of National Academy of Sciences–Earth Sciences Division's Geological Sciences Committee.
- Heard report of Office of Water Resources Research.
- Discussed activities of the American Petroleum Institute.
- Heard report of the U.S. Bureau of Mines.
- Heard report on the American Geological Institute.
- Heard committee reports: Balloting, Auditing, Honorary Members, Future Meetings, Resolutions, Environmental.
- Sent $200 contribution to American Geological Institute.
- Appointed Ian Campbell to devise procedure for handling deaths of former members.
- Designated president-elect as ex-officio member of Liaison Committee.
- Appointed ad hoc committee to investigate problems of the outer continental shelf.
- Approved resolution concerning the potential impact of the NATURE program on topographic mapping efforts.
- Appointed committees: Liaison, Environmental Geology, National Research Council, AGI House of Representatives, AAPG Public Relations, Water Use for Public Use, Personnel, American Commission on Stratigraphic Nomenclature, AGI Commission on Minority Groups.

1973, May 28–30, Stone Mountain, Ga.

Host: Sam M. Pickering Jr. and Geological Section of the Georgia Department of Natural Resources, Earth and Water Division.

Officers:

> President: Norman F. Williams
> President-elect: Kenneth N. Weaver
> Vice President: James L. Calver
> Secretary-Treasurer: Charles J. Mankin
> Editor: Edwin A. Noble
> Statistician: Robert R. Jordan
> Historian: Charles G. Doll

Members Present:

> G.W. Swindle, Alabama
> William H. Dresher, Arizona
> Norman F. Williams, Arkansas
> Wesley G. Bruer, California
> John W. Rold, Colorado
> Robert R. Jordan, Delaware
> Charles W. Hendry Jr., Florida
> Sam M. Pickering Jr., Georgia
> Rolland R. Reid, Idaho

John C. Frye, Illinois

John B. Patton, Indiana

William B. Hambleton, Kansas

Wallace W. Hagan, Kentucky

Leo W. Hough, Louisiana

Walter Anderson, Maine

Kenneth N. Weaver, Maryland

Joseph Sinnott, Massachusetts

Arthur E. Slaughter, Michigan

Alvin R. Bicker Jr., Mississippi

Wallace B. Howe, Missouri

Sid L. Groff, Montana

Vincent H. Dreeszen, Nebraska

Glenn W. Stewart, New Hampshire

Kemble Widmer, New Jersey

Don H. Baker Jr., New Mexico

James F. Davis, New York

Stephen G. Conrad, North Carolina

Edwin A. Noble, North Dakota

Charles J. Mankin, Oklahoma

Raymond E. Corcoran, Oregon

Arthur A. Socolow, Pennsylvania

Norman K. Olson, South Carolina

Merlin Tipton, South Dakota

Robert E. Hershey, Tennessee

William L. Fisher, Texas

William P. Hewitt, Utah

Charles G. Doll, Vermont

James L. Calver, Virginia

Vaughn E. Livingston Jr., Washington

Robert B. Erwin, West Virginia

Meredith E. Ostrom, Wisconsin

Daniel N. Miller, Wyoming

Business Session:

- Introduced guests.
- Heard treasurer's report.
- Heard report of American Geological Institute representative.
- Heard report on National Research Council.
- Heard report on AAPG Public Relations Committee.
- Heard report on Committee on Water Data for Public Use.
- Heard report of Personnel Committee.

- Assigned meeting committees: Auditing, Balloting, Future Meetings, Resolutions, Honorary Members, Offshore Drilling, Personnel Matters.
- Heard report of American Commission on Stratigraphic Nomenclature.
- Heard editor's report.
- Heard historian's report.
- Heard statistician's report.
- Heard report of Liaison Committee.
- Heard report on American Petroleum Institute.
- Heard U.S. Geological Survey report.
- Heard report on American Geological Institute.
- Heard analysis of minerals industry from the industrial viewpoint.
- Heard report of U.S. Bureau of Mines.
- Heard report of ad hoc Offshore Drilling Committee.
- Heard report on AAPG's Geological Highway Map Program.
- Heard report on Interstate Mining Compact.
- Heard report of the Environmental Committee.
- Heard report of the ad hoc Committee on Personnel Matters.
- Heard report of Registration Committee.
- Heard report of Auditing Committee.
- Heard report of Honorary Members Committee.
- Heard report of Future Meetings Committee.
- Heard report of Resolutions Committee.
- Accepted report of Balloting Committee.
- Appointed standing committees for coming year: Liaison, Environmental Geology, Outer Continental Shelf, National Research Council, AGI House of Representatives, AAPG Public Relations, Personnel, American Commission on Stratigraphic Nomenclature, Water Data for Public Use, Registration, Personnel, Honorary Members.
- Established position of Culture Chairman.

1974, June 9–12, Bend, Ore.

Host: Raymond E. Corcoran and the
Oregon Department of Geology and Mineral Industries
Officers:

    President: Kenneth N. Weaver
    President-elect: James L. Calver
    Vice President: Charles J. Mankin
    Secretary-Treasurer: Daniel N. Miller Jr.
    Historian: Charles G. Doll
    Statistician: Robert R. Jordan
    Editor: Edwin A. Noble

Members Present:

Donald C. Hartman, Alaska
William H. Dresher, Arizona
Norman F. Williams, Arkansas
James E. Slosson, California
John W. Rold, Colorado
Hugo F. Thomas, Connecticut
Robert R. Jordan, Delaware
Charles W. Hendry Jr., Florida
Sam M. Pickering Jr., Georgia
John C. Frye, Illinois
John B. Patton, Indiana
Samuel J. Tuthill, Iowa
William W. Hambleton, Kansas
Wallace W. Hagan, Kentucky
Leo W. Hough, Louisiana
Kenneth N. Weaver, Maryland
Arthur E. Slaughter, Michigan
Matt S. Walton, Minnesota
William H. Moore, Mississippi
Wallace B. Howe, Missouri
Sid Groff, Montana
Vincent H. Dreeszen, Nebraska
Arthur Baker III, Nevada
Glenn W. Stewart, New Hampshire
Kemble Widmer, New Jersey
Frank E. Kottlowski, New Mexico
James F. Davis, New York
Stephen G. Conrad, North Carolina
C.B. Folsom, North Dakota
Charles J. Mankin, Oklahoma
Raymond E. Corcoran, Oregon
Arthur A. Socolow, Pennsylvania
Norman K. Olson, South Carolina
Duncan J. McGregor, South Dakota
William L. Fisher, Texas
Donald T. McMillan, Utah
Charles G. Doll, Vermont
James L. Calver, Virginia
Vaughn E. Livingston Jr., Washington
Robert B. Erwin, West Virginia
Meredith E. Ostrom, Wisconsin
Daniel N. Miller Jr., Wyoming

Business Session:

- Introduced guests.
- Appointed meeting committees: Auditing, Balloting, Future Meetings, Resolutions, Honorary Members.
- Heard treasurer's report.
- Heard editor's report.
- Heard historian's report.
- Heard statistician's report.
- Heard report of Water Data for Public Use.
- Heard report of ad hoc Outer Continental Shelf Committee.
- Heard report of American Commission on Stratigraphic Nomenclature.
- Heard Liaison Committee report.
- Heard report of AGI Governing Board.
- Heard U.S. Geological Survey report.
- Heard report on American Geological Institute.
- Heard report on American Institute of Professional Geologists.
- Heard report on Interstate Mining Compact.
- Heard AAPG Liaison Committee report.
- Heard report of U.S. Bureau of Mines.
- Heard report on Atomic Energy Commission.
- Heard report of Office of Coastal Zone Management.
- Heard report of Soil Conservation Service.
- Heard report of National Research Council.
- Heard Personnel Committee report.
- Heard Environmental Geology Committee report.
- Heard ad hoc Personnel Committee report.
- Heard ad hoc Constitution and Bylaws Committee report.
- Heard Honorary Members Committee report.
- Heard Auditing Committee report.
- Heard report on Task Force on Midwest Energy Requirements and Environmental Protection.
- Heard report on the Association of Engineering Geologists; all state geologists urged to join.
- Announced that "AASG represents the strongest publicly oriented, geological group in the nation and functions as a non-partisan organization. We should evaluate our membership relative to future positions in the Federal government as Assistant Under-Secretaries within the Department of Interior." Recommended appointing a committee to accomplish this.
- Heard report from the Library of Congress.
- Heard Resolutions Committee report.
- Heard report of Future Meetings Committee.
- Heard report of the Balloting Committee.
- Appointed committees for coming year.

1975, May 19–22, Asheville, N.C.

Host: Stephen G. Conrad and North Carolina Division of Land Resources

Officers:

President: James L. Calver

President-elect: Charles J. Mankin

Vice President: William L. Fisher

Secretary-Treasurer: Daniel N. Miller Jr.

Historian: Charles G. Doll

Editor: Edwin A. Noble

Statistician: Robert R. Jordan

Members Present:

Philip E. LaMoreaux, Alabama

Richard Moore, Arizona

Norman F. Williams, Arkansas

James E. Slosson, California

John W. Rold, Colorado

Hugo F. Thomas, Connecticut

Robert R. Jordan, Delaware

Charles W. Hendry Jr., Florida

Sam M. Pickering Jr., Georgia

John G. Bond, Idaho

Jack A. Simon, Illinois

John B. Patton, Indiana

Oliver Van Eck, Iowa

William W. Hambleton, Kansas

Wallace W. Hagan, Kentucky

Leo W. Hough, Louisiana

Kenneth N. Weaver, Maryland

Joseph A. Sinnott, Massachusetts

Arthur E. Slaughter, Michigan

Matt S. Walton, Minnesota

William H. Moore, Mississippi

Wallace B. Howe, Missouri

Sid Groff, Montana

Vincent H. Dreeszen, Nebraska

Glenn W. Stewart, New Hampshire

Kemble Widmer, New Jersey

Frank E. Kottlowski, New Mexico

James F. Davis, New York

Stephen G. Conrad, North Carolina

Edwin A. Noble, North Dakota

Charles J. Mankin, Oklahoma

R.E. Corcoran, Oregon

Arthur A. Socolow, Pennsylvania

Norman K. Olson, South Carolina

Duncan J. McGregor, South Dakota

Robert E. Hershey, Tennessee

Charles S. Groat, Texas

Donald T. McMillan, Utah

James L. Calver, Virginia

Vaughn E. Livingston Jr., Washington

Robert B. Erwin, West Virginia

Meredith E. Ostrom, Wisconsin

Daniel N. Miller Jr., Wyoming

Business Session:

- Introduced guests.
- Appointed group discussion leaders for evening discussion sessions on the outer continental shelf and coal.
- Heard treasurer's report.
- Heard editor's report.
- Heard Water Data for Public Use report.
- Heard report of the U.S. Bureau of Mines.
- Heard report of the Energy Research and Development Administration.
- Heard report of the U.S. Geological Survey.
- Heard report of the Nuclear Regulatory Commission.
- Heard report of the American Geological Institute.
- Heard report of the Soil Conservation Service.
- Heard report of the Library of Congress.
- Heard report on the Interstate Mining Compact.
- Heard historian's report.
- Heard report of the American Commission on Stratigraphic Nomenclature.
- Heard Environmental Geology Committee report.
- Heard report of Committee on Registration of Geologists.
- Heard statistician's report.
- Introduced Walter B. Jones, state geologist of Alabama from 1927 to 1961.
- Heard report on AGI Management Board.
- Heard report of Committee on Continental Margins.
- Discussed National Coal Data Committee.
- Resolved to support AASG being an advisory committee to the National Coal Data Committee.

- Heard Liaison Committee report.
- Heard Honorary Members Committee report.
- Heard report on National Research Council.
- Heard report of Constitution and Bylaws Committee.
- Heard AAPG Liaison Committee report.
- Heard Core and Sample Library Committee report.
- Discussed publications exchange.
- Heard report on American Association for the Advancement of Science.
- Heard report of ad hoc Editor's Advisory Committee.
- Approved recommendations in report of Registration of Geologists Committee.
- Heard report of Future Meetings Committee.
- Heard report of Honorary Members Committee.
- Heard report of Auditing Committee.
- Discussed Federal-State Power Plant Siting Conference.
- Heard Resolutions Committee report.
- Discussed expenses of AASG and authorization of funds.
- Approved paying expenses of state geologists' travel to Liaison Committee meetings, if their surveys cannot provide support.
- Contributed $500 to American Geological Institute.
- Held moment of silence for former members Robert O. Vernon and Walter F. Pond.
- Heard Balloting Committee report.
- Appointed committees for coming year.

1976, June 20–25, Vail, Colo.

Host: John W. Rold and the Colorado Department of Natural Resources–Geological Survey Division

Officers:

President: Charles J. Mankin
President-elect: Duncan J. McGregor
Vice President: Arthur A. Socolow
Secretary-Treasurer: Daniel N. Miller Jr.
Historian: Charles G. Doll
Editor: Edwin A. Noble
Statistician: Robert R. Jordan

Members Present:

Philip E. LaMoreaux, Alabama
Ross G. Schaff, Alaska
William H. Dresher, Arizona
Norman F. Williams, Arkansas

Thomas E. Gay Jr., California
John W. Rold, Colorado
Hugo G. Thomas, Connecticut
Robert R. Jordan, Delaware
Charles W. Hendry Jr., Florida
Sam M. Pickering Jr., Georgia
Maynard M. Miller, Idaho
Jack A. Simon, Illinois
John B. Patton, Indiana
Stanley C. Grant, Iowa
William W. Hambleton, Kansas
Wallace W. Hagan, Kentucky
Leo W. Hough, Louisiana
Kenneth N. Weaver, Maryland
Arthur E. Slaughter, Michigan
Matt S. Walton, Minnesota
William H. Moore, Mississippi
Wallace B. Howe, Missouri
Sid Groff, Montana
Vincent H. Dreeszen, Nebraska
John H. Schilling, Nevada
Kemble Widmer, New Jersey
Frank E. Kottlowski, New Mexico
Stephen G. Conrad, North Carolina
Edwin A. Noble, North Dakota
Charles J. Mankin, Oklahoma
Raymond E. Corcoran, Oregon
Arthur A. Socolow, Pennsylvania
Antonio Segovia, Puerto Rico
Duncan J. McGregor, South Dakota
Robert E. Hershey, Tennessee
Charles G. Groat, Texas
Donald T. McMillan, Utah
James L. Calver, Virginia
Vaughn E. Livingston Jr., Washington
Robert B. Erwin, West Virginia
Meredith E. Ostrom, Wisconsin
Daniel N. Miller Jr., Wyoming

Business Session:

- Heard president's review of year's activities.
- Heard secretary-treasurer's report.
- Heard editor's report.
- Heard statistician's report.
- Appointed meeting committees: Future Meetings, Auditing, Balloting, Resolutions.
- Heard Liaison Committee report.
- Heard Water Data for Public Use Committee report.
- Heard report of Geological Society of America liaison.
- Heard report on American Committee on Stratigraphic Nomenclature.
- Heard report of U.S. Geological Survey.
- Heard report of U.S. Department of the Interior.
- Heard report on the Federal Energy Administration.
- Heard report on the Energy Research and Development Administration.
- Heard report on the Library of Congress.
- Heard report of the U.S. Bureau of Mines.
- Heard report on American Petroleum Institute.
- Heard report on American Geological Institute.
- Heard report of the Nuclear Regulatory Commission.
- Heard report on the upcoming International Carboniferous Conference.
- Recognized honorary members.
- Heard report of the Registration of Geologists Committee.
- Heard report of Interim Study Committee on Materials.
- Heard Continental Margins Committee report.
- Heard National Coal Data Coordinating Committee report.
- Heard Honorary Members Committee report.
- Announced that Congress failed to pass a 90-day extension for Federal Energy Administration activities.
- Heard report of Energy Research and Development Administration.
- Passed motion to appoint committee to work with the Energy Research and Development Administration on nuclear waste disposal programs.
- Discussed confidentiality of statistician's report.
- Passed motion to ask the American Geological Institute to discontinue reference to AASG endorsement of its Data Collecting System proposal to the National Science Foundation.
- Heard reports of meeting committees: Auditing, Future Meetings, Resolutions, Balloting.

1977, June 5–9, Newark, Del.
Host: Robert Jordan, Delaware Geological Survey
Officers:

> President: Duncan J. McGregor
> President-elect: Arthur A. Socolow
> Vice President: Robert B. Erwin
> Secretary-Treasurer: Daniel N. Miller Jr.
> Historian: Charles G. Doll
> Editor: Edwin A. Noble
> Statistician: Robert R. Jordan

Members Present:

> Thomas A. Joiner, Alabama
> Ross G. Schaff, Alaska
> Richard Moore, Arizona
> Norman F. Williams, Arkansas
> Thomas E. Gay Jr., California
> John W. Rold, Colorado
> Hugo G. Thomas, Connecticut
> Thomas E. Pickett, Delaware
> Charles W. Hendry Jr., Florida
> Sam M. Pickering Jr., Georgia
> Jack A. Simon, Illinois
> John B. Patton, Indiana
> Orville Van Eck, Iowa
> William W. Hambleton, Kansas
> Wallace W. Hagan, Kentucky
> Robert G. Doyle, Maine
> Kenneth N. Weaver, Maryland
> Joseph A. Sinnott, Massachusetts
> Arthur E. Slaughter, Michigan
> Matt S. Walton, Minnesota
> William H. Moore, Mississippi
> Wallace B. Howe, Missouri
> Vincent H. Dreeszen, Nebraska
> Glenn W. Stewart, New Hampshire
> Kemble Widmer, New Jersey
> Frank E. Kottlowski, New Mexico
> Stephen G. Conrad, North Carolina
> Edwin A. Noble, North Dakota
> Charles J. Mankin, Oklahoma

Ralph S. Mason, Oregon

Arthur A. Socolow, Pennsylvania

Duncan J. McGregor, South Dakota

William L. Fisher, Texas

Donald T. McMillan, Utah

Charles A. Ratté, Vermont

James L. Calver, Virginia

Vaughn E. Livingston Jr., Washington

Robert B. Erwin, West Virginia

Meredith E. Ostrom, Wisconsin

Daniel N. Miller Jr., Wyoming

Business Session:

- Assigned Future Meetings Committee.
- Heard report of Balloting Committee.
- Heard president's report.
- Heard secretary-treasurer's report.
- Heard editor's report.
- Heard report of Auditing Committee.
- Heard report of Resolutions Committee.
- Heard historian's report.
- Heard statistician's report.
- Introduced honorary members.
- Noted the passing of Gerald E. Eddy and Walter B. Jones.
- Heard report by U.S. Bureau of Mines.
- Heard report by Energy Research and Development Administration.
- Heard report by Uranium Resources, Division of Uranium Resources and Enrichment.
- Heard report by Nuclear Regulatory Commission.
- Heard report by U.S. Geological Survey.
- Heard report by USGS Topographic Division.
- Heard report by USGS Water Division Cooperative Program.
- Heard report by USGS Conservation Division.
- Reminded Association of the forthcoming International Carboniferous Congress.
- Heard report by USGS Geologic Division.
- Introduced panel of state geologists and ex-state geologists who were, or had been, associated with the "Washington scene."
- Took annual group photograph.
- Heard Liaison Committee report.
- Heard Energy Research and Development Administration– Nuclear Waste Disposal Advisory Committee report.
- Heard report by the AASG Review Group.

- Heard GeoSat Committee report.
- Heard Potential Gas Committee report.
- Heard Auditing Committee report.
- Heard Core and Sample Library Committee report.
- Heard AAPG Liaison Committee report.
- Heard Committee on Water Data for Public Use report.
- Heard AGI Management report.
- Heard report on registration of geologists.
- Heard National Coal Data Committee report.
- Heard Continental Margins Committee report.
- Heard Honorary Members Committee report.
- Heard Interim Study Committee on Materials report.
- Heard Resolutions Committee report.
- Heard National Coal Data Committee report.
- Heard report of GSA Liaison Committee.
- Heard report of International Surveys Liaison Committee.
- Heard report of Public Issues Committee.
- Heard president's report.
- Heard treasurer's report.
- Heard Liaison Committee report.

1978, June 11–15, Jackson, Wyo.
Host: Daniel N. Miller Jr., Wyoming Geological Survey
Officers:

President: Arthur A. Socolow
President-elect: Robert B. Erwin
Vice President: Daniel N. Miller Jr.
Secretary-Treasurer: Robert R. Jordan
Historian: Arthur E. Slaughter
Editor: Edwin A. Noble
Statistician: Wallace B. Howe

Members Present:

Thomas A. Joiner, Alabama
Ross G. Schaff, Alaska
H. Wesley Pierce, Arizona
Norman F. Williams, Arkansas
James F. Davis, California
John W. Rold, Colorado
Hugo F. Thomas, Connecticut
Robert R. Jordan, Delaware

Charles W. Hendry Jr., Florida
Sam M. Pickering, Georgia
Maynard M. Miller, Idaho
Jack A. Simon, Illinois
John B. Patton, Indiana
Dean Lebestky, Kansas
Wallace W. Hagan, Kentucky
Charles G. Groat, Louisiana
Robert G. Doyle, Maine
Kenneth N. Weaver, Maryland
Arthur E. Slaughter, Michigan
Matt S. Walton, Minnesota
William H. Moore, Mississippi
Wallace B. Howe, Missouri
Sid Groff, Montana
Vincent H. Dreeszen, Nebraska
John H. Schilling, Nevada
Glenn W. Stewart, New Hampshire
Kemble Widmer, New Jersey
Frank E. Kottlowski, New Mexico
Robert Fakundiny, New York
Lawrence Rickard, New York
Stephen G. Conrad, North Carolina
Lee C. Gerhard, North Dakota
Charles J. Mankin, Oklahoma
Arthur A. Socolow, Pennsylvania
Norman K. Olson, South Carolina
Duncan J. McGregor, South Dakota
Robert E. Hershey, Tennessee
William L. Fisher, Texas
Donald T. McMillan, Utah
Charles A. Ratté, Vermont
James L. Calver, Virginia
Robert B. Erwin, West Virginia
Meredith E. Ostrom, Wisconsin
Daniel N. Miller Jr., Wyoming

Business Session:

- President Socolow extended a special welcome to two newly appointed state geologists.
- Recognized honorary members of AASG attending.

- Introduced staff members in attendance from the several state geological surveys and the invited guests of AASG.
- Heard necrology report.
- Heard president's report
- Appointed meeting committees.
- Transferred the secretary-treasurer duties.
- Approved and distributed minutes of the 69th annual meeting, with corrections.
- Heard report of the secretary-treasurer.
- Heard report of the editor.
- Heard report of the historian.
- Heard report of the statistician.
- Heard report of the Liaison Committee.
- Heard reports of the U.S. Geological Survey: Conservation Division, Land Information Analysis Program, Administration Division.
- Heard report of the U.S. Bureau of Mines.
- Heard report of AAPG's Correlation of Stratigraphic Units of North America (COSUNA) project.
- Heard report of National Uranium Resource Evaluation and Bendix.
- Heard report of the Office and Technology Assessment.
- Heard report of the Interstate Mining Compact Commission.
- Heard report from the National Research Council.
- Heard report of the National Academy of Science.
- Heard report of the Nuclear Waste Disposal Committee.
- Heard report of the GeoSat Committee.
- Heard report of the Potential Gas Committee.
- Heard report from the AAPG liaison officer.
- Heard report from the Core and Sample Library Committee.
- Heard report from the Water Data for Public Use Committee.
- Heard report from the National Coal Data Committee.
- Heard report from the Continental Margins Committee.
- Heard report from the American Commission on Stratigraphic Nomenclature.
- Heard report from the Committee on Registration of Geologists.
- Heard report from the AGI representative.
- Heard report on the Ian Campbell Memorial Fund.
- Heard report from the International Carboniferous Congress.
- Heard report on the Petroleum Data System.
- Heard report on the withdrawal of lands from mineral access.
- Reviewed the RARE II (Roadless Area Review and Evaluation) program of the U.S. Forest Service.
- Heard report from the Library of Congress.

- Heard report on the New Jersey mapping program.
- Heard report on the national magnetic anomaly map.
- Heard report from the Honorary Members Committee.
- Reviewed invitations to host AASG meeting.
- Heard report from the Resolutions Committee.
- Heard report from the Balloting Committee.
- Outgoing president introduced incoming president.
- Appointed new committee members.

1979, June 4, Little Rock, Ark.

Host: Norman F. Williams, Arkansas Geological Commission

Officers:

President: Robert B. Erwin

President-elect: Daniel N. Miller Jr.

Vice President: Stephen G. Conrad

Secretary-Treasurer: Robert R. Jordan

Historian: Arthur E. Slaughter

Editor: Vincent H. Dreeszen

Statistician: Wallace B. Howe

Members Present:

Thomas J. Joiner, Alabama

Larry D. Fellows, Arizona

Norman F. Williams, Arkansas

James F. Davis, California

John W. Rold, Colorado

Hugo F. Thomas, Connecticut

Robert R. Jordan, Delaware

Charles W. Hendry Jr., Florida

William McLemore, Georgia

Jack A. Simon, Illinois

John B. Patton, Indiana

Stanley C. Grant, Iowa

William W. Hambleton, Kansas

Donald C. Haney, Kentucky

Charles G. Groat, Louisiana

Kenneth N. Weaver, Maryland

Arthur E. Slaughter, Michigan

Matt S. Walton, Minnesota

Alvin R. Bicker Jr., Mississippi

Wallace B. Howe, Missouri

Sid Groff, Montana

Vincent H. Dreeszen, Nebraska

John H. Schilling, Nevada

Glenn W. Stewart, New Hampshire

Kemble Widmer, New Jersey

Frank E. Kottlowski, New Mexico

Robert H. Fakundiny, New York

Stephen G. Conrad, North Carolina

Lee C. Gerhard, North Dakota

Charles J. Mankin, Oklahoma

Arthur A. Socolow, Pennsylvania

Merlin J. Tipton, South Dakota

Robert E. Hershey, Tennessee

William L. Fisher, Texas

Donald T. McMillan, Utah

Robert C. Milici, Virginia

Vaughn E. Livingston, Washington

Robert B. Erwin, West Virginia

Meredith E. Ostrom, Wisconsin

Daniel N. Miller, Wyoming

Business Session:

- Introduced honorary members.
- Heard necrology report.
- Appointed meeting committee chairmen.
- Heard report of the Auditing Committee.
- Heard report of the Resolutions Committee.
- Heard report of the Future Meetings Committee.
- Heard report from the secretary-treasurer.
- Heard report from the editor.
- Heard report from the historian.
- Heard report from the statistician.
- Heard report of the Liaison Committee.
- Heard report of the U.S. Geological Survey.
- Heard report of the USGS Topographic Division.
- Heard report of the USGS Conservation Division.
- Heard report of the U.S. Bureau of Mines.
- Heard report of the American Geological Institute.
- Heard report from the Aero Service Corp.
- Reviewed the history of the Correlation of Stratigraphic Units of North America (COSUNA) project.
- Heard report of the state–National Research Council cooperative.
- Heard report of the Interstate Mining Compact Commission.

- Heard report of the Board of Mineral and Energy Resources.
- Heard report of the Alaska coal study.
- Heard report on groundwater and coal.
- Heard report on science and technology in Bureau of Land Management decision-making.
- Heard report on radioactive waste management.
- Heard report of the Surface Mining and Reclamation Committee.
- Heard report of the Offshore Energy Technology Committee.
- Heard report of the Energy Information Administration.
- Heard report on the USGS Geographic Names Committee.
- Heard report on the USGS communications system.
- Heard report on AM International.
- Welcomed new state geologists to AASG.
- Heard report of the Future Meetings Committee.
- Heard report of the American Commission on Stratigraphic Names Committee.
- Heard report of the AAPG Liaison Committee.
- Heard report from the Water Data for Public Use Committee.
- Heard report of the GSA Liaison Committee.
- Heard report of the Potential Gas Committee.
- Discussed results of the poll of state surveys about core and sample libraries.
- Heard report of the GeoSat Liaison Committee.
- Heard report of the International Surveys Liaison Committee.
- Heard report of the Nuclear Waste Management Committee.
- Heard report on the National Coal Data System.
- Heard report of the Registration of Geologists Committee.
- Distributed U.S. Geological Survey centennial pin.
- Heard auditor's report.
- Heard report on AASG finances and dues.
- Heard report of the Metrication Board.
- Extended invitation for participation of foreign surveys.
- Heard report on AASG constitution and bylaws.
- Discussed U.S. Bureau of Mines.
- Heard report on U.S. Geological Survey conflict of interest interpretations.
- Heard report on USGS communications system.
- Heard report on USBM Liaison Officer Program.
- Heard report on simulated aperture radar imagery.
- Discussed publication exchange.
- Heard report on Strategic Arms Limitations Talk (SALT II).
- Appointed a Washington contact person.
- Heard report of the Honorary Members Committee.
- Heard report of the Continental Margins Committee.

- Heard report of the Ian Campbell Memorial Fund Committee.
- Heard report of the Resolutions Committee.
- Heard report on Three Mile Island accident.
- Heard report of the Balloting Committee.
- Outgoing President Erwin welcomed and congratulated the new president of AASG.

1980, April 27–May 1, South Padre Island, Tex.

Host: William L. Fisher, Texas Bureau of Economic Geology

Officers:

> President: Daniel N. Miller Jr.
> President-elect: Stephen G. Conrad
> Vice President: William L. Fisher
> Secretary-Treasurer: Robert R. Jordan
> Historian: Arthur E. Slaughter
> Editor: Vincent H. Dreeszen
> Statistician: Wallace B. Howe

Members Present:

> Thomas J. Joiner, Alabama
> Ross G. Schaff, Alaska
> Larry D. Fellows, Arizona
> Norman F. Williams, Arkansas
> James F. Davis, California
> John W. Rold, Colorado
> Hugo F. Thomas, Connecticut
> Robert R. Jordan, Delaware
> Charles W. Hendry Jr., Florida
> William McLemore, Georgia
> Maynard M. Miller, Idaho
> Jack A. Simon, Illinois
> John B. Patton, Indiana
> Donald Koch, Iowa
> William B. Hambleton, Kansas
> Charles G. Groat, Louisiana
> Walter A. Anderson, Maine
> Kenneth N. Weaver, Maryland
> Arthur E. Slaughter, Michigan
> Matt S. Walton, Minnesota
> Wallace B. Howe, Missouri
> Sid Groff, Montana
> Vincent H. Dreeszen, Nebraska

John H. Schilling, Nevada

Glenn W. Stewart, New Hampshire

Frank E. Kottlowski, New Mexico

Robert H. Fakundiny, New York

Stephen G. Conrad, North Carolina

Lee C. Gerhard, North Dakota

Charles J. Mankin, Oklahoma

Donald A. Hull, Oregon

Arthur A. Socolow, Pennsylvania

Norman K. Olson, South Carolina

Duncan J. McGregor, South Dakota

William L. Fisher, Texas

Donald T. McMillan, Utah

Charles A. Ratté, Vermont

Robert C. Milici, Virginia

Vaughn E. Livingston, Washington

Robert B. Erwin, West Virginia

Meredith E. Ostrom, Wisconsin

Daniel N. Miller Jr., Wyoming

Business Session:

- Called the roll.
- Introduced members of staff of the state geological surveys.
- Introduced honorary members.
- Heard necrology report.
- Approved the minutes from the 71st annual meeting.
- Heard report of the secretary-treasurer.
- Heard report of the editor.
- Heard report of the historian.
- Heard report of the statistician.
- Appointed meeting committees: Auditing, Balloting, Future Meetings, Resolutions.
- Heard report from the Department of Energy on geothermal programs.
- Heard report from the Committee on USGS Contracting Initiative.
- Heard report from the Liaison Committee.
- Heard presentation of the Environmental Atlas on the Brownsville-Harlington part of the Texas coast.
- Heard reports from the U.S. Geological Survey: Water Resources Division, National Mapping Division, Conservation Division.
- Heard report from the U.S. Bureau of Mines.
- Announced resignation of Stanley Grant.
- Heard report from the American Association of Petroleum Geologists liaison.

- Heard report from the Geological Society of America liaison.
- Heard report on the American Association for the Advancement of Science.
- Heard report on the American Geological Institute.
- Heard report from the NRC Site Safety Research Branch.
- Heard report from the Interstate Mining Compact Commission.
- Heard report from the National Academy of Sciences Continental Drilling Program.
- Heard report from the GSA Committee on Geology and Public Policy.
- Heard report from the North American Commission on Stratigraphic Nomenclature.
- Heard report from the International Surveys Committee.
- Heard report from the Department of Energy Technical Review Committee on Nuclear Waste Storage.
- Heard report from the Core and Sample Library Committee.
- Heard report from the Committee on Water Data and Public Use.
- Heard report from the Potential Gas Committee.
- Heard report from the American Institute of Professional Geologists.
- Heard report from the Continental Margins Committee.
- Heard report from the National Academy of Science.
- Heard report from the National Coal Resources Data Committee.
- Heard report from the Registration of Geologists Committee.
- Heard report from the Constitution and Bylaws Committee.
- Heard report from the AGI Governing Board.
- Heard report from the Future Meetings Committee.
- Heard report from the Honorary Members Committee.
- Heard report from the Public Issues Committee.
- Heard report from the Cultural chairman.
- Heard miscellaneous reports and notes.
- Heard report from the Auditing Committee.
- Heard report from the Resolutions Committee.
- Heard report from the Balloting Committee.
- Heard remarks from outgoing president.
- Heard comments of incoming president

1981, June 7–11, Baltimore, Md.

Host: Kenneth N. Weaver, Maryland Geological Survey

Officers:

 President: Stephen G. Conrad

 President-elect: William L. Fisher

 Vice President: Meredith E. Ostrom

 Secretary-Treasurer: Robert R. Jordan

Historian: Arthur E. Slaughter

Editor: Vincent H. Dreeszen

Statistician: Wallace B. Howe

Members Present:

Richard N. Raymond, Alabama

Ross G. Schaff, Alaska

Larry D. Fellows, Arizona

Norman F. Williams, Arkansas

James F. Davis, California

John W. Rold, Colorado

Hugo F. Thomas, Connecticut

Robert R. Jordan, Delaware

Charles W. Hendry Jr., Florida

William McLemore, Georgia

Robert Bergstrom, Illinois

John B. Patton, Indiana

Donald L. Koch, Iowa

William H. Hambleton, Kansas

Donald C. Haney, Kentucky

Charles G. Groat, Louisiana

Walter A. Anderson, Maine

Kenneth N. Weaver, Maryland

R. Thomas Segall, Michigan

Matt S. Walton, Minnesota

Alvin R. Bicker Jr., Mississippi

Wallace B. Howe, Missouri

Sid Groff, Montana

Vincent H. Dreeszen, Nebraska

Robert I. Davis, New Hampshire

Frank J. Markewicz, New Jersey

Frank E. Kottlowski, New Mexico

Robert H. Fakundiny, New York

Stephen G. Conrad, North Carolina

Lee C. Gerhard, North Dakota

Charles J. Mankin, Oklahoma

Arthur A. Socolow, Pennsylvania

Norman K. Olson, South Carolina

Robert E. Hershey, Tennessee

William L. Fisher, Texas

Robert C. Milici, Virginia

Vaughn Livingston Jr., Washington

Meredith E. Ostrom, Wisconsin

Business Session:

- Introduced members of staffs of the state geological surveys.
- Heard necrology report.
- President Conrad read a message from Jack Simon.
- Approved minutes of 1980 annual meeting.
- Heard report of the secretary-treasurer.
- Heard report of the editor.
- Heard report of the historian.
- Heard report of the statistician.
- President Conrad appointed the meeting committees: Auditing, Balloting, Future Meetings, Resolutions.
- Discussed establishment of the Ian Campbell Medal.
- Heard Liaison Committee report.
- Discussed joint planning and cooperation with the U.S. Geological Survey.
- Heard report from the U.S. Geological Survey.
- Heard report from the U.S. Bureau of Mines.
- Heard report from the Interstate Mining Compact Commission.
- Heard report from the Consortium for Continental Reflection Profiling.
- Heard report from the state geologists' Technical Advisory Committee to the Department of Energy.
- Heard report from the Nuclear Regulatory Commission.
- Heard presentation on the eruption of Mount St. Helens.
- Heard report from the National Academy of Sciences.
- Heard report from the Continental Margins Committee.
- Heard report from the Geological Sciences Board.
- Heard report from the American Geological Institute.
- Heard report from the AGI Management Council.
- Heard report on the COSUNA project.
- Heard report from the North American Commission on Stratigraphic Nomenclature.
- Heard report of the Geological Society of America liaison.
- Heard report on the Committee on Registration of Geologists.
- Heard report from the American Institute of Professional Geologists.
- Heard report from the state geologists' Technical Review Group (Department of Energy).
- Heard report from the Committee on Water Data for Public Use.
- Heard report from the National Coal Resources Data Committee.
- Heard report from the American Association for the Advancement of Science.
- Heard Honorary Members Committee report.
- Heard report from the American Association of Petroleum Geologists liaison.
- Heard report from the Core and Sample Library Committee.

- Discussed liaison officer program, state survey cartographers, prohibition of exploration, joint planning and cooperation with USGS.
- Heard report on the U.S. Bureau of Mines liaison program.
- Heard report from the state geologists' Technical Advisory Committee (Department of Energy).
- Considered requests for an AASG logo.
- Discussed problems with publications of state surveys.
- Discussed administrative items.
- Called for support of the Department of the Interior.
- Noted Allen Agnew was retiring from the Library of Congress, and called for letters in support of offering AASG's assistance in filling the position.
- Heard Honorary Members Committee report.
- Heard report of Auditing Committee.
- Heard report of Future Meetings Committee.
- Heard report of Resolutions Committee.
- Heard report of Special Recognition Committee.
- Heard report of the Balloting Committee.

1982, June 6–10, Hershey, Pa.

Host: Arthur A. Socolow, Pennsylvania Department of Environmental Resources.

Officers:

 President: William L. Fisher

 President-elect: Meredith E. Ostrom

 Vice President: Robert R. Jordan

 Secretary-Treasurer: Charles W. Hendry Jr.

 Historian: Robert E. Hershey

 Editor: Vincent H. Dreeszen

 Statistician: Wallace B. Howe

Members Present:

 Ernest A. Mancini, Alabama

 Ross G. Schaff, Alaska

 Larry D. Fellows, Arizona

 Norman F. Williams, Arkansas

 John W. Rold, Colorado

 Hugo G. Thomas, Connecticut

 Robert R. Jordan, Delaware

 Charles W. Hendry Jr., Florida

 William McLemore, Georgia

 Robert E. Bergstrom, Illinois

 John B. Patton, Indiana

 Donald L. Koch, Iowa

William W. Hambleton, Kansas

Donald C. Haney, Kentucky

Charles G. Groat, Louisiana

Walter A. Anderson, Maine

Kenneth N. Weaver, Maryland

Joseph A. Sinnott, Massachusetts

R. Thomas Segall, Michigan

Matt S. Walton, Minnesota

Wallace B. Howe, Missouri

Sid Groff, Montana

Vincent H. Dreeszen, Nebraska

John H. Schilling, Nevada

Frank Markewicz, New Jersey

Frank E. Kottlowski, New Mexico

Robert H. Fakundiny, New York

Stephen G. Conrad, North Carolina

Donald L. Halvorson, North Dakota

Charles J. Mankin, Oklahoma

Arthur A. Socolow, Pennsylvania

Norman K. Olson. South Carolina

Cleo M. Christensen, South Dakota

Robert E. Hershey, Tennessee

William L. Fisher, Texas

Genevieve Atwood, Utah

Charles A. Ratté, Vermont

Robert C. Milici, Virginia

Robert B. Erwin, West Virginia

Meredith E. Ostrom, Wisconsin

Business Session:

- Heard necrology report.
- Approved the minutes of the 73rd annual meeting.
- President Fisher appointed the following ad hoc committees to serve during the meeting: Auditing, Balloting, Future Meetings, Resolutions.
- Heard report of the secretary-treasurer.
- Heard report of the editor.
- Heard report of the historian.
- Heard report of the statistician.
- Heard report from the Honorary Members Committee.
- Heard report from the Liaison Committee.
- Heard report from the ad hoc Federal Minerals Management Committee.
- Heard report on joint planning and cooperation with the U.S. Geological Survey.

- Heard report from the state geologists' Technical Review Group (Department of Energy).
- Heard report from the American Association of Petroleum Geologists.
- Held roundtable discussion.
- Heard report from the U.S. Department of the Interior.
- Heard report from the Bureau of Land Management.
- Heard reports from the U.S. Geological Survey: National Mapping Division, Water Resources Division.
- Heard report from the U.S. Bureau of Mines.
- Heard report of meeting between William L. Fisher and Charles J. Mankin and Secretary of the Interior Watt.
- Heard report from the North American Commission on Stratigraphic Nomenclature liaison.
- Heard report from the American Geological Institute Governing Board liaison.
- Heard report from the American Association of Petroleum Geologists liaison.
- Heard report from the Geological Society of America liaison.
- Heard report from the American Association for the Advancement of Science liaison.
- Heard report from the American Institute of Professional Geologists liaison.
- Heard report on the registration of geologists.
- Heard Honorary Members Committee report.
- Heard report on the Geological Society of America.
- Heard report on the American Geological Institute.
- Heard report on the National Academy of Sciences.
- Heard report on the Interstate Mining Compact Commission.
- Heard report from the Potential Gas Committee liaison.
- Heard report from the National Academy of Sciences liaison.
- Heard report from the ad hoc Committee on Mineral Land Assessment.
- Heard report from the Continental Margins Committee.
- Heard report from the Core and Sample Library Committee.
- Heard report from the Water Data for Public Use Committee.
- Heard report from the National Coal Resources Data Committee.
- Heard report of the Auditing Committee.
- Heard report of the Future Meetings Committee.
- Heard report of the Balloting Committee.
- Heard report of the Resolutions Committee.
- Heard report of the social chairman.
- Heard comments from the outgoing president.
- Heard comments from the incoming president.

1983, June 5–9, Anchorage, Alaska
Host: Ross G. Schaff, Alaska Division of Geological and
Geophysical Surveys
Officers:

> President: Meredith E. Ostrom
> President-elect: Robert R. Jordan
> Vice President: James F. Davis
> Secretary-Treasurer: Charles W. Hendry Jr.
> Historian: Robert E. Hershey
> Editor: Vincent H. Dreeszen
> Statistician: Wallace B. Howe

Members Present:

> Ernest A. Mancini, Alabama
> Ross G. Schaff, Alaska
> Larry D. Fellows, Arizona
> Norman F. Williams, Arkansas
> James F. Davis, California
> John W. Rold, Colorado
> Hugo G. Thomas, Connecticut
> Robert R. Jordan, Delaware
> Charles W. Hendry Jr., Florida
> Maynard M. Miller, Idaho
> Robert E. Bergstrom, Illinois
> John B. Patton, Indiana
> Donald L. Koch, Iowa
> William W. Hambleton, Kansas
> Donald C. Haney, Kentucky
> Andy Tolman, Maine
> Kenneth N. Weaver, Maryland
> Joseph A. Sinnott, Massachusetts
> R. Thomas Segall, Michigan
> Glen Morey, Minnesota
> Wallace B. Howe, Missouri
> Edward C. Bingler, Montana
> Vincent H. Dreeszen, Nebraska
> John H. Schilling, Nevada
> Frank Markewicz, New Jersey
> Frank E. Kottlowski, New Mexico
> Robert H. Fakundiny, New York
> Stephen G. Conrad, North Carolina

Donald L. Halvorson, North Dakota

Charles J. Mankin, Oklahoma

Donald A. Hull, Oregon

Arthur A. Socolow, Pennsylvania

Norman K. Olson, South Carolina

Merlin J. Tipton, South Dakota

William L. Fisher, Texas

Genevieve Atwood, Utah

Robert C. Milici, Virginia

Meredith E. Ostrom, Wisconsin

Gary B. Glass, Wyoming

Business Session:

- Called the roll.
- Introduced other members of staff.
- Recognized honorary members.
- Approved the minutes of the 74th annual meeting.
- Appointed ad hoc committees to serve during the meeting:
  Auditing, Balloting, Future Meetings, Resolutions, Honorary Members.
- Heard report of the secretary-treasurer.
- Heard report of the editor.
- Heard report of the historian.
- Heard report of the statistician.
- Heard necrology report.
- Heard report of the Liaison Committee.
- Heard report of the Honorary Members Committee.
- Heard report from the North American Commission
  on Stratigraphic Nomenclature liaison.
- Heard report from the American Geological
  Institute Governing Board liaison.
- Heard report from the Geological Society of America liaison.
- Heard report from the American Association for
  the Advancement of Science liaison.
- Heard report from the American Institute of
  Professional Geologists liaison.
- Heard report from the Board on Earth Sciences liaison.
- Heard report from the American Petroleum Institute liaison.
- Heard report from the National Academy of Sciences liaison.
- Heard report from the Outer Continental Shelf Policy Committee liaison.
- Heard report from the state geologists' Technical
  Review Group (Department of Energy).
- Heard report of the ad hoc committee on U.S. Bureau of
  Mines Minerals Availability System Program Evaluation.

- Heard report of the ad hoc committee on the Minerals Management Service.
- Heard report of the ad hoc committee on registration of professional geologists.
- Heard report on joint AASG–USGS Coordinating Committee (Implementation for Coordination).
- Heard report of the social chairman.
- Heard report from the Consortium for Continental Reflection Profiling liaison.
- Heard report from the Water Resources Cooperative Program Review Committee.
- Heard report from the Advisory Committee on Water Data for Public Use.
- Heard report of the Continental Margins Committee.
- Heard report of the Core and Sample Library Committee.
- Discussed National Coal Resources Data System.
- Heard report of U.S. Department of Interior.
- Heard report from the U.S. Geological Survey.
- Heard report from the Minerals Management Service.
- Heard report from the U.S. Bureau of Mines.
- Heard report from the Bureau of Land Management.
- Heard report from the Interstate Mining Compact Commission.
- Heard report from the Geological Society of America.
- Heard report from the American Association of Petroleum Geologists.
- Heard report from the American Geological Institute.
- Heard report from the National Academy of Sciences.
- Heard report from the Potential Gas Agency.
- Heard report from the State Geologists Technical Review Group (Department of Energy).
- Heard report from the National Academy of Sciences Advisory Committee to the U.S. Geological Survey.
- Heard report on trends, needs, and priorities for the geological sciences in the coming decade.
- Heard report on the state geological survey well log and sample libraries.
- Heard Honorary Members Committee report.
- Heard Auditing Committee report.
- Heard Future Meetings Committee report.
- Heard Resolutions Committee report.
- Heard further comments from the cultural chairman.
- Heard report of the Balloting Committee.
- Heard comments of the retiring president.
- Heard comments of the incoming president.

1984, June 3–7, Duluth, Minn.
Host: Matt S. Walton, Minnesota Geological Survey
Officers:

President: Robert R. Jordan
President-elect: James F. Davis
Vice President: Frank E. Kottlowski
Secretary-Treasurer: Charles W. Hendry Jr.
Historian: Robert E. Hershey
Editor: Vincent H. Dreeszen
Statistician: Wallace B. Howe

Members Present:

Ernest A. Mancini, Alabama
Ross G. Schaff, Alaska
Larry D. Fellows, Arizona
Norman F. Williams, Arkansas
James F. Davis, California
John W. Rold, Colorado
Hugo F. Thomas, Connecticut
Robert R. Jordan, Delaware
Charles W. Hendry Jr., Florida
William McLemore, Georgia
Maynard M. Miller, Idaho
Morris W. Leighton, Illinois
John B. Patton, Indiana
Donald L. Koch, Iowa
William W. Hambleton, Kansas
Donald C. Haney, Kentucky
Charles G. Groat, Louisiana
Walter A. Anderson, Maine
R. Thomas Segall, Michigan
Matt W. Walton, Minnesota
Wallace B. Howe, Missouri
Edward C. Bingler, Montana
Vincent H. Dreeszen, Nebraska
John H. Schilling, Nevada
Lincoln R. Page, New Hampshire
Frank E. Kottlowski, New Mexico
Robert H. Fakundiny, New York
Stephen G. Conrad, North Carolina
Donald L. Halvorson, North Dakota

Charles J. Mankin, Oklahoma

Arthur A. Socolow, Pennsylvania

Norman K. Olson, South Carolina

Merlin J. Tipton, South Dakota

Robert E. Hershey, Tennessee

William L. Fisher, Texas

Genevieve Atwood, Utah

Charles A. Ratté, Vermont

Robert C. Milici, Virginia

Eric Schuster, Washington

Robert B. Erwin, West Virginia

Meredith E. Ostrom, Wisconsin

Gary B. Glass, Wyoming

Business Session:

- Called roll.
- Introduced staff of state geological surveys.
- Introduced guests.
- Appointed ad hoc committees to serve during the meeting: Auditing, Balloting, Future Meetings, Resolutions, Honorary Members, Parliamentarian.
- Heard report of the president.
- Heard report of the secretary-treasurer.
- Heard report of the editor.
- Heard report of the historian.
- Heard report from the American Geological Institute Exploration Affairs liaison.
- Heard report from the North American Commission on Stratigraphic Nomenclature liaison.
- Heard report of the statistician.
- Heard report from the Liaison Committee.
- Heard report from the ad hoc committee on the future of the Association.
- Announced luncheon speaker.
- Heard report from the U.S. Department of the Interior.
- Heard report from the U.S. Bureau of Mines.
- Heard report from the Bureau of Land Management.
- Heard report from the Minerals Management Service.
- Heard report from the U.S. Geological Survey.
- Invited all to attend lecture.
- Heard report from the Interstate Mining Compact Commission.
- Heard report from the Continental Margins Committee.

- Heard report from the American Geological Institute Governing Board liaison.
- Heard report from the American Association of Petroleum Geologists liaison.
- Heard report from the Geological Society of America liaison.
- Heard report from the American Association for the Advancement of Science liaison.
- Heard report from the American Institute of Professional Geologists liaison.
- Heard report from the Canadian Provincial Surveys Committee.
- Heard report from the Board of Earth Science liaison.
- Heard report from the National Academy of Sciences.
- Heard report from the Potential Gas Agency.
- Heard report from the Advisory on Water Data for Public Use.
- Heard report on the registration and certification of geologists.
- Heard necrology report.
- Heard report from the National Coal Resources Data System liaison.
- Discussed Consortium for Continental Reflection Profiling.
- Heard report from the ad hoc committee on the U.S. Bureau of Mines.
- Heard report from the Council of State Governments liaison.
- Heard report from the AASG–U.S. Geological Survey Joint Planning Committee.
- Heard culture report.
- Heard Honorary Members Committee report.
- Heard report of Committee on Radioactive Waste Isolation.
- Heard report from the Geologic Review Group liaison.
- Heard report on AASG–U.S. Geological Survey cooperative water programs.
- Heard report of the historian (continued).
- Heard report from the Core and Sample Library Committee.
- Heard report from the ad hoc Awards Committee.
- Heard report of the Honorary Members Committee.
- Heard report of the ad hoc Committee on the Future of the Association (continued).
- Heard reports of meeting ad hoc committees: Auditing, Future Meetings, Resolutions, Balloting.
- Appointed committees of AASG.
- Heard comments from the retiring president.
- Heard comments from the incoming president.

1985, June 3–6, Mystic, Conn.
Host: Hugo F. Thomas, Connecticut Geological and Natural History Survey
Officers:

President: James F. Davis
President-elect: Frank E. Kottlowski
Vice President: Charles W. Hendry Jr.
Secretary-Treasurer: R. Thomas Segall
Historian: Robert E. Hershey
Editor: Ernest A. Mancini
Statistician: Larry D. Fellows

Members Present:

Ernest A. Mancini, Alabama
Larry D. Fellows, Arizona
Norman F. Williams, Arkansas
James F. Davis, California
John W. Rold, Colorado
Hugo F. Thomas, Connecticut
Robert R. Jordan, Delaware
Charles W. Hendry Jr., Florida
William McLemore, Georgia
Maynard M. Miller, Idaho
Morris W. Leighton, Illinois
John B. Patton, Indiana
Donald L. Koch, Iowa
William W. Hambleton, Kansas
Donald C. Haney, Kentucky
Charles G. Groat, Louisiana
Walter A. Anderson, Maine
Kenneth N. Weaver, Maryland
Joseph A. Sinnott, Massachusetts
R. Thomas Segall, Michigan
Matt S. Walton, Minnesota
Wallace B. Howe, Missouri
Henry McLernan, Montana
Vincent H. Dreeszen, Nebraska
Lincoln R. Page, New Hampshire
Haig F. Kasabach, New Jersey
Frank E. Kottlowski, New Mexico
Robert H. Fakundiny, New York
Stephen G. Conrad, North Carolina

Donald L. Halvorson, North Dakota

Charles J. Mankin, Oklahoma

Arthur A. Socolow, Pennsylvania

Norman K. Olson, South Carolina

Robert E. Hershey, Tennessee

Edward C. Bingler, Texas

Genevieve Atwood, Utah

Robert C. Milici, Virginia

Raymond Lasmanis, Washington

Meredith E. Ostrom, Wisconsin

Business Session:

- Called roll.
- Recognized guest and honorary members.
- Heard report of Department of Interior, Water and Science.
- Held forum on regional geologic mapping.
- Held forum on nonfuel mineral resource assessment.
- Heard report from the Council of Environmental Quality.
- Held forum on water quality and toxic waste management.
- Appointed ad hoc committees to serve during the meeting: Future Meetings, Resolutions, Parliamentarian.
- Held forum on energy resource data and policies.
- Heard report of the Liaison Committee.
- Heard report from the U.S. Geological Survey.
- Heard report from the U.S. Bureau of Mines.
- Heard report from the National Academy of Sciences.
- Heard report from the Geological Society of America.
- Heard report from the Interstate Mining Compact Commission.
- Heard report on geology in education.
- Heard necrology report.
- Heard statistician's report.
- Heard secretary-treasurer's report.
- Heard COGEOMAP report.
- Heard Coal Committee report.
- Heard High-Level Radioactive Waste Committee report.
- Heard report of the Federal Land Policy Committee.
- Heard report on the U.S. Geological Survey cluster meetings.
- Heard report from the Minerals Management Service.
- Heard report from the Bureau of Land Management.
- Heard report from the American Geological Institute.
- Heard report from the Culture Committee.
- Passed resolutions.

- Heard report from the U.S. Forest Service.
- Heard report from the Continental Margins Committee.
- Heard report on the AASG newsletter.
- Heard report from the Board on Earth Sciences.
- Heard report from the Low-Level Radioactive Waste Committee.
- Heard historian's report.
- Heard necrology report.
- Heard report from the Core Repository Committee.
- Heard report from the Honorary Members Committee.
- Heard report from the Geological Society of America liaison.
- Heard report from the Consortium for Continental Reflection Profiling liaison.
- Heard report from the North American Commission on Stratigraphic Nomenclature liaison.
- Heard Audit Committee report
- Heard Future Meetings Committee report.
- Heard Balloting Committee report.
- Heard report of American Institute of Professional Geologists liaison.
- Discussed registration and certification.
- Heard report of the Advisory Committee on Water Data for Public Use.
- Heard Resolutions Committee report.
- Heard president's remarks.
- Heard report of Awards Committee.
- Heard incoming president's remarks.
- Appointed AASG committees.

1986, June 9–12, Long Beach, Calif. (aboard the *Queen Mary*)
Host: James F. Davis, California Department of Conservation
Officers:

> President: Frank E. Kottlowski
> President-elect: Charles W. Hendry Jr.
> Vice President: Wallace B. Howe
> Secretary-Treasurer: R. Thomas Segall
> Historian: John B. Patton
> Editor: Ernest A. Mancini
> Statistician: Larry D. Fellows

Members Present:

> Ernest A. Mancini, Alabama
> Larry D. Fellows, Arizona
> Norman F. Williams, Arkansas
> James F. Davis, California

John W. Rold, Colorado
Richard Hyde, Connecticut
Robert R. Jordan, Delaware
Charles W. Hendry Jr., Florida
Maynard M. Miller, Idaho
Morris W. Leighton, Illinois
John B. Patton, Indiana
Donald L. Koch, Iowa
William W. Hambleton, Kansas
Donald C. Haney, Kentucky
Charles G. Groat, Louisiana
Walter A. Anderson, Maine
Kenneth N. Weaver, Maryland
R. Thomas Segall, Michigan
Matt S. Walton, Minnesota
James H. Williams, Missouri
Hal James, Montana
Vincent H. Dreeszen, Nebraska
John H. Schilling, Nevada
Haig F. Kasabach, New Jersey
Frank E. Kottlowski, New Mexico
Robert H. Fakundiny, New York
Stephen G. Conrad, North Carolina
Sidney B. Anderson, North Dakota
Ken Johnson, Oklahoma
Donald A. Hull, Oregon
Arthur A. Socolow, Pennsylvania
J. Allan Cain, Rhode Island
Norman K. Olson, South Carolina
Merlin J. Tipton, South Dakota
William T. Hill, Tennessee
William L. Fisher, Texas
Genevieve Atwood, Utah
Charles A. Ratté, Vermont
Robert C. Milici, Virginia
Raymond Lasmanis, Washington
Meredith E. Ostrom, Wisconsin

Business Session:

- Called roll.
- Introduced guests and honorary members.
- Appointed committees: Future Meetings, Balloting, Auditing, Resolutions.
- Held forum on state geological survey management.

- Heard report of the secretary-treasurer.
- Heard report of the editor.
- Heard report of the statistician.
- Heard report of the historian.
- Heard report from the American Association of Petroleum Geologists liaison.
- Heard report from the Potential Gas Committee.
- Heard report from the Geological Society of America.
- Heard report from the National Academy of Sciences.
- Heard report from the American Institute of Professional Geologists liaison.
- Heard report from the American Geological Institute.
- Heard report from the Federal Liaison Committee.
- Heard report from the AASG–U.S. Geological Survey Cooperative Planning Committee.
- Heard special presentation: "Evolving Role of State Geological Surveys, 1954–1984."
- Heard report from the National Geologic Mapping Program and COGEOMAP.
- Heard report from the U.S. Bureau of Mines.
- Heard report from the U.S. Geological Survey.
- Heard report on Minerals Management Service/ AASG Symposium on Coastal Studies.
- Heard report from the Minerals Management Service.
- Heard report on federal lands.
- Discussed future of the Association.
- Heard report from the U.S. Geological Survey on state grant funding problems.
- Heard report on high-level radioactive waste disposal.
- Heard report from the AASG Review Committee on U.S. Geological Survey High-Level Radioactive Waste Disposal.
- Heard report from the Advisory on Water Data for Public Use.
- Heard report from the Water Resources Division Co-op Committee.
- Heard report on the National Coal Resources Database.
- Heard report from the Registration/Certification Committee.
- Heard report on the AASG/American Geological Institute/ National Academy of Sciences Earth Science Education Project.
- Heard report from the Consortium for Continental Reflection Profiling.
- Heard report from the North American Commission on Stratigraphic Nomenclature.
- Heard report from the Core and Sample Repository Committee.
- Heard report from the Core Data Standards Work Group.
- Heard report from the Core Preservation Communications System.
- Heard report on geographic information systems.

- Heard recommendations for new honorary members.
- Heard Honorary Members Committee report.
- Heard Audit Committee report.
- Heard Balloting Committee report.
- Heard Resolutions Committee report.
- Heard report of the 1987 meeting.
- Heard necrology report.
- Heard Future Meetings Committee report.
- Presented awards.
- Heard outgoing president's remarks.
- Heard incoming president's remarks.
- Appointed AASG committees.
- Heard report from the Culture Committee.

1987, June 8–10, Traverse City, Mich.

Host: R. Thomas Segall, Michigan Geological Survey

Officers:

President: Charles W. Hendry Jr.
President-elect: Charles G. Groat
Vice President: Larry D. Fellows
Secretary-Treasurer: Ernest A. Mancini
Historian: John H. Schilling
Editor: Robert C. Milici
Statistician: Morris W. Leighton

Members Present:

Ernest A. Mancini, Alabama
Robert B. Forbes, Alaska
Larry D. Fellows, Arizona
Norman F. Williams, Arkansas
John W. Rold, Colorado
Hugo F. Thomas, Connecticut
Robert R. Jordan, Delaware
Charles W. Hendry Jr., Florida
William H. McLemore, Georgia
Maynard M. Miller, Idaho
Morris W. Leighton, Illinois
Norman C. Hester, Indiana
Donald L. Koch, Iowa
Donald W. Steeples, Kansas
Donald C. Haney, Kentucky
Charles G. Groat, Louisiana

Walter A. Anderson, Maine

Kenneth N. Weaver, Maryland

R. Thomas Segall, Michigan

Matt S. Walton, Minnesota

Conrad A. Gazzier, Mississippi

James H. Williams, Missouri

Edward T. Ruppel, Montana

Perry B. Wigley, Nebraska

Haig F. Kasabach, New Jersey

Frank E. Kottlowski, New Mexico

Robert H. Fakundiny, New York

Stephen G. Conrad, North Carolina

Kenneth S. Johnson, Oklahoma

Donald M. Hoskins, Pennsylvania

Norman K. Olson, South Carolina

Merlin J. Tipton, South Dakota

Edward C. Bingler, Texas

Genevieve Atwood, Utah

Charles A. Ratté, Vermont

Robert C. Milici, Virginia

Raymond Lasmanis, Washington

Meredith E. Ostrom, Wisconsin

Business Session:

- Called roll.
- Recognized new state geologists, honorary members, and guests.
- Approved minutes from previous year's meeting.
- Appointed ad hoc committees to serve during the meeting: Auditing, Balloting, Future Meetings, Resolutions.
- Heard report of the secretary-treasurer.
- Heard report of the editor.
- Heard report of the historian.
- Heard reports from federal agencies: U.S. Bureau of Mines, Minerals Management Service, Bureau of Land Management, Office of Surface Mining, UNC-Geotech, Provincial Geologists Committee, U.S. Geological Survey (National Mapping Division, Water Resources Division, Information Systems Division, Geologic Division).
- Held forum on state/federal coastal erosion programs.
- Heard report from the Liaison Committee.
- Heard report of the statistician.
- Heard report from the Continental Margins Committee.
- Heard report from the Honorary Members Committee.
- Heard report from the American Association for the Advancement of Science liaison.

- Heard report from the American Association of Petroleum Geologists liaison.
- Heard report from the American Geological Institute liaison.
- Heard report from the Geological Society of America and International Geological Congress liaison.
- Heard report from the North American Commission on Stratigraphic Nomenclature liaison.
- Heard report on honorary members' activities.
- Heard report from the Potential Gas Committee liaison.
- Heard report from the Low-Level Radioactive Waste Committee.
- Heard report from the Consortium for Continental Reflection Profiling/EDGE Committee.
- Heard report from the Core Curation and Data Management Committee.
- Heard COGEOMAP report.
- Heard report from the Environmental Affairs Committee.
- Heard report from the Federal Lands Committee.
- Heard report from the Public Information Committee.
- Heard report from the Geographic Information Systems Committee.
- Heard report from the superconducting supercollider discussion.
- Heard report from the Survey Histories Committee.
- Heard report from the National Coal Resources Data Systems Committee.
- Heard report from the Professional Affairs Committee.
- Heard report from the Water Resources Policy Committee.
- Heard report from the High-Level Radioactive Waste Committee.
- Heard report from the Repository Geotechnical Information Committee.
- Heard report from the Earth Sciences National Research Council liaison.
- Heard report on the Earth Sciences Education Project.
- Heard report from the Advisory Committee on Water Data for Public Use.
- Heard necrology report.
- Heard report of the Auditing Committee.
- Heard report of the Balloting Committee.
- Heard report of the Resolutions Committee.
- Heard report of the Future Meetings Committee.
- Heard report of the Culture Committee.
- Heard comments by outgoing President Hendry.
- Heard comments by incoming President Groat.
- Appointed AASG standing and special committees.

1988, June 13–15, Lexington, Ky.
Host: Donald C. Haney, Kentucky Geological Survey
Officers:

President: Charles G. Groat
President-elect: Larry D. Fellows
Vice President: Donald C. Haney?
Secretary-Treasurer: Ernest A. Mancini
Historian: John H. Schilling
Editor: Robert C. Milici
Statistician: Morris W. Leighton

Members Present:

Ernest A. Mancini, Alabama
Robert B. Forbes, Alaska
Larry D. Fellows, Arizona
Norman F. Williams, Arkansas
Theodore C. Smith, California
John W. Rold, Colorado
Ralph S. Lewis, Connecticut
Robert R. Jordan, Delaware
Walter Schmidt, Florida
William H. McLemore, Georgia
Robert W. Bartlett, Idaho
Morris W. Leighton, Illinois
Norman C. Hester, Indiana
Donald L. Koch, Iowa
Lee C. Gerhard, Kansas
Donald C. Haney, Kentucky
Charles G. Groat, Louisiana
Walter A. Anderson, Maine
Kenneth N. Weaver, Maryland
R. Thomas Segall, Michigan
Conrad A. Gazzier, Mississippi
James H. Williams, Missouri
Edward T. Ruppel, Montana
Perry B. Wigley, Nebraska
Larry Garside, Nevada
Haig F. Kasabach, New Jersey
Frank E. Kottlowski, New Mexico
Robert H. Fakundiny, New York
Stephen G. Conrad, North Carolina

Sidney B. Anderson, North Dakota
Ronald G. Rea (for Dennis Hull), Ohio
Charles J. Mankin, Oklahoma
Donald A. Hull, Oregon
Donald M. Hoskins, Pennsylvania
Norman K. Olson, South Carolina
Merlin J. Tipton, South Dakota
Edward T. Luther, Tennessee
William L. Fisher, Texas
Genevieve Atwood, Utah
Robert C. Milici, Virginia
Raymond Lasmanis, Washington
Larry D. Woodfork, West Virginia
Meredith E. Ostrom, Wisconsin

Business Session:

- Called roll.
- Recognized new state geologists, state survey staff members, honorary members, and guests.
- Approved minutes.
- Appointed ad hoc committees to serve during the meeting: Auditing, Balloting, Future Meetings, Resolutions.
- Heard report of the secretary-treasurer.
- Heard report of the editor.
- Heard reports from federal and other agencies: U.S. Geological Survey, Minerals Management Service, U.S. Bureau of Mines, Bureau of Land Management, Environmental Protection Agency, Department of Energy, Office of Surface Mining.
- Heard report from the American Geological Institute.
- Heard report from the Public Information Committee– Forum on Education and Public Information.
- Heard Liaison Committee report.
- Heard report of the statistician.
- Heard report from the National Geologic Mapping Committee.
- Heard report from the U.S. Geological Survey/Minerals Management Service Oil and Gas Assessment.
- Heard report on COGEOMAP.
- Heard report from the Continental Margins Committee.
- Heard report from the Environmental Affairs Committee.
- Heard report from the Geographic Information Systems Committee.
- Heard report on the superconducting supercollider.
- Heard report from the High-Level Radioactive Waste Committee–Repository Geotechnical Information Committee.

- Heard report from the Low-Level Radioactive Waste Committee.
- Heard report from the Federal Lands Committee.
- Heard report from the Core/Sample Committee.
- Heard report from the Water Resources Policy Committee.
- Heard report from the Advisory Committee on Water Data for Public Use.
- Heard report from the Professional Affairs Committee.
- Heard report on AASG/U.S. Geological Survey cooperative planning.
- Heard report from the Survey Histories Committee.
- Heard report from the Honorary Members Committee.
- Heard report from the Consortium for Continental Reflection Profiling/EDGE Committee.
- Heard report from advisory boards/committees.
- Heard report from the American Geological Institute Governing Board.
- Heard report from the American Association of Petroleum Geologists.
- Heard report from the American Association for the Advancement of Science.
- Heard report from the Interstate Mining Compact Commission.
- Heard report from the North American Commission on Stratigraphic Nomenclature.
- Heard report from the Honorary Members Committee.
- Heard report from the Culture Committee.
- Heard report of the Auditing Committee.
- Heard report of the Balloting Committee.
- Heard report of the Future Meetings Committee.
- Heard report of the Resolutions Committee.
- Heard comments by outgoing President Groat.
- Heard comments by incoming President Fellows.
- Appointed AASG committees.

1989, May 13–19, Oklahoma City, Okla.

Host: Charles J. Mankin, Oklahoma Geological Survey

Officers:

President: Larry D. Fellows

President-elect: Ernest A. Mancini

Vice President: Robert H. Fakundiny

Secretary-Treasurer: Donald A. Hull

Historian: Norman K. Olson

Editor: Robert C. Milici

Statistician: Morris W. Leighton

Members Present:

Ernest A. Mancini, Alabama
Robert B. Forbes, Alaska
Larry D. Fellows, Arizona
Norman F. Williams, Arkansas
Brian E. Tucker, California
John W. Rold, Colorado
Sidney Quarrier, Connecticut
Thomas E. Pickett, Connecticut
Robert R. Jordan, Delaware
Walter Schmidt, Florida
William H. McLemore, Georgia
Robert W. Bartlett, Idaho
Morris W. Leighton, Illinois
Norman C. Hester, Indiana
Donald L. Koch, Iowa
Lee C. Gerhard, Kansas
Donald C. Haney, Kentucky
Charles G. Groat, Louisiana
John Williams, Maine
Kenneth N. Weaver, Maryland
Jack L. Van Alstine, Michigan
Arthur E. Slaughter, Michigan
Michael Bograd, Mississippi
Curtis W. Stover, Mississippi
James H. Williams, Missouri
Edward T. Ruppel, Montana
Perry B. Wigley, Nebraska
Jonathan G. Price, Nevada
Haig F. Kasabach, New Jersey
Frank E. Kottlowski, New Mexico
Robert H. Fakundiny, New York
Stephen G. Conrad, North Carolina
Sidney B. Anderson, North Dakota
Thomas M. Berg, Ohio
Charles J. Mankin, Oklahoma
Donald A. Hull, Oregon
Donald M. Hoskins, Pennsylvania
Norman K. Olson, South Carolina
Merlin J. Tipton, South Dakota
William T. Hill, Tennessee

William L. Fisher, Texas

Genevieve Atwood, Utah

Robert C. Milici,, Virginia

Raymond Lasmanis, Washington

Larry D. Woodfork, West Virginia

Meredith E. Ostrom, Wisconsin

Business Session:

- Called roll.
- Recognized new state geologists and honorary members.
- Approved minutes of previous year's meeting.
- Appointed ad hoc committees to serve during the meeting: Balloting, Auditing, Awards, Future Meetings, Resolutions.
- Heard report of the secretary-treasurer.
- Heard report of the editor.
- Heard report of the historian.
- Heard necrology report.
- Heard report of the statistician.
- Heard report of the Liaison Committee.
- Summarized oil and gas assessment.
- Heard status report on National Academy of Sciences/National Research Council.
- Heard report on the National Geologic Mapping Program.
- Heard report on environmental affairs.
- Heard report on professional affairs.
- Heard report from the Public Information Committee.
- Heard report from the U.S. Department of Energy.
- Heard report from the U.S. Forest Service.
- Heard report from the U.S. Geological Survey.
- Heard report from the Bureau of Land Management.
- Heard report from the Minerals Management Service.
- Heard report from the U.S. Bureau of Mines.
- Heard report on water programs.
- Heard report from the U.S. Geological Survey.
- Heard report from the National Academy of Sciences.
- Heard report on geologic hazards.
- Heard report from the American Geological Institute.
- Heard report on digital cartographic standards.
- Heard report from the Exclusive Economic Zone Symposium.
- Heard Auditing Committee report.
- Heard Balloting Committee report.
- Heard Future Meetings Committee report.

- Heard Honorary Members Committee report.
- Heard Resolutions Committee report.
- Heard closing comments by incoming President Haney.

1990, June 9–13, Madison, Wis.

Host: Meredith E. Ostrom, Wisconsin Geological and Natural History Survey

Officers:

President: Donald C. Haney

President-elect: Ernest A. Mancini

Vice President: Robert H. Fakundiny

Secretary-Treasurer: Donald A. Hull

Historian: Norman K. Olson

Editor: Robert C. Milici

Statistician: Morris W. Leighton

Members Present:

Forty states were represented (list of those attending was not found).

Business Session:

- Called roll.
- Recognized new state geologists.
- Approved minutes of previous year's meeting.
- Appointed ad hoc committees to serve during meeting: Auditing, Awards, Balloting, Culture, Future Meetings, Resolutions.
- Heard report of the secretary-treasurer.
- Heard report of the editor.
- Heard report of the historian.
- Heard report of the statistician.
- Heard report of the Liaison Committee.
- Heard report of the Radon Committee.
- Heard report on National Academy of Sciences/National Research Council review of oil and gas assessment.
- Heard report of the National Geologic Mapping Program.
- Heard report of the Consortium for Continental Reflection Profiling Committee.
- Heard report of the Professional Affairs Committee.
- Heard report of the National Research Council Marine Board Committee.
- Heard report of the Public Information and Education Committee.
- Approved constitutional amendment.
- Heard report of the Continental Margins Committee.
- Reviewed USGS cluster meetings.
- Approved Geological Society of America Memorial Fund.

- Heard report on the U.S. Department of Energy initiative in fossil energy.
- Heard report from the U.S. Geological Survey.
- Heard report from the USGS National Mapping Division.
- Heard report from the USGS Water Resources Division.
- Heard report from the USGS Geologic Division.
- Heard report from the U.S. Department of Energy.
- Heard report from the Minerals Management Service.
- Heard report from the National Academy of Sciences.
- Heard report from the Drilling, Observation, and Sampling of the Earth's Continental Crust group.
- Heard report from the Interstate Mining Compact Commission.
- Held forum on AASG geologic mapping program.
- Heard report from the American Heritage Center.
- Heard report from the American Geological Institute.
- Reviewed resolution to the National Academy of Sciences/National Research Council.
- Heard Audit Committee report.
- Heard Resolutions Committee report.
- Heard Honorary Members Committee report.
- Heard Awards Committee report.
- Heard necrology report.
- Heard Future Meetings Committee report.
- Established new officers.
- Appointed committee chairs.

1991, May 4–7, Saratoga Springs, N.Y.
Host: Robert H. Fakundiny, New York State Geological Survey
Officers:

> President: Ernest A. Mancini
> President-elect: Robert H. Fakundiny
> Vice President: Morris W. Leighton
> Secretary-Treasurer: Donald M. Hoskins
> Historian: Norman K. Olson
> Editor: Robert C. Milici
> Statistician: Haig F. Kasabach

Members Present:

> Ernest A. Mancini, Alabama
> Thomas E. Smith, Alaska
> Larry D. Fellows, Arizona
> Norman F. Williams, Arkansas
> James F. Davis, California

John W. Rold, Colorado
Richard C. Hyde, Connecticut
Robert R. Jordan, Delaware
Walter Schmidt, Florida
E.A. Shapiro, Georgia
Earl H. Bennett, Idaho
Morris W. Leighton, Illinois
Norman C. Hester, Indiana
Donald L. Koch, Iowa
Lee C. Gerhard, Kansas
Donald C. Haney, Kentucky
Charles G. Groat, Louisiana
Walter A. Anderson, Maine
Kenneth N. Weaver, Maryland
Joseph A. Sinnott, Massachusetts
R. Thomas Segall, Michigan
Priscilla C. Grew, Minnesota
S. Cragin Knox, Mississippi
James H. Williams, Missouri
Edward T. Ruppel, Montana
Perry B. Wigley, Montana
Jonathan G. Price, Nevada
Haig F. Kasabach, New Jersey
Charles E. Chapin, New Mexico
Robert H. Fakundiny, New York
Charles H. Gardner, North Carolina
John P. Bluemle, North Dakota
Thomas M. Berg, Ohio
Charles J. Mankin, Oklahoma
Donald A. Hull, Oregon
Donald M. Hoskins, Pennsylvania
Norman K. Olson, South Carolina
L. Hedges, South Dakota
Marcus Milling, Texas
Charles Ratté, Vermont
Robert C. Milici, Virginia
Raymond Lasmanis, Washington
Larry D. Woodfork, West Virginia
Ronald G. Hennings, Wisconsin
Gary B. Glass, Wyoming

Business Session:

- Called roll.
- Introduced state survey staff members and honorary members.
- Approved minutes of previous year's meeting.
- Appointed ad hoc committees to serve during the meeting: Auditing, Awards, Balloting, Future Meetings, Resolutions.
- Heard report of the vice president.
- Heard report of the secretary-treasurer.
- Heard report of the historian.
- Heard report of the editor.
- Heard report of the statistician.
- Heard Liaison Committee report.
- Heard Radon Committee report.
- Heard report of special committee on AASG– U.S. Geological Survey cluster meeting.
- Heard report on the national geologic mapping initiative: legislation, cost-benefits, priorities.
- Heard report on national and regional seismic networks.
- Heard report on the criteria for honorary membership.
- Heard Honorary Members Committee report.
- Heard special committee report on geological fees and services.
- Discussed undiscovered mineral resource assessment.
- Heard coastal erosion report.
- Heard report on the assistance to New Hampshire.
- Heard Future Meetings Committee report.
- Heard report from the U.S. Geological Survey.
- Heard report from the U.S. Bureau of Mines.
- Heard report from the Minerals Management Service.
- Held panel discussion on access to public lands.
- Heard report from the Environmental Affairs Committee.
- Heard report from the U.S. Department of Energy on national energy strategy.
- Heard report from the National Historic Landmarks Program.
- Heard report from the National Academy of Sciences/National Research Council Board on Earth Sciences and Resources.
- Heard report from the Interstate Mining Compact Commission.
- Heard report from the American Geological Institute.
- Heard report from the High-Level Radioactive Waste Committee.
- Heard report from the Professional Affairs Committee.
- Heard report from the Digital Cartography Standards and Protocols Committee.

- Heard report from the Water Policy Committee.
- Heard report from the Advisory Committee on Water Data for Public Use.
- Heard report on the Consortium for Continental Reflection Profile/EDGE activities.
- Heard Public Information and Education Committee report.
- Heard reports of committees: Audit, Ballot, Honorary Members, Resolutions, Memorials, Awards, Future Meetings.
- Heard retiring president's comments.
- Heard president-elect's comments.

1992, June 13–17, Tuscaloosa, Ala.

Host: Ernest A. Mancini, Geological Survey of Alabama

Officers:

President: Robert H. Fakundiny

President-elect: Morris W. Leighton

Vice President: Donald A. Hull

Secretary-Treasurer: Donald M. Hoskins

Historian: Norman K. Olson

Editor: Thomas M. Berg

Statistician: Haig F. Kasabach

Members Present:

Ernest A. Mancini, Alabama

Thomas E. Smith, Alaska

Larry D. Fellows, Arizona

Norman F. Williams, Arkansas

James E. Davis, California

John W. Rold, Colorado

R. Lewis, Connecticut

Robert R. Jordan, Delaware

Walter Schmidt, Florida

William H. McLemore, Georgia

Earl H. Bennett, Idaho

Morris W. Leighton, Illinois

Norman C. Hester, Indiana

Donald L. Koch, Iowa

Lee C. Gerhard, Kansas

Donald C. Haney, Kentucky

Charles G. Groat, Louisiana

Walter A. Anderson, Maine

Kenneth N. Weaver, Maryland

Joseph A. Sinnott, Massachusetts

E.E. Eltzroth, Michigan

S. Cragin Knox, Mississippi

James H. Williams, Missouri

Perry B. Wigley, Nebraska

Jonathan G. Price, Nevada

Haig F. Kasabach, New Jersey

James M. Robertson, New Mexico

Robert H. Fakundiny, New York

Charles H. Gardner, North Carolina

John P. Bluemle, North Dakota

Thomas M. Berg, Ohio

Charles J. Mankin, Oklahoma

Donald A. Hull, Oregon

Donald M. Hoskins, Pennsylvania

Norman K. Olson, South Carolina

Edward T. Luther, Tennessee

William L. Fisher, Texas

Diane Conrad, Vermont

Stanley S. Johnson, Virginia

Raymond Lasmanis, Washington

Larry D. Woodfork, West Virginia

Ronald Hennings, Wisconsin

Business Session:

- Called roll.
- Introduced state survey staff members and honorary members.
- Approved minutes from previous year's meeting.
- Appointed ad hoc committees: Balloting, Auditing, Resolutions, Awards, Future Meetings.
- Heard reports of officers: president, vice president, secretary-treasurer, historian, editor, statistician.
- Heard Liaison Committee report and discussed.
- Heard report on the AASG–USGS cluster meetings.
- Heard report from the Coastal Erosion Committee.
- Heard report from the Continental Margins Committee.
- Heard report from the Radon Committee.
- Heard National Geologic Mapping Committee reports.
- Heard report from the Federal Lands Committee.
- Heard report from the Honorary Members Committee.
- Heard report from the Minerals Policy Committee.
- Heard report from the Intergovernmental Task Force on Monitoring Water Quality.

- Heard report from the National Historical Landmarks Committee.
- Heard report from the High-Level Radioactive Waste Committee.
- Heard report from the Professional Affairs Committee.
- Heard Central United States Earthquake Consortium report.
- Heard report from the U.S. Department of the Interior.
- Heard report from the U.S. Geological Survey.
- Heard report from the U.S. Bureau of Mines.
- Heard report from the Minerals Management Service.
- Heard report from the Bureau of Land Management.
- Heard report from the Office of Surface Mining.
- Held national geologic mapping panel discussion.
- Heard report from the U.S. Department of Energy.
- Heard report from the National Academy of Sciences.
- Heard report from the American Geological Institute.
- Heard report from the Interstate Mining Compact Commission.
- Heard report from the U.S. Environmental Protection Agency.
- Heard report from the Digital Mapping Committee.
- Heard report from the Earth Science Education Committee.
- Heard report from the Water Resources Policy Committee.
- Heard report from the Energy Policy Committee.
- Reprised discussion on national mapping.
- Heard report from the Environmental Affairs Committee.
- Heard additional committee reports.
- Heard meeting committee reports: Necrology, Audit, Balloting, Honorary Members, Future Meetings, Awards/Culture, Resolutions.
- Heard comments from retiring president.
- Heard comments from incoming president.

1993, June 5–8, Coeur d'Alene, Idaho
Host: Earl H. Bennett, Idaho Geological Survey
Officers:

    President: Morris W. Leighton

    President-elect: Donald A. Hull

    Vice President: Donald M. Hoskins

    Secretary-Treasurer: Walter Schmidt

    Historian: Donald L. Koch

    Editor: Thomas M. Berg

    Statistician: Haig F. Kasabach

    Members Present:

    Ernest A. Mancini, Alabama

    Thomas E. Smith, Alaska

Larry D. Fellows, Arizona
Norman F. Williams, Arkansas
James F. Davis, California
Vicki J. Cowart, Colorado
R. Lewis, Connecticut
Robert R. Jordan, Delaware
Walter Schmidt, Florida
William H. McLemore, Georgia
Earl H. Bennett, Idaho
Morris W. Leighton, Illinois
Norman C. Hester, Indiana
Donald L. Koch, Iowa
Lee C. Gerhard, Kansas
Donald C. Haney, Kentucky
William E. Marsalis, Louisiana
Walter A. Anderson, Maine
Emery T. Cleaves, Maryland
Richard N. Foster, Massachusetts
Priscilla C. Grew, Minnesota
S. Cragin Knox, Mississippi
James H. Williams, Missouri
Edward T. Ruppel, Montana
Perry B. Wigley, Nebraska
Jonathan G. Price, Nevada
Haig F. Kasabach, New Jersey
Charles E. Chapin, New Mexico
Robert H. Fakundiny, New York
Charles H. Gardner, North Carolina
John P. Bluemle, North Dakota
Thomas M. Berg, Ohio
Charles J. Mankin, Oklahoma
Donald A. Hull, Oregon
Donald M. Hoskins, Pennsylvania
Cleo M. Christensen, South Dakota
Edward T. Luther, Tennessee
William L. Fisher, Texas
M. Lee Allison, Utah
Stanley S. Johnson, Virginia
Raymond Lasmanis, Washington
Larry D. Woodfork, West Virginia
James M. Robertson, Wisconsin

Business Session:

- Called to order.
- Called roll.
- Introduced guest, other state survey staff, members, honorary members, and new members.
- Approved 1992 midyear minutes.
- President appointed ad hoc committees to serve during the meeting: Auditing, Balloting, Resolutions, Awards, Future Meetings.
- Heard reports of the officers: president, vice president, secretary-treasurer, historian, editor, statistician.
- Heard Liaison Committee report.
- Heard report from the AASG–USGS cluster meetings.
- Heard report from the Honorary Members Committee.
- Discussed National Geologic Mapping Act strategy.
- Heard report from the Digital Mapping Committee.
- Heard report from the Association for Women Geoscientists.
- Heard report from the Federal Lands Committee.
- Heard report from the Continental Margins Committee.
- Heard report from the Minerals Policy Committee.
- Heard report from the Energy Policy Committee.
- Heard report from the Environmental Affairs Committee.
- Heard report from the National Association of Science Teachers.
- Heard report from the Geologic Hazards Policy Committee.
- Heard report from the Water Policy Committee.
- Heard report from the Radioactive Waste Committee.
- Heard report from the Professional Affairs Committee.
- Heard report from the U.S. Geological Survey.
- Heard report on the implementation of the National Geologic Mapping Act.
- Heard report from the U.S. Department of Agriculture–Forest Service.
- Heard report from the U.S. Department of Energy.
- Heard report from the U.S. Environmental Protection Agency.
- Heard report on the Mineral Issues Mini-Forum: Subpanel on Mining Reform Legislation, Subpanel on Mineral Assessment and Availability.
- Heard report from the Minerals Management Service.
- Heard report from the U.S. Bureau of Land Management.
- Heard report from the World Geological Organization.
- Heard report from the American Geological Institute.
- Heard report from the Educational Outreach Committee.
- Heard report from the National Academy of Sciences/National Research Council.
- Heard report from the Endowment Fund Steering Committee.

- Heard meeting committee reports: American Association for the Advancement of Science, American Association of Petroleum Geologists, North American Commission on Stratigraphic Nomenclature, American Geological Institute, Consortium for Continental Reflection Profiling, Coastal Erosion, EDMAP.
- Discussed old business: survey personnel exchange questionnaire, Awards Committee recommendations.
- Discussed new business: Honorary Members Committee report, necrology report, Auditing Committee report, Balloting Committee report, Resolutions Committee report, Awards Committee report, Culture Committee report, Future Meetings Committee report.
- Discussed next year's annual meeting.
- Heard concluding comments from the retiring president.
- Heard comments from the incoming president.

1994, June 4–8, Maumee Bay, Ohio
Host: Thomas M. Berg, Division of Geological Survey, Ohio Department of Natural Resources
Officers:

    President: Donald A. Hull

    President-elect: Donald M. Hoskins

    Vice President: Norman C. Hester

    Secretary-Treasurer: Walter Schmidt

    Historian: Donald L. Koch

    Editor: Thomas M. Berg

    Statistician: Haig F. Kasabach

Members Present:

    Ernest A. Mancini, Alabama

    Thomas E. Smith, Alaska

    Larry D. Fellows, Arizona

    Norman F. Williams, Arkansas

    James F. Davis, California

    Vicki J. Cowart, Colorado

    Robert R. Jordan, Delaware

    Walter Schmidt, Florida

    E. Shapiro, Georgia

    Earl H. Bennett, Idaho

    Morris W. Leighton, Illinois

    Norman C. Hester, Indiana

    Donald L. Koch, Iowa

    Lee C. Gerhard, Kansas

    Donald C. Haney, Kentucky

William E. Marsalis, Louisiana
Walter A. Anderson, Maine
Emery T. Cleaves, Maryland
Richard N. Foster, Massachusetts
R. Thomas Segall, Michigan
David L. Southwick, Minnesota
S. Cragin Knox, Mississippi
James H. Williams, Missouri
Perry B. Wigley, Nebraska
Harold Bonham Jr., Nevada
Haig F. Kasabach, New Jersey
Robert H. Fakundiny, New York
Charles H. Gardner, North Carolina
John P. Bluemle, North Dakota
Thomas M. Berg, Ohio
Charles J. Mankin, Oklahoma
Donald A. Hull, Oregon
Donald M. Hoskins, Pennsylvania
Edward T. Luther, Tennessee
William L. Fisher, Texas
Laurence R. Becker, Vermont
Stanley S. Johnson, Virginia
Raymond Lasmanis, Washington
Larry D. Woodfork, West Virginia
James M. Robertson, Wisconsin

Business Session:

- Called roll.
- Discussed historical development of the Maumee Bay State Park.
- Approved 1993 midyear meeting minutes.
- Appointed ad hoc committees to serve during the meeting: Auditing, Balloting, Future Meetings, Resolutions.
- Heard reports of the officers: president, vice president, secretary-treasurer, historian, editor, statistician.
- Heard Liaison Committee report.
- Heard report from the Coastal Erosion Committee.
- Heard report from the Continental Margins Committee.
- Heard report from the Digital Mapping Committee.
- Heard report from the Earth Science Education Committee.
- Heard Consortium for Continental Reflection Profiling report.

- Heard report from the Endowment Fund Committee.
- Heard report from the Energy Policy Committee.
- Heard report from the Environmental Affairs Committee.
- Heard report from the Federal Lands Committee.
- Heard report from the Professional Affairs Committee
- Heard report from the Mineral Policy Committee.
- Heard report from the Water Policy Committee.
- Heard report from the Honorary Members Committee.
- Heard report from the National Geologic Mapping Program panel of chairs on implementation and STATEMAP committees.
- Regional caucuses held meetings.
- Held Executive Committee meeting.
- Held demonstration of Geologic Information Visualization System.
- Heard briefing on the Ontario Geological Survey.
- Heard report from the U.S. Geological Survey.
- Heard report from the Minerals Management Service.
- Heard report from the U.S. Bureau of Land Management.
- Heard report from the U.S. Bureau of Mines.
- Heard report from the National Park Service.
- Heard report from the U.S. Forest Service.
- Heard report from the U.S. Army Corps of Engineers.
- Heard report from the Radioactive Waste Committee.
- Heard report from the Minerals Management Service.
- Heard report from the Geologic Hazards Policy Committee.
- Heard report on the Missouri Basin Mapping Initiative.
- Heard report from the Advisory Committee on Water Data for Public Use.
- Heard report from the Auditing Committee.
- Heard report from the Balloting Committee.
- Heard report from the Future Meetings Committee.
- Passed 1995 annual meeting promotional fliers among members.
- Heard report from the American Association for the Advancement of Science.
- Heard Honorary Members Committee report.
- Heard Resolutions Committee report.
- Heard addresses from the American Geological Institute during lunch meeting.
- Held open comment period.
- Heard concluding remarks from the outgoing president.
- Heard comments from the new president.

1995, June 12–15, Reno, Nev.

Host: Jonathan G. Price, Nevada Bureau of Mines and Geology

Officers:

    President: Donald M. Hoskins

    President-elect: Walter Schmidt

    Vice President: Norman C. Hester

    Secretary-Treasurer: Earl H. Bennett

    Historian: Donald L. Koch

    Editor: Thomas M. Berg

    Statistician: Haig F. Kasabach

Members Present:

    Ernest A. Mancini, Alabama

    Larry D. Fellows, Arizona

    James F. Davis, California

    Vicki J. Cowart, Colorado

    Robert R. Jordan, Delaware

    Walter Schmidt, Florida

    William H. McLemore, Georgia

    Earl H. Bennett, Idaho

    William W. Shilts, Illinois

    Norman C. Hester, Indiana

    B. Hoyer, Iowa

    Lee C. Gerhard, Kansas

    Donald C. Haney, Kentucky

    William E. Marsalis, Louisiana

    Robert Marvinney, Maine

    Emery T. Cleaves, Maryland

    Richard N. Foster, Massachusetts

    David L. Southwick, Minnesota

    S. Cragin Knox, Mississippi

    James H. Williams, Missouri

    John C. Steinmetz, Montana

    Perry B. Wigley, Nebraska

    Jonathan G. Price, Nevada

    Haig F. Kasabach, New Jersey

    Charles E. Chapin, New Mexico

    Robert H. Fakundiny, New York

    Charles H. Gardner, North Carolina

    Thomas M. Berg, Ohio

    Charles J. Mankin, Oklahoma

Donald A. Hull, Oregon

Donald M. Hoskins, Pennsylvania

Cleo M. Christensen, South Dakota

N. Tyler, Texas

M. Lee Allison, Utah

Laurence R. Becker, Vermont

Stanley S. Johnson, Virginia

Raymond Lasmanis, Washington

Larry D. Woodfork, West Virginia

James M. Robertson, Wisconsin

Gary B. Glass, Wyoming

Business Session:

- Called to order.
- Welcomed colleagues and friends.
- Called roll.
- Introduced new state geologists and acting state geologists.
- Introduced honorary members, state geological survey staff.
- Appointed annual meeting committees: Auditing, Future Meetings, Resolutions, Balloting.
- Conducted new balloting for president-elect.
- Heard reports of the officers: president, vice president, secretary/treasurer, editor, statistician, historian.
- Heard reports of standing committees: Honorary Members, Liaison, Bylaws and Constitution, Earth Science Education, Energy Policy, Environmental Affairs, Geologic Hazards Policy.
- Donald C. Haney discussed problem with topographic maps from U.S. Geological Survey.
- Heard reports of other standing or special committees: National Cooperative Geologic Mapping Act Peer Review Committee, National Cooperative Geologic Mapping Act Advisory Committee.
- Discussed the future of the AASG.
- Heard cluster meeting reports.
- Heard federal agency reports: U.S. Geological Survey, Minerals Management Service, Federal Emergency Management Agency, Environmental Protection Agency, National Park Service, Bureau of Land Management, American Geological Institute–Governmental Affairs Program, National Academy of Sciences/National Research Council, U.S. Bureau of Mines.
- USGS held workshop on the National Cooperative Geologic Mapping Program.
- Discussed reauthorization of National Geologic Mapping Act: Reopened discussion on the budget section.
- Heard report on the future of cluster meetings.

- Heard report of Constitution and Bylaws Committee.
- Heard report of Honorary Members Caucus.
- Heard report of the Awards Committee.
- Heard reports of the special annual meeting committees: Auditing, Balloting, Future Meetings, Resolutions.
- Heard information on next year's meeting.
- Heard comments from Walter Schmidt, incoming AASG president.
- Discussed American Geological Institute Governmental Affairs Program contribution.

1996, June 2–4, Charlottesville, Va.

Host: Stanley S. Johnson, Virginia Division of Mineral Resources

Officers:

President: Walter Schmidt
President-elect: Earl H. Bennett
Vice President: Charles H. Gardner
Secretary-Treasurer: Jonathan G. Price
Historian: Donald L. Koch
Editor: Thomas M. Berg
Statistician: Haig F. Kasabach

Members Present:

Ed Osborne, Alabama
Milton A. Wiltse, Alaska
Larry D. Fellows, Arizona
William F. Bush, Arkansas
James F. Davis, California
Vicki J. Cowart, Colorado
Ralph S. Lewis, Connecticut
Robert R. Jordan, Delaware
Walter Schmidt, Florida
William H. McLemore, Georgia
Earl H. Bennett, Idaho
William W. Shilts, Illinois
Norman C. Hester, Indiana
Donald L. Koch, Iowa
Lee C. Gerhard, Kansas
Donald C. Haney, Kentucky
William E. Marsalis, Louisiana
Robert G. Marvinney, Maine
Emery T. Cleaves, Maryland
Lynne Boyd, Michigan

David L. Southwick, Minnesota

S. Cragin Knox, Mississippi

James H. Williams, Missouri

John C. Steinmetz, Montana

Perry B. Wigley, Nebraska

Jonathan G. Price, Nevada

Haig F. Kasabach, New Jersey

Robert H. Fakundiny, New York

Charles H. Gardner, North Carolina

Thomas M. Berg, Ohio

Charles J. Mankin, Oklahoma

Donald A. Hull, Oregon

Donald M. Hoskins, Pennsylvania

Lisbeth Hyman, Puerto Rico

Cleo M. Christensen, South Dakota

Ronald P. Zurawski, Tennessee

Rob Finely, Texas

M. Lee Allison, Utah

Laurence R. Becker, Vermont

Stanley S. Johnson, Virginia

Raymond Lasmanis, Washington

Larry D. Woodfork, West Virginia

James M. Robertson, Wisconsin

Business Session:

- Recognized new state geologists and honorary members.
- Appointed ad hoc committees to serve during the meeting: Auditing, Balloting, Future Meetings, Awards, Resolutions.
- Heard reports of the officers: president, vice president, secretary-treasurer, editor, statistician, historian.
- Heard Liaison Committee report.
- Heard reports of the bylaws affiliation representatives, other affiliates, and AASG committees: American Commission on Stratigraphic Nomenclature, America Geological Institute liaison, Earth Science Education Committee, American Association for the Advancement of Science, American Association of Petroleum Geologists, Federal Emergency Management Agency, Geological Society of America, Association of State Boards of Geology, Water Policy Committee, Digital Mapping and Standards Committee, Geologic Hazards Policy Committee, Environmental Affairs Committee, Continental Margins Committee.
- Heard report on the National Cooperative Geologic Mapping Program.
- Discussed other USGS issues.
- Heard report from the U.S. Geological Survey.
- Heard report from the Minerals Management Service.

- Heard report from the National Park Service.
- Heard report from the U.S. Department of Energy.
- Virginia Secretary of Commerce and Trade welcomed the Association.
- U.S. House of Representatives, Subcommittee on Energy and Mineral Resources discussed changes in Congress.
- Heard report from the National Research Council.
- Heard report from the U.S. Environmental Protection Agency.
- Heard report from the American Geological Institute.
- Heard report from the National Mining Association.
- Heard report from the Interstate Mining Compact Commission.
- Held informal discussion on geologic and topographic mapping.
- Discussed changes to separate positions of secretary and treasurer.
- Discussed new business.
- Heard report from the Honorary Members Committee.
- Heard report of the Auditing Committee.
- Heard report of the Balloting Committee.
- Heard report of the Future Meetings Committee.
- Heard Necrology report.
- Heard Awards and Resolutions Committee report.

1997, June 21–24, Breckenridge, Colo.
Host: Vicki J. Cowart, Colorado Geological Survey
Officers:

President: Earl H. Bennett

President-elect: Charles H. Gardner

Vice President: Larry D. Woodfork

Secretary: James M. Robertson

Treasurer: Jonathan G. Price

Historian: Emery T. Cleaves

Editor: John P. Bluemle

Statistician: Vicki J. Cowart

States Represented:

Alabama

Alaska

Arizona

Arkansas

California

Colorado

Connecticut

Delaware

Florida

Georgia
Idaho
Illinois
Indiana
Iowa
Kansas
Kentucky
Louisiana
Maine
Maryland
Minnesota
Mississippi
Missouri
Montana
Nebraska
Nevada
New Jersey
New Mexico
New York
North Carolina
North Dakota
Ohio
Oklahoma
Oregon
Pennsylvania
Puerto Rico
South Dakota
Tennessee
Texas
Utah
Vermont
Virginia
Washington
West Virginia
Wisconsin
Wyoming

Business Session:

- Called roll.
- Introduced new state geologists and honorary members.
- Appointed annual meeting committees.

- Heard reports of officers: president-elect, vice president, secretary, treasurer, editor, publications manager, newsletter manager, statistician, historian.
- Heard Liaison Committee report.
- Heard reports of special affiliations representatives: American Commission on Stratigraphic Nomenclature, American Geological Institute, American Association for the Advancement of Science, Geological Society of America, National Association of State Boards of Geology, U.S. Geological Survey/Environmental Protection Agency, Potential Gas Committee, National Water-Quality Assessment Program Council, American Institute of Professional Geologists.
- Heard reports of special committees: Coastal Processes, Continental Margins, Earth Science Education, Energy and Minerals Policy, Environmental Affairs, Geologic Hazards Policy, Professional Affairs, Water Policy.
- Coordinated publications transfer from U.S. Geological Survey to states.
- Discussed National Geologic Mapping Act: status of reauthorization.
- Heard report on the U.S. Geological Survey National Mapping Division topographic map program.
- Received update on Natural Disaster Protection and Insurance Act.
- Heard Digital Geologic Mapping Committee report.
- Received update on National Cooperative Geologic Mapping Program.
- Heard report from the Department of the Interior, Deputy Assistant Secretary for Water and Science.
- Heard report from the U.S. Geological Survey–Geological Division.
- Heard report from the U.S. Geological Survey–Water Resources Division.
- Heard report from the U.S. Geological Survey– National Mapping Division.
- Heard report from the Minerals Management Service.
- Heard report from the National Park Service.
- Heard report from the U.S. Forest Service.
- Heard report from the Environmental Protection Agency.
- Heard report from the National Research Council.
- Heard report from the American Geological Institute.
- Heard report from the National Mining Association.
- Heard report from the Federal Emergency Management Agency.
- Heard report from the U.S. Geological Survey.
- Heard report from the Interstate Mining Compact Commission.
- Heard reports of annual meeting committees: Resolutions, Auditing, Balloting, Future Meetings.
- Discussed Environmental Protection Agency opportunities: Surf Your Watershed.
- Held cluster lunches.
- Discussed AASG Washington, D.C., meeting.

- Heard necrology report.
- Heard information on 1998 annual meeting.
- Heard AASG president's remarks.
- Introduced President-elect Charles H. Gardner.

1998, June 14–16, Portland, Maine
Host: Robert G. Marvinney, Maine Geological Survey
Officers:

President: Charles H. Gardner
President-elect: Larry D. Woodfork
Vice president: James M. Robertson
Secretary: S. Cragin Knox
Treasurer: Jonathan G. Price
Historian: Emery T. Cleaves
Editor: John P. Bluemle
Statistician: Vicki J. Cowart

States Represented:

Forty-four states represented (list of the states
represented or the attendees was not found).

Business Session:

- Called roll.
- Introduced new members, acting state geologists, honorary
  members, and state geological survey staff.
- Heard reports of the officers: treasurer, editor, historian,
  statistician, vice president, president-elect.
- Heard Liaison Committee report.
- Heard report on the American Commission on Stratigraphic Nomenclature.
- Heard report from the American Geological Institute liaison.
- Heard report on the American Association for the Advancement of Science.
- Heard report on the American Association of Petroleum Geologists.
- Heard report from the Federal Emergency Management Agency.
- Heard report from the Geological Society of America.
- Heard report from the National Association of State Boards of Geology.
- Heard report from the Potential Gas Committee.
- Heard report from the American Institute of Professional Geologists.
- Heard report from the Continental Margins Committee.
- Heard report from the Energy and Mineral Policy Committee.
- Heard report from the Earth Science Education Committee.
- Heard report from the Geologic Hazards Policy Committee.
- Heard report from the Water Policy Committee.

- Heard report from the National Cooperative Geologic Mapping Program.
- Heard report from the Topographic Map Subcommittee.
- Heard report from the U.S. Geological Survey.
- Heard additional presentations by USGS.
- Heard report from the Minerals Management Service.
- Heard report from the Bureau of Land Management.
- Heard report from the National Park Service.
- Heard report from the Department of Energy.
- Heard report from the Federal Emergency Management Agency.
- Discussed Institute of Business and Home Safety.
- Discussed Environmental Protection Agency.
- Discussed National Oceanic and Atmospheric Administration.
- Discussed American Geophysical Institute.
- Discussed National Research Council.
- Discussed *The State Geological Surveys: A History*.
- Heard report of the Honorary Members Committee.
- Heard report of the Honorary Members Caucus.
- Heard report of the Auditing Committee.
- Heard report of the Balloting Committee.
- Discussed National Geologic Mapping Advisory Committee.
- Heard report of the Awards and Resolutions Committee.
- Discussed introduction of HR 2354.
- Heard report of the Future Meetings Committee.
- Heard necrology report.
- Heard president's report.

Appendix 3:
Biographies of Founding Members of AASG

Eugene Allen Smith *(Alabama)*
Lewis Dean *(Alabama Geological Survey)*

Eugene Allen Smith was born at Washington, Autauga County, Alabama, on October 27, 1841. He attended school in nearby Prattville and graduated Central High School in Philadelphia, Pa., in 1859. In 1860 he entered the junior class at the University of Alabama, where he received the A.B. degree in 1862. Studying in Germany, he received the Ph.D., summa cum laude, from the University of Heidelberg in 1868. On his return to the states, Smith was appointed assistant professor of chemistry at the University of Mississippi and also served as assistant with State Geologist Woldemar Hilgard of the Mississippi Geological Survey until 1871. In 1872, Smith married Jane Garland, the daughter of Landon C. Garland, a distinguished educator. There were five children, two of whom died in the teenage years.

Upon the reorganization of the University of Alabama in 1871 (the campus having been destroyed by federal forces in 1865), the school's board of trustees authorized the newly elected professor of geology, Dr. Eugene Allen Smith, to devote as much spare time as available in examining the geology of the state. The subject of state support for the geological survey was brought before the Alabama legislature, and in April of 1873, a legislative act was passed "to revive and complete the geological and agricultural survey of the state of Alabama." Smith was appointed Alabama's second state geologist, a position he would hold for the next 54 years. A modest appropriation of $500 per year was authorized for expenses associated with the Survey.

During the next 10 years, Smith devoted the greater part of his 3-month summer vacation toward making geological excursions, forgoing any personal salary for the work. During this period, Smith published four annual reports and three biennial reports dealing chiefly with the economic geology of the state. Smith also published a comprehensive agricultural report on the state in 1883, and in 1887 co-authored with L.C. Johnson U.S. Geological Survey Bulletin 43, which was the first detailed study of Gulf Coastal Plain Cretaceous and Tertiary stratigraphy in Alabama.

The results of the first 10 years of Smith's work were more than sufficient to impress upon the Alabama legislature the value of the geological survey to the state, and legislators passed a bill in 1883 providing an annual appropriation of $5,000 per year for the next decade. With these funds, Smith was able to enlist the aid of numerous assistant geologists, who completed several benchmark reports describing every geologic province of the state. Smith arranged for numerous reports and maps to be published for public distribution, the only cost to the public being a modest request for postage in filling the thousands of requests for information on the results of studies completed under the supervision of Smith. Cooperative studies with the federal geological survey were initiated by Smith and resulted in the first topographic map surveys of the state for use in undertaking detailed geologic mapping. Smith initiated collections for paleontology and natural history, which became the nucleus of the present Alabama Museum of Natural History.

In 1910, the University of Alabama dedicated the completion of the new Alabama Museum of Natural History building, appropriately named Smith Hall, which also housed the Geological Survey of Alabama for over half a century. Smith also served as president of the Geological Society of America in 1913.

In the 1920's, Smith lobbied for increased legislative support, which allowed him to mark the end of his career with the publication in 1926 of the exceptional report and map, produced jointly with the U.S. Geological Survey, on the geology of Alabama; it was one of the most comprehensive studies made in any state up until the 1920's. At the time of his death in Tuscaloosa on September 7, 1927, he had published over 120 titles on Alabama and southeastern geology, spanning the period from 1872 to 1927.

One of the lasting legacies of Smith's work is the recognition that his research is considered to be of the highest standards and, even today, his published reports are consulted on a variety of topics regarding the geology of Alabama.

Albert H. Purdue *(Arkansas, Tennessee)*
J. Michael Howard *(Arkansas Geological Commission)*

Albert Homer Purdue was born near Yankeetown, Ind., on March 29, 1861. Raised on a farm, he received what limited education he could from the local Yankeetown school. He entered Indiana State Normal School at Terre Haute and graduated in 1886 when he was 25. He then taught school in Missouri and served as assistant superintendent of the U.S. Indian School at Albuquerque, N.M.

In 1893, A.H. Purdue received an A.B. degree from Leland Stanford University, after which he took a year of graduate work. During part of 1892 and 1893, he worked for the Arkansas Geological Survey, under Dr. John C. Branner, state geologist.

During 1894 and 1896, he completed graduate work in geology at the University of Chicago, and upon leaving, he became professor of geology at the University of Arkansas. In 1902, mining was added to his chair, and in 1912 the university conferred upon him the degree of LL.D. From 1907 to 1912, he was ex officio state geologist of Arkansas.

Meanwhile, beginning in 1895, he worked several summers with the U.S. Geological Survey in Arkansas, spending much of his time doing detailed mapping. During his later years in Arkansas, he was given a steady increase in committee and other administrative work. Also, the state of Arkansas had ceased funding the state survey after T.B. Comstock's report on gold and silver in the state, under Dr. Branner, which exposed widespread deception and outright fraud by promoters. Purdue wanted to continue his scientific investigations, so in March of 1912 he resigned from the University of Arkansas to become state geologist of Tennessee.

While ex officio state geologist of Arkansas, Purdue oversaw the completion of three publications under the auspices of the Arkansas Geological Survey: *Slates of Arkansas,* 1909, authored by Purdue; *Bibliography on the Geology of Arkansas,* by J.C. Branner, in *Slates of Arkansas,* 1909; and *Coal Mining in Arkansas, Parts I and II* (privately published), 1910, by A.A. Steele. Purdue was an early advocate of conservation, speaking out in 1910 concerning uncontrolled and unregulated mineral development and its problems.

While at the University of Arkansas, A.H. Purdue had a student, H.D. Miser, who eventually became a co-worker and for a short time after Purdue's departure, was even ex officio state geologist of Arkansas while on leave from the U.S. Geological Survey.

In *Slates of Arkansas,* Purdue described and named many of the oldest formations exposed in the Ouachita Mountains, including the Collier Shale and the Crystal Mountain Sandstone. In 1907, publication of U.S. Geological Survey Folio 154 marked the beginning of cooperative work by Purdue for the U.S. Geological Survey.

In 1912, Purdue picked up the administrative duties of the Tennessee Geological Survey with an experienced hand. By 1914, he had authored two administrative reports on the Survey's activities for 1912 through 1914. He also authored a state survey publication, *The Zinc Deposits of Northeastern Tennessee,* in 1912. In 1917, Purdue and Miser co-authored U.S. Geological Survey Folio 202, Eureka Springs-Harrison, part of his continued association with the USGS. During his appointment as state geologist of Tennessee, he authored a series of short, popular-interest pamphlets and publications, relating the study of geology, industry, and its benefits to the citizens of Tennessee.

While at the Tennessee survey, he continued his predecessor's efforts, hired a permanent chemist to the staff, and was involved in the establishment of a Division of Forestry, headed by a forester. He believed that the public should benefit from the efforts of the state survey and was less concerned with abstract topics of geology.

Purdue died in Nashville, Tenn., on December 12, 1917, at the age of 56. He was buried in Little Rock, Ark.

Purdue's former student, friend, and co-worker, Hugh D. Miser, carried on Purdue's geologic work in Arkansas, which resulted in a number of co-authored publications after his passing. In 1918, U.S. Geological Survey Bulletin 691-J, *Asphalt Deposits and Oil Conditions in Southwestern Arkansas,* was published, followed by USGS Atlas Folio 215, for Hot Springs, in 1923. Finally, in 1929, U.S. Geological Survey Bulletin 808, *Geology of DeQueen and Caddo Gap Quadrangles, Arkansas,* completed Purdue's professional authorship and was a fitting ending to his geologic career.

Biography adapted from Wilson (1981).

Elias Howard Sellards *(Florida)*
Frank Rupert *(Florida Geological Survey)*

Elias Howard Sellards was born May 2, 1875, at Carter, Ky., the son of Wiley W. and Sarah Menach Sellards. His early school years were spent in Carter, and his family later moved to Kansas while Sellards was a youth. He continued his schooling at Scranton, Kan., completing high school in 1894. Sellards enrolled at Washburn Academy in Topeka, Kan., and later attended the University of Kansas in Lawrence, from which he received his B.A. degree in 1899 and an M.A. degree in 1900.

In 1899, while a student at the University of Kansas, Sellards discovered the Elmo fossil site, an extremely rich deposit that yielded some 6,000 specimens of Permian insects and plants, exceeding in volume all such material collected from American sites during the previous century. He continued his graduate study in paleontology at Yale University, and received his Ph.D. degree in 1903.

After a brief stint at the Carnegie Museum in Pittsburgh, Sellards began a teaching career as instructor in geology and mineralogy at Rutgers College in New Brunswick, N.J., during the 1903–04 school year. In 1904, he accepted the chair of professor of geology and zoology at the newly formed University of Florida in Gainesville. While at the University of Florida, Sellards also served as the state entomologist during 1904–05.

In June of 1907 the Florida legislature established funding for a permanent state geological survey, and Gov. Napoleon Broward appointed Sellards to the new state geologist position. Sellards moved to Tallahassee to start the fledgling Florida Geological Survey. On September 4, 1907, he married Anna Alford, with whom he would later have two daughters, Helen and Daphne.

Sellards spent his first year at the Florida survey creating the new agency from scratch, first occupying an unused committee meeting room in the capitol, and later in a two-room office shared with the state chemist. By 1908, Sellards had hired Herman Gunter as his assistant, and engaged the services of George Matson and Frederick Clapp to prepare a report on the general geology and stratigraphy of the state and coordinate activities with the U.S. Geological Survey. He also established the Florida Geological Survey library and its first museum collections. In addition to attending the inaugural meeting of the Association of American State Geologists in 1908, Sellards was invited to the first Conference for the Preservation of

Natural Resources, held the same year in Washington, and presided over by President Theodore Roosevelt.

Sellards devoted considerable attention to Florida's fossil vertebrates, especially early man. In 1913, human remains were found in the undisturbed wall of a canal at Vero (now Vero Beach), Fla., seemingly in association with extinct Pleistocene fauna. Since this discovery suggested that man may have arrived in Florida much earlier than previously thought at the time, the discovery resulted in a conference of noted scientists at the site in 1916. Subsequent controversy over the true age of "Vero Man" plagued Sellards for much of his career, but nonetheless fortified his interest in early human cultures.

Sellards served the Florida Geological Survey with distinction until April of 1919. He had firmly established the foundation of a successful agency that would grow throughout the next century along with the state it served. During his 12-year tenure at the Florida survey he published 12 annual reports, two bulletins, a geologic map, and numerous articles. These publications were primers on the geology, groundwater, and mineral resources of Florida, and set the pace for subsequent research into the solid earth systems so vital to Florida's developing economy.

In 1919, Sellards resigned from the Florida survey to take a more lucrative position as a research geologist with the Texas Bureau of Economic Geology and Technology, in Austin. One of his first assignments, given him by the Texas attorney general, was to determine the original boundary between Oklahoma and Texas along the Red River. Oil had recently been discovered in the river valley, and a long-running interstate dispute over land ownership prompted what would become one of the first judicial trials to utilize expert witnesses. Sellards presented his painstaking research so thoroughly that the Supreme Court of the United States ruled favorably for Texas (see chapter 5 of this volume, 1928). His knowledge, talents, and ability to carry an extraordinary workload served him well. He was appointed associate director of the Bureau in 1925, and he became director in 1932, a position he held until 1945. Concurrently, he was appointed professor of geology and a member of the graduate faculty at the University of Texas in 1926 and was director of the Texas Memorial Museum in Austin from 1938 until his retirement in 1957. As time permitted, Sellards remained active in field work. He directed a paleontological project that assembled an outstanding collection of Pleistocene fossils for the Texas Memorial Museum, and he made other numerous significant paleontological and anthropological discoveries around Texas. Through this period Sellards also served as president of the Society of Economic Paleontologists and Mineralogists in 1938, councilor of the Geological Society of America from 1938 to 1940, president of the Paleontological Society in 1942, and vice president of the Geological Society of America in 1943.

In spite of his administrative responsibilities, Sellards found time to teach, write, and edit extensive reports on the geology, mineral resources, and early human inhabitants of Texas. He authored or co-authored 179 publications during his remarkable career, which spanned nearly 60 years. Among his most noted published contributions are the two-volume compendium *The Geology of Texas*, and a book, *Early Man in America,* including a bibliography of literature on the subject. Sellards also taught stratigraphy at the UT Department of Geology and supervised 17 master's students and one Ph.D. student. He was instrumental in the creation of the Petroleum Engineering Department of the university. For his distinguished service and devotion to the science of petroleum geology, Sellards was awarded honorary membership in the American Association of Petroleum Geologists in 1946. He was named director emeritus of the Texas Bureau of Economic Geology in 1945, a position he held until his death, in Austin, on February 4, 1961.

Biography adapted from Texas State Historical Association (2006) and Jackson School of Geosciences (2006).

Samuel W. McCallie *(Georgia)*

Professor Samuel W. McCallie was appointed state geologist and director of the Georgia Geological Survey following the death of Professor Yeates on February 18, 1908. After coming to the Georgia survey in 1893, he published a number of important publications under the supervision of Yeates. He also published a number of bulletins after he was appointed director. In many ways, he followed the general plan of the survey previously established by Yeates: that is, the system of completely covering the state as far as possible for each commercial mineral, one at a time. By this method, whoever wished to mine a mineral commodity could take the report of that specific mineral, and with the assistance of the state geologist, attempt to locate and establish a new mining industry. This system obviously was modified by public demand. In some cases, a commercial mineral would be industrially replaced by some other mineral or artificial product; thus, no succeeding or follow-up report was made. On the other hand, minerals such as clays, which were steadily becoming more important, were periodically reexamined, calling for later and more modern reports.

Also, by this time, the urban population of Georgia began to require considerable surface and groundwater for municipal water supplies. From the beginning, McCallie recognized that water and knowledge of water resources were among the most important factors for the development of industry and for the preservation of health and economic standing of the state.

Mr. McCallie stands out among other state geologists of this country in having accomplished much with very little. There were times when he did not know whether or not he would have a budget sufficient to operate a survey, and unpredictable events often made it difficult for the Survey to continue. Mr. McCallie died on October 26, 1933.

H. Foster Bain *(Illinois)*
Myrna M. Killey *(Illinois State Geological Survey)*
Beverly L. Herzog *(Illinois State Geological Survey)*

H. Foster Bain was the first secretary of AASG, serving 2 years in that position, 1908 and 1909. The tremendous role he played in the creation of AASG is well documented in preceding chapters. He became the first director of the Illinois State Geological Survey in November 1905. His 1931 account of the people and conditions under which the Illinois State Geological Survey was founded pays tribute to the vision, courage, and ability of the founders and political leaders of the time, but Bain himself was also a person of remarkable vision who was chosen to give the Survey its start because of his unique set of qualifications and his capacity for hard work. He set the Survey on the road toward fulfilling its mission of research and service.

Harry Foster Bain was born in Seymour, Ind., on November 2, 1871, and was known as Hal. He attended Moores Hill College (Indiana), Johns Hopkins University, and the University of Chicago, where he obtained his Ph.D. in 1897. He began his professional career at the Iowa Geological Survey, during which time he authored a number of county reports and eight papers on glacial and physiographic geology. He also published reports on coals of Arkansas and on the Western Interior Coal Field. In 1901–02, he worked at mining in Colorado before joining the U.S. Geological Survey in 1903 and publishing a series of reports on the fluorspar deposits of Kentucky and Illinois and the lead-zinc deposits of the Upper Mississippi Valley.

Upon joining the newly established Illinois State Geological Survey in November 1905, Bain built an organization designed to investigate all phases of geology and the important mineral resources of the state. He recruited a small permanent staff but utilized specialists and graduate students from several universities of the state, an arrangement that continues in one form or another to this day.

Bain thought that the Survey should serve both educational and economic needs and that the latter should be interpreted broadly. This resulted in a special series of educational bulletins and local material for use in Illinois classrooms. Topographic mapping was recognized as a basic necessity, and a priority, and the cooperative agreement made with the U.S. Geological Survey has been maintained to the present day. Bain also called a meeting in 1906 in Chicago to organize the Association of State Geologists of the Mississippi Valley, which led to the formation 2 years later of the Association of American State Geologists. This association's mission was to promote the development of expertise and cooperation among state surveys and the independent thinking needed for scientific endeavors in the states' best interests, separate from those of the U.S. Geological Survey's interests, which were focused on federal priorities.

Bain arranged cooperative programs with federal and state agencies concerned with geology, mining, topographic mapping, reclamation of land subject to overflow, highway building, and water supplies. He also enlisted the goodwill of coal operators and miners, clay operators, railroad officials, engineering societies, the technical press, and high school teachers. The Survey quickly became known as an important agency for scientific research and distribution of information for the development of the state. There are many other examples of Bain's vision and intense hard work toward the establishment and fulfillment of the Survey's goals for the future.

Bain stepped down as ISGS director in 1909 to become editor of the Mining and Scientific Press, then went to London to become editor of *Mining Magazine* in 1915. While in England, Bain became a member of the Commission for Relief in Belgium, service for which he received the Medal of King Albert. He spent most of 1916–20 in minerals exploration of Africa and the Far East, but returned to the United States for a brief period to serve as assistant director of the U.S. Bureau of Mines, working on several subjects related to the war. He served as director of the Bureau of Mines from 1921 to 1924 and as secretary of the American Institute of Mining and Metallurgical Engineers from 1925 to 1931. Bain entered private industry in 1931 and continued to conduct much of his work overseas. In 1937, he moved to Manila to plan the Philippines Bureau of Mines, which included a geological survey. He stayed on to head the new organization and was trapped there when World War II came. In 1942, at the age of 71, he was interned by the Japanese in the Santo Tomas University prison camp. Upon his release 2 years later, he returned to the United States and his private consulting work. This work took him back to Manila, where he passed away from a sudden illness on March 9, 1948.

Samuel Calvin *(Iowa)*
Robert D. Libra *(Iowa Geological Survey)*

Samuel Calvin was born in Wigtonshire, Scotland, on February 2, 1840. He and his parents came to America when he was 11 years old. For 3 years the family lived on a farm near Saratoga, N.Y., before relocating to a farm in Buchanan County in eastern Iowa. While little is recorded from his youth, his devotion to knowledge and teaching showed itself early; at the age of 16 he was hired to teach in a one-room schoolhouse near the town of Quasqueton. He received his college education at Lenox College, in Hopkinton, Iowa, and later received an M.A. from Cornell College in Mount Vernon, Iowa, and a Ph.D. from Lenox.

When he was 24 years old he enlisted in the army and served for a few months in the Civil War. After returning from the war, he held a teacher of science position at Lenox College for 4 years. While there, he met and married Mary Louise Jackson, the daughter of one of the college's founders. They had two children, Alice and John William.

In 1869, Calvin resigned from Lenox to become principal of a school in Dubuque, Iowa, where he taught science and gave public lectures in geology. In 1874, he was elected to a professorship of natural science in the University of Iowa in Iowa City. Here, at first, he had charge of botany, zoology, geology, and physiology. Later, he was made professor of geology, a position he filled with distinction until his death in 1911. While at the university, Calvin gained a national reputation as a scientist and writer. His main focus was invertebrate paleontology, and in the course of his work he named some 30 species of fossils and had 11 species named for him. He also discovered the fossil remains of fish in the nearby Devonian strata, and a remarkable interglacial fauna containing horse, mastodon, camel, giant stag, and giant ground sloth remains.

In 1892, Dr. Calvin was elected state geologist of Iowa, and held that position, with a 2-year hiatus, until his death. The Iowa Geological Survey under his directorship published about 20 volumes of reports dealing with the geology and mineral resources of the state, covering all but nine Iowa counties by 1909. The findings of his Survey were published in the annual reports, and the quality of the Survey enabled important industrial development in the state. Although Calvin understood the utilitarian application of his work, and heartily cooperated in its material application, his sensitivity to the cultural value of his science was never subordinated. He gladly joined his skill and wisdom to the rising crusade calling for conservation and was invited to, and attended, Theodore Roosevelt's conservation conference at the White House in 1908.

Calvin contributed over 70 scientific articles that were published in Iowa Geological Survey annual reports, the *Bulletin from the Laboratories of Natural History from the State University of Iowa, American Journal of Science, Journal of Geology,* and many others. Calvin was one of the founders of the Baconian Club, formed for the mutual interchange of thought and the discussion of scientific topics. He was also an active member of the Geological Society of America (of which he became president in 1908), the Paleontological Society of America, the American Association for the Advancement of Science, the National Geographic Society, the Iowa Academy of Sciences, and the Davenport Academy of Sciences. He was one of the founders and editors of *The American Geologist.*

Samuel Calvin's legacy of accomplishments has influenced generations of Iowa geologists. Even today, he is regarded as Iowa's premier geologist among the many scientists to have worked in the state. Calvin was recognized by the Iowa Academy of Sciences (1911) for having given shape, proportion, and character to the work of the Iowa Geological Survey and for having effectively combined its scientific and economic aspects. His colleagues found in his example of service to the state, to education, and to science "the purest inspiration for future effort and devotion." Dr. Calvin died in the early morning of April 17, 1911. The university suspended classes the day of his funeral service. He is buried in Oakland Cemetery in Iowa City, about a mile from the center of the university and the Iowa Geological Survey offices, where his influence and philosophy are a continuing presence.

Biography adapted from Kay (1911), Thornton (1947), and Witzke (1992).

Erasmus Haworth *(Kansas)*

Erasmus Haworth was born in Warren County, Iowa, on April 17, 1855. His family moved to Galena, Kan., when he was 11. Haworth earned an undergraduate degree from the University of Kansas in 1881 and a Ph.D. from Johns Hopkins University in 1889. He taught at Penn College in Oskaloosa, Iowa, until 1892, when he was brought to Kansas, probably by Chancellor Francis Snow to help with the fledgling University Geological Survey. Haworth was already familiar with the state's geology when he returned to Kansas. In the 1880's, he published several articles about the geology and minerals of southeastern Kansas.

There were early incarnations of a geological survey in Kansas in 1864 and 1865. After letting the Survey lapse for 24 years, the Kansas legislature recreated it at KU in 1889. When Haworth returned to Kansas, he joined Samuel Wendell Williston and E.H.S. Bailey in forming the Survey's nucleus. Though the legislature appropriated no funding for the Survey, Haworth organized field work that led to extensive publication about the geology and topography of eastern Kansas, including some of the first detailed and accurate cross sections developed by Survey staff members. In 1896, he was listed as the author of the first Survey publication since its establishment at KU. Mainly a reconnaissance of the geology of eastern Kansas, it was titled simply *The University Geological Survey of Kansas, vol. 1.* Haworth was probably less of an author than he was editor of the report; a number of the chapters were written by other staff members. In short, though the Survey had no official state geologist or director, Haworth was clearly the leader of the band.

Between 1896 and 1907 the Survey published nine volumes on the geology of Kansas, including books on the paleontology, coal, mineral waters, oil and gas, and other resources of the state. It published overviews of the state's geology, including the first detailed geologic map of the state. These were handsome, well-illustrated books that stood the test of time. Through these publications, the Survey established its scientific credentials and credibility, becoming a recognized, consistently funded part of state government.

In 1907, the Survey underwent a statutory redefinition that gave it new responsibilities and a new name: the State Geological Survey of Kansas. By 1908, many of the personnel were different. Haworth was now shown as state geologist, as legally required by the new statute, though he had been using the title on publications since 1903.

After 1907, the number of Haworth's publications decreased significantly. Unlike in his earlier years at the Survey when he was editing or writing books at the rate of better than one per year, he produced only two Survey publications in a period of 8 years (these were the only two publications from the Survey between 1908 and 1917). Some of that lack of productivity may be simply the result of aging. Perhaps also there was less legislative pressure to publish, with the appearance of the earlier Survey volumes that captured much about the geology of Kansas. Finally, consulting and other business interests, particularly related to oil and gas, may have taken increasing amounts of Haworth's time, perhaps to the detriment of his publication record. In addition to leading the Survey and teaching in the geology department, Haworth was appointed as geologist in the State Irrigation Commission by the 1896 legislature, and he continued in that role into the 20th century. He was also head of the mining and mineralogy school at KU. The sum of those activities must have weighed heavily on Haworth, and probably had something to do with his resignation as head of the Survey in 1915. From 1889 to 1915, Haworth was the only director that the modern Survey had known.

Though Haworth left the Survey, he retained the position as chairman of the KU geology department. He also consulted, working now with his son Henry. In 1920, he resigned from the geology department, blaming a low salary and the need for additional outside income. From 1920 until 1931, he was active in the state's oil and gas business, and he regularly consulted on and was involved with business activities related to geology. He died on November 18, 1932, in Wichita, where he is buried.

In his years in Kansas, Haworth worked throughout the state, becoming known as a consummate field geologist. He was well regarded by students, who called him "Daddy" Haworth. Today, Haworth's name is closely associated with the mapping of surface features that led to the discovery of the El Dorado Oil Field in Butler County, the study of the Equus Beds aquifer in central Kansas, and several geologically related capital ventures that met with varying degrees of success. His memory is preserved at KU mainly through the campus hall that carries his name (though it houses KU's biological sciences division and not the geology department). But more important, Haworth (along with other early Survey staff) carved a scientific niche for the Survey. He took a little-known line in the university's budget and turned it into a productive, relevant institution. That change was as dramatic and important, perhaps, as any during the Survey's history. That foundation allowed the Survey to survive, flourish, and evolve into the institution it is today.

Gilbert D. Harris *(Louisiana)*

Gilbert Dennison Harris was the fourth state geologist of Louisiana, a position he held for 10 years, although he carried the title of geologist in charge. He was born near Jamestown, N.Y., in 1864. He received a scholarship to Cornell University in Ithaca, N.Y., as an undergraduate in 1883 and graduated with a Ph.D. in 1886. Harris joined the Arkansas Geological Survey in 1888 and a year later began work with the U.S. Geological Survey. He also worked briefly with the Texas Geological Survey and was hired as an instructor in paleontology by Cornell University in 1894.

He began his work with the Louisiana Geological Survey in 1899. The Survey at that time was part of the Agricultural Experiment Station. He continued this work until 1909, and his was the most productive of the early surveys. The Experiment Station had contracted for Harris to spend his summers working on the geology of the state. Harris was by then a well-known professor of geology at Cornell. According to the transmittal letter for the first report (1899), the director of the Experiment Station stated that Harris was "the recognized authority in this country on Tertiary geology." The final report of the Harris survey was the 52-page Bulletin 8 of 1909, *Oil and Gas in Northwestern Louisiana, with Special Reference to the Caddo Field*, by Harris, I. Perrine, and W.E. Hopper. This report proved of significant scientific interest, not only in paleontology, but also in economic terms, because Harris was among the first to identify a relationship between salt domes and oil and gas accumulation. Harris and his associates authored a number of geologic reports and publications during his tenure at the Louisiana survey.

Harris divided his time for 10 years between the Louisiana survey and teaching at Cornell. Many of his Survey assistants were Cornell students. He obtained the cooperation of the U.S. Geological Survey, the U.S. Coast and Geodetic Survey, and the Bureau of Soils of the U.S. Department of Agriculture. Harris's work was very accurate, especially under the conditions of the time. His efforts, and those of his assistants, contributed not only significantly to the geologic knowledge but to the development of the natural resources of the state. Thus, he accomplished much with a very small budget. Each of these federal organizations placed parties in the field, and thereby contributed support many times the $2,500 that appears to have been the largest amount that the Harris survey received in any year. It was through Harris's determination and the arrangement he made that a great deal of extremely valuable topographic and cartographic work was accomplished.

The attitude of the geologists of the Harris survey is best expressed in the letter of transmittal for the 1899 report, in which the director of the Experiment Station said "… they have persistently followed their work through freezes and sunshine, over intolerable roads, impelled by an enthusiasm known only to lovers of science." He was a pioneer in Tertiary paleontology. He devoted his life to a study of the rocks and fossils of the Cenozoic Era, first in Arkansas, Louisiana, and Texas, and later in Europe and various parts of South and Central America and the Caribbean. In association with his students, he amassed a huge collection of specimens and was an author of definitive studies on many Tertiary species.

Harris was also a scientific entrepreneur. He was always interested in economic geology, and throughout his career maintained dual appointments for the academic and the applied aspects of geology. He was granted leave during the spring term in exchange for teaching field studies during the summer term, together with a normal teaching load during the fall term. During the early part of the year he devoted his time to consulting, either working as a member of the Geological Survey of Louisiana or accepting consulting work with a growing number of oil companies in various parts of the world. This combination of activities proved to be very beneficial, bringing hundreds of specimens to Ithaca from every corner of the globe and providing access to geologic information that would otherwise have been unobtainable.

Harris was particularly sympathetic toward the interests of women in geology, and not only enrolled them in field camp before this was an accepted practice, but also supervised their graduate studies when few other faculty would do so. His relations with them were not always harmonious, but he was clearly an early advocate of women's interests.

Harris wanted to be sure that, once he retired from Cornell, his massive collections of Tertiary fossils would be appropriately preserved. For these reasons, he slowly developed the idea of establishing an institution, free-standing and wholly independent of Cornell, that would house his collections and provide a basis for continuing research and study. The germ of this idea had in fact begun in 1895 when he started his own printing operation because he had difficulty in finding copies of older paleontologic publications and getting his own work published in a timely manner. Harris founded two journals, *Bulletins of American Paleontology* in 1895 and *Palaeontographica Americana* in 1916. He printed them on his own presses, and they continue to be published today. It was about this time that the Paleontological Research Institution gradually grew, housed first in a small cinderblock building that

Harris constructed on the grounds of his home in Ithaca, and later moved to the present building on the west shore of Cayuga Lake. The provisional charter of PRI was approved by the New York State Board of Regents in 1933, a year before his retirement, and a permanent charter was granted in 1936. While he was well into his 80's, Harris was still operating the presses of the institution he created.

Harris had a very remarkable career as professor of paleontology, state geologist of Louisiana, international consultant, publisher, and founder of the Paleontological Research Institution. Being a founding member of AASG can also be added to his list of outstanding accomplishments.

Biography adapted from Socolow (1988) and Brice (1996).

William Bullock Clark *(Maryland)*
Jeffrey Halka *(Maryland Geological Survey)*

At the inaugural meeting of the AASG in 1908, William Bullock Clark had served as state geologist of Maryland for 12 years. Elected state geologist in 1896, he served until his death in 1917. Clark combined to an unusual degree thorough training, a broad outlook, exceptional leadership skills, outstanding organizational skills, and exceptional interpersonal skills. He was born in Brattleboro, Vt., on December 15, 1860, and died unexpectedly at his summer home at North Haven, Maine, on July 27, 1917. He graduated from Amherst College in 1884, specializing in geology, and received his Ph.D. in 1887 from the University of Munich. While in Europe, he did field work for geological surveys in Prussia and Great Britain.

Employed by Johns Hopkins University in fall 1894, he became professor of geology and chairman of the geology department in 1894. In 1888, Clark was appointed assistant geologist with the U.S. Geological Survey. His chosen field was the Coastal Plain of the Atlantic Seaboard, and he prepared a bulletin on the Eocene deposits of America and monographs on Mesozoic and Cenozoic echinodermata of the United States.

Clark was not a cloistered scientist and readily placed his knowledge at the service of the public. In 1892 he was appointed director of the State Weather Service, in 1896 elected as state geologist, in 1906 became executive officer of the State Board of Forestry, and in 1910 was appointed as a state roads commissioner.

Clark was equally active in professional societies: among others, the National Academy of Sciences (chairman of the geology section), American Philosophical Society, America Academy of Arts and Sciences, Mining and Metallurgical Society of America, American Association for the Advancement of Science, Geological Society of America (councilor and treasurer), and Association of American State Geologists (president).

During his tenure as state geologist, the Survey published county topographic, geologic, forestry, and soil maps; county reports (featuring sections on physiography, geology, mineral resources, soils, climate, hydrography, magnetic declination, and forests); systematic reports (e.g., Eocene, Miocene, Cretaceous, and Devonian); volumes featuring sections such as "Report on Resurvey of the Mason and Dixon Line," "The Geography of Maryland," and "The Surface and Underground Water Resources of Maryland, Delaware and the District of Columbia." Overall, the Survey published 30 reports and 57 county maps and two state geologic maps from 1896 through 1917.

"In all these numerous and diversified efforts for betterment of the State of his adoption, Professor Clark has shown untiring energy, unselfish zeal and devotion..." (Mathews, 1918).

Alfred C. Lane *(Michigan)*

Alfred Church Lane (1863–1948) was state geologist of Michigan from 1899 to 1909. In 1893, Dr. Lane was appointed the assistant state geologist under Dr. Lucius Hubbard. When Dr. Hubbard resigned in 1899, the Board of Geological Survey elected Dr. Lane as his replacement. Dr. Lane moved the Survey's headquarters from Houghton to Lansing and refocused the work of the Survey to include more geology in the Lower Peninsula. The first thorough topographic survey of Michigan was started under his direction. Dr. Lane was president of the Michigan Engineering Society for several years concurrent with the state geologist position. He also worked for Calumet and Hecla and other copper mining companies, a committee of the Boston Stock Exchange, and was vice president of Allen-Lane Co. Dr. Lane resigned his position as state geologist to accept a position as Pearson Professor of Geology and Mineralogy at Tufts University. He was known for research on the age of the earth, and is also known by some atomic scientists as the "Forgotten Man" of atomic research for his role in early work on splitting the atom.

He was a descendent of Thomas Dudley, a founder and four-time governor of the Massachusetts Bay Colony. He was born on January 29, 1863, in Boston and attended Boston Latin High School. After graduating from Harvard in 1883, he remained at the institution as a mathematics instructor. From 1885 to 1887 he studied at the University of Heidelberg, returning to Harvard in 1888 to receive his doctorate. The following year he worked as petrographer of the Michigan Geological Survey and as instructor in the Michigan College of Mines. He remained at the college until his resignation in 1936, protesting the state's teachers' oath. In 1940, he was the recipient of the Ballou Medal for distinguished service to education and the nation, awarded by Tufts College.

Working with Otto Hahn, a German scientist, Lane helped to inaugurate an international plan for the exchange of scientific information on smashing the atom in 1926. Lane was the first American to receive notice from Hahn about his successful splitting of a uranium atom in 1938, and he immediately passed the information on to Washington. In 1929, Lane became the first consultant in science ever appointed at the Library of Congress. Over the course of his lifetime, he published 1,087 articles and reports in both scientific and general journals.

He was a past president of the Geological Society of America and was affiliated with several international geologic and academic associations. He also supported the YMCA and was a dedicated servant of the Boy Scouts of America. A peleochoric amphibole mineral, known as lanenite, is named in his honor.

Lane Hall, home to the geology department, was dedicated in Lane's honor in 1968. There is also a memorial tablet in Goddard Chapel. Lane died on April 14, 1948, in Cambridge, Mass. He was survived by his wife and three children.

Biography adapted from Encyclopædia Brittanica Online (2007), Socolow (1988), and Tufts University Digital Collections and Archives (2007).

Albert F. Crider *(Mississippi)*

Albert F. Crider was state geologist of Mississippi from 1906 to 1909 and attended the founding meeting of the Association of American State Geologists in Washington, D.C. During his 3 years as state geologist, bulletins were published on cement materials, clays, lignite, and forestry. A "Provisional Geologic and Topographic Map of Mississippi" was bound into Bulletins 1 through 3, all published in 1907. This map, at a scale of 1 inch equals 13 miles, was a refinement of the 1905 map of Eckel and Crider. Crider was based in Biloxi, Miss., and covered the state from there. His reports were published in Jackson, the state capital.

In 1903 Crider had been assigned by the USGS to work with the Geological and Industrial Survey organized at Mississippi A&M College. The Geological and Industrial Survey was created to fill the needs of a state geological survey in the absence of state support and legislation. He worked with E.C. Eckel in geology and M.L. Fuller in water resources.

Crider was a native Kentuckian, the third son of William B. Crider and Martha J.A. Crider of Marion, Crittenden County, Kentucky, where he was born on January 13, 1873. He received the A.B. degree in geology in 1902 and B.S. degree in geology in 1903 at what is now the University of Kentucky in Lexington. He was hired by the U.S. Geological Survey as assistant geologist in 1903. He did field investigations on clays of western Kentucky and Tennessee, mineral resources of Mississippi, and groundwater of the Coastal Plain for the USGS. He was influenced by his association with L.W. Stephenson on the geology of the Coastal Plain. He became chair of the geology department at the University of Mississippi in 1906. He then became director of the Mississippi Geological Survey. In 1912 he returned to Kentucky as assistant state geologist under Joseph Hoeing, state geologist. His energies during the 4 following years were devoted to an intensive study of coal and tar sands; his bibliography reflects the zeal with which he attacked this topic.

The rising tide of petroleum geology, sweeping through the nation in 1916, attracted his attention. He began a career in petroleum geology that lasted for almost 30 years. His start in the oil business was with Atlas Oil Co. (later the Palmer Corp.), located in Tulsa, Okla. From 1916 to 1920, he did geologic investigations in the Midcontinent for Atlas Oil. He was credited with mapping the Jennings Field in Pawnee County, Oklahoma. Of greater significant was his observations in Claiborne Parish, Louisiana, where he recorded evidence for an oil play west of Homer. The manager for Palmer Oil stated that Crider was solely responsible for his company's highly favorable acreage position in the prolific and highly profitable Homer Field. Following his success at Homer, Crider—now known far and wide in the industry as "Doc"—stepped into a position with the Dixie Oil Co. in Shreveport, where from 1920 to 1929 he served that organization, directing work in the development of "chalk-rock" oil and in prospecting the then-new Glen Rose and Travis Peak zones of Caddo Parish, Louisiana. From 1929 to the end of his career, Crider maintained a consulting office in Shreveport. The high regard in which his work was held is evidenced by the fact that though past retirement age, he was retained by Sohio Petroleum, a relationship that lasted until March 15, 1945, only 6 months preceding his death.

Albert Crider was united in marriage with Rosa Rhee Kevil on November 15, 1905. The couple had a son, Foster Kevil Crider (who became a geophysicist), a daughter, and four grandchildren.

Crider, the geologist, will be remembered because of the association of his name with the Wilcox Group of the Gulf Coast Tertiary section; the group name, which seems destined to retain its place in North American stratigraphy, was introduced in his early bulletins on Mississippi geology. He was an early president of the Shreveport Geological Society. His name is inscribed on the bronze plaque in AAPG headquarters giving the names of the founders of that society, which was founded in 1917.

Crider, the man, was held in high esteem as a citizen of Shreveport. He was an active member of the First Presbyterian Church. He maintained connections to his native state of Kentucky and was devoted to his adopted state of Mississippi. He was chosen to represent the University of Kentucky at the dedication of the new Louisiana State University at Baton Rouge in 1926.

Biography adapted from Moody (1946) and Socolow (1988).

Henry A. (Chief) Buehler *(Missouri)*
Bill Duley *(Missouri Division of Geology and Land Survey)*

Henry Andrew Buehler was born to Andrew and Catherine Buehler in Monroe, Wis., on May 27, 1876. His father was a blacksmith. Henry attended the University of Wisconsin and earned a bachelor of science degree in chemical engineering in 1901. He moved to Rolla shortly after, upon the request of W.R. Buckley. Buckley, who had served as state geologist of Wisconsin, accepted the position of state geologist for Missouri in 1901 and asked Buehler to come to Missouri to serve as assistant state geologist. Buehler served in that capacity until 1907, when he left his state position for a brief stint in the private sector. The following year, the position of state geologist was vacated because of Buckley's resignation, and Buehler was chosen to fill the position. Buehler served in the office of Missouri state geologist for 36 years, longer than any other. He was appointed to the position by 10 consecutive governors: five Democrats and five Republicans. At Buehler's funeral, Gov. Forrest Donnell commented, "to have been selected by ten consecutive governors without regard to politics is a striking testimony to the quality of work and the character of the man."

Buehler's support of Missouri's mineral resource development helped turn a $15 million industry into one that produced $75 million annually in 1944. During Buehler's tenure, the Survey produced publications on coal, oil, gas, water resources, fireclay, and pyrite. The state geologic map was revised. Staff did extensive research on insoluble residues, principally as a means for zoning Cambrian-Ordovician dolomites.

He served as president of the Rolla Chamber of Commerce in 1922, 1926, 1927, and 1933. The June 15, 1920, minutes of this organization reflect receiving "two telegrams from Mr. Buehler, who is in Washington [D.C.] looking after the interests of Rolla, in the securing of the zinc and lead experiment station" (that later materialized as the U.S. Bureau of Mines office in Rolla).

In 1921, Buehler was appointed as ex officio member of the first Missouri Highway Commission. It is said that U.S. 63 was paved so Buehler could get to Jefferson City easier, and was often called "Chief Buehler's Highway."

The Missouri School of Mines awarded Buehler the degree of doctor of science, honoris causa, in 1925 in appreciation of his professional work, his loyal support, and his untiring efforts on behalf of the school.

The chief was a founding member of the American Association of Petroleum Geologists. In 1935, he was installed as president of the prestigious American Institute of Mining and Metallurgical Engineers in New York City. Buehler was preceded in service as president of AIMME by U.S. President Herbert Hoover, who was elected as the organization's president in 1920.

Buehler belonged to the Missouri Planning Commission, Missouri Resources Museum Commission, Conservation Committee of the Missouri Academy of Science, Natural Resources Committee of the State Defense Council, Geological Society of America, St. Louis Science Academy, Tau Beta Pi, and numerous other organizations. He also served as state engineer on the Civil Works Administration, director of the State Rehabilitation Corporation, and director of a WPA project. In 1940, Buehler was voted a life member of the Board of Directors of the Rolla Chamber of Commerce. In 1939, he served on Missouri's Committee of the World's Fair Commission.

On March 14, 1944, Rolla, along with the state and nation, were shocked and saddened to learn of the death of Henry Andrew Buehler. Buehler died of heart disease while in Jefferson City, preparing to attend a State Highway Commission meeting. He was 67. Buehler's funeral was held in Parker Hall on the Missouri School of Mines campus. So many attended that 3,000 had to stand outside the auditorium and listen to the ceremony via speakers. Buehler was laid to rest in the Rolla Cemetery. His grave is adorned with a lichen-covered pink granite boulder. The chief's wishes were for a "simple granite rock, unpolished, from one of these Missouri hills." Buehler was buried with full Masonic honors.

Buehler's death was followed by numerous tributes from the state of Missouri and professional organizations. The 1943–44 Constitutional Convention of Missouri honored Buehler through resolution 39, offered by Mr. Allen McReynolds. After highlighting his service as state geologist and its many facets, McReynolds wrote,

> Few people have known his politics—no one cared. The important thing was that here was a great disinterested public servant who devoted his life to the development of the natural resources of the State in order that mankind might be benefited. It is said that no man is indispensable. This may be true, but it will require many days to find a man of the stature and capacity and unselfish devotion to succeed to the work of H.A. Buehler, as State Geologist of Missouri.

The state geological survey has been housed in a number of locations, but in 1946 it was moved to the first Buehler Building in Rolla, the old USO building at the corner of 9th and Rolla Streets. At the dedication ceremonies, Gov. Donnell said of Buehler,

> The building which we proudly dedicate today has been named the Buehler Building. It is so named in memory of one of our greatest geologists, Dr. Henry

> Andrew Buehler, whose life and career were so intimately associated with the advancement of his beloved state as he labored in the great field of geological research, planning, and investigation. It has been said of him that every mineral industry in the State of Missouri felt the wisdom and influence of Buehler. His advice and counsel were in constant demand.

The current home of the Division of Geology at 111 Fairgrounds was also named in honor of Buehler upon its completion in 1963. In July 2000, Gov. Mel Carnahan signed a proclamation in honor of Buehler's contributions to the state of Missouri on the occasion of Missouri's hosting of the 92nd annual meeting of the Association of American State Geologists in St. Louis.

Biography adapted from Marler (2001) and Weaver (2001).

Erwin Hinckley Barbour *(Nebraska)*
Charles A. Flowerday
(Editor, Conservation and Survey Division/
School of Natural Resources, University of Nebraska–Lincoln)

Erwin Hinckley Barbour, the first director of the Nebraska Geological Survey, was born in 1856 near Oxford, Ohio, and was educated at Miami University (Ohio). He received his Ph.D. from Yale University, where he worked under noted geologists O.C. Marsh and J.D. Dana, graduating in 1882. He was assistant paleontologist with the U.S. Geological Survey from 1882 to 1888.

He then taught at Grinnell College in Iowa before coming to the University of Nebraska as a professor of geology and paleontology in 1891, as well as being named acting state geologist. In 1893, the legislature made him head professor of geology and geologist for the state. And from those humble beginnings, a state geological survey began to take shape. Barbour's principal interest was paleontology. He organized the University of Nebraska State Museum and became its first curator. But he also recognized that bone-hunting wasn't something the boosters of a young state would think full of commercial potential. He also understood the need to explore for economic minerals. And against conventional wisdom, he recognized that in a coal-poor, drought-prone region lacking in precious metals, mineral resources would and should include water.

His prescience about the state's groundwater resources was only slowly recognized, but his early studies laid the foundation for an agriculture that now stands second in the nation in irrigated acres only to California and makes use of more than 100,000 registered irrigation wells. A conservationist, Barbour's interest in groundwater led him in 1897–98 to investigate and report on homemade windmills along the Platte River. He published a pamphlet that encouraged the building of windmills, and in 1904 received a silver medal from the U.S. Department of Agriculture for the best-designed homemade windmill.

Barbour also saw the sparse materials available at the university with which to teach geology, so he soon took an assistant into the field to look for fossils and mineral samples. Soon enough, renting a covered wagon, he and a group of graduate assistants ventured to the farthest corner of the state, northwestern Nebraska's Sioux County and its Badlands and Pine Ridge, to look for fossils. On their first day out, they found large corkscrew fossils he called the "devil's corkscrew" *(Daemonelix),* later determined to be the burrows, or trace fossils, of a large ancient rodent. It was the first of many fossil discoveries Barbour would make. Most of these went to the university's State Museum, making it one of the most notable in vertebrate paleontology in the world.

Barbour taught, fossil-hunted, and did rudimentary geological survey on a meager budget, eventually supplemented by private money from boosters such as Regent Charles Morrill, whose name graces the building housing all the displays and some of the offices of the state museum.

The university finally gave the Survey $500 in 1899, then only $250 a year for 1900–02. This may have been because it received $1,200 from the state in the last two of those years. The appropriations for the state survey increased incrementally until it was given $10,000 in 1911, along with an authorization to enter into cooperative agreements with the U.S. Geological Survey to build efficiency.

After 20 years of work, it seemed the geological survey had at last achieved a reliable funding base. But that same year, the legislature passed two other bills that would begin to undermine Barbour's hold on the Survey: the head professor of geology was no longer the state geologist, instead being chosen from the teaching staff by the regents; and a new entity, the Conservation and Soil Survey, was born and given a $6,000 budget. It was headed by George E. Condra, a large, garrulous, Teddy Roosevelt–like figure with a passion for both conservation and economic development who immediately set about documenting Nebraska's people, landscapes, and natural resources. Condra and Barbour could not have been more dissimilar: Condra was a geographer, Barbour a geologist; Condra was a tall, stocky former athlete who spoke loudly and plainly and was not afraid to step on toes; Barbour was also tall but slender, soft-spoken and gentle, well-liked by almost everyone.

Condra joined the faculty in 1902 and a year later his dissertation was published by Barbour's survey. Eventually, Condra's greater political savvy would give him control of earth-science survey in Nebraska while Barbour would be given charge of his first love, the state's fossil resources via its natural history museum.

In 1913, funding for the Conservation and Soil Survey was doubled to $12,000, even as Barbour's survey received $10,000. Then, in 1915, Condra's survey was given that same amount, but funding for Barbour's survey was cut to $7,500. Condra by this time was also serving on the Conservation and Public Welfare Commission with the governor, the chancellor of the university, and two other state officials, with the charge, in part, of advising himself and Barbour as directors of the state surveys.

In the next legislative session, 1917, Condra's soil survey received $25,000 and Barbour's nothing. He was still state geologist, but his version of the state geological survey was done. In 1919, during the next biennial session of the legislature, Condra's survey was given some geological duties, while Barbour remained head of the state museum—not entirely left out in the cold, still tending to his main passion, paleontology.

Barbour would continue to be an important figure in the state and national scientific communities, but in 1921, the newly named Conservation and Survey Division, headed by Condra, was charged with investigating the geologically related natural resources of the state.

Barbour and Condra loom as the two largest figures on the state's scientific landscape in its early days. They cast long shadows, and the story of one must include the other. Both were well known across the state by 1921. Barbour continued to head the geology department until 1934 and was head of the state museum until 1941. From 1919 to 1929, he was also chair of the geography department.

Barbour's legacy in paleontology makes him one of the early giants in the field. In 1905, at James Henry Cook's Agate Springs Ranch in Sioux County, he opened two quarries he named University Hill, which the University of Nebraska explored for fossils, and Carnegie Hill, which was largely excavated in those days by the Carnegie Museum.

These widely known fossil quarries are part of an area designated in 1965 as Agate Fossil Beds National Monument. They have yielded some of the most extraordinary vertebrate fossils in North America and the world, particularly of fossil mastodons and mammoths. Other important fossil finds include the *Paleocaster,* an ancient beaver, the rhino-like *Diceritherium,* and the *Titanothere,* which resembles a giant-size tapir.

Barbour was also the Nebraska representative at the Columbian Exposition in Chicago in 1893. At the Trans-Mississippi Exposition in Omaha, 1897–98, he was superintendent of mining, forestry, and university educational exhibits. In 1903, he was superintendent of education, mining, and resources at the Louisiana Purchase Exposition in St. Louis.

Barbour wrote more than 400 scientific reports and books. He received many awards and medals for his work at the expositions and in scientific organizations. He died in Lincoln on May 11, 1947.

Henry Barnard Kummel *(New Jersey)*
Irving G. Grossman *(New Jersey Geological Survey)*

Henry Barnard Kummel was the first president of AASG, although in 1908 that position was referred to as chairman. He served as president for the first 4 years of AASG's existence (1908–12). He then served 2 more years as vice president (1913–14). He was obviously dedicated to AASG and seeing this fledgling organization off to a good start. He was born in Milwaukee, Wis., on May 25, 1867. His undergraduate studies at Beloit College led to an A.B. degree in 1889. He remained in Beloit College Academy for 2 years as instructor and moved to Harvard University, where he served as assistant in the department of geology. He earned his A.M. degree there in 1892.

The following summer, he was employed by Professor R.D. Salisbury, of the University of Chicago, in mapping the glacial deposits of northern New Jersey. His work led to a fellowship in geology at the University of Chicago. While attending the University of Chicago, Kummel met and later married Charlotte F. Coe. Theirs was a happy marriage and it produced two daughters. Three years later, he received a Ph.D. for his thesis, entitled "Lake Passaic—An Extinct Glacial Lake."

From 1896 to 1899, Kummel was an assistant professor of physiography at Lewis Institute in Chicago. During the summer months he mapped the Triassic formations of central and northern New Jersey, the professional work for which he is best known. Kummel's geologic mapping was done on foot, bicycle, horseback, or with horse and buggy. He became thoroughly familiar with the surficial and bedrock geology of all parts of New Jersey. Among his many reports published from 1908 to 1914 are five folios co-authored as part of the Atlas of New Jersey. His bibliography lists 47 titles.

When John C. Smock retired as state geologist in January 1902, Kummel succeeded him. Despite heavy administrative duties, he found time to supervise the preparation and publication of many geologic reports.

In 1906, a group of seven state geologists had organized the Association of State Geologists of the Mississippi Valley. When an enlarged ASGMV met in Washington, D.C., with the U.S. Geological Survey in 1908, it voted to include all the states and metamorphose into the Association of American State Geologists. The chairman of the conference, Henry Kummel, was elected president. He was reelected in 1909 and 1910. He subsequently served on the Executive Board in 1912 and 1913.

Kummel's activities were numerous and varied. He was a founding member of the Society of Economic Geologists and a fellow of the American Association for the Advancement of Science. In 1937, he was the representative of the AASG on the National Research Council. From 1897 to 1901, he was associate editor of the *Journal of Geography*. In 1931, he was elected vice president of the Geological Society of America.

Kummel retired in June 1937, having served as state geologist for 35 years, longer than anyone before or after. He had also served concurrently as director of the state Department of Conservation and Development for 15 years.

In 1934, widower Kummel (his wife had died in 1933) married Anna Goets Williams, an old friend. Kummel died in Trenton on October 23, 1945. The wide esteem in which he was held is attested by those who attended his funeral, including two former governors of New Jersey and representatives of many state and national organizations.

John Mason Clarke *(New York)*
William M. Kelly
(New York State Museum and Science Service)

John Mason Clarke was born in Canandaigua, N.Y., on April 15, 1857. He attended Amherst College in 1873, where he studied under B.K. Emerson. Upon graduation from Amherst, he taught at several institutions, including the Canandaigua Academy (1877–79), Amherst (1879–80), the Utica Free Academy (1880–81), Smith College (1881–85), and the Massachusetts Agricultural College (1885). Clarke variously taught geology, mineralogy, zoology, and German.

John Clarke became associated with the New York State Geological Survey in January of 1886 when he started work under James Hall. Upon Hall's death in 1898, Clarke was appointed state paleontologist. In 1904, when Frederick Merrill, second New York state geologist after Hall, retired, Clarke was named state geologist and director of the State Museum and Science Division of the Education Department. He held these titles until his death. Clarke was elected to approximately 50 scientific and historical societies in the United States, Canada, England, Germany, France, and Russia. He authored or co-authored over 300 papers. His most important work was in the last volumes of *Paleontology of New York*, by Hall and Clarke. Clarke named 135 genera and 870 new species of fossils, specializing in brachiopods, eurypterids, trilobites, and sponges, mostly from the Devonian.

Clarke was the first president of the Paleontological Society in 1909 and was president of the Geological Society of America in 1916. He was awarded the Prix de Léonide Spindiaroff by the International Geological Congress in 1910 and the Thompson Gold Medal of the National Academy of Sciences shortly before his death, having been a member of the latter organization from 1909. Clarke also received gold medals from the Permanent Wild Life Protection Fund and the Philadelphia Academy of Sciences. He was awarded honorary degrees from the University of Marburg, Colgate University, the University of Chicago, Princeton University, Amherst College, and Johns Hopkins University.

Under the direction of John Clarke, New York entered into what has been called the "golden age" of geology and paleontology in the state. Research, sponsored both by the state and academia, was greatly encouraged and supported generously. Clarke favored various branches of science in addition to his own interests in paleontology and stratigraphy. He equally supported economic and purely scientific research. Under Clarke's direction the geological survey, in cooperation with university professors, mapped two-thirds of the bedrock of New York, cataloging rock structures, fossils, and mineral resources. Clarke was also interested in publishing large scientific works that would appeal to the general public. Thus were published E.H. Eaton's *Birds of New York* (two quarto volumes, 106 color plates) and H.D. House's *Wild Flowers of New York* (two quarto volumes, 264 color plates).

Unlike his predecessor James Hall, who was often tyrannical, Clarke was described as being firm and persuasive, a quiet, polite man of compromise. Clarke was very successful in obtaining gifts of artifacts and large amounts of money for building exhibits. Shortly after Clarke assumed his duties as director of the state museum, space for exhibits and storage for research collections became a critical problem. Exhibits were housed in eight separate buildings in Albany, and the research materials were stored in seven different buildings, with every corner, corridor, and stair landing jammed with boxes and cabinets of specimens. Clarke declared that the conditions were "intolerable" and began working in earnest on a new building for the museum. In 1915, the museum was moved into an entire floor of the newly constructed Education Building.

As state museum director and state geologist, Clarke was interested in the preservation of several geologically unique sites in New York. He arranged for these sites to be donated to the state museum and designated "scientific reservations" to be used as outdoor exhibits. Most of these were absorbed into the state park system in the 1950's, but two of the smaller ones remain under the care of the New York State Museum.

In the last years of his life, John Clarke was inclined to look on the general, philosophic aspect of science. His *Life of James Hall* is in fact a history of geology in the United States during the time that Hall lived. He became interested in ceramics and the early history of the Pennsylvania Dutch, which had been hobbies but which he treated, and published upon, in a scientific manner. John Mason Clarke passed away on May 29, 1925, after a brief illness.

Biography adapted from New York State Museum (1926), University of the State of New York (1964), Fisher (1978), and Landing (2004).

Joseph Hyde Pratt *(North Carolina)*
Kenneth B. Taylor *(North Carolina, Associate)*

Joseph Hyde Pratt was the first executive committeeman of AASG in 1908. He returned to that office for 4 years from 1914 to 1917. The title of executive committeeman was changed in 1937 to vice president. He was born in Hartford, Conn., on February 3, 1870, the son of James Church and Jennie Abbey (Peck) Pratt, and died in Chapel Hill, N.C., on June 2, 1942. He was educated in the Hartford public schools and the Sheffield Scientific School of Yale University, where he received the Ph.B. degree in 1893 and the Ph.D. degree in 1896. As an undergraduate, his chief interest was in chemistry, in which he made a brilliant record. He received the senior appointment and was commencement speaker. A collecting trip through western North Carolina in 1892 with S.L. Penfield and J.A. Holmes shifted his interest from chemistry to geology and mineralogy, in which he majored for his Ph.D. degree in 1896.

Pratt came to North Carolina in 1897 as state mineralogist, and made his home in Chapel Hill the remainder of his life. His choice of a southern state as a permanent residence was not entirely accidental. Prior to the Civil War, his father, James Church Pratt, had lived on a sugar plantation in Louisiana for several years. At the outbreak of the Civil War, he enlisted and served as a captain in the Confederate army. Pratt was state mineralogist from 1897 to 1905 and state geologist from 1906 to 1924. He served as a member of the International Jury of Awards at the St. Louis Exposition of 1904, director of briquetting experiments of the U.S. Geological Survey Coal Testing Plant at St. Louis in 1904–05, chief of the Department of Mines and Metallurgy at the Jamestown Exposition in 1907, and a special expert to the U.S. Twelfth Census. As state mineralogist, his work was devoted almost entirely to mineralogy and geology. He was the discoverer or co-discoverer of four new minerals: pirssonite, wellsite, rhodolite, and mitchellite. During this period he was author or co-author of eight reports on the geology and mining industry of North Carolina. His method of determining ferrous iron in silicates is still standard procedure. As a mineralogist, he was interested in gems and gem materials of the state and was awarded gold medals and diplomas for his exhibits of North Carolina gem materials at the Pan-American Exposition at Buffalo in 1901 and the Charleston Exposition in 1902.

In 1906, he was appointed state geologist in the enlarged agency known as the North Carolina Geological and Economic Survey and immediately took advantage of the enlarged program of work available. He took a leading part in the movement to establish forest reservations in the southern Appalachians and worked incessantly for the passage of the Weeks Law authorizing the acquisition of land for national forests. He organized the Southern Forestry Congress, the North Carolina Forestry Association, and good roads associations; he sponsored good road days, conducted good roads institutes, and sponsored fisheries and drainage conventions.

Following the declaration of war on April 6, 1917, he was commissioned a major in the Reserve Corps on April 24, 1917, and assigned to the 105th Regiment of Engineers, where he was promoted to lieutenant colonel on November 11, 1917, and colonel on October 9, 1918. He received the Distinguished Service Medal for his services overseas. After the war, he returned home with impaired health, from which he never recovered. Being unable to perform the duties of state geologist, he resigned the position in February 1924. With improved health in 1933, he served in various engineering positions with different federal agencies through 1940.

Pratt was one of North Carolina's most prominent and useful citizens, and during his period of active service to the state, probably contributed more to its progress and well-being than any other one person. Although impaired health prevented him from following his programs to their conclusion, he lived to see most of them become a vital part of the state's life. The U.S. Forest Service has acquired thousands of acres of land in the Pisgah, Nantahala, and Croatan National Forests, and the National Park Service has established the Great Smoky Mountains National Park along the Great Smoky Mountains in North Carolina and Tennessee. The legislature of 1921 inaugurated a road-building program that made North Carolina outstanding for many years as the good roads state, while legislation of 1925 converted the Geological and Economic Survey into the more inclusive Department of Conservation and Development, which, within 2 years, contained divisions of Forestry, Game and Inland Fisheries, Commercial Fisheries, Water Resources and Engineering, Mineral Resources, Commerce and Industry, and Public Relations.

Upon the resignation of J.A. Holmes in the fall of 1905 to accept a full-time position with the U.S. Geological Survey, Dr. Joseph Hyde Pratt became acting state geologist and was appointed to the position of state geologist by Gov. R.B. Glenn. Dr. Pratt had been associated with Professor Holmes as state mineralogist on the North Carolina Geological Survey since the middle of 1897, and was aware of and in accord with the program that had been laid for good roads, forestry, water power, and conservation in general; in fact, he had contributed to the laying of the foundation policy for these programs. The North Carolina Geological and Economic Survey, which the legislature of 1905 had established, gave him the opportunity to enlarge the program of work and he immediately took advantage of it. The publications of the Survey between 1905 and 1925 include, in addition to a number of valuable bulletins and volumes on geology and minerals, reports on forests and forest-fire prevention, terracing of farm lands, water power, drainage, fisheries and the fishing industry, and public roads.

During Dr. Pratt's tenure as state geologist, the Survey published 12 bulletins, two volumes, and six economic papers on the geology and mineral resources of the state. Dr. Pratt was author of one bulletin, Bulletin 25, *Zircon, Monazite and Other Minerals Used in the Production of Chemical Compounds Employed in the Manufacture of Lighting Apparatus,* and the six economic papers that dealt with minerals and mining. Six of the 12 bulletins were prepared by Survey personnel, consisting of especially qualified assistants, while the remaining six bulletins and two volumes were prepared by the personnel of cooperating agencies. Four of the 12 bulletins dealt with the metallic minerals and their setting, seven dealt with nonmetallic minerals and rocks, and one was a bibliography of North Carolina geology, mineralogy, and geography.

Volume III and volume V were the most important reports of the Survey from the standpoint of pure science. Volume III, *The Coastal Plain of North Carolina,* published in 1912, was a volume of 552 pages, including two maps. One map showed the surficial formations of the Coastal Plain and the other showed the geologic formations of the Coastal Plain of North Carolina, exclusive of the surficial formations. This report, which was prepared by geologists of the U.S. Geological Survey in cooperation with the North Carolina Geological and Economic Survey, was the most complete report ever prepared and published on the Coastal Plain of North Carolina. This report was in two parts. Part I contained detailed historical accounts and descriptions of Coastal Plain geologic formations and their fossils. Part II contained detailed accounts of the water resources of the Coastal Plain. It was published at a time when the information it contained was important to securing safe drinking water in the Coastal Plain.

Volume V, *The Cretaceous Formations of North Carolina,* published in 1923, was a volume of 604 pages and one geologic map, plus 102 pages of plates, 94 of which illustrated the fossil content of the formations. This report was prepared by geologists of the U.S. Geological Survey in coop-eration with the North Carolina Geological and Economic Survey. This report was a major contribution to the geology of Cretaceous formations.

The failure of Dr. Pratt to prepare more than seven reports on the geology and mineral resources of North Carolina for publication by the Geological and Economic Survey during the 19 years he served as state geologist did not indicate any lack of interest in either the geology and mineral resources of the state or publications relating to them. The work of the Survey was so diversified, covering as it did geology and minerals, forests and forest-fire prevention, drainage of swamp lands, water power, groundwater supplies, terracing of farm lands, fisheries and the fishing industry, and public roads, that administrative duties and the preparation of reports that he could best do left little time for the necessary field work to make possible the preparation of geologic and mineral reports.

In addition to the seven reports on the geology and minerals of North Carolina noted above, he prepared, during his tenure as state geologist, nine biennial reports, seven economic papers on roads and road-building, five economic papers on commercial fisheries, and eight economic papers on drainage; he also supervised the preparation of five others. All 34 pub-lications were published by the Geological and Economic Survey. Dr. Pratt was a prolific writer, as shown by the fact that his lifetime bibliography contained slightly over 225 entries, approximately 125 of which, including the 34 mentioned above, were prepared during the 19 years he served as state geologist.

It is very probable that the Geological and Economic Survey, between 1905 and 1925, affected the economic welfare of the state of North Carolina as much as or more than any other state agency. The following state agencies have developed from the Geological and Economic Survey and its programs: the Department of Conservation and Development, State Highway Commission, Wildlife Resources Commission, and Department of Water Resources.

Arthur Gray Leonard *(North Dakota)*
Edward C. Murphy *(North Dakota Geological Survey)*

Arthur Gray Leonard was born on March 15, 1865, in Clinton, N.Y. His father was a Congregational minister, which resulted in the family moving several times while Leonard was a boy. He graduated from Salt Lake Academy in Utah and from Oberlin College in 1889. Leonard returned to Oberlin College and obtained his master's degree in 1895. He worked on and off for the Iowa Geological Survey between 1893 and 1903. The Iowa survey provided him with valuable field experience and training that he applied later in his career. He taught geology in Western Toledo, Iowa, during the winter months of 1894–96. In 1896, he became assistant state geologist of the Iowa Geological Survey. Shortly thereafter, he went to Johns Hopkins University in Baltimore, Md., obtaining his Ph.D. in 1898. He returned to the Iowa Geological Survey as assistant state geologist and remained there until 1903, except for 1 year's leave of absence to teach at the University of Missouri.

Dr. Leonard became state geologist of North Dakota and a professor of geology at the University of North Dakota in 1903. North Dakota had become a state in 1889. The North Dakota Geological Survey was formed in 1895, and had been under the direction of two previous state geologists (Earle Babcock, 1895–1902; Frank Wilder, 1902–03) prior to Leonard. He was to hold that position until his death on December 17, 1932. Leonard's 29-year tenure as North Dakota state geologist is the longest in state history, although Dr. Wilson M. Laird, state geologist from 1941–69, comes very close with 28 years.

Much of Dr. Leonard's early career in North Dakota was spent mapping the coal-bearing rocks of the Fort Union Group (Paleocene) in the badlands of western North Dakota. He typically traveled from Grand Forks to Dickinson, Williston, Minot, or Bismarck by train and then rented or purchased horses and a wagon for the summer field season. From 1904 to 1923, his field seasons typically began as soon as classes ended in the spring and ended in mid-September when he returned to resume teaching. He neatly filled 19 field notebooks with his insightful scientific observations. Although he did not complain about hardships in the field, these notebooks document the difficulty of finding spring water fit for drinking and the skill that was required to cross deep, narrow coulees and ravines without high-centering the wagon at the base of the draw. The North Dakota Geological Survey still retains his cumbersome, but portable, dark room and numerous glass negatives that he took in the field.

Forty-eight articles on the geology of North Dakota were published by Leonard. Most of the articles appeared in North Dakota Geological Survey bulletins and biennial reports, roughly half focused on the coal resources of western and central North Dakota. The subjects of his other articles were wide-ranging and included such things as the purpose and value of a state geological survey, the gravel and clay resources of North Dakota, a geological history of the state that was written to be used in schools, Pleistocene drainage changes in western North Dakota, the first geologic map of the state, natural gas resources of the area, the state's landforms, and the oil and gas potential of North Dakota.

By all accounts, Leonard was a well-respected scientist, administrator, and teacher. His long tenure in the Survey provided much needed stability for the new agency. His time as state geologist was not without its difficulties, however. The state legislature did not provide funding for the geological survey for 9 of those years and appropriated only $1,000 per year for another 14. Perhaps his greatest contribution, beyond his advancement of the science of geology in North Dakota, was to keep the state survey operating under such deplorable funding conditions.

The University of North Dakota Department of Geology and Geological Engineering is housed in Leonard Hall, named in honor of his many accomplishments. That building, constructed in 1964, also housed the North Dakota Geological Survey until the agency was moved to Bismarck in 1989. In 1991, the Department of Geology and Geological Engineering began awarding the A.G. Leonard Award in recognition of outstanding contributions to the field of geology by department alumni.

John A. Bownocker *(Ohio)*
Thomas M. Berg *(Ohio State Geologist, Honorary)*

John Adams Bownocker, fifth state geologist of the state of Ohio, was among the founders of the Association of American State Geologists. His participation in the 1908 founding of the Association came early in his 22-year career as state geologist (1906–28). He had considerable prior experience in the geology of Ohio, having come under the tutelage of Dr. Edward Orton Sr. at Ohio State University. After receiving his B.Sc. degree at Ohio State in 1889, he studied at the University of Chicago and at Yale, and returned to Ohio State, where he served as an assistant to Dr. Orton, Ohio's third state geologist. Bownocker received his D.Sc. from Ohio State University in 1897. He advanced along the academic track to the position of professor and chairman of the Department of Geology, a position that he held from 1918 to 1928. During his academic progress, he served as a geologic assistant for the Ohio and New Jersey surveys, and was appointed Ohio's state geologist in 1906.

John A. Bownocker was born near St. Paul in Fairfield County, Ohio, on March 11, 1865. Raised on the family farm 15 miles south of Columbus, he demonstrated a great thirst for knowledge. On hearing a lecture in his community by Dr. Edward Orton Sr., he resolved to attend the state university. After saving his money, he entered the preparatory department of Ohio State in the fall of 1883. Under the influence of Dr. Orton, Bownocker decided to enter the field of geology, and spent the rest of his career at OSU.

As state geologist of Ohio, Bownocker was clearly dedicated to unraveling as many aspects of the state's geology as he could for the people of Ohio. He accomplished a great deal in this quest—without sacrificing concerns for OSU and its students. This was a balancing act that many state geologists have had to face, but he did it well. In addition to balancing his academic and research activities, Bownocker gave significant and important attention to the relationship between the Ohio Geological Survey and its sister state surveys. In 1906, the very year he was appointed state geologist, he attended a seminal meeting of central U.S. state geological surveys at the University of Chicago, to help form an organization of Mississippi Valley state geologists, with the objective of collaboration and mutual support to advance the work of the surveys. In May of 1908, Dr. Bownocker traveled to Washington, D.C., to participate with 21 other state geologists in formation of the nationwide Association of American State Geologists.

In examining the early records of AASG, it appears that Bownocker was usually faithful in attending the meetings of the association, although he did miss a few gatherings. It does not appear that he ever served as an AASG officer—again a reflection of his pursuit of proper balance in his professional life. In 1923 and 1924 in particular, he worked very actively through AASG in support of the congressional Temple Bill on topographic mapping in the United States (HR 10057, introduced by Rep. Temple of Pennsylvania). He contacted members of the Ohio delegation seeking strong support of the Temple Bill and its appropriations for this important national effort. The hard work of Bownocker and his fellow state geologists is very reminiscent of AASG's efforts during the late 1980's and early 1990's in support of the National Geologic Mapping Act. Bownocker continued his strong and leading efforts for national topographic-mapping legislation until his death in 1928.

Dr. Bownocker devoted his professional career to teaching geology at OSU beginning in 1895, and administering the Department of Geology as its chairman from 1918 to 1928. Equal devotion was given to administering the Ohio Geological Survey and the work and contributions of students, former students, OSU faculty, and faculty from other universities. During much of his time as state geologist, Bownocker employed the services of Wilber Stout (who succeeded Bownocker as state geologist) and Raymond E. Lamborn—both outstanding Ohio geologists in their own right. In his memorial of Bownocker published by the Geological Society of America, Clinton Stauffer said,

> Much detailed work was planned and accomplished during his tenure as State Geologist. The results of this work were published in a series of twenty-five bulletins and several state maps. These publications deal with nearly every phase of geology and are particularly valuable in their dealings with the mineral resources of the State.

It is axiomatic that a good state geologist should be familiar with almost every aspect of his or her state's geology. Bownocker's list of publications shows very clearly that he was well armed to speak on almost any aspect of Ohio geology. Early on in his geological career, however, he became fascinated by oil and natural gas resources, Ohio's subsurface stratigraphy, and petroleum genesis. The majority of his publications focus on these subject areas. He also published on Ohio's glacial geology, paleontology, geomorphology, coal resources, industrial minerals, salt occurrences, building stones, molding sands, glass sands, and of considerable importance, geologic mapping of all kinds. The latter subject held high value for Bownocker, as it should for any state geologist. It was not until 2006 that Bownocker's 1920 statewide bedrock geologic map of Ohio was finally revised—a testimony to its high quality and lasting value.

Stauffer described John Bownocker's passing:

> In the latter part of February 1928, Dr. Bownocker underwent a serious operation, from which he only partially recovered. He was able to be at his office in Orton Hall part of the time, but he never resumed his teaching. During the late summer he grew steadily worse and died at his home on October 21, 1928.

It is a strange oversight that Stauffer does not mention AASG and Bownocker's activity in that association. Bownocker traveled to the AASG meeting in Washington, D.C., in late April of 1927. The number-one topic was appropriations for the Temple Bill. Bownocker also attended the December 30, 1927, meeting of the Association held in Cleveland, Ohio, and no doubt assisted in planning that meeting.

All can look to Bownocker in AASG's history as an outstanding state geologist who helped found the Association, and struck an exemplary balance among teaching, researching the geology of his home state, and service to AASG.

Richard Roberts Hice *(Pennsylvania)*
Clifford H. Dodge *(Pennsylvania Department of Conservation and Natural Resources)*

Richard Roberts Hice is remembered today primarily for his role as state geologist of the Third Geological Survey (or Commission) of Pennsylvania (1899–1919). Yet, as "a man of broad interests and a keen observer" (Ashley, 1926, p. 95), Hice was also an accomplished businessman, consulting geologist, and expert on the economic geology of western Pennsylvania. In addition, he was a strong conservationist. Hice was affiliated with several scientific and technical organizations, and devoted considerable attention to some. He loved geology and enjoyed research and writing; his work was published in a number of scientific journals. He also had a keen interest in other fields of science, such as astronomy. He traveled extensively in the United States, and maintained a winter home in Fort Myers, Fla., where he cultivated orange trees. Hice was known to many for his engaging personality and strong physique. Blue-eyed and fair-haired, he was described by Ashley (1926, p. 94) as having "a breezy, hearty manner that made him good company wherever he went."

The second child of Judge Henry and Ruth Ann (née Ralston) Hice, a prominent western Pennsylvania family, Richard Hice was born on August 19, 1865, in the town of Beaver—about 25 miles northwest of Pittsburgh. Sadly, Hice was only 7 when his mother died in 1872, though his father later remarried. Hice was a lifelong resident of Beaver. He was educated at local public schools and graduated from Geneva College, Beaver Falls, Pa., in 1886, with a baccalaureate in natural sciences. Held in high esteem for a very successful career, he was later awarded an honorary Sc.D. by his alma mater in 1913. Following graduation from college, Hice read law under his father, but discontinued his studies 6 months before completion. It was decided that he should pursue a career involving outdoor work, owing to health concerns (Ashley, 1926).

Hice initially worked for a fledgling natural gas company, but around 1891 joined the newly founded Fallston Fire Clay Co. located several miles north of Beaver. He held several supervisory and executive positions with this company until late 1909. The Fallston Fire Clay Co. specialized in the manufacture of face brick and mined its own clay from the "lower productive" coal measures (Middle Pennsylvanian Allegheny Formation). By 1890, Hice's enthusiasm for geology solidified, particularly as it pertained to western Pennsylvania. His earliest published research dealt with Pleistocene river terraces and preglacial drainage of the Beaver and Ohio River Valleys. Within a few years, he was a recognized expert on the local geology and clay occurrences of Beaver County (Hopkins, 1898, p. 6).

On April 12, 1893, Hice married May Kells in her hometown of Citra, Fla. Tragically, their first child was stillborn the following year. Thereafter, they had one daughter, Eva Kells Hice. During the 1890's, Hice joined the National Brick Manufacturers Association, an industry trade group. Just before the start of the 13th annual convention of the NBMA, held in Columbus, Ohio, in 1899, Hice attended the organizational meeting of the American Ceramic Society and became a charter member. The Society was initially a separate part of the NBMA, and its purpose was to promote scientific research in all fields of ceramics. Hice remained deeply committed to the Society and its principles throughout his life, and was elected its president for 1915–16.

By the end of the 19th century, the geology of the commonwealth had been investigated by both the First (1836–42, 1851–58) and Second (1874–95) Geological Surveys of Pennsylvania. Nevertheless, growing demand by the public for an accurate topographic map of the state and by business interests for more detailed information on the economic geology of western Pennsylvania compelled the Pennsylvania General Assembly to consider a Third Geological Survey. Thus, a bill was introduced in the state legislature, entitled "an act to authorize the topographic and geological survey of the State in co-operation with the United States Geological Survey." Signed into law by Gov. William A. Stone on April 28, 1899, Act 78 called for the governor to appoint a commission consisting of three unpaid citizens of the state, who would confer and negotiate with the U.S. Geological Survey to develop and implement a cooperative topographic and geologic mapping program. The commission would also provide oversight to protect and ensure state interests. Emphasis was on topographic mapping. The law allowed for the expenditure by the state of up to $20,000 per year for the first 2 years (the legislative biennial cycle), provided that the USGS spent an equivalent amount. Independent of this, the USGS also bore all the expenses for printing and publication. The three original commissioners of the Topographic and Geologic Survey Commission of Pennsylvania were George W. McNees, Simon Harrold, and Fred D. Barker, and they signed the cooperative agreement with Charles D. Walcott, director of the USGS, on July 12, 1899. With the death of Harrold in 1902, Hice was selected to replace him.

As time went on, Hice became the secretary and chief representative of the Commission. One of his important assignments resulted from President Theodore Roosevelt's growing national conservation movement. From May 13–15, 1908, the president convened a Conference of Governors at the White House to call attention to the management and use of the nation's natural resources. Just prior to the conference, state geologists met with the director and staff of the USGS in Washington, D.C., to discuss conservation issues, including the need for increased topographic mapping. Commissioner Hice represented the Topographic and Geologic Survey of Pennsylvania. Before the 2-day meeting ended on May 12, 1908, the state geologists also organized the Association of American State Geologists to achieve greater political clout through a unified voice on matters of common interest.

Much good work was accomplished by the USGS during the first few years of the Third Survey, including unprecedented quantitative geologic mapping in parts of western Pennsylvania and detailed reports on areal economic resources. (Other geologic mapping by the USGS was conducted in the eastern part of the state that was not part of the cooperative agreement.) Topographic surveys, involving many persons, resulted in dozens of 15-minute quadrangles being controlled and mapped. Some highlights and contributions of the Topographic and Geologic Survey Commission of Pennsylvania were discussed by Sevon (1987).

Though acknowledging the importance and success of the cooperative program with the USGS, the commissioners recognized the urgent need to create an independent and "permanent geological survey" at the state level to conduct geologic investigations. A state survey with a proper annual appropriation would ensure ongoing collection, analysis, dissemination, and preservation of detailed geologic information from throughout Pennsylvania and would encourage conservation in the mineral industries (Pennsylvania Geological Survey, 1911). The act creating the independent state geological survey was finally approved and signed into law on May 13, 1909.

The independent state survey operated under the purview of the Topographic and Geologic Survey Commission. The Commission now had the legislative authority to appoint a state geologist and selected one of its own—Richard Hice—who accepted the position in October 1909. Hice, by background and temperament, was a practical scientist and businessman and believed that "the primary purpose of a Geological Survey is the encouragement of the mineral production of the State" (Hice, 1912, p. 156). Hice maintained the office of state geologist in Beaver.

Unfortunately, thereafter, the Third Survey was chronically underfunded. The inadequate biennial appropriations of the legislature were further cut by successive governors "because of insufficient State revenue" (Pennsylvania Geological Survey, 1912, p. 22). No new cooperative geologic mapping was initiated. Cooperative topographic mapping continued on a reduced scale. Independent geologic work had to rely on Pennsylvania academicians and college upperclassmen, whose studies were often already under way prior to Survey involvement. The Third Survey could only afford to pay per diem wages and some field expenses. Other than for some clerical support, there was no money for permanent staff or full-time geologic assistants. Hice spent most of his time collecting and compiling geologic information and statistics in cooperation with the USGS, answering service requests, performing administrative duties, and editing and producing the various state reports.

In 1915, the appropriation bill for the Survey was vetoed by the governor, and the work of the Third Survey ceased on June 1. Little is known of Hice's activities during the next 2 years. He may have continued to function as state geologist for a while, but then probably became a consulting geologist to support his family. He was also more involved with the American Ceramic Society as its president for 1 year, though the work was largely ceremonial.

Funds for the Third Survey were restored during the 1917 legislative session. With the entry of the United States into World War I and the involvement of the USGS in the war effort, little cooperative work was accomplished in Pennsylvania over the next 2 years, however. Some additional independent state investigations were begun, but only one state geologic report was completed. Two years later, new legislation was passed and signed into law by the governor on June 7, 1919, creating the modern Fourth

Geological Survey of Pennsylvania, which was designated the Bureau of Topographic and Geologic Survey, initially in the Pennsylvania Department of Internal Affairs. The act also abolished the Topographic and Geologic Survey Commission, and Hice's formal tenure with the Survey came to an end.

Given the generally lukewarm support of the general assembly and the inadequate biennial appropriations, Hice and the Topographic and Geologic Survey Commission of Pennsylvania probably accomplished as much as could be expected. The total estimated cost of the Third Survey, excluding printing and publications, was $540,000 ($310,000 from the state and $230,000 from the USGS). The cooperative work with the USGS resulted in topographic-map coverage for 56 percent of the state (U.S. Geological Survey, 1919, p. 125). In addition, cooperative geologic mapping was initiated in 31 quadrangles; 27 of the resulting maps were published in folios before 1919. A number of associated economic bulletins were released as well. The USGS also mapped the geology of several other quadrangles on its own in southeastern, south-central, and western Pennsylvania. The Topographic and Geologic Survey Commission independently produced six progress reports and 12 numbered reports.

Hice showed no interest in applying for the office of state geologist in the new Survey, but urged quick action in filling the position so that the appointee could attend an upcoming AASG meeting. Nevertheless, Hice was asked to stay on as acting state geologist until his replacement was selected (Hice, 1919; McNees, 1919). In late August 1919, Dr. George H. Ashley was appointed first state geologist of the Fourth Geological Survey, and his employment began on September 1. Ashley (1919) asked Hice to finish his current Survey work before leaving, which involved the location and testing of sources of limestone aggregate in western Pennsylvania for the Highway Department. Hice completed his study in October 1919.

Hice spent the remainder of his career in private practice as a consulting geologist. He devoted much of his attention to the analysis and evaluation of natural gas reserves throughout the United States. In his work, he traveled frequently to Louisiana, Oklahoma, Texas, and West Virginia.

By 1922, Hice was in declining health, and the following year, he spent several months resting at his winter home in Florida to comply with doctor's orders (Hice, 1922, 1923). He continued to travel and consult extensively, however. Thus, friends and colleagues alike were surprised by his unexpected death at his home in Beaver on March 27, 1925. He was buried locally at the Beaver Cemetery. Hice was a charter member and former president of the American Ceramic Society and a fellow of the Geological Society of America. He was also a member of the Association of American State Geologists, American Institute of Mining Engineers, Engineers Society of Western Pennsylvania,

American Association for the Advancement of Science, and American Geographical Society. He was a lifelong member of the Presbyterian Church.

Virginia M. Caldwell and Kae H. Kirkwood, Geneva College, and Greg R. Geiger and Mark J. Mecklenborg, the American Ceramic Society, provided useful information and historical references that pertained to the life and career of Richard Roberts Hice.

Earle Sloan *(South Carolina)*
C. William (Bill) Clendenin
(South Carolina State Geologist)

Earle Sloan (1858–1926) was a native-born South Carolinian. His quick perceptive mind, strong inherent drive, and charismatic personality helped him to become a successful Charleston businessman, and a nationally recognized chemical, civil, and mining engineer. Early in his career, he gained renown for his painstaking field study of the 1886 Charleston earthquake. His professionalism resulted in his appointment as head of the South Carolina Geological Survey on May 1, 1901. He served in this position until 1911.

Sloan was born on Cherry Hill Plantation near Pendleton, S.C., on October 18, 1858. He was a descendant of the prominent Earle family of Virginia and South Carolina. His father served as a colonel in South Carolina's Fourth Regiment during the Civil War. Three of his great-grandfathers also fought in the Revolutionary War. Sloan attended country schools before his family moved to Charleston. In 1878, he enrolled at the University of Virginia, where his academic interests were toward chemistry and geology. Following his graduation in 1881, he pursued further graduate studies in chemistry and geology until 1882, but his career interests were in petrography, engineering, and mining.

In 1883 and 1884, Sloan worked as a mining consultant for the Norfolk and Ouray Mining Co. of Ouray, Colo. From 1884 to 1886, he was involved with exploration for iron and coal deposits in Alabama. Early in 1886, he formed a partnership with William H. Echols; together they built railroads, founded the town of Ensley, Fla., and prospected for minerals. The partnership disbanded in 1887.

When the Charleston earthquake struck on August 31, 1886, Sloan left his consulting business to study the impact of the earthquake. W.J. McGee, U.S. Geological Survey, met him in September 1886, and was so impressed with Sloan's credentials that McGee quickly recruited him as an assistant geologist to help in the study of the Charleston earthquake. Before McGee left South Carolina, he gave Sloan the assignment to carry out field studies of the epicenters of the earthquake. Sloan produced an acclaimed report for the USGS on October 16, 1886 (Peters, 1986). The University of Virginia was so impressed with his observations that it conferred a doctorate degree on him.

From 1888 to 1890, Sloan prospected for bauxite, iron, and coal in northwestern Georgia and Alabama. During this time, he became interested in phosphate deposits in South Carolina, which could be used as agricultural fertilizers. For the next two decades, Sloan played an instrumental role in the development of South Carolina's phosphate industry. During that period, he worked as a mine superintendent at one company and as president at another. Later he was a co-owner of the Etiwan Phosphate works.

In 1901, he became state geologist of South Carolina, a post he held until 1911. Because State appropriations were not enough, much of the field work that he conducted was at his own expense. Most of his work was on the Coastal Plain, but he did investigate the metamorphic rocks in the Piedmont. During his tenure as state geologist, Sloan discovered a number of previously unclassified fossils. Many of his specimens were personally donated to the Charleston Museum and to the Smithsonian Institution. He also wrote several valuable papers on clay, mineral resources, and different geologic formations. During this period, four of Sloan's reports were published by the State, the most complete of these being *Catalogue of the Mineral Localities of South Carolina*, published in 1908. His greatest contribution, however, was in his assistance to others by pointing out prominent exposures, helping to collect fossils, and providing information on mineral resources.

In his lifetime, Earle Sloan was involved in many different organizations. Professionally, he was a member of the American Association for the Advancement of Science, the American Museum of Natural History, the Association of American State Geologists, and the American Institute of Mining Engineers. Socially, he was a member of a number of clubs in Charleston. He succumbed to cancer on August 19, 1926, at the age of 68.

George Henry Perkins *(Vermont)*
Laurence R. Baker *(Vermont State Geologist)*

George Henry Perkins, born in Cambridge, Mass., in 1844, became the first professional to hold the position of state geologist of Vermont, and was appointed by Gov. Josiah Grout September 7, 1898, and reappointed each biennium by subsequent governors until he died in office September 12, 1933, at the age of 89. A petition in 1898 suggested Perkins for state geologist as "a man most eminently fitted by character, profession, and training" (Bassett, 1976, p. 20) for the job. Over 150 signatures, representing half the towns, and all the counties and principal villages of Vermont, had been gathered and given to the governor.

In the eyes of most Vermonters, the title of state geologist was honorific. No one deserved this honor more than Perkins, who had been interpreting popular science to rural Vermonters for a generation. Perkins steadily preached, at farmers' institutes all over the state and during the winter "short course" in agriculture on the campus of the University of Vermont, that the science provided at UVM could help the farmer.

He was a professional by his training, teaching, and research, although only a part-time geologist. He had graduate training as a natural scientist at the Sheffield Scientific School of Yale University. Perkins was a specialist in mollusks. His 1869 Ph.D. (the fifth ever granted by Yale) was accomplished with a thesis describing the snails and shellfish of the New Haven area. Since 1869 he had taught geology, along with other biological sciences, at the University of Vermont. He took the seniors on geological trips to Boston (1883) and New York (1884) and his geology class to Ausable Chasm. He had published, up to his appointment in 1898, five articles in the realm of earth science. Three were on Winooski marble, one on Illinois geodes, and one, in a field bordering meteorology and surficial geology, a short piece entitled "Notice of a Recent Landslide on Mount Passaconaway" (New Hampshire).

Besides being the first professional, Perkins established the Vermont Geological Survey as a continuing program of state government. The act of 1886 initiated the practice of publishing annual summaries of answers to a questionnaire, but his predecessor had only minimal cooperation from quarry and mine operators and did not publish a complete series. The act of 1896 asked for only one report, in 1898. Perkins, however, by delivering a 64-page report based on visits to 75 marble, granite, and slate quarries in less than 6 weeks after his commission was signed, showed that he was the man to keep on that job.

The state geologist did conceive of a systematic survey, and started one without special appropriations. The completion of 1:62,500-scale or 15-minute (1 inch to the mile) topographic maps of most of southern Vermont and the Lake Champlain strip by 1900, and most of the Champlain Valley by 1920, encouraged additional work on the west side of the state.

He was the center for the study of Vermont geology, and he put a good deal of his accumulated knowledge into his reports. A detailed, 70-page chronological summary of previous work, his third bibliography, appeared in his 1922 report. This shows which of his special studies appeared in the bulletins of the U.S. Geological Survey and in the learned journals. It also shows that both in quantity and quality the Vermont state geologist's report was the primary outlet for Vermont studies. Each report continued and expanded previous annual summaries of stone and mineral workings, referred to the testing of hundreds of ore samples, and to "the very large correspondence which [prevents] ... the office from being a sinecure" (Bassett, 1976, p. 23). Soon after the germ theory of disease spread from Europe in the 1880's, Dr. C.S. Caverly's Vermont Board of Public Health pioneered in raising public consciousness of the dangers of water pollution. To this movement Perkins contributed a landmark study, "The Drinking Waters of Vermont."

From about 1908 on, the state geologist tried to attend the meetings of the Geological Society of America, the Geological Section of the American Association for the Advancement of Science, and the Association of American State Geologists whenever they were near enough for his small budget to stand the expense. He attended at least five meetings of the AASG, from 1912 to 1921, all in the Northeast. As one of the senior geologists in the United States, he presided at the Christmas 1918 meeting of AAAS geologists in New York City, in the absence of the president. Perkins's 18 biennial reports were bound in covers of marble, for his first and last reports glorify the Vermont Marble Co., the producer most cooperative with the state geologist. His 1933 report on marble is an imposing volume of nearly 400 pages. One might wonder how a man laid up with rheumatism, lecturing to his students from his easy chair in the sun room, could have made the necessary investigations. It appears, however, to be his own compilation, updating the section of his first report by fitting together all the work of 35 years.

As geology was not his only interest, he had always done what seemed necessary at the moment, if it meant preparing four widely different courses, being helpful in answering letters, encouraging a boy curious about a rock, or gently promoting the theory of evolution. As his burdens were lifted, he became what he always wanted to be: a religious philosopher.

He was a peace-loving man, preeminently a conciliator, and a giver of approval. One professor who had known him on the faculty for 28 years wrote in the memorial issue of the University of Vermont *Alumni Weekly* that in all that time he had only once or twice heard Perkins speak a word of adverse criticism, and then in the gentlest tone of voice. One keeps such a man in office, who has found so much good in so many.

Biography adapted from Fleetwood (1902) and Bassett (1976).

Israel C. White *(West Virginia)*

Born on a farm in Monongalia County, W.Va., in 1848, Israel Charles White became a pioneer and leader in many ways. He was a member of the entering class of West Virginia University when it opened in 1867. He received his A.B. degree in 1872, an A.M. in 1875, and his Ph.D. from the University of Arkansas in 1880.

His early professional career began with the Second Survey of Pennsylvania (1875–84). He then worked as an assistant geologist for the U.S. Geological Survey between 1884 and 1888. His work with the Second Survey of Pennsylvania led to his becoming chair of geology at West Virginia University in 1876. The following year, he was appointed the first chairman of the newly formed Department of Geology, which was split from the Department of Natural Science. He left the department in 1892 to pursue full-time his work in a petroleum company that grew out of his research in oil occurrence.

White was appointed the first state geologist with the creation of the West Virginia Geological and Economic Survey in 1897. He directed the Survey until his death in 1927. Major accomplishments during his tenure included cooperative work with the U.S. Geological Survey to determine true meridians in every county, complete a set of topographic quadrangle maps covering the entire state, and establish gages on all principal rivers; and cooperative work with the U.S. Bureau of Soils to study, describe, and map soils in 48 of the 52 counties in the state.

The more than 22,000 pages of reports and maps published during the 30 years he directed the Survey stand as a testament to his energy and organization. Survey staff during this period averaged about 10 employees. Publications included 25 volumes describing the geology and mineral resources of 51 counties, and general volumes on oil and gas, coal, limestone and cement, clays, iron ores, salt, sandstones, forestry and wood industries, and the living and fossil flora of the state. The county reports with accompanying maps and data continue to be sold today, albeit in digital format.

In addition to his public and academic service, he worked as a geologic consultant for Hope Natural Gas Co. and the Baltimore and Ohio Railroad. During 1904–06, he made a survey of coal and oil resources in Brazil for that country's government. He was a speaker at the first White House Conference of State Governors on the subject of fuel conservation in 1908.

Instrumental in the founding of the Geological Society of America, he served as treasurer from 1892 to 1906 and president in 1920.

White is probably best known outside West Virginia as an early advocate of the anticlinal theory of oil accumulation. Although not the originator of the theory—he duly credited others for the idea—he tested the concept successfully with the drilling of the discovery well in the Mannington Oil Field in West Virginia. The effectiveness and role of the theory in development of the petroleum industry remains controversial to this day; nevertheless, it certainly was claimed as an important tool by the fledgling discipline of petroleum geology. White went on to become the second vice president and the third president of the new American Association of Petroleum Geologists.

Very active in the affairs of the AASG during its first two decades, White served as its second president from 1913 to 1915. He died in 1927 while still state geologist of West Virginia.

Biography adapted from Price (1963).

William Otis Hotchkiss *(Wisconsin)*
James M. Robertson *(Wisconsin State Geologist)*

William Otis Hotchkiss was born in Eau Claire, Wis., on September 17, 1878, the son of Lyman Palmer and Almeda (Smith) Hotchkiss. He was graduated from the University of Wisconsin with a B.S. in general engineering–geology (1903), a C.E. (1908), and a Ph.D. in economic geology (1916). He began his career in 1902 while still an undergraduate; his early professional work included mining engineering in Minnesota, construction engineering in Wisconsin, and minerals exploration in Ontario, Canada.

In 1906, Hotchkiss began work at the Wisconsin Geological and Natural History Survey, where he was put in charge of economic geology. From 1904 until 1907, Hotchkiss held a joint appointment as an instructor of mineralogy and petrography in the University of Wisconsin's Department of Geology. In addition to his economic geology responsibilities, Hotchkiss became chief of the Wisconsin survey's newly established Highway Division in 1907, and assistant state geologist in 1908. Hotchkiss was appointed state geologist in 1909, although E.A. Birge continued as director and superintendent. In 1919, Birge resigned from the Survey to take the job of president of the University of Wisconsin. Survey leadership responsibilities and titles were then consolidated, and Hotchkiss became state geologist, director, and superintendent.

During Hotchkiss's tenure at the Wisconsin survey, he was instrumental in the creation of a separate State Highway Commission that was formally created by the state legislature in 1911. He served on the commission from its inception and was secretary from 1911 to 1922 and chairman from 1923 to 1925. Hotchkiss supervised the writing and publication of many bulletins that dealt with the state's natural resources. He co-authored statutes directing the Survey to collect data for the evaluation of mines and mineral lands and to specifically assess the lead and zinc deposits of southwestern Wisconsin. He secured increased funding for topographic mapping. Hotchkiss authored or co-authored numerous Survey publications, including *Rural Highways of Wisconsin, Limestone Road Materials of Wisconsin, Geological and Road Map of Wisconsin, Mineral Land Classification,* and *Mineral Lands of Northern Wisconsin.*

Hotchkiss served on many state and federal committees and was a member of numerous professional societies. During World War I he was a member of the War Minerals Committee and spent considerable time in Washington, D.C., planning for the development of strategic and critical mineral supplies. He participated in the founding meeting of the Association of American State Geologists in May 1908. He was secretary-treasurer of AASG from 1915 to 1917, and served as president of that organization from 1918 to 1920. He was vice president of the Geological Society of America in 1937, and treasurer from 1945 to 1948. He also served as president of the Society of Economic Geologists in 1946.

In 1925, Hotchkiss resigned from the Wisconsin survey to accept the position of president of the Michigan College of Mining and Technology. Hotchkiss left Michigan in 1935 to become the president of Rensselaer Polytechnic Institute in Troy, N.Y. He retired from Rensselaer in 1943. He remained actively engaged in consulting work throughout North America until his death.

Hotchkiss married Edith Rachel Balsley on September 20, 1904, and they had three children. He died on June 20, 1954, while doing consulting work for the New Jersey Zinc Exploration Co. in Franklin, N.J.

References Cited

Ashley, G.H., 1919, Unpublished letter from George H. Ashley, State Geologist, Harrisburg, Pa., to Richard R. Hice, Beaver, Pa., September 5, 1919: Pennsylvania Geological Survey files, 2 p.

Ashley, G.H., 1926, Memorial of Richard R. Hice: Geological Society of America Bulletin, v. 37, p. 94–96.

Bassett, T.D.S., 1976, A history of the Vermont Geological Survey and state geologists: Vermont Geological Survey, p.

Brice, W.R., 1996, Gilbert Dennison Harris, a life with fossils: Bulletin of American Paleontology, v. 109, no. 350, 154 p.

Encyclopædia Britannica Online, 2005, Lane, Alfred Church:

Fisher, D.W., 1978, Laudable legacy: A synopsis of the titans of geology and paleontology, *in* New York state: New York State Geological Association, 50th annual field trip guidebook, p. 1–24.

Fleetwood, F.G., Secretary of State, 1902, Vermont legislative directory, biennial session, 1902: Biographical notes.

Hice, R.R., 1912, The mineral production of Pennsylvania: Pennsylvania Geological Survey, 3rd ser., Biennial Report 1910–12, Appendix G, p. 156–177.

Hice, R.R., 1919, Unpublished letter from Richard R. Hice, Beaver, Pa., to Hon. James F. Woodward, Secretary, Internal Affairs, Harrisburg, Pa., August [6], 1919: Pennsylvania Geological Survey files, 3 p.

Hice, R.R., 1922, Unpublished letter from Richard R. Hice, Beaver, Pa., to Dr. George H. Ashley, State Geologist, Harrisburg, Pa., June 28, 1922: Pennsylvania Geological Survey files, 2 p.

Hice, R.R., 1923, Unpublished letter from Richard R. Hice, Fort Myers, Fla., to Dr. George H. Ashley, State Geologist, Harrisburg, Pa., March 31, 1923: Pennsylvania Geological Survey files, 1 p.

Hopkins, T.C., 1898, Clays and clay industries of Pennsylvania: Pennsylvania State College, Annual Report 1897, 183 p.

Jackson School of Geosciences, 2006: www.jsg.utexas.edu/foundation/mem/sellards.html [accessed July 2006].

Kay, G.F., 1911, Samuel Calvin: Science, v. 34, no. 865, p. 106–107.

Landing, E., 2004, America's first science parks: John M. Clarke's scientific reservations [abs.]: Geological Society of America, Abstracts with Programs, v. 36, no. 2, p. 115.

Marler, L.A., 2001, Hail to "The Chief": No Standing News, v. 1, no. 82, p. 1–2.

Mathews, E.B., 1918, Maryland Geological Survey, v. 10, p. 37.

McNees, G.W., 1919, Unpublished letter from G.W. McNees, Kittanning, Pa., to Hon. James F. Woodward, Department of Internal Affairs, Harrisburg, Pa., August 9, 1919: Pennsylvania Geological Survey files, 1 p.

Moody, C.L., 1946, [Obituary of Albert Foster Crider]: American Association of Petroleum Geologists Bulletin, v. 30, no. 4, p. 633–639.

New York State Museum, 1926, In memoriam, John Mason Clarke: Twenty-first report of the director of the State Museum and Science Service: New York State Museum, Bulletin 267, p. 7–11.

Pennsylvania Geological Survey, 1911, Topographic and geologic survey, 1908–1910: Pennsylvania Geological Survey, 3rd ser., Biennial Report 1908–10, 104 p.

Pennsylvania Geological Survey, 1912, Topographic and Geological Survey of Pennsylvania, 1910–1912: Pennsylvania Geological Survey, ser. 3, Biennial Report 1910–12, 182 p.

Peters, K.E., 1986, biographic sketch of Earle Sloan, *in* Peters, K.E., and Hierrmann, R.B., eds., First-hand observations of the Charleston earthquake of August 31, 1886, and other earthquake materials: South Carolina Geological Survey, Bulletin 41, p. 41–43.

Price, P.H., 1963, The West Virginia Geological and Economic Survey—An inventory of progress, *in* Latimer, I.S., Jr., Ludlum, J.C., Welden, J.c., and Tucker, R.C., eds., West Virginia Geological and Economic Survey—Its accomplishments and outlook: West Virginia Geological and Economic Survey, v. 23, p. 1–30.

Sevon, W.D., 1987, The Third Geological Survey of Pennsylvania: The topographic years: Pennsylvania Geology, v. 18, no. 1, p. 16–22.

Socolow, A.A., ed., 1988, The state geological surveys: A history: Association of American State Geologists, 499 p.

Texas State Historical Association, 2006, Handbook of Texas online: www.tshaonline.org/handbook/online/articles/SS/fse17.html [accessed July 2006].

Thornton, H.J., 1947, Samuel Calvin: Iowa City, University of Iowa Press, 73 p.

Tufts University Digital Collections and Archives, 2007, Alfred Church Lane papers (MS127), biographical sketch

U.S. Geological Survey, 1919, Fortieth annual report of the director of the United States Geological Survey to the Secretary of the Interior for the fiscal year ended June 30, 1919: U.S. Geological Survey Annual Report 40, 200 p.

University of the State of New York, 1964, The New York State Museum, a short history: University of the State of New York, 31 p.

Weaver, H.D., 2001, The Chief: Big man; bigger mission: Missouri Resources, v. 17, no. 4, p. 3–8.

Wilson, C.W., 1981, State geological surveys and state geologists of Tennessee: A history of the development of the Division of Geology, Department of Conservation: Tennessee Division of Geology, 62 p.

Witzke, B.J., 1992, Samuel Calvin, pioneering geologist: Iowa Geology, no. 17, p. 5.

Appendix 4:
Historical Directory of State Geological Surveys
George F. Hanson
(Wisconsin State Geologist, Honorary; AASG Historian, 1961–72)

Preface

As an undergraduate I was blessed with a professor who had a keen interest in the historical development of geology in the United States, hence soon became acquainted with the outstanding accomplishments of the early state surveys and their directors. Upon becoming a state geologist myself it was apparent that many changes had taken place in state surveys since their beginning years.

The early state surveys were usually formed for a specific task, such as to "complete a study of the geology of the state." Once the task was completed, and indeed often before, the surveys were disbanded. Around the turn of the century the need for continuing geological work became evident and geological surveys became permanent units of state government, but over the years not only their missions changed to reflect the differing resources and needs of the various states, but also so did their affiliation in the governmental framework.

Upon being elected the historian of the Association of American State Geologists in 1961, I thought it would be of interest to my fellow state geologists to attempt to tabulate the changes in the titles of the organizations over the years, as well as the names, titles, and periods of tenure, of their directors; but although much had been written on the history of state surveys, and their contribution to American geology, it soon became apparent that not only was there inadequate published information to make the proposed tabulation, but also some of it was contradictory. Trying to use the publications of the state surveys as a primary source of information only magnified the confusion. I therefore took the easy way out and appealed to my fellow state geologists for help. Much correspondence flowed back and forth as it was found that the task was not as simple as first imagined. In 1962 a report was given to the Association at its annual meeting, and a revised report was presented in 1969. In 1972 a second revision was presented to the Association, at which time the members voted that it be printed.

I am therefore entirely indebted to my many colleagues for the information contained herein, and apologize for the inconsistencies in format and for some informational gaps that still persist. I trust that it will nonetheless serve as a useful reference for those interested in the growth and vicissitudes of state surveys.

In 2007, the Kentucky Geological Survey updated George Hanson's historical directory. As he pointed out, there are gaps and inconsistencies that still exist. We agree with him that the effort is worthwhile and should be again updated in the future.

Alabama
Geological Survey of Alabama

Michael Tuomey	State Geologist	1848–57
Eugene Allen Smith	State Geologist	1873–1927
Walter Bryan Jones	State Geologist	1927–61
Philip Elmer LaMoreaux	State Geologist	1961–76
Thomas Johnson Joiner	State Geologist	1976–81
Richard Nowlin Raymond	Acting State Geologist	1981–82
Ernest Anthony Mancini	State Geologist	1982–96
James Danny Moore	Acting State Geologist	1996
Donald Frederick Oltz	State Geologist	1996–2002
Berry H. (Nick) Tew Jr.	State Geologist	2002–present

Note: Although Tuomey was appointed state geologist in 1848, no funds were appropriated for the geological survey until 1854. During this period, Professor Tuomey conducted his work at the expense of the University of Alabama.

Alaska

Territorial Department of Mines

B.D. Stewart	Commissioner of Mines	1935–50
Leo Saarela	Commissioner of Mines	1950–52
Phil R. Holdsworth	Commissioner of Mines	1952–59

Division of Mines and Minerals, Department of Natural Resources

James A. Williams	Director	1959–70

Division of Geological Survey, Department of Natural Resources

James A. Williams	State Geologist	1970–71
William C. Fackler	State Geologist	1971-73
Donald Hartman	State Geologist	1973–75
Ross G. Schaff	State Geologist	1975–86
Robert B. Forbes	State Geologist	1987–90
Thomas E. Smith	State Geologist	1991–95
Milton A. Wiltse	State Geologist	1995–2002
Rodney A. Combellick	State Geologist	2003–January 2005
Mark D. Myers	State Geologist	February–October 2005
Robert F. Swenson	State Geologist	November 2005–present

Note: When Alaska attained statehood, Phil R. Holdsworth was appointed commissioner of the newly created Department of Natural Resources.

Arizona

Office of the Territorial Geologist (1888–90, 1898–1912)

John F. Blandy	Territorial Geologist	1888–90

University of Arizona Bureau of Mines

Theodore B. Comstock	Director	1893–95
William P. Blake	Director	1895–1905
William P. Blake	Territorial Geologist	1898–1904
Cyrus F. Tolman	Territorial Geologist	1911–12

Arizona Bureau of Mines

Charles F. Willis	Director	1913–18
Gurdon M. Butler	Director	1918–40
Thomas G. Chapman	Director	1940–56
James D. Forrester	Director	1956–70
William H. Dresher	Director	1971–78

Arizona Bureau of Mines and Mineral Technology

William H. Dresher	Director	1979–81
Richard A. Swalin	Director	1984–86
Larry D. Fellows	State Geologist and Assistant Director	1979–88

Arizona Geological Survey

Larry D. Fellows	State Geologist and Director	1989–2005
Rose Ellen McDonnell	Acting Director	2005
Jon E. Spencer	Acting Director	2005
M. Lee Allison	State Geologist and Director	2005–present

Source: Socolow, A.A., ed., 1988, Arizona, *in* The state geological surveys: A history: Association of American State Geologists, p. 14.

Arkansas

"First Survey" (Owen Survey)

David Dale Owen	State Geologist	1857–60

"The Civil War Years" (Geological Survey Activity Suspended) 1861–65

"Second Survey" (Reconstruction Surveys)

W.F. Roberts Sr.	State Geologist	1871–73
George Haddock	State Geologist	1873–74
William Hazeldine	State Geologist	January–June 1874
Arnold Syberg	State Geologist	June 1874–January 1875

"Branner Survey"

John C. Branner	State Geologist	1887–93
Albert H. Purdue	Ex officio State Geologist	1896–1912
N.F. Drake	Ex officio State Geologist	1912–20
Gilbert H. Cady	Ex officio State Geologist	1920–26

Geological Survey of Arkansas

George C. Branner	State Geologist	1923–42
Richard J. Anderson	Acting State Geologist	1942–43
Joe W. Kimzey	State Geologist	1943–45
Harold B. Foxhall	Director and State Geologist	1945–51
Norman F. Williams	Director and State Geologist	1951–55

Arkansas Geological and Conservation Commission

Norman F. Williams	Director and State Geologist	1955–63

Arkansas Geological Commission

Norman F. Williams	Director and State Geologist	1963–95
William Bush	Director and State Geologist	1995–2002
Mac B. Woodward	Director and State Geologis	2003–05
Rebecca C. White	Director and State Geologist	2005–07

Arkansas Geological Survey (effective 7/1/07)

Rebecca C. White	Director and State Geologist	2007–present

Note: Roberts was appointed in 1871 but in 1873 Gov. Hadley reported to the Assembly that Roberts returned to Pennsylvania "last July and I have not heard from him since."

From 1907–23 the professor of geology, University of Arkansas, acted ex officio as part-time state geologist. Office holders were A.H. Purdue, N.H. Drake, and G.H. Cady.

Natural Research Council bulletin (National Research Council, Comittee on State Geological Surveys, 1932, Summary information on the state geological surveys and the United States Geological Survey: Bulletin of the National Research Council, no. 88, 136 p.) gives name as "The Office of State Geologist" as opposed to Geological Survey of Arkansas.

California

"Trask Survey" or "First Geological Survey"

John B. Trask	State Geologist	1853–56

State Geological Survey of California

Josiah D. Whitney	State Geologist	1860–73

California State Mining Bureau

Henry G. Hanks	State Mineralogist	1880–86
William Irelan Jr.	State Mineralogist	1886–92
J.J. Crawford	State Mineralogist	1892–96
Augustus S. Cooper	State Mineralogist	1896–1901
Lewis E. Aubury	State Mineralogist	1901–11
William H. Storms	State Mineralogist	1911–13
Fletcher Hamilton	State Mineralogist	1913–23
Lloyd Root	State Mineralogist	1923–27

Division of Mines and Mining, Department of Natural Resources

Lloyd Root	State Mineralogist	1927–28
Walter H. Bradley	State Mineralogist	1928–29

Division of Mines, Department of Natural Resources

Walter H. Bradley	State Mineralogist	1929–46
W. Burling Tucker	Interim State Mineralogist	1946–47
Olaf P. Jenkins	State Mineralogist and Chief, Division of Mines	1947–58
Gordon B. Oakeshott	Interim State Mineralogist and Chief, Division of Mines	1958–59
Ian Campbell	State Mineralogist and Chief, Division of Mines	1959–61

Division of Mines and Geology, Department of Conservation

Ian Campbell	State Geologist and Chief, Division of Mines and Geology	1961–69
Wesley G. Bruer	State Geologist and Chief, Division of Mines and Geology	1969–73

James E. Slosson	State Geologist and Chief, Division of Mines and Geology	1973–75
Thomas E. Gay	Acting State Geologist and Chief, Division of Mines and Geology	1975–78
James F. Davis	State Geologist and Chief, Division of Mines and Geology	1978–2003
Michael S. Reichle	Acting State Geologist and Chief, Division of Mines and Geology	2003–05

California Geological Survey, Department of Conservation

John G. Parrish	State Geologist and Chief, California Geological Survey	2005–present

Note: Tucker was the last state mineralogist to be appointed directly by the governor, and served only 5 months as an honor for his long service to the Division. Jenkins through Slosson were appointed from eligible lists of Civil Service employees determined by competitive examinations. Later, permanent appointments were made by the director of the Department of Conservation from a list of candidates nominated by the State Mining and Geology Board, which is appointed by the governor.

The tenure dates given for Irelan, Crawford, and Cooper are those lettered on their portraits and are used as official dates by the California Geological Survey. However, U.S. Geological Survey Bulletin 465 lists their respective tenures as 1886–93, 1893–97, and 1897–1901 (personal communication, Mary Hill, 1967).

Between 1867–70 there were no appropriations to the Geological Survey, and Whitney carried on some work at his own expense.

During the period from Campbell's retirement in October 1969 and Bruer's temporary appointment in December of 1969, the Division operated without a state geologist. Administration of the Division at this time was assigned to John Mayfield, deputy director of the Department of Conservation. Bruer's permanent appointment as state geologist was made in September 1970.

Colorado

J. Alden Smith	State Geologist	1874–83
Ernest LeNeve Foster	State Geologist	1883–85
J. Alden Smith	State Geologist	1885–87
Fred J. Bulkley	State Geologist	1887–89
George E. Kedzie	State Geologist	1889–95
Thomas A. Rickard	State Geologist	1895–1901

| John W. Finch | State Geologist | 1901–06 |
| B.A. Langridge | State Geologist | 1906–07? |

State Geological Survey

| R.D. George | State Geologist | 1907–29 |

Geological Survey Division, Department of Natural Resources

John W. Rold	State Geologist and Director	1969-90
Vicki J. Cowart	State Geologist and Director	1992–2003
Vincent Matthews III	State Geologist and Director	2004–present

Note: The appointment of a state geologist was authorized by the Territorial Legislature in 1872, but "no compensation for services, nor for any expense whatever, shall be paid by the state to or for said State Geologist." It was not until the State Geological Survey was organized that funds became available and then not until 1908.

In 1929 the Colorado Geological Survey was reorganized with offices in the State Museum Building at Denver, and under the control of a board consisting of the governor, the commissioner of Mines, the president of the Colorado Mining Association, and the president of the University of Colorado, the Colorado School of Mines, and the College of Agriculture. This board dealt with cooperative U.S. Geological Survey programs; other geologic matters were handled by free cooperative services of other state organizations (National Research Council, Comittee on State Geological Surveys, 1932, Summary information on the state geological surveys and the United States Geological Survey: Bulletin of the National Research Council, no. 88, 136 p.). In 1968 the Colorado Geological Survey was reestablished as a division of the Department of Natural Resources, and in February 1969 John W. Rold was appointed state geologist and director. He retired in 1992.

In 1992, the Geological Survey was placed under the Division of Minerals and Geology. In 1993, Vicki J. Cowart was appointed state geologist. She resigned in 2003.

Vincent Matthews III was appointed state geologist in 2004. In 2005, the Colorado Geological Survey was removed from the Division of Minerals and Geology and made a co-equal division with the other eight divisions within the Department of Natural Resources.

Connecticut
"Geological and Mineralogical Survey"

| J.G. Percival | Geologist | 1835–41 |
| C.U. Shepard | Mineralogist | 1835–41 |

State Geological and Natural History Survey

William North Rice	Superintendent	1903–16
Herbert Ernest Gregory	Superintendent	1916–21
Henry Hollister Robinson	Superintendent	1921–25
Wilton Everett Britton	Superintendent	1925–39
Edward Leffingwell Troxell	Superintendent	1939–54
John Becker Lucke	Director	1954–60
Joe Webb Peoples	Director	1960–71

State Geological and Natural History Survey, Department of Environmental Protection

Hugo F. Thomas	Director and State Geologist	1972–89
Richard C. Hyde	Director and State Geologist	1989–97
Ralph S. Lewis	State Geologist	1997–2003
Margaret A. Thomas	Acting State Geologist	2006–present

Note: In 1959 the Geological and Natural History Survey was placed in a new Department of Agriculture and Natural Resources.

The Survey was located during the various tenures as follows: Rice at Wesleyan University; Gregory and Robinson at Yale; Britton at the Connecticut Agricultural Experiment Station; Troxell at Trinity College; Lucke at University of Connecticut; Peoples at Wesleyan. Percival and Shepard had no titles but were appointed as a committee to carry out the Survey.

Delaware
Geological and Mineralogical Survey

James C. Booth	State Geologist	1837–41

Delaware Geological Survey

Johan J. Groot	State Geologist	1951–69
Robert R. Jordan	State Geologist	1969–2003
John H. Talley	State Geologist	2003–present

Note: On February 18, 1837, the Delaware General Assembly passed a measure to "Procure to make (sic) a Geological and Mineralogical Survey of the State." Three commissioners were appointed to contract with a geologist and on June 1, 1837, they signed articles of agreement with James C. Booth, which established him as "State Geologist."

No separate autonomous agency was created beyond the commission and its appointee. Booth's appointment was to run "… as long as he is in the service of the State." Presumably, this terminated in January 1841, when he submitted his report to the commission.

The present organization was established by state law in 1951 as the Delaware Geological Survey. Jordan served as acting state geologist from July 1965 through June 1966, during a year-long leave of absence taken by Johan J. Groot.

Florida

Florida State Geological Survey

Elias H. Sellards	Director and State Geologist	1907–19
Herman Gunter	Director and State Geologist	1919–58
Robert O. Vernon	Director and State Geologist	1958–61

Division of Geology, State Board of Conservation

Robert O. Vernon	Director and State Geologist	1961–69

Bureau of Geology, Florida Department of Natural Resources

Robert O. Vernon	Chief and State Geologist	1969–71
Charles W. Hendry Jr.	Chief and State Geologist	1971-83

Florida Geological Survey, Florida Department of Natural Resources

Charles W. Hendry Jr.	Chief and State Geologist	1983–85
Walter Schmidt	Chief and State Geologist	1985–93

Florida Geological Survey, Florida Department of Environmental Protection

Walter Schmidt	Chief and State Geologist	1993–2007

Florida Geological Survey, Florida Department of Environmental Protection

Walter Schmidt	Director and State Geologist	2007–present

Note: Gen. Francis L. Dancy occupied the position of "State Engineer and Geologist" from 1852 to 1855; however, he had no staff. John Kost, a physician, made geologic reports to the governor for the state published in 1883 and 1886, but was never designated as state geologist. In 1907, legislation creating the Florida Geological Survey was passed designating its head as director and state geologist. With the 1961 reorganization of state government agencies, the Florida Geological Survey was subordinated to the Division of Geology, in the State Board of Conservation. The Division was organized into two sections for administrative purposes: (1) the Geological Survey and (2) the Oil and Gas Section, of which Vernon was administrator.

In 1969 the Florida state government was reorganized under a new constitution. The Division of Geology became the Bureau of Geology under the Department of Natural Resources; this included the Oil and Gas regulatory responsibilities. On December 3, 1971, Hendry was appointed chief of the Bureau of Geology and state geologist and replaced Dr. Vernon, who was appointed the director, Division of Interior Resources, Department of Natural Resources. In 1983 the title of "Florida Geological Survey" was again reestablished for the Bureau. In 1985, Walter Schmidt was appointed chief and state geologist upon Hendry being appointed director of the Division of Resource Management. In 2007 the Florida Geological Survey was reassigned within the Florida Department of Environmental Protection to report directly to the deputy secretary of Land and Recreation, renaming the head of the Florida Geological Survey as director. Oil and Gas responsibilities were reassigned to the Bureau of Mines and Mineral Resources within the Department of Environmental Protection.

Georgia (no response as of 7/25/07)

Geological Survey of Georgia

John R. Cotting	State Geologist	1836–40

Geological, Mineralogical and Physical Survey

George Little	State Geologist	1874–79

Geological Survey

J.W. Spencer	State Geologist	1890–93
W.S. Yeats	State Geologist	1893–1908

Georgia Geological Survey, Department of Forestry and Geological Development

Samuel W. McCallie	State Geologist	1932–33
Richard W. Smith	State Geologist	1933–37

Division of Mines, Mining, and Geology, Department of Natural Resources

Richard W. Smith	Director	1937–38
Garland Peyton	Director	1938–43

Department of Mines, Mining, and Geology, State Division of Conservation

Garland Peyton	Director	1943–64
A.S. Furcron	Acting Director	1964–65
A.S. Furcron	Director	1965–69
Jesse H. Auvil Jr.	Director	1969–72

Department of Natural Resources, Earth and Water Division, Geological Section

Sam M. Pickering Jr.	Division Director and State Geologist	1972

Idaho

Idaho Bureau of Mines and Geology

Francis A. Thomson	Secretary	1919–28
Ernest W. Ellis	Acting Secretary	1928
A.W. Fahrenwald	Secretary	1929–30
John W. Finch	Director	1930–34
A.W. Fahrenwald	Director	1934–54
J.D. Forrester	Director	1954–56
E.F. Cook	Director	1956–64
Rolland R. Reid	Acting Director	1963–65
Rolland R. Reid	Director	1965–74
Maynard M. Miller	Director	1975–84

Idaho Geological Survey

Maynard M. Miller	Director and State Geologist	1984–87
Robert W. Bartlett	Director	1987–97
Earl H. Bennett	State Geologist	1987–97
Earl H. Bennett	Director and State Geologist	1997–2003
Roy M. Breckenridge and Kurt L. Othberg	Directors	2003–present
Roy M. Breckenridge	State Geologist	2003–present

Note: Cook was on leave of absence 1963–64.

Illinois

Geological Survey of Illinois

Joseph G. Norwood	State Geologist	1851–58
Amos H. Worthen	Director	1858–75

State Historical Library and Natural History Museum

Amos H. Worthen	Curator	1877–88
Joshua Lindahl	Curator	1888–93
W.F.E. Gurley	Curator	1893–97

State Geological Survey, State Geological Commission

H. Foster Bain	Director	1905–09
Frank W. De Wolf	Director	1909–17

State Geological Survey, Board of Natural Resources and Conservation

Frank W. De Wolf	Chief	1917–23
Morris M. Leighton	Chief	1923–54
John C. Frye	Chief	1954-74
Jack A. Simon	Chief	1974–81
Robert E. Bergstrom	Chief	1981–83
Morris W. Leighton	Chief	1983–94
Jonathan H. Goodwin	Acting Chief	1994–95
William W. Shilts	Chief	1995–present

Note: All provision for Worthen's survey ended in 1875; however, an act was passed in 1885 that volume VIII of the Geological Survey of Illinois be prepared by "the Curator of the State Historical and Natural History Museum, who is required to perform such duties as may be by law required of the State Geologist." Lindahl, who completed this task in 1890 following Worthen's death in 1888, was in fact listed as state geologist on the title page.

Indiana

David Dale Owen	Appointed Geologist of the State of Indiana	1837–39
Ryland Thomas Brown	Served as Geological Agent for the State Board of Agriculture	1851–53

| David Dale Owen | Recommissioned to make Second Survey. Died in 1860. | 1859–60 |
| Richard Owen | Brother of D.D. Owen and Principal Assistant with the Survey State Geologist | 1859–60 1860–61 |

Geological Survey of Indiana

| Edward Travers Cox | State Geologist | 1869–79 |

Indiana Department of Statistics and Geology

| John Collett | Chief of Bureau | 1879–81 |

Indiana Department of Geology and Natural History

John Collett	State Geologist	1881–84
James Maurice Thompson	State Geologist	1885–88
Sylvester Scott Gorby	State Geologist	1888–89

Indiana Department of Geology and Natural Resources

Sylvester Scott Gorby	State Geologist	1889–94
Willis Stanley Blatchley	State Geologist	1895–1910
Edward Barrett	State Geologist	1910–18

Division of Geology, Indiana Department of Conservation

William Newton Logan	State Geologist	1919–36
Ralph Emerson Esarey	State Geologist	1936–45
Charles Frederick Deiss	State Geologist	1945–51

Geological Survey, Indiana Department of Conservation

| Charles Frederick Deiss | State Geologist | 1951–59 |
| John Barratt Patton | State Geologist | 1959–65 |

Geological Survey, Indiana Department of Natural Resources

| John Barratt Patton | State Geologist | 1965–86 |
| Norman Curtis Hester | State Geologist | 1986–92 |

Geological Survey, Indiana University

Norman Curtis Hester	State Geologist	1992–98
John Charles Steinmetz	State Geologist	1998–present

Iowa
Geological Survey of Iowa

James Hall	State Geologist	1855–59

State Geological Survey

Charles A. White	State Geologist	1866–69

Iowa Geological Survey

Samuel Calvin	State Geologist and Director	1892–1904
Frank A. Wilder	State Geologist and Director	1904–06
Samuel Calvin	State Geologist and Director	1906–11
George F. Kay	State Geologist and Director	1911–34
Arthur C. Trowbridge	State Geologist and Director	1934–47
H. Garland Hershey	State Geologist and Director	1947–69
Samuel J. Tuthill	State Geologist and Director	1969–75
Stanley C. Grant	State Geologist and Director	1975–80
Donald L. Koch	State Geologist and Director	1980–2002
Robert D. Libra	State Geologist and Director	2002–present

Kansas
(First) State Geological Survey of Kansas

Benjamin F. Mudge	State Geologist	1864–65

(Second) State Geological Survey of Kansas

George C. Swallow	State Geologist	1865–66

University Geological Survey of Kansas

Erasmus Haworth	State Geologist	1895–1907

State Geological Survey of Kansas

Erasmus Haworth	State Geologist and Director	1907–15
William H. Twenhofel	State Geologist and Director	1915–16
Raymond C. Moore	State Geologist and Director	1916
	State Geologist	1917–37
	State Geologist and Director	1937–45
	State Geologist and Director of Research	1945–54
Kenneth K. Landes	Assistant State Geologist	1927–37
	Co-State Geologist and	
	Assistant Director	1937–41
John C. Frye	Assistant State Geologist and	
	Assistant Director in Charge	1941–45
	Executive Director	1945–52
	State Geologist and Executive Director	1952–54
Frank C. Foley	State Geologist and Director	1954–70
William W. Hambleton	Assistant State Geologist	
	and Assistant Director	1955–56
	Associate State Geologist and	
	Associate Director	1956–70
Paul C. Franks	Acting Associate State Geologist	
	and Acting Associate Director	1959–60
Paul L. Hilpman	Assistant Director and	
	Assistant State Geologist	1964–65
Ernest E. Angino	Associate State Geologist and	
	Associate Director	1970–72
Charles K. Bayne	Associate State Geologist and	
	Associate Director	1972–
William W. Hambleton	State Geologist and Director	1970–86
Lee C. Gerhard	State Geologist and Director	1986–99
M. Lee Allison	State Geologist and Director	1999–2004
William Harrison	State Geologist and Director	2004–present

Note: The third survey was formally established in 1889 by the state legislature as the University Geological Survey of Kansas. No appropriation was made and no personnel named until 1895 when the University of Kansas Board of Regents declared the Survey to be organized. Although Haworth is listed as state geologist of the University Geological Survey from 1895–1907, reflecting his leadership, no formal appointment was made until 1903.

Landes and Frye at times held the title of state geologist concurrently with Moore. Landes was co-state geologist from 1937 to 1941. Moore was on military leave from 1942–45, during which time Frye was in charge of the Survey. After Moore's return, Frye was executive director, and Moore was state geologist and director of research. In 1945, Frye gained the additional title of state geologist.

Franks was acting associate state geologist and acting associate director while Hambleton was on sabbatical leave. Hilpman served as assistant director and assistant state geologist while Foley was on leave.

Kentucky

| William W. Mather | State Geologist | 1838 |

Kentucky Geological Survey

| David Dale Owen | State Geologist | 1854–57 |
| Nathaniel S. Shaler | State Geologist and Director | 1873–80 |

Kentucky Geological Survey and Bureau of Immigration

| John R. Proctor | State Geologist and Director | 1880–92 |

Kentucky Geological Survey

| Charles J. Norwood | Director | 1904–12 |
| Joseph B. Hoeing | State Geologist | 1912–18 |

Department of Geology and Forestry

| Joseph E. Barton | Commissioner | 1918–19 |
| Willard R. Jillson | Deputy Commissioner and State Geologist | 1919–20 |

Kentucky Geological Survey

| Willard R. Jillson | Director and State Geologist | 1920–32 |

Bureau of Mineral and Topographic Survey, University of Kentucky

| Arthur C. McFarlan | Director and State Geologist | 1932–34 |

Division of Geology, Department of Mines and Minerals

| Daniel J. Jones | State Geologist | 1948–58 |

Kentucky Geological Survey, University of Kentucky

Arthur C. McFarlan	Director	1948–58
Wallace W. Hagan	Director and State Geologist	1958-78
Donald C. Haney	State Geologist and Director	1978–99
James C. Cobb	State Geologist and Director	1999–present

Note: David Dale Owen left Kentucky to become state geologist of Arkansas. Robert Peter, state chemist, brought manuscripts to completion and saw them through press. This survey was therefore probably active until about 1860.

Louisiana

Topographical and Geological Survey of Louisiana

Frederick V. Hopkins	State Geologist	1869–72

Geological and Agricultural Survey of Louisiana

Otto Lerch	Geologist in Charge	1892
	State Geologist	1893
William W. Clendenin	Geologist	1894–97
Gilbert D. Harris	Geologist in Charge	1899–1902

Geological Survey of Louisiana

Gilbert D. Harris	Geologist in Charge	1903–09

Louisiana Soil and Geological Survey

Frederick E. Emerson	Geologist	1914–19

Bureau of Scientific Research, Minerals Division, Department of Conservation

Cyril K. Moresi	Geologist	1931–34

Louisiana Geological Survey

Cyril K. Moresi	State Geologist	1934–40
John Huner Jr.	State Geologist	1940–46
Paul Montgomery	Acting State Geologist	April–December 1946
James M. Cunningham	Acting State Geologist	December 1946–July 1947
Gerard O. Coignet	Acting Director	July–October 1947
Leo W. Hough	State Geologist	1947–77
Harry L. Roland, Jr.	Assistant State Geologist	February 1977–July 1978
Charles G. Groat	Director and State Geologist	July 1978–July 1990
John E. Johnston III January 1992	Acting State Geologist	August 1990–
Charles G. Groat	Director and State Geologist October 1992	February 1992–

| William E. Marsalis | Director and State Geologist | November 1992– September 1997 |
| Chacko J. John | Director and State Geologist | October 1997–present |

Note: Clendenin was professor of mineralogy at Louisiana State University and served half-time as geologist for the Survey. Dr. Emerson was professor of geology at Louisiana State University and died in 1919. The University was without a geologist until the arrival of Henry V. Howe in 1922. All geological matters were handled by Dr. Howe until the present Survey was established in 1934.

Charles G. Groat went on leave from August 1990–January 1992, during which time John E. Johnston III, who was the Louisiana Geological Survey deputy director, served as acting state geologist.

Maine

Geological Survey, Massachusetts Bay Colony and State of Maine

| Charles T. Jackson | Geologist | 1836–38 |

Maine Board of Agriculture

| Charles H. Hitchcock | Geologist | 1861–62 |

Topographic Survey Commission

| Leslie A. Lee | State Geologist | 1903–05 |

State Survey Commission

Leslie A. Lee	State Geologist	1905–08
Franklin C. Robinson	State Geologist	1908–10
C. Vey Holman	State Geologist	1910–11

State Geologist

| Freeman F. Burr | State Geologist | 1914–16 |

Maine Public Utilities Commission

| Freeman F. Burr | Geologist | 1916–19 |

Maine Water Power Commission

| Freeman F. Burr | Geologist | 1919–20 |

Geological Survey

Lucius H. Merrill	State Geologist	1929–31
Joseph Conrad Twinem	State Geologist	1931–32
Freeman F. Burr	State Geologist	1937–42

Maine Geological Survey, Maine Development Commission

Joseph M. Trefethen	State Geologist	1942–52

Maine Geological Survey, Department of Development of Industry and Commerce

Joseph M. Trefethen	State Geologist	1953–56
John R. Rand	State Geologist	1956–57

Maine Geological Survey, Department of Economic Development

John R. Rand	State Geologist	1957–59
Robert G. Doyle	State Geologist	1959–71

Maine Geological Survey, Maine Forest Service

Robert G. Doyle	State Geologist	1971–73

Maine Geological Survey, Maine Department of Conservation

Robert G. Doyle	State Geologist	1973–79
Walter A. Anderson	State Geologist	1979–95
Robert G. Marvinney	State Geologist	1995–present

Maryland

J.T. Ducatel	Geologist	1834–42
James Higgins	State Agricultural Chemist	1848–58
Philip T. Tyson	State Agricultural Chemist	1858–62

Maryland Geological Survey (Geological and Economic Survey)

William Bullock Clark	State Geologist	1896–1917
Edward Bennett Mathews	State Geologist	1917–41

Department of Geology, Mines and Water Resources

Edward Bennett Mathews	Director	1941–43
Joseph T. Singewald Jr.	Director	1943–62
Ernst Cloos	Acting Director	1962–63
Kenneth N. Weaver	Director	1963–64

Maryland Geological Survey

Kenneth N. Weaver	Director	1964-92
Emery T. Cleaves	Director	1992–2006
Jeffrey P. Halka	Acting Director	2007–present

Note: The Maryland Geological Survey operated under that name from 1896–1917, although it was established by the legislature as the Geological and Economic Survey.

Massachusetts

First and Second "Survey of the Geology and Natural History of Massachusetts"

Edward Hitchcock	"Geological Surveyor"	1830–33
Edward Hitchcock	"Geological Surveyor"	1837–39

Department of Public Works

Joseph A. Sinnott	State Geologist	1971-92

Executive Office of Environmental Affairs

Richard N. Foster	State Geologist	1992–2002

University of Massachusetts

Stephen B. Mabee	State Geologist	2002–present

Note: The dates of Hitchcock's official tenure are somewhat in doubt.

Michigan

"First Geological Survey"

Douglass Houghton	State Geologist	1837–45

"Second Geological Survey"

Alexander Winchell	State Geologist	1859–62

Michigan Geological and Biological Survey

Alexander Winchell	State Geologist	1869–71
Carl L. Rominger	State Geologist	1871–85
Charles E. Wright	State Geologist	1885–88
M.E. Wadsworth	State Geologist	1888–93
Lucius L. Hubbard	State Geologist	1893–99
Alfred C. Lane	State Geologist	1899–1909
Rollan C. Allen	State Geologist	1909–19
Richard A. Smith	State Geologist	1919–20

Geological Survey Division, Department of Conservation

Richard A. Smith	Division Chief and State Geologist	1920–46
Gerald E. Eddy	Division Chief and State Geologist	1946–51
Franklin G. Pardee	Division Chief and State Geologist	1951–52
William L. Daoust	Acting State Geologist and Division Chief	1952–54
William L. Daoust	Division Chief and State Geologist	1954–64

Geological Survey Division, Department of Natural Resources

Gerald E. Eddy	Division Chief and State Geologist	1964–71
Arthur E. Slaughter	Division Chief and State Geologist	1971–81
R. Thomas Segall	Division Chief and State Geologist	1981–96

Geological Survey Division, Department of Environmental Quality

Harold R. Fitch	Division Chief and State Geologist	1996–2002

Geological and Land Management Division, Department of Environmental Quality

Harold R. Fitch	Division Chief and State Geologist	2002–04

Office of Geological Survey, Department of Environmental Quality

Harold R. Fitch	Office Director and State Geologist	2004–present

Minnesota

A.H. Hanchett	State Geologist	1864–65
H.H. Eames	State Geologist	1865–67

Minnesota Geological and Natural History Survey

Newton Horace Winchell	Director	1872–1900

Minnesota Geological Survey

William Harvey Emmons	Director	1911–44
Frank Fitch Grout	Director	1944–46
George Melvin Schwartz	Director	1946–61
Paul Kibler Sims	Director	1961–73
Matt Savage Walton	Director	1973–86
Priscilla C. Grew	Director	1986–93
David L. Southwick	Director	1993–2002
L. Harvey Thorleifson	Director	2003–present

Mississippi

Agricultural and Geological Survey of the State

John N. Millington	Chief Geologist	1850–53
John C. Keeney	State Geologist	1853–54
Lewis Harper	State Geologist	1854–57
Eugene Woldemar Hilgard	State Geologist	1858–66
George Little	State Geologist	1866–70
Eugene Woldemar Hilgard	State Geologist	1870–72
William Newton Logan	State Geologist	1903–05 *(unofficial)*

Mississippi Geological Survey

Albert Foster Crider	State Geologist	1906–09
Ephraim Noble Lowe	State Geologist	1909–33
William Clifford Morse	State Geologist	1934–58

Mississippi Geological, Economic and Topographical Survey

Tracy Wallace Lusk	State Geologist	1958–62
Frederic Francis Mellen	Director and State Geologist	1962–65
William Halsell Moore	Director and State Geologist	1965-80
Alvin Raymond Bicker Jr.	Acting Director and State Geologist	February 1980–April 1, 1980
Alvin Raymond Bicker Jr.	Director and State Geologist	1980–86
Edwin Ellis Luper	Acting Director and State Geologist	July 1986–May 5, 1987
Conrad A. Gazzier	Director and State Geologist	1987–90
Charles E. Clevenger	Acting Director and State Geologist	January 1990–July 1990
Samuel Cragin Knox	Director and State Geologist	1990–2004
Michael B.E. Bograd	Acting Director and State Geologist	July 2004–June 2006
Michael B.E. Bograd	Director and State Geologist	2006–present

Missouri

Geological Survey of Missouri

G.C. Swallow	State Geologist	1853–61

Missouri Bureau of Geology and Mines

A.D. Hager	State Geologist	1870–71
Joseph G. Norwood	Temporary State Geologist	August–November 1871
Raphael Pumpelly	State Geologist	1871–73
G.C. Broadhead	State Geologist	1873–75
C.P. Williams	State Geologist	1875–78

Missouri Bureau of Geology and Mines

Arthur Winslow	State Geologist and Director	1889–93
C.R. Keyes	State Geologist and Director	1893–97
J.A. Gallaher	State Geologist and Director	1898–1900

Leo Gallaher	Acting State Geologist and Acting Director	1900–01
E.R. Buckley	State Geologist and Director	1901–08
Henry A. Buehler	State Geologist and Director	1908–33

Missouri Geological Survey and Water Resources

Henry A. Buehler	State Geologist and Director	1933–44
E.L. Clark	State Geologist and Director	1944–45

Missouri Division of Geological Survey and Water Resources, Department of Business and Administration

E.L. Clark	State Geologist and Director	1945–55
Thomas R. Beveridge	State Geologist and Director	1955–64
William C. Hayes	State Geologist and Director	1964–71
Wallace B. Howe	State Geologist and Director	1971–74

Division of Geology and Land Survey, Department of Natural Resources

Wallace B. Howe	State Geologist and Director	1974–86
James H. Williams	State Geologist and Director	1986–2000
Mimi R. Garstang	State Geologist and Director	2000–present

Montana

Montana Bureau of Mines and Geology

Charles H. Clapp	Director	1919–21
George W. Craven	Director	1921–28

Montana Bureau of Mines and Geology

Francis A. Thomson	Director	1928–50
Arthur E. Adami	Director	1950–51
J. Robert Van Pelt	Director	1951–56
Walter S. March Jr.	Associate Director	1956–62
Edwin G. Koch	Director	1957–69
Uuno M. Sahinen	Associate Director	1962–69
Uuno M. Sahinen	Director and State Geologist	1969–71

Sid Groff	Acting Director and State Geologist	1971–72
	Director and State Geologist	1972–82
Edward C. Bingler	Director and State Geologist	1982–84
Henry McLernan	Acting Director and State Geologist	1984–86
Edward T. Ruppel	Director and State Geologist	1986–94
John C. Steinmetz	Director and State Geologist	1994–98
Edmond G. Deal	Director and State Geologist	1998–present

Note: The Montana Bureau of Mines and Geology was established in 1919 as the Montana State Bureau of Mines and Metallurgy, a department in the Montana State School of Mines (now Montana Tech of the University of Montana). Originally, the president of the School of Mines was designated as the director of the Bureau; however, his responsibilities did not necessarily coincide with those of a "state geologist." Thus, during the period 1957 to 1969, the associate director was in effect the "state geologist." During the 1969 legislature, a bill was enacted that made the director of the Bureau the state geologist and required that said director be either a certified professional geologist or a registered mining engineer.

Nebraska

Nebraska Geological Survey

Samuel Aughey	State Geologist	1871–83
Lewis E. Hicks	State Geologist	1884–90
Erwin H. Barbour	State Geologist	1891–1918
George E. Condra	State Geologist	1919–21

Conservation and Survey Division, University of Nebraska

George E. Condra	State Geologist	1921–53
Eugene C. Reed	Director and State Geologist	1954–67
Vincent. H. Dreeszen	Director and State Geologist	1968-87
Perry B. Wigley	State Geologist and Director	1987-98
Mark S. Kuzila	State Geologist and Director	1998-present

Note: Samuel Aughey was chairman of the Department of Natural Sciences at the University of Nebraska from 1871–85 and acted as unofficial "state geologist."

Byron P. Russell was hired as a "geologist" by the State during the drilling of a well at Lincoln, 1885–89.

In National Research Council Bulletin 88 (National Research Council, Comittee on State Geological Surveys, 1932, Summary information on the state geological surveys and the United States Geological Survey: Bulletin of the National Research Council, no. 88, 136 p.), Condra reported that Barbour was appointed acting state geologist in 1891, that the Survey was created in 1893, and organized into its existing form in 1919.

Nevada

Office of the State Geologist

Created by the Nevada legislature in its first session, in 1865, but the position was not filled.

Office of the State Mineralogist

R.H. Stretch	State Mineralogist	1866
A.F. White	State Mineralogist	1867–70
H.R. Whitehill	State Mineralogist	1871–78

School of Mining and Mackay School of Mines at the University of Nevada

Robert D. Jackson	Director	1888–99
Charles P. Brown	Director	1899
George J. Young	Director	1900–14
Francis Church Lincoln	Director	1914–24
John A. Fulton	Director	1924–39
Jay A. Carpenter	Director	1939–51
Vernon E. Scheid	Dean	1951–72
Arthur Baker III	Dean	1973–84
James V. Taranik	Dean	1984–87

State Analytical Laboratory

Robert D. Jackson	Director	1895–99
Charles P. Brown	Director	1899
George J. Young	Director	1900–14
Francis Church Lincoln	Director	1914–24
Walter S. Palmer	Director	1924–51

Nevada Bureau of Mines

John A. Fulton	Director	1929–39
Jay A. Carpenter	Director	1939–51
Vernon E. Scheid	Director	1951–71

Nevada Bureau of Mines and Geology

Vernon E. Scheid	Director	1971–72
John H. Schilling	Director/State Geologist	1973–87
Jonathan G. Price	Director/State Geologist	1988–present

Note: The School of Mining was named the Mackay School of Mines in 1906. The School's name was changed to the Mackay School of Earth Sciences and Engineering in 2004. The Nevada Bureau of Mines and Geology is managed as a research and public service unit of the School. Until 1973, the director or dean of the Mackay School of Mines was also the director of the Nevada Bureau of Mines or its predecessor, the State Analytical Laboratory. Deans of the Mackay School of Mines since 1987 included Richard Bradt, James L. Hendrix, and Jane C.S. Long. James V. Taranik, who served as president of the Desert Research Institute from 1987 until 1998, when he returned to the University as a Regents Professor and Arthur Brant Chair of Geophysics, was called back into service as the acting dean of the Mackay School of Mines in 2003 and became the first director of the Mackay School of Earth Sciences and Engineering in 2004.

The State Analytical Laboratory was created by the Nevada legislature in 1895 as a public service unit of the School of Mining. The Nevada Bureau of Mines was created by the Nevada legislature in 1929 as a separate public service unit of the University of Nevada. The State Analytical Laboratory became part of the Nevada Bureau of Mines in 1972. From 1960 through 1972, although the director of the Bureau was also the director of the Mackay School of Mines, the Bureau was administered by an associate director. Associate directors included S.E. Jerome (1960–65), Robert C. Horton (1965–67), Arthur Baker III (1967–72), and John Shilling (1972–73).

The Nevada Bureau of Mines and Geology was given its current name by the Nevada legislature in 1971. James V. Taranik served as acting director of the Bureau between May 1987 and July 1987, James L. Hendrix served as acting director from July 1987 through August 1988, and Larry J. Garside served as acting associate director from May 1987 through August 1988. Harold F. Bonham Jr. was the acting director from February 1993 to February 1995, while Jonathan Price was on loan from the University of Nevada–Reno to the National Research Council in Washington, D.C., where he served as the staff director of the Board on Earth Sciences and Resources.

New Hampshire
"Geological and Mineralogical Survey of the State"

Charles T. Jackson	State Geologist	1839–44
Charles H. Hitchcock	State Geologist	1868–78
James W. Goldthwaite	State Geologist	1917–37

New Hampshire Department of Resources and Economic Development, Division of Economic Development, Office of the State Geologist

Theodore R. Meyers	State Geologist	1942–63
Glenn W. Stewart	State Geologist	1963–81
Robert I. Davis	State Geologist	1981–84
Lincoln R. Page	State Geologist	1984–85

New Hampshire Department of Environmental Services, Office of the State Geologist

Eugene L. Boudette	State Geologist	1986–2000

New Hampshire Department of Environmental Services, New Hampshire Geological Survey

David R. Wunsch	State Geologist	2000–present

Note: The first geological survey of New Hampshire commenced in 1839 as ordered by Gov. John Page. The formal office of state geologist was created May 9, 1967. The New Hampshire Geological Survey was statutorily established June 19, 2001.

New Jersey

"Rogers Survey"

Henry D. Rogers	State Geologist	1835–40

"Kitchell Survey"

William Kitchell	State Geologist	1854–56

Geological Survey of New Jersey

George H. Cook	State Geologist	1864–89
John C. Smock	State Geologist	1889–1901
Henry B. Kummel	State Geologist	1901–15

Division of Geology and Waters, Department of Conservation and Development

Henry B. Kummel	State Geologist	1915–25

Division of Geology and Topography, Department of Conservation and Development

Henry B. Kummel	State Geologist	1925–37
Meredith E. Johnson	State Geologist and Chief of Division of Geology and Topography	1937–47

Bureau of Geology and Topography, Division of Planning and Development, Department of Conservation and Economic Development

Meredith E. Johnson	State Geologist and Chief, Bureau of Geology and Topography	1947–58
Kemble Widmer	State Geologist and Chief, Bureau of Geology and Topography	1958–61

Bureau of Geology and Topography, Division of Resource Development, Department of Conservation and Economic Development

Kemble Widmer	State Geologist and Chief, Bureau of Geology and Topography	1961–71

Bureau of Geology and Topography, Division of Water Resources, Department of Environmental Protection

Kemble Widmer	State Geologist and Chief, Bureau of Geology and Topography	1971–81
Frank Markewicz	Acting State Geologist and Chief, Bureau of Geology and Topography	1981–83

Geological Survey Element, Division of Water Resources, Department of Environmental Protection

Haig F. Kasabach	Deputy and Acting State Geologist	1983–85
Haig F. Kasabach	State Geologist	1985–92

Geological Survey, Division of Science and Research, Department of Environmental Protection

Haig F. Kasabach	State Geologist	1992–99
Karl W. Muessig	State Geologist	1999–2002

Geological Survey, Land Use Management, Department of Environmental Protection

Karl W. Muessig	State Geologist and Director	2002–present

New Mexico

Bureau of Mines and Mineral Resources, New Mexico School of Mines

E.H. Wells	President and Director	1927–39
C.E. Needham	President and Director	1939–42

R.H. Reece	President and Director	1942–44
John M. Kelly	Director (part-time)	1944–45
A.D. Hahn	Director (part-time)	February–July 1945
E.C. Anderson	Director	1945–49
Eugene Callaghan	Director	1949–51

Bureau of Mines and Mineral Resources, New Mexico Institute of Mining and Technology

Eugene Callaghan	Director	1951–57
Alvin J. Thompson	Director	1957–68
Frank E. Kottlowski	Acting Director	1968–69
Don H. Baker Jr.	Director	1969-73
Frank E. Kottlowski	Acting Director	1973–74
Frank E. Kottlowski	Director	1974–91
Charles E. Chapin	Director	1991–99
Peter A. Scholle	Director	1999–2001

Bureau of Geology and Mineral Resources, New Mexico Institute of Mining and Technology

Peter A. Scholle	Director	2001–present

Note: From 1927–43 the president of the School of Mines served as director of the Bureau of Mines and Mineral Resources. Staff of the school served as part-time personnel. The first full-time director was appointed in 1945. The term "New Mexico School of Mines" was retained for fiscal purposes only until 1960.

The name of the organization was changed by legislative act to the Bureau of Geology and Mineral Resources in 2001 to reflect the broadening of geoscience responsibilities that had occurred since founding in 1927.

Since 1969, the director is responsible to the Board of Regents and reports through the president of the University.

New York
"State Geological and Natural History Survey"

William W. Mather	Geologist, First District	1836–43
Ebenezer Emmons	Geologist, Second District	1836–43
Lardner Vanuxem	Geologist, Third District	1836–43
Timothy A. Conrad	Geologist, Fourth District	1836–37

| James Hall | Geologist, Fourth District | 1837–43 |
| James Hall | State Geologist | 1843–65 |

State Cabinet of Natural History

| James Hall | Curator | 1865–70 |

New York State Museum of Natural History

| James Hall | Director | 1870–83 |

Office of Geology and Office of Paleontology
(in New York State Museum)

James Hall	State Geologist, State Paleontologist and Director	1883–94
F.J.H. Merrill	State Geologist	1894–98
James Hall	State Paleontologist and Director	1894–98
F.J.H. Merrill	State Geologist and Director	1898–1904
John M. Clarke	State Geologist, State Paleontologist and Director	1904–26
David H. Newland	State Geologist	1927–41
C.A. Hartnagel	State Geologist	1941–44
John G. Broughton	In Charge	1944–45

New York State Museum and Science Service

John G. Broughton	Acting State Geologist	1945–49
John G. Broughton	State Geologist	1949–68
James F. Davis	Acting State Geologist	1968–70
James F. Davis	State Geologist	1970-78
Robert H. Fakundiny	State Geologist	1978–2004
William M. Kelly	Acting State Geologist	2004–05
William M. Kelly	State Geologist	2005–present

Note: When Hall, who had been an assistant to Emmons, became geologist of the fourth district in 1837, Conrad continued as state paleontologist until 1843. The offices of geology and paleontology were not merged until 1955. State paleontologists prior to the merger, and not noted above, were John Clarke, 1898–1904, when he also became state geologist; Rudolph Ruedemann, 1926–37; Winifred Goldring, 1937–54.

North Carolina
Board of Agriculture

Denison Olmsted	Professor, Chemistry and Mineralogy University of North Carolina	1824–25
Elisha Mitchell	Professor, Chemistry and Mineralogy University of North Carolina	1825–27

Geological Survey of North Carolina

Ebenezer Emmons	State Geologist	1851–63
W.C. Ken	State Geologist	1864–66

Geological, Mineralogical, Agricultural, and Botanical Survey

W.C. Ken	State Geologist	1866–85
J.A. Holmes	State Geologist	1891–1905

Geological and Economic Survey of North Carolina

Joseph Hyde Pratt	Acting State Geologist	1905–06
Joseph Hyde Pratt	State Geologist	1906–24
Brent S. Drane	State Geologist	1924–25

Division of Mineral Resources, Department of Conservation and Development

Jasper L. Stuckey	State Geologist	1925–26
Herman J. Bryson	State Geologist	1926–40
Jasper L. Stuckey	State Geologist	1940–64

Division of Land Resources

Stephen G. Conrad	State Geologist	1964–90
Charles H. Gardner	State Geologist	1990–2002
James D. Simons	State Geologist	2002–present

Note: Although W.C. Ken was appointed state geologist in 1864 following the death of Emmons, the Survey was inactive during the last 2 years of the Civil War.

North Dakota

North Dakota Geological Survey

Earle J. Babcock	State Geologist	1895–1900
Frank A. Wilder	State Geologist	1901–02
Arthur G. Leonard	State Geologist	1903–32
Howard E. Simpson	State Geologist	1933–38
Frank C. Foley	State Geologist	1939–41
Wilson M. Laird	State Geologist	1941–69
Edwin A. Noble	State Geologist	1969-78
Lee C. Gerhard	State Geologist	1978–82
Donald L. Halvorson	State Geologist	1982–85
Sidney B. Anderson	Acting State Geologist	1985–88
Frank R. Karner	State Geologist	1988–89
Sidney B. Anderson	Acting State Geologist	1989–90
John P. Bluemle	State Geologist	1990–2004
Edward C. Murphy	Acting State Geologist	2004–05
Edward C. Murphy	State Geologist	2005–present

Ohio

"First Geological Survey of Ohio"

| William W. Mather | State Geologist | 1837–38 |

"Second Geological Survey of Ohio"

| J.S. Newberry | State Geologist | 1869–79 |
| Edward Orton Sr. | State Geologist | 1882–88 |

Third Geological Survey of Ohio

| Edward Orton Sr. | State Geologist | 1889–99 |

Fourth Geological Survey of Ohio

Edward Orton Jr.	State Geologist	1900–06
John A. Bownocker	State Geologist	1906–28
Wilbur Stout	State Geologist	1928–46

| George W. White | State Geologist | 1946–47 |
| John H. Melvin | State Geologist | 1947–49 |

Division of Geological Survey, Ohio Department of Natural Resources

John H. Melvin	Division Chief/State Geologist	1949–57
Ralph J. Bernhagen	Division Chief/State Geologist	1957–68
Horace R. Collins	Division Chief/State Geologist	1968-89
Thomas M. Berg	Division Chief/State Geologist	1989–2006
Lawrence H. Wickstrom	Division Chief/State Geologist	2006–present

Note: The present Survey is considered essentially as a continuation of the "Fourth Survey."

Oklahoma

Oklahoma Territory Department of Geology and Natural History Survey

| Albert H. Van Vleet | Director | 1898–1907 |

Oklahoma Geological Survey

Charles N. Gould	Director and State Geologist	1908–11
Daniel W. Ohern	Director and State Geologist	1911–14
Charles W. Shannon	Director and State Geologist	1914–23
Charles N. Gould	Director and State Geologist	1924–31
Robert H. Dott	Director and State Geologist	1935–52
William E. Ham	Acting Director and State Geologist	1952–54
Carl C. Branson	Director and State Geologist	1954–67
Charles J. Mankin	Director and State Geologist	1967–2007

Note: The Survey was inactive from July 1, 1923, to June 30, 1924, and from 1931–1935 with Charles E. Decker as custodian during both periods.

Oregon

Oregon Bureau of Mines and Geology

| Henry M. Parks | Director | 1913–23 |

State of Oregon Department of Geology and Mineral Industries

Earl K. Nixon	Director	1937–44
Fay W. Libbey	Director	1944–54
Hollis M. Dole	Director and State Geologist	1955–69
Raymond E. Corcoran	Director and State Geologist	1969-77
Ralph S. Mason	Director and State Geologist	1977–78
Donald A. Hull	Director and State Geologist	1978–99
John Beaulieu	Director and State Geologist	1999–2003
Vicki S. McConnell	Director and State Geologist	2003–present

Note: Libbey, Dole, and McConnell were appointed acting director for a short period prior to their appointment as director. (Hollis Dole was appointed Assistant Secretary of Interior on March 20, 1969.)

Pennsylvania

Geological Survey of Pennsylvania (First Geological Survey of Pennsylvania)

Henry Darwin Rogers	State Geologist	1836–42
Henry Darwin Rogers	State Geologist	1851–58

Second Geological Survey of Pennsylvania

J. Peter Lesley	State Geologist	1874–95

Topographic and Geologic Survey Commission

(Third Geological Survey of Pennsylvania)

Richard R. Hice	State Geologist	1909–19

Bureau of Topographic and Geologic Survey

(Pennsylvania Geological Survey or Fourth Geological Survey of Pennsylvania),

Department of Internal Affairs

Richard R. Hice	Acting State Geologist	August 1919
George H. Ashley	State Geologist	September 1919–23

Department of Forests and Waters

George H. Ashley	State Geologist	1923–27

Department of Internal Affairs

George H. Ashley	State Geologist	1927–46
Ralph W. Stone	State Geologist	August–December 1946
Stanley H. Cathcart	State Geologist	1947–53
Ralph W. Stone	Acting State Geologist	April–October 1953
Carlyle Gray	Acting State Geologist	October 1953–October 1955
Carlyle Gray	State Geologist	1955–61
Alan R. Geyer	Acting State Geologist	October–December 1961
Arthur A. Socolow	State Geologist	1961–69

State Planning Board

Arthur A. Socolow	State Geologist	1969–71

Department of Environmental Resources

Arthur A. Socolow	State Geologist	1971–86
Donald M. Hoskins	Acting State Geologist	August 1986–December 1986
Donald M. Hoskins	State Geologist	1987–93

Department of Conservation and Natural Resources

Donald M. Hoskins	State Geologist	1993–2000
Samuel W. Berkheiser Jr.	Acting State Geologist	January–June 2001
Jay B. Parrish	State Geologist	2001–02
Samuel W. Berkheiser Jr.	Acting State Geologist	September–November 2002
Jay B. Parrish	State Geologist	2002–present

Note: Names in parentheses are commonly used alternatives today.

The Third or Commission Survey (1899–1919) was established to engage in cooperative topographic and geologic mapping with the U.S. Geological Survey. During the Third Survey's existence, three (generally) citizens of the Commonwealth of Pennsylvania were appointed as commissioners by the governor to provide oversight of the state's half of the cooperative program. In 1909, the Commission received legislative approval to undertake independent geologic investigations and authorization to appoint a state geologist. Hice, one of the three active commissioners at the time, was named state geologist in October 1909.

Transfers to various agencies and departments did not affect the Fourth Survey's basic organizational structure or bureau title.

Puerto Rico (sent letter that they would try to get the information)

Mineralogy and Geology Section of the Department of Industrial Research of the Economic Development Administration of Puerto Rico

Mort D. Turner	Chief Geologist	1954–58
John Q. St. Clair	Chief Geologist	1959–60
Jose F. Cadilla	Chief Geologist	1961–69
Eduardo Aguilar-Cortes	Director and State Geologist Geology and Mineral Resources	1969–

Note: Prior to 1957 the Section was called the Division of Mineralogy and Geology.

Rhode Island (no response as of 7/25/07)

"Jackson Survey"

Charles T. Jackson	Geological and Agricultural Surveyor	1839–40

Natural Resources Survey of Rhode Island

Charles Wilson Brown	Superintendent	1909–13

South Carolina

Geological and Mineralogical Survey of South Carolina

Lardner Vanuxem	Professor of Geology and Mineralogy University of South Carolina	1825–26

Agricultural Survey of South Carolina

Edmund Ruffin	Agricultural Surveyor of the State	1842–43

Geological and Agricultural Survey of the State of South Carolina

Michael Tuomey	State Geological Surveyor	1843–46
Oscar M. Lieber	Mineralogical, Geological, and Agricultural Surveyor	1856–60

South Carolina Geological Survey

Earle Sloan	State Geologist	1902–10
M.W. Twitcheft	State Geologist	1911–12
Stephen Taber	State Geologist	1912–47
Laurence L. Smith	State Geologist	1947–61

Division of Geology, State Development Board

Henry S. Johnson Jr.	State Geologist	1961–69
Norman K. Olson	State Geologist	1969–95

South Carolina Geological Survey, State Budget and Control Board

Norman K. Olson	State Geologist	1995–97

South Carolina Geological Survey, Department of Natural Resources

C. William Clendenin	State Geologist	1995–97

South Carolina Geological Survey, Department of Natural Resources; Land, Water, and Conservation Division

C. William Clendenin	State Geologist	1997–2005

Note: From 1912 until the formation of the State Development Board, there were no funds appropriated for geological investigations, and the state geologist served principally in an advisory capacity on a part-time basis. The report of Vanuxem's survey was published in the newspapers of the state in 1826 and was the first geological report issued by any state in America.

South Dakota
South Dakota Geological and Natural History Survey

J.E. Todd	State Geologist	1893–1903
Elwood C. Perisho	State Geologist	1903–14
Freeman Ward	State Geologist	1915–26
Edgar P. Rothrock	State Geologist	1926–32

State Geological Survey

Edgar P. Rothrock	State Geologist	1932–57
Allen F. Agnew	State Geologist	1957–63
Duncan J. McGregor	State Geologist	1963–81
Merlin J. Tipton	State Geologist	1981–92
Cleo M. Christensen	State Geologist	1992–97
Derric L. Iles	State Geologist	1997–present

Tennessee

Gerard Troost	State Geologist	1831–50
James M. Safford	State Geologist	1854–69

Tennessee State Geological Survey

George H. Ashley	State Geologist	1910–12
Albert H. Purdue	State Geologist	1912–17
L.C. Glenn	Acting State Geologist	1918
Wilbur Nelson	State Geologist	1918–23

Division of Geology of the Department of Education

Wilbur Nelson	State Geologist	1923–25
Hugh D. Miser	State Geologist	1926
Walter F. Pond	State Geologist	1927–37

Division of Geology, Department of Conservation

Walter F. Pond	State Geologist	1937–45
H.B. Burwell	State Geologist	1945–51
Herman W. Ferguson	State Geologist	1951–52
William D. Hardeman	State Geologist	1952–59

Division of Geology, Department of Conservation and Commerce

William D. Hardeman	State Geologist	1959–63

Division of Geology, Department of Conservation

William D. Hardeman	State Geologist	1963–69

Robert E. Hershey	Director and State Geologist	1969–85
William T. Hill	Director and State Geologist	1985–90
Edward T. Luther	Director and State Geologist	1990–91

Division of Geology, Department of Environment and Conservation

| Edward T. Luther | Director and State Geologist | 1991–95 |
| Ronald P. Zurawski | Director and State Geologist | 1996–present |

Texas

"Geological and Agricultural Survey of Texas"

(First Texas Geological Survey—"Shumard Survey")

Benjamin F. Shumard	State Geologist	1858–60
Francis Moore Jr.	State Geologist	1860–61
Benjamin F. Shumard	State Geologist	1861 (brief)

Note: Samuel B. Buckley was placed in charge of the above Survey
when it was briefly reactivated in 1866 following the Civil War.

Geological and Agricultural Survey of Texas

(Second Texas Geological Survey—"Buckley Survey")

| John W. Glenn | State Geologist | 1873–74 |
| Samuel B. Buckley | State Geologist | 1874–75 |

Geological Survey of Texas (of the Department of Agriculture, Insurance,

Statistics, and History of the State of Texas—Third Texas Geological Survey, "Dumble Survey")

| Edwin T. Dumble | State Geologist | 1888–94 |

The University of Texas Mineral Survey

| William B. Phillips | Director | 1901–05 |

Bureau of Economic Geology and Technology, University of Texas—

name changed in 1925 to Bureau of Economic Geology, University of Texas;
University name changed in 1967 to The University of Texas at Austin

| William B. Phillips | Director | 1909–15 |
| Johan A. Udden | Director | 1915–32 |

| Elias H. Sellards | Director | 1932–45 |
| John T. Lonsdale | Director | 1945–60 |

Note: Since 1967, formal name is "Bureau of Economic Geology,
The University of Texas at Austin."

Peter T. Flawn	Director	1960–70
William L. Fisher	Acting Director	1970–71
William L. Fisher	Director	1971–94
Noel Tyler	Director	1994–98
William L. Fisher	Interim Director	1998–2000
Scott W. Tinker	Director	2000–present

Note: In 2003, the Bureau became part of the John A. and Katherine G. Jackson School
of Geosciences at The University of Texas at Austin. It remains known as
"Bureau of Economic Geology, The University of Texas at Austin."

Utah

Utah Geological and Mineralogical Survey, Department of Publicity and Industrial Development

| Arthur L. Crawford | Senior Investigator | 1941–44 |
| Arthur L. Crawford | Director and Commissioner | 1946–49 |

Utah Geological and Mineralogical Survey, College of Mines and Mineral Industries, University of Utah

| Arthur L. Crawford | Director | 1949–61 |
| William P. Hewitt | Director | 1961–74 |

Utah Geological and Mineral Survey, Utah Department of Natural Resources

| Donald T. McMillan | Director | 1974–81 |
| Genevieve Atwood | Director | 1981–89 |

Utah Geological Survey, Utah Department of Natural Resources (name changed, 1991)

| Lee M. Allison | Director | 1989–99 |
| Richard G. Allis | Director | 2000–present |

Note: The Geological and Mineralogical Survey was authorized by legislature in 1931 but not formally activated until 1941. During these 10 years and indeed prior to this time, several geologists acted as consultants to various state agencies as occasion demanded and were sometimes unofficially referred to as "state geologist." Among these were J.E. Talmage, F.J. Pack, W. Peterson, E.H. Burdick, F. Gunnell, J.A. March, H.H. Higgs, and A.M. Buranek.

Vermont
Vermont Geological Survey (Vermont Division of Geology and Mineral Resources)

Charles Baker Adams	State Geologist	1845–48
Zadock Thompson	State Geologist	1849–56
Judge Augustus Young	State Geologist	1856
Edward Hitchcock	State Geologist	1856–61
Albert D. Hagar	State Geologist and Curator	1864–70
H.A. Cutting	State Geologist and Curator	1870–86
George W. Perry	State Geologist and Curator	1886–98
George Henry Perkins	State Geologist and Curator	1898–1933
Elbridge C. Jacobs	State Geologist and Curator	1933–47
Charles G. Doll	State Geologist	1947–76
Charles A. Ratté	State Geologist and Director	1976–91
Diane L. Conrad	State Geologist and Director	1991–95
Laurence R. Becker	State Geologist and Director	1995–present

Note: The 1861 Geological Map of Vermont was "traced out and compiled by members of the Geological Survey." The first reference to the "Vermont Geological Survey" is in the 1913–14 report of Perkins. The term has apparently been in general use since then and appears on publications since that time, but the "Office of State Geologist" was in official use until 1989. The position of curator of the Cabinet was held by the state geologist, but the title is obsolete. The Cabinet was a natural history collection and display at Montpelier, and from 1864–98 the curatorship was the primary function of the state geologist. In 1989, the Vermont Geological Survey became known in statute as the Vermont Division of Geology and Mineral Resources directed by the state geologist.

Virginia
Geological Survey of Virginia, Board of Public Works

William Barton Rogers	Director	1835–44

Geological Survey of Virginia, Department of Agriculture and Immigration

Thomas Leonard Watson	Geologist in Charge	1904–07

Virginia Geological Survey, University of Virginia

Thomas Leonard Watson	Director	1908–24
Albert William Giles	Acting Director	1924
Wilbur A. Nelson	State Geologist	1925–28

Virginia Geological Survey, State Department of Conservation and Development

Linwood H. Warwick	Acting Head	1928–29
Arthur C. Bevan	State Geologist	1929–47
William M. McGill	State Geologist	1947–54

Division of Geology, Department of Conservation and Development

William M. McGill	State Geologist	1954–57

Division of Mineral Resources, Department of Conservation and Development

James L. Calver	Commissioner of Mineral Resources and State Geologist	1957–58

Division of Mineral Resources, Department of Conservation and Economic Development

James L. Calver	Commissioner of Mineral Resources and State Geologist	1958–78

Division of Mineral Resources, Department of Conservation and Economic Development

Robert C. Milici	Commissioner of Mineral Resources and State Geologist	1979–85

Division of Mineral Resources, Department of Mines, Minerals and Energy

Robert C. Milici	Commissioner of Mineral Resources and State Geologist	1985–91

Division of Mineral Resources, Department of Mines, Minerals, and Energy

Stanley S. Johnson	Director of Mineral Resources and State Geologist	1992–2001

Division of Mineral Resources, Department of Mines, Minerals and Energy

C.R. Berquist Jr.	Director of Mineral Resources and State Geologist	2002–04

Division of Mineral Resources, Department of Mines, Minerals, and Energy

Edward E. Erb Jr.	Director of Mineral Resources and State Geologist	2005–present

Note: In 1956 the Division of Mineral Resources was created within the Department of Conservation and Development. In 1957 all functions of the Division of Geology were transferred to the Division of Mineral Resources.

Washington

State Mining Bureau

George A. Bethune	State Geologist	1890–92

State Geological Survey of the State of Washington

Henry Landes	State Geologist	1901–21

Division of Geology, Department of Conservation and Development

Solon Shedd	Supervisor	1921–25
Harold E. Culver	Supervisor	1925–45

Division of Mines and Geology, Department of Conservation and Development

Sheldon Glover	Supervisor	1945–57

Division of Mines and Geology, Department of Conservation

Marshall T. Huntting	Supervisor	1957–67

Division of Mines and Geology, Department of Natural Resources

Marshall T. Huntting	Supervisor	1967–71
Vaughn E. Livingston Jr.	Supervisor and State Geologist	1971-82
Raymond Lasmanis	Division Manager and State Geologist	1982–2001
Ron Teissere	Division Manager and State Geologist	2001–present

Note: The State Mining Bureau was legally in existence until 1901 but was inactive from 1893 due to lack of appropriations.

West Virginia
West Virginia Geological and Economic Survey

Israel C. White	State Geologist	1897–1927
David Reger	Geologist in Charge	1927–29
James D. Sisler	State Geologist	1930–34
Paul H. Price	Director and State Geologist	1934–69
Robert B. Erwin	Director and State Geologist	1969–88
Larry D. Woodfork	Director and State Geologist	1988–2001
Carl J. Smith	Director and State Geologist	2002–05
Michael Ed Hohn	Director and State Geologist	2005–present

Wisconsin
State Geological Survey

Edward Daniels	State Geologist	1853–54
J.G. Percival	State Geologist	1854–56

"Geological and Agricultural Survey"

James Hall Ezra Carr Edward Daniels	Joint Commissioners	1857–62

"Survey of the Lead District"

John Murrish	Commissioner	1870–72

"Complete Geological Survey"

Increase A. Lapham	State Geologist	1873–74
O.W. Wight	State Geologist	1875
T.C. Chamberlin	Chief Geologist	1876–82

Geological and Natural History Survey

E.A. Birge	Superintendent	1897–1900
E.A. Birge	Director and Superintendent	1900–19
William O. Hotchkiss	State Geologist	1908–19
William O. Hotchkiss	State Geologist, Director and Superintendent	1919–25
Ernest F. Bean	Acting State Geologist, Director and Superintendent	1925–26
Ernest F. Bean	State Geologist, Director and Superintendent	1926–31
Ernest F. Bean	State Geologist	1931–53
George F. Hanson	Director and State Geologist	1953–72
Meredith E. Ostrom	Director and State Geologist	1972–90
Juergen Reinhardt	Director and State Geologist	1991
Ronald Hennings	Acting State Geologist and Director	1990–92
James M. Robertson	Director and State Geologist	1993–present

Note: The Geological and Natural History Survey had an ex officio governing board until 1931 when it was placed under the Board of Regents of the University of Wisconsin. In 1966 it became a part of the reorganized University of Wisconsin–Extension.

Wyoming

Y.G. Murphy	Territorial Assayer	1878
Fred J. Stanton	Territorial Geologist	1881–82
Samuel Aughey	Territorial Geologist	April–August 1882
Gilbert Bailey	Territorial Geologist	1882–85
Samuel Aughey	Territorial Geologist	1885–87
Louis D. Ricketts	Territorial Geologist	1887–90
Henry C. Beeler	State Geologist	1903–09
Edwin Hal	State Geologist	1909–11

C.E. Jamison	State Geologist	1911–13
Loyal W. Trumbull	State Geologist	1913–19
G.B. Morgan	State Geologist	1919–23
Albert B. Bartlett	State Geologist	1923–27
John G. Marzel	State Geologist	1927–33

Wyoming State Geological Survey

S.H. Knight	State Geologist	1933–41
Horace D. Thomas	State Geologist and Director	1941–67
D.L. Blackstone Jr.	State Geologist and Director	1967–69
Daniel N. Miller Jr.	State Geologist and Director	1969–81
Gary B. Glass	State Geologist and Director	1981–99
Lance Cook	State Geologist and Director	1999–2004
Ronald C. Surdam	State Geologist and Director	2004–present

Note: Prior to 1933, there was simply the Office of the Territorial or State Geologist. In 1933, legislation was passed creating the Wyoming State Geological Survey. In 1969, the status of the Wyoming survey was changed to include a full-time state geologist.

Appendix 5:
Selected Group Photographs

Group photographs have been taken at all recent AASG annual meetings. This practice has been under way for many decades. A collection of these photographs was beyond the scope of this history, but should be undertaken at some time. Currently, several decades of group photographs are on the AASG Website in the historical archives section. The following group photographs are presented for interest's sake, and were not chosen for any particular reason. They are a reminder, however, that a great number of photographs exist, but are not yet organized as an archive. This is a job yet to be done.

1923

State geologists and others at Franklin, Tenn., on October 2, 1923. From left to right: Morris M. Leighton (Illinois), Ralph W. Stone (Pennsylvania), D. Thompson (USGS), Thomas L. Watson (Virginia), David White (USGS), Phillip Smith (USGS), Samuel W. McCallie (Georgia), Henry B. Kummel (New Jersey), A. C. Lawson (California), Oliver Bowles (U.S. Bureau of Mines), Richard M. Field (Princeton University), Charles Schuckert (Yale University), and Edward B. Mathews (Maryland). Courtesy of the New Jersey Geological Survey.

1939

State geologists at 1939 annual meeting in the conference room of the director of the U.S. Geological Survey in Washington, D.C. (note photographs of Dr. George Otis Smith and Maj. John Wesley Powell behind the group). Front row, left to right: Henry B. Kummel (New Jersey), Wilson M. Laird (North Dakota), Jasper L. Stuckey (North Carolina), Walter F. Pond (Tennessee), Arthur Bevan (Virginia), Ralph E. Esarey (Indiana), Edward L. Troxell (Connecticut). Back row, left to right: Robert H. Dott (Oklahoma), Richard A. Smith (Michigan), William H. Emmons (Minnesota), Raymond C. Moore (Kansas), Meredith E. Johnson (New Jersey), Paul H. Price (West Virginia), Arthur C. Trowbridge (Iowa), Harold E. Culver (Washington), and C.A. Hartnagel (New York). Courtesy of the New Jersey Geological Survey.

1990

State geologists at the 1990 annual meeting in Wisconsin. Index identifies the members shown.

Photo of State Geologists - 1990

1. Haig Kasabach, 2. Charles Ratté, 3. Vince Dreeszen, 4. Sid Anderson, 5. Ed Ruppel, 6. Walter Anderson, 7. Bob Fakundiny, 8. Jim Davis, 9. Art Socolow, 10. Larry Fellows, 11. Bud Hendry, 12. George Hanson, 13. Walt Schmidt, 14. Larry Woodfork, 15. Ken Weaver, 16. Charlie Mankin, 17. Jon Price, 18. Robert Forbes, 19. John Rold, 20. Jim Williams, 21. Donald Hoskins, 22. Ole Olson, 23. Bill Williams, 24. Perry Wigley, 25. Tom Berg, 26. Frank Kottlowski, 27. Don Hull, 28. Art Slaughter, 29. Norman Hester, 30. Priscilla Grew, 31. Don Haney, 32. Dan Miller, 33. Ned Noble, 34. Tom Segall, 35. Ray Lasmanis, 36. Phil LaMoreaux, 37. Robert Jordan, 38. Charles Gardner, 39. Bill Hambleton, 40. Earl Bennett, 41. Steve Conrad, 42. Buzz Ostrom, 43. Lee Gerhard, 44. Ernie Mancini, 45. Robert Milici, 46. Allen Agnew

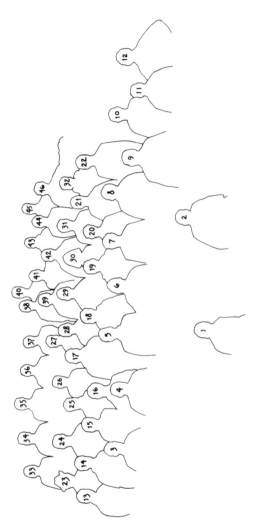

2000

State geologists at the 2000 annual meeting in St. Louis, Mo. Index identifies the members shown.